RETRIEVER THEORY

entitled

RETRIEVER THEORY

C. A. McMahan

Fall 1970 / Equivalent to the current entry fee / 861 + pages
for one open all-age stake--$25.00.

Limited Edition Only: Each copy numbered and signed.

Collector's Item

A systematic source book (in symbolic gobbledegook) addressed to questions most retriever field trial enthusiasts have never asked.

CONTENTS: Head-Piece. Art and Science of Judging. Retriever Dogma. Ideal Judge. The Drawing. The Triple Mark. Retriever Probability. Retrievership Expectancy. [Technical Notes] Changing a Test. Measuring Retriever Performance. Pontchippi Mathematics. Callbacks and One Judge. [Technical Note] Callbacks and Two Judges. [Technical Note] A Judge Judges His Judgment. Conferences for Judges. Tail-Piece. APPENDICES: Assumed Reader Wisdom. My Ideal Judge. Pontchippi Survey of Retriever Field Trial Judges, 1968. On Tossing a Dummy. Tidbits from My British Journal. Index.

PONTCHIPPI
TRADEMARK

© 1961 by C. A. McMahan

RETRIEVER THEORY

C. A. McMahan

Distributed by
EDWARDS BROTHERS, INC.
Ann Arbor, Michigan

For Alex and Jerry and You-all

PREFACE

Conventionally, the final chore of writing a book is to prepare a short subjective introduction; such a part of the book is placed first and probably read least. In view of the materials presented in this particular book such a prolegomenon seems uncommonly superfluous.

The scientific aspects of this book run the gamut from the pure to the applied. In a narrow sense, this book concerns judgment methods with particular emphasis on the method of paired comparisons fetched all the way from Fechner in 1860. In a broad sense, the concern is with theories of measurement where each theory is associated with a distinct level of measurement.

In the preparation of this volume and in determining the order in which the various topics should be dealt with, a major consideration has been convenience. After all, many of the methods applied in this book were used by the author in the 1940's and published as far back as 1950; portions of this book were written more than 10 years ago; moreover, rewriting "hieroglyphical" material is a risky undertaking. In addition it was desirable to attempt to separate the author's opinion from more objective matter, although that endeavor was not success-ful, lock, stock, and barrel. A bird's eye view of the field covered, and the two major subdivisions--chapters and appendices--can be ob-tained by consulting the table of contents. However, it is not obvious that each element within a major subdivision may (or may not) have one or more technical notes, one or more notes, as well as a section entitled addenda. Some of the technical notes may not be particularly technical; moreover, notes may contain materials that could just as well have been included under another subheading.

After all, in the present state of the art of judging American retriever field trials, the order of presentation is probably of little import. If a retriever enthusiast doesn't understand the judging process, at most this book may possibly suggest to him some methods so that if he's planning to judge, he'll at least not be like some would-be judges, of whom the retriever field trial fraternity is much too full, who don't understand what they're doing, do not know they don't know, but who are trying to do it.

C. A. McMahan

Pontchippi-on-Canal
New Orleans
May, 1970

ACKNOWLEDGMENTS

This book has been more than a decade in the making; a decade or two or no, this book could never have been written alone. The author is indebted to many for help and encouragement, in particular, to the following two persons:

Raymond I. Fields,

Lynne K. Hammett.

An especial acknowledgment is due Dr. Fields, Professor and Chairman, Department of Applied Mathematics and Computer Science, University of Louisville, for his substantial original contributions to this book. Special acknowledgment and thanks are due my colleague Lynne K. Hammett for creative suggestions, constructive criticisms, cartographic and photographic contributions, as well as for preparing notes about the author and for other dedicated assistance.

The author acknowledges his debt to associates in dog training, field trialing, and hunting endeavors, both past and present, who have greatly influenced the ideas presented in this tome, even though it may be difficult to identify the particular contribution of each. Clearly then, I am indebted to all those whose ideas and terminology I may have unwittingly adopted as my own. Not only am I indebted to those persons who kindly tried to share their knowledge with me, but also to those who *thought* they were keeping their secrets from me.

My thanks also go to all those individuals who aided the cause by providing photographs or by granting permission to use photographs and materials published elsewhere; in the main, acknowledgment has been made at the pertinent place in the book. Multiple and/or extended excerpts from selected authors, articles, and publications call for special notice here. The editors of the following publications were most generous as well as helpful: *American Field, The Field, Shooting Times and Country Magazine*. Excerpts from several articles by Peter R. A. Moxon, as well as the photograph of Her Majesty's kennels (Sandringham), have been reproduced with his approval.

Materials from *Rudiments of Biometry* were adapted and reproduced without explicit reference to that publication in most instances.

Many laborious tasks and checking procedures were performed at the Biometry Computing Center, Louisiana State University Medical Center, for which sincere appreciation is expressed. I take this opportunity to thank my students and colleagues throughout the years for the innumerable helpful questions and suggestions in the quest for reliable knowledge.

Indebtedness is expressed to members of my family as follows: to my wife, Mable Shockley McMahan, for tolerating me, my dogs, and my field trial interests over a time interval reckoned in dogs, say 200 plus or minus a few; to my sons, W. Jerry McMahan, M. D., and C. Alex McMahan, Ph. D., for personal conduct and scholarly activities becoming true southern gentlemen and top-rank distinguished field trial devotees, for participating with me in dog training, sporting, and trial activities, and for comments and queries that motivated me to take more care, probe more deeply, and be more outspoken than I might have been otherwise.

Finally, I thank Mrs. Kathleen R. Bennett for dedicated assistance in translating my manuscript into beautiful typescript ready to be photocopied for the press, keeping the voluminous materials in good order, as well as calling my attention to glaring errors.

Because I was around during the complete life of this project, obviously, none of these persons is in any way responsible for the subject-matter included, the opinions stated, nor for the errors or shortcomings which remain; these are solely my responsibility.

C. A. McM.

TABLE OF CONTENTS

A pittance of practice may be worth a tome of theory.

CHAPTER ONE

HEAD-PIECE

When an author writes a book, it seems to me, the reader is justified in asking the question: Where are you going? In the present instance, my answer is as follows: "I'm going to see a man about a dog." More explicitly, this book is focused on theoretical and ideal concepts; more plainly, it concerns the methods a composite judge might use to evaluate the retrieving performance of that dog I went to see a man about.

The range of potential topics for discussing judging of retriever performance in the field is at least as broad as the range of classifications of retriever behavior and human behavior in all possible two-way combinations. For a long time, it has seemed to me that in order to advance knowledge for judging in the whole area of retriever field trials, the "body of facts" which appears to exist within the field trial fraternity needs to be interrelated and strengthened with a little genuine theory.

At the outset, I have proposed some miniature theories on at least a few topics, always having kept in mind that the proper test of soundness of theory is the comparison of prediction with experience.

For practical men, and especially for a notoriously practical man such as the author, it may be worthwhile to elaborate on selected (not mutually exclusive) aspects of the usefulness of theory, to include theoretical models.

Theory may assist judges in planning their tests and in conducting stakes.

Theory or models may be of service to judges in deciding what observations on a retriever's performance to make and record;

contrariwise, models or theory may serve judges in deciding not to record excessive and/or irrelevant data.

Theory or models may help judges be more consistent in the process of judging.

Theory or models should be of assistance to judges in selection, classification, scoring or grading procedures, and ranking procedures; in short, they should assist judges in deciding on appropriate methods and techniques.

Theory should improve the judges' capabilities to make wise decisions with limited information.

Theory, to include models, may assist judges in understanding the relationships of apparently independent happenings.

Theoretical models may assist judges in determining what they can and cannot measure reliably.

"Little theories" may lead to the formulation of more comprehensive theoretical models.

Theories and models may aid other aspects of judging and the retriever game.

It is common knowledge that each of us who judges tends to see the retriever field trial "game" not as it really is, but through our own eyes. Unfortunately, but almost inescapably, they are biased. Some retriever enthusiasts might assert that such bias needs to be reduced, even minimized. At the very outset, let it be known that I see the game through the eyes of a gundog fanatic; by gundog fanatic, I mean that for over 40 years, when shooting (hunting) upland game and wildfowl, I have derived more than half my pleasure from owning, training, and working a useful gundog. During my lifetime of association with dogs, game, and guns, all along the way, I have enjoyed many delightful treasures which have been revealed when wing-shooting activities and the field trial game (beagles, bird dogs, and retrievers) have been reflected upon within a limited framework of the mathematics of uncertainty.

Moreover, my frame of reference has been greatly influenced by

a lifetime devoted to making sound estimates and spotting winners--
obtaining reliable knowledge; in fact, I seem to be interested in reliable knowledge in most all my activities. It is my avocation and my
vocation. (This leads to an illustration; see Notes to Chapter One.)

Clearly, then, this is not another book written within the limitations imposed by a title on "how to ... ." In fact, I have lost count
of the number of books designed to appeal to beginners in the retriever
field trial game. I refer to books on how to train retrievers, and the
like, which take for granted that the reader knows nothing about the
game, and begin by telling him "how to ... ." Furthermore, not
only is this not a book on training, it is not a manual, nor is it a handbook; nor for that matter is this merely *Memoirs of Another Retriever
Enthusiast*.

This book is "aimed at" highly motivated, dedicated, senior field-
trialers only, since novice or barely post-novice field-trialers seem
not to realize that the game existed long before they arrived on the
stage, that the present and the future are mere extensions of the past.
It follows, then, that the reader is expected to be knowledgeable (as is
indicated in Appendix A) concerning the literature on retrievers, and
to be both retriever-wise and trial-wise.

Some consideration has necessarily been given to distinguishing
between the art and the science of judging (Chapter Two). The author
believes that judging, just as love making, should not be (completely)
scientific. His essay on the art of versus the science of judging does
imply that he expects the judge to be able always to distinguish among
science, authority, and opinion. Clearly, certain methods and techniques underlie the "art" of judging. Yet a man could spend years
studying this book and/or books on "how to judge" and never become
a competent judge. Details, minute as well as large, serve to indicate
whether real art is present or absent in judging. One may learn techniques from books, but development of the art of judging is a growth
process, a learn-as-you-go operation.

In essence, the fourth chapter of this book (and Appendix B) is really a footpath to nowhere, to an abstraction, namely, to a theoretical concept of an "ideal judge." Clearly, the theoretical concept of Appendix B is not a complete operational definition, not even a description of the ideal judge, merely a composite of selected aspects which one "retriever-scholar" has chosen to make a matter of record.

In retriever training and judging, certain questions crop up again and again; one might consider this book as being designed to provide a framework for answering some of those questions regarding judging. Admittedly, this book is written for those retriever enthusiasts (RE's) affluent enough to participate extensively in American retriever trials. Moreover, these participants know that training of a judge, in the main, is informal training inasmuch as one can neither purchase the know-how nor go to school to learn to be a judge. However, even if one does not look or aspire beyond informal training, this book is not an invitation to enter my house of wisdom; nor is it a proclamation of great wisdom. It is an invitation to become involved in a cooperative project of exploring the process of learning about judging retriever trials--more explicitly, learning to approach certain important problems systematically. It is up to the responsible individual to scrutinize carefully not only the logic *per se*, but also the scientific aspects of this book, assimilate any portions that he thinks are useful to him, and make his own application to judging in any particular trial.

Selected Premises

1.   The new retriever enthusiast and new ("young") judge must reach back into history not only to learn, but also to understand the time-honored judicial practices; then he must understand what we are doing currently.

2.   Changing times requires that adjustments must be made not only in our time-honored practices, but in our current practices as well.

3.   Carefully thought-out, explicit arguments (concerning these practices), by either new votaries or old, do have merit.

4. A wide exchange of such clearly thought-out, explicit viewpoints is desirable, because better guidelines for the future will indubitably result from extensive debate--but not from damning alone.

5. The basis on which reasoning proceeds throughout this entire work is that usually the author (or any other retriever enthusiast for that matter) cannot "know for sure" in any particular case. This implies repeated use of weasel words; but to avoid such excessive usage, I have set down my opinions in what may appear to be "dogmatic fashion." No such meaning is intended; they are set forth most humbly always recognizing that I don't know it all. *Bewilderment:* It is unmistakable to the reader from my mode of expression that I am not a novelist. Furthermore, I assume that the reader recognizes how perplexing it must have been for me to set down my opinions in dogmatic fashion. This is especially true inasmuch as most of my writings over a lifetime have been in a scientific framework--based for the most part on empirical data. Moreover, the *crux criticorum* is even more irritating with the recognition that some of my opinions must undoubtedly be contrary to facts--just plain wrong; that is, where I appreciate so well that these incorrect opinions will be so obvious to me too when someone points them out.

6. Brains, gentlemen, please! Even though the reader may know all that is included in the early chapters of this book, I have dared to set down *my* ideas, under the assumption that exact observation and careful description modify many a cherished illusion--including my own. Once something is pointed out, unquestionably it is obvious; but "let's be on with it."

A pittance of practice may be worth a tome of theory.

Comment: Analogies, anecdotes, and asides are used frequently throughout this book. For convenience, most of them may be found grouped together at the end of selected chapters.

1. One Attempt to Obtain Reliable Knowledge

So-called heartworms in dogs is a very real problem in the deep South. In 1958, I started prophylactic treatment of a retriever named Kube with a drug which will be called "C." I treated Kube periodically (systematically) and unfailingly from 1958 through the fall of 1966, a period exceeding 8 years. When we tested her for microfilaria in December, 1966, we were unable to find any present. This is not conclusive evidence that Kube is free of adult heartworms; C might have killed the microfilaria. Based on this evidence, one might be tempted to conclude that C prevented the heartworms. The thoughtful person, however, might ask, would Kube have had heartworms given $\overline{C}$ (read "C-bar," meaning given no drug C, or not given drug C)?

Hankie, a beagle who was whelped in February, 1958 (one month earlier than Kube), was used as a control. She was kennelled side-by-side with Kube; both were allowed to sleep in a screened enclosure at night to reduce exposure to mosquitoes (it is assumed that the reader understands the role played by the mosquito in the epidemiology of heartworms). Hankie was treated with $\overline{C}$ (no drug C) and no other drug. In December, 1966, we likewise could find no microfilaria in blood specimens from Hankie.

This is a small sample, too small to draw a conclusion. The pertinent point is, at least I made a meager attempt to obtain reliable knowledge--not just to gather data.

2. Some Notes Should the "Not-So-Senior" Field-Trialer
   Come Across this Book

Many people who own a pedigreed dog want him to come up to his potential--to be something more than just a mutt. Many of these dog owners want to compare and test the breeding, care, and/or training of their dogs against others. There are at least three ways in which this is often done: conformation contests ("dog shows"), obedience trials, and other trials to include field

KUBE (1965)

Among retrievers in "Greater New Orleans" Kube was a pioneer achiever. According to the calendar, no other retriever was awarded a ribbon in a licensed open stake at an earlier trial. Derby: She was first to obtain silver in a licensed derby stake, Lone Star Retriever Club, October 2, 1959. Qualifying: She was first to win a licensed qualifying stake, Port Arthur Retriever Club, March 11, 1961. Amateur: She was first to obtain championship points (awarded second place in the amateur stake, licensed trial, North Louisiana Retriever Club, April 1, 1962). (Photo by VPA)

The author photographed by the waters of Bayou St. John, Nouvelle Orléans, 1970.

trials. In the conformation shows success may rest on fine points of such characteristics as coat, color, gait, set of the ears, ... , and the like. In obedience trials the dog, within a relatively confined space, must perform certain acts on command or by rote--heel, sit-stay, down-stay, come, or jump. To forget, hurry, or lag may cause the dog to lose out. In (field) trials the dog must do certain things, possibly with a certain style. He may cover considerable distances and have to respond to whistle or hand signals from afar. He may even be required to find efficiently, hold or flush, and/or retrieve in a certain manner.

In all cases there are human judges who must decide whether the dog's appearance or performance is acceptable, good, superior, or disqualifying. There are "standards"--guides, rules, and requirements--meant to guide the judge in picking winners. These criteria are often nebulous, subjective, and may be all but impossible of exact application. In many cases the judge is not obligated to say how or why he reached his decision. He may serve his "apprenticeship," gain experience, and "be certified" by the accrediting organization. To many it is enough that the judge "know dogs" and be honest. To others he should be a combination of King Solomon, George Washington, King Arthur, and Natty Bumppo.

In a field trial, many of the dogs may perform in an excellent manner, but only one can "win." Is one dog clearly so superior to all others? What fine points determine a "winner" over another excellent performer? Or, conversely, what petty points go against the excellent performer that does not win?

Men and women who "run" dogs give certain judges reputations for having various preferences, biases, prejudices--that they are predictably attracted to and repelled by certain traits, actions, and qualities in dogs. Judges are also responsible for seeing what others cannot see, or to be more knowledge- able about what they see than others. Sometimes the performances of dogs are so nearly the same that we must wait for one to commit some little bob- ble, then the other dog can clearly be winner. Actually, is not the winner the winner of this moment, before this judge? As in boxing, two different judges sometimes see the same round entirely differently. A particular dog loses one day and wins another, loses under one judge and wins under another.

What is being judged? How is it being done? Can it be explained to me? Is there "proof"? All these questions give pause to many thoughtful breeders, handlers, judges, and buffs. The interested and trained observer can record many bits of data. The meaning may be beyond any one mind, but human intelligence plus the assistance of modern methods, know-how, and computers may give us some insights about judging that have never been seriously questioned or analyzed.

One aim of this book is to try to help us sort out some of the things that are known and some of the things that are not known about dogs that perform and men who judge those performances. How much "science" and how much "art" is there in judging dogs? This ought to be discernible; if it is not, we may be making assumptions about dogs that are baseless. For the good of the breed, for edification of the fancier, for the adventure of questing for knowledge, let us join together to analyze what we know and define what we desire to know to the end that theory, lore, and fact can be sorted out--or an effort be made in that direction.

3.   On Theorists and Theory

Particularly since the 1930's, letter abbreviations have been fashionable, but have been lampooned often; it has been traditional (but not without some basis, no doubt) for the theorist to be a target of caricature. Prior to the "atomic era," a person with an advanced university degree was especially vulnerable.

Without regard for the foregoing, I think most of us would willingly lend an ear to arguments contrary to our beliefs, provided these arguments were not restricted to the narrow-mindedness of the purely selfish, and provided they paid due and proper respect to the welfare of our retriever game. I think this book is concerned with the good of the retriever game, but I warn that it may antagonize many a reader in that he will be forced to think, which is disquieting for most of us.

I have not made a willful effort to make the material in this book obscure. I do not claim that all the thoughts in this book are profound and conclusive. Much of the book is heavy going, like walking up-hill over a wet, sticky, plowed field in the red clay Piedmont area of South Carolina. At least, I do admit that each and every word may not be lucid and self-explanatory. In justification, I have made limited use of some modern elementary tools which I didn't learn at school "either."

The reader may find that in a narrative I go from one subject to another, then tack on a recollection or an illustration as an afterthought. Moreover, many points are stated as though they were matters of fact. I must emphasize that such statements are only my thoughts at the time of this writing, and are subject to change. It is my way of presenting a point of view that I hope will be challenging.

Throughout this book, many topics are tackled by simply asking a question. If I am confronted with this by a reader, I shall reply that I am not answering, but merely asking, the question. When I make such a plea, I must admit that for many of the questions, I have an idea that I may know (some of) the answers. In order to involve the reader, to make him part and parcel of this project, elemental items are provided in the form of "action items" which are intended to stimulate discussion and perhaps even heated arguments.

In view of the foregoing comments, clearly this book is not intended to be popular with the so-called "wheels" who play the role of "Lords-of-the-Trials," who charm the local field trial enthusiasts, and then at judging conferences try to campaign for or against practices and policies based on incidents which have been either unpleasant or embarrassing to them.

4.   Qualifications of the Author

The author believes himself to be uniquely qualified to write this book, because he is a rare combination of special interests, skills, and experience.

Judging will obviously be referred to as an art long after this book has been written; however, we must not forget that techniques of an art can be learned, tested, and improved. Sometimes observation and analysis by one who is not too firmly entrenched in a subject can highlight more clearly some procedures and practices that have become accepted routine (to others). The fact that I am not an insider in the American retriever-world may make it possible for me to write a much sounder, more objective book than if I were a member of the "in-group." To expand on an earlier point, when one becomes too entangled with subgroups in a power structure, clear thinking becomes difficult; in fact, one might be compromised by just such pressure and knowledge.

As an afterthought, probably my best qualification for writing such a book as this one is that I am either bold enough, or foolish enough, to try it; moreover, no one else has attempted it before me; I like the challenge of plowing new ground--those stumps make it dangerous but interesting!

I am interested in retriever trials; I want to see something good become even better. There are methods, knowledge, and tools now available to us in retriever judging that are not being used or are being used only partially. I want to put some of these before my fellow retriever enthusiasts to the end that retriever judging will approach somewhat more closely the goal of being as good, as fair, and as enjoyable as possible.

Which is the "Best" Whistle?

Given six whistles, which one is the best? In the picture, whistles have been assigned to lanyard and position on each lanyard in random order. Many years ago I conducted several well-designed experiments in an attempt to find out which whistle would be expected to stop a retriever at the greatest distance (the best). Intensity (loudness using a sound-level meter), frequency (pitch using an oscilloscope and associated equipment), time or duration of "blast," distance from the line, and wind were all explicitly considered; several retriever-handler teams were used; and of course, replication and randomization were incorporated.

Her Majesty the Queen, with one of her black Labradors, Wren, at heel, making her way up the hill to watch the North of Scotland Gundog Association's retriever trials at Balmoral ... [1967]. Photo by and reproduced by permission of Central Press Photos Ltd; courtesy of The Field.

Dr. McMahan's flat-coated retriever Wynk on the way to the line with his owner (note nylon slip), licensed derby stake, Bonnet Carré Spillway, Saturday, February 24, 1968 (photo by JPI).

CHAPTER TWO

ART AND SCIENCE OF JUDGING

Such a chapter title is a formidable one; indeed, every retriever enthusiast (RE) knows so broad an area of subject matter cannot be treated conclusively in a book which has "gone to the dogs." Perforce, there is no intention of attempting to fully outline, even in an abbreviated manner, all of these matters. To begin, a few questions and assertions will have to suffice. (After all, Karl Pearson wrote an entire book in 1892 on *The Grammar of Science.*[1])

All things having been considered, man has been interested in these subjects for centuries, and tons of copy on these subjects have been printed in recent years and eagerly received by avid readers as a result of these interests.

Even so, repeatedly, not only "qualified judges" but other RE's as well, glibly and, apparently uncritically, invoke the assertion that judging American retriever trials is an art. Plainly, the word *art* (like science) means many things to many people, and it means many different things to the same person at different times. Do some RE's find it useful to consider "something," say a way of interpreting phenomena, on a continuum (a scale of degrees) that assists them in distinguishing science from non-science, even art from science, in some such manner as the following scale suggests?

(Black)   (Gray)   (White)

←—————————————— · · · ——————————————→

Not science,   Exact
even art   science

11

What do these RE's mean by art? Do they mean "tricks of the trade"? Do they mean skill in handling people who are interested in retrievers-- practical techniques of influencing human behavior and attitudes? Or, do they mean that judging of retriever performance in the field is based on subtle qualities which are difficult to put into words and impossible to state in figures? Or, do they imply that a judge of a licensed retriever trial possesses a capacity (say, a particular type of aesthetic judgment) not present in most humans and not granted the average retriever enthusiast? Or, is it not reasonable to suspect that some invoke this label (art) as a cover-up for inaccurate, inexact, unreliable judging performances in general, as well as for some particular performance. *Analogy:* Some people assert that selected behavior in retrievers is determined by instinct. Does this connotation of *instinct* really help explain retriever behavior or might it be a screen for ignorance? [Even more elementary, why does a homing pigeon return to his loft? Instinct!] But then again, precisely what does one mean by instinct? Have not scientific advances rearranged some long standing assumptions about instinct?

On selected dictionary meanings of art.--Certainly, these judges (and other RE's) do not mean the fine arts such as drawing, painting, sculpture, and ceramics. Do they mean creative work generally? Do they mean black magic? No doubt some judges would say they mean "skill, dexterity, or the power of performing certain actions, acquired by experience, study or observation; ... ." It may be revealing to examine some synonyms of the word *art* in this context.

Some synonyms of art follow: aptitude, readiness, skill, dexterity, adroitness, contrivance, cunning, artifice, deceit, duplicity. Is it not enlightening to make sentences about judging and judges using these synonyms as a substitute for the word *art*?

Understanding the Art

For the moment, suppose we do assume that judging retriever trials is an art (undefined) and ask the question: How can guidance be provided for truly appreciating that art? Clearly, in view of differences of opinion, there can be no one approach for providing such guidance. Basically, appreciation of this art may involve understanding the essential principles of judging; all the while, the student of the art of judging must apparently be concerned with why. A teacher of art appreciation might say: "He must 'see' the principles of judging; he must 'feel' these principles; he must 'think' about these principles. Repeatedly, he must think through why these principles operate. He must go to the best teachers and see judging of acknowledged high quality and why--repeatedly, why." What is the sense of the word *why* in this context? Does it have the same meaning as in the following question: Do the RE's who claim that judging is an art do so because science does not purport to explain why? Certainly, science progresses by justifying wider and wider, more comprehensive, generalizations, even though it is admitted that a sphere of ignorance remains. Science does attempt to concisely describe how changes take place. We add the concept causation; and if we are interested in or believe that such changes will occur in the future, we use the concept probability.

In contrast, does art concisely describe how changes take place, or does it merely portray an artist's feelings and emotions as of a particular instant of time? Does any final art form attempt prediction or even imply the concept of probability? Is the judge of retriever performance in the field required to see, feel, and understand cause and effect in their relation to retriever performance? Must he apply the concept of probability? If not, why not?

The judge of a licensed retriever trial is required to classify and rank, to measure, retriever performances in the field; and he is required to do more. Is this art? The following quotation appeared for many years in the "annual editions" of *Standing Recommendations of the Retriever Advisory Committee* in the section entitled evaluation of dog work: "Judging can never be precise; it is not an exact science, merely an art, and simply because there are so many shades of gray between black and white. " Does this statement really say what it purports to say? Is the process of judging American retriever trials merely an art because there are so many shades of gray between black and white? On the other hand, any senior retriever enthusiast who is familiar with essentials of the scientific method would probably agree with the statement "... it [judging] is not an exact science ... ." Note, clearly, that this does not state that the method of science is necessarily inapplicable. Certainly, judges are expected to collect carefully and classify accurately their facts and observations, note their sequence, relationships, and relative significance, and to form judgments (make inferences) based upon the facts, not on personal emotions, whims, or prejudices.

Neither Art nor Science

Operationally, doctrine, wisdom, philosophy, poetry, and history, each appears to be useful to man, yet neither is science. Moreover, meticulous collection of isolated facts alone, as has been accomplished for sections of this book, does not make a science; neither does measurement alone make science.

Geoffrey Chaucer[2] stated: "In everything there lieth measure." Any thoughtful senior RE knows that the end product of a judging assignment is measurement (on a scale no more complex than a ranking scale [see Chapter Ten]). If one follows this (Chaucer's) line of reasoning, where does it lead him?

Medicine: Both Art and Science

Medicine, like judging, is a broad concept. Relationships of disease, medicine, and art have been studied extensively. Even the practice of medicine is said to be an art. Most retriever enthusiasts would probably agree that this is partly true in the sense that imagination, intuition, and skill are important as well as indispensable. To elaborate, Wolf (in 1939) wrote *A History of Science, Technology, and Philosophy in the 16th and 17th Centuries.*[3] He stated that "medicine is essentially a practical art ... people rarely distinguish between recovery *after* a certain treatment, recovery *because* of it, and recovery *in spite of it,* ... ." Clearly, the practice of medicine includes far more than the physician's actions. Even if one focuses on the latter, even though the physician takes action based on both experience and theory, ideas on magic, religion, philosophy, as well as science, may guide him.

Even when the practice of medicine is considered an art, it is clear that much of medicine is founded on the so-called basic sciences (as well as the more specialized medical sciences); in fact, each year in the United States, millions of dollars are spent on research to provide an even stronger scientific foundation for the health sciences. In contrast, when we consider judging American retriever trials as an art, as far as I can tell, no attempt has been made to systematically build (establish) a foundation on which to improve the state of that art (known as the judging of retriever field trials). Because it is to this that we address our attention, let's face up to the truth.

Truth and Science

Assertions: Most judges probably know only "half the truth." In fact, there is no final truth even in science.

Truth.--At times many of us get away from the facts: Most people deplore a lie, but the same people may change the definition of lie to suit themselves; they may explain that self-protection or normal politesse required "slight" departures from hard facts. By somebody-or-other's definition, undoubtedly all of us are liars, but some lies are out-and-out offensive.

Science.--Oversimplified, the "scientific circle" is composed of observation, hypothesis, prediction, verification (and observation):

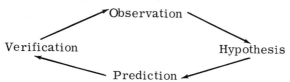

Observation: The scientist observes what happens; he collects and studies facts relevant to his problem. Hypothesis: To explain the observed facts, he formulates his "hunches" into a hypothesis expressing the pattern he thinks he has detected in the data (he makes use of induction); he reasons from particular cases to the general case. Prediction: From the hypothesis or theory he makes deductions; assuming the theory is satisfactory, these deductions ("predictions") constitute new knowledge, not known empirically; he makes use of the process of deduction; he reasons from the general to the particular using the *if* ... *then* ... statement--*if* the theory is true, *then* this ... should follow. Verification: He collects new facts to test the predictions and then the cycle starts over again. If the hypothesis or theory is substantiated, it is put to more severe tests; if the theory is contradicted, a new hypothesis is formulated consistent with the new facts. Thus, the scientist is back where he started; again he is collecting new data.

As man has groped through the ages to organize and systematize his knowledge, and especially in recent centuries as he has strived to become more scientific and hopefully more accurate, he has felt the need to generate hypotheses. Experience, imagination, "sudden insight," and analogy are among the factors which may give rise to hypotheses; I shall make use of all these factors in this book. (But the reader must beware, and I assume that he will because he is forewarned.)

Quote from Karl Pearson [1857-1936]

"All great scientists have, in a certain sense, been great artists; ... ."

Quote from Claude Bernard [1813-1878]

"A modern poet has characterized the personality of art and the impersonality of science as follows: Art is I: Science is We."

Joe (Statistic), the 13-inch beagle, on the day he won the "Texas Derby," 1956, posed by Alex, aged 12.   (Note the painted identification number still visible.)

Hankie and Alex at home, February, 1959.

MIDNIGHT (1947-1960)

Photographed with his owner, Jerry, about 1959. Midnight out-
lasted many of our dogs; he provoked many of them at one time or
another, and even frequently rode Judy, an English Setter, bareback.

ACTION ITEMS

Item 1.-- Attempt to distinguish between science (*a* or *the* science) of judging and philosophy of judging. After all, philosophy and science have not always been distinguished from each other.

Item 2.-- Iwan Ries & Company (tobacconist since 1857), 17 South Wabash, Chicago, makes the following assertion and request: "Pipe smoking is an art. Let us teach you."

Have you ever heard that judge of retriever trials who routinely invokes "judging is an art" follow up with "let me teach you"? Discuss.

Item 3.--Assertion: In *some* respects, the judging of retriever trials is an art rather than a science--an art to be acquired by "practice" (attempting to do), as are all other arts. Do you agree with the foregoing statement? What are artifices? In the framework of this action item, are artifices to be acquired by "practice"? Discuss.

Item 4.-- Obviously, a judge cannot evaluate retriever performance in the field with abstract principles of logic alone. In fact, probably one can assert with considerable justification that art, logic, and science are all tools of the imagination. Moreover, in judging retrievers, logic and emotion seem to be inseparable. Pascal (1623-1662) put it this way: "The heart has its reasons which reason knows nothing of."

Consider the above and discuss before reading Chapter Three.

Item 5.--Pontchippi judging jukebox (PJ*J): Some judging tricks are quite easy; others appear to be enormously difficult. If we assume that judging is an art, then it follows that proficiency can be acquired in that art only by regular practice. He who attains that facility must judge and judge and judge. Yet, such opportunities are not usually available. For many years I have observed the need for an inexpensive contraption to train the individual RE on knowledge of the rules and procedures and on the mechanical facets of judging; in short, on selected aspects of judging. Moreover, I reasoned that such a contraption would assist me in examining, analyzing, and improving my judging performance; hence, I (took a tip from my friend Kenneth Olson and his associates and) applied some ideas to the PJ*J.

The basic unit chosen is an ordinary 160-selection jukebox. I removed part of the works and added a viewing screen and 2 random-access slide projectors. The capacity of each projector is 81 slides, 9 groups of 9 each; thus, 162 slides could be shown. The gadget makes use of stereo and step-switches; speech is controlled on one channel and control tones on another channel. A tape recorder was added to record the title of each record as it is played--a built-in use rating system.

Programmed instruction is provided; performance of the would-be judge is evaluated by means of multiple choice questions, where the would-be judge answers by pushing buttons. If the trainee judge fails the test, a leg-lifting retriever appears on the screen ... . On the other hand, if he scores a passing grade on the examination, a camera is set to take a picture of the trainee judge; hence, a permanent record is kept. Such a gadget can be built for less than $5,000 and could be circulated among retriever field trial clubs.

REFERENCES

1. Pearson, Karl. *The Grammar of Science* (third edition), New York: The Macmillan Company, 1911 (first edition, 1892).

2. Chaucer, Geoffrey. *Troilus and Criseyde*, circa 1375.

3. Wolf, A. *A History of Science, Technology, and Philosophy in the 16th and 17th Centuries*, New York: The Macmillan Company, 1939.

A pittance of practice may be worth a tome of theory.

NOTES TO CHAPTER TWO

1. Analogy and Parable

To explicitly alert the reader, analogy is worth discussing *per se* since this fertile source of ideas has not only been used extensively in this book, but indeed has led to much judging stupidity. Warning repeated: I shall present many analogies, but I shall depend upon the reader to be astute and to identify the superficial ones which can lead to error. Remember, what we want is the correct analogy for our particular purpose. Each time I use an analogy, recall that a high proportion of cartoons in newspapers are analogies; moreover, as a method of proof, reasoning from analogy is generally condemned. Recall also that the parable is a form of analogy which even the untutored mind can understand. What is the parable anyway? Succinctly put, a parable involves a story of an authentic situation with a point of parallelism to another real situation. How many hundreds of times have you heard just such reasoning submitted as proof of the proper solution to a judging situation? In short, one purpose of this book is to attempt to take one short, easy step away from "proof by parable"--analogy.

2. Retriever and Shotgun Folklore

Analogy (danger).--As the retriever game has become institutionalized, a folklore has developed; a folklore which contains much misinformation. It is somewhat analogous to the folklore regarding shotguns and upland bird shooting which I learned as a youth. I recall being told that there were noticeable differences (that one could "tell" the difference) in how "hard" and far a gun would shoot. For example, the longer the barrel, the farther it would shoot; that a 30-inch barrel shoots "harder" than a 28-inch or a 26-inch barrel. If a dime wouldn't go into the muzzle of a 12 gauge shotgun, it was full choke; that given the same degree of choke, a 16 or 20 gauge would throw a smaller pattern than the 12 gauge. After much critical reading and some rather careful studies of my own, to include consideration of variability among shells, regardless of what the truth is, I must admit that these notions about shotguns don't stand up very well.

People can go on forever uncritically accepting hearsay, lore, traditional tales as fact or they may test a few things out for themselves. Is it not up to each man, or woman, as an individual "to know" and not just to accept?

3. On Old Prints

The retriever has been part and parcel of my life as long as I can recollect. My father and mother had an old framed print of a flat-coated retriever, with a duck at his feet, hanging on the wall of the den, to the right of the door leading to the kitchen. That print hung there until 1943 ; then it disappeared after my father died. Furthermore, throughout my own lifetime, I have collected "genuine" old sporting prints, particularly those of gundogs by British artists. This hobby is relatively inexpensive (although one could invest a "tidy sum" over a period of several years). Even so, as I have gained more and more first-hand experience with dogs, and as I have learned to appreciate the skills and insights of some of the old artists and craftsmen, this hobby has become ever more fascinating.

ARCHIBALD ALEXANDER McMAHAN
1863-1943

A true Southern gentleman. My father always had time to do things with me. He provided me direct access to knowledge of nineteenth century field sports and nature in the South, and diminished my ignorance considerably concerning life in general as well as things both afield and astream.

THE HOMEPLACE

Partial view of the front of the author's boyhood home and family residence, 1917-1943, Nr. Seneca, South Carolina.

UNCLE JEFF'S PLACE

Home of Jefferson Davis McMahan (1861-1942) and his family, Richland, South Carolina. The author has spent many pleasant hours bird shooting here on this plantation.

SNIPE SHOOTING.

From a color print in the author's private Pontchippi Collection. Engraved by J. Greig from a painting by L. Clennell. Published by Sherwood, Neely, & Jones, Paternoster Row, Nov. 1, 1817.

CLUMBER SPANIEL RETRIEVING DUCK

An old signed print by G. Vernon Stokes in the author's private Pontohippi Collection.

CHAPTER THREE

RETRIEVER DOGMA

People who are genuinely interested in retriever field trials, re-triever enthusiasts (RE's), wile away many hours in discussion on the subject. To make a case, they may use what they think are facts or they may even use statistics and/or lies. As a controversy pro-gresses, a spectator may observe that some RE's get in a tizzy while others merely grunt to make a shrewd comment.

Eventually, however, as debate ensues and as more and more gullet-scorching liquid is consumed, invariably someone resorts to demanding that "words be defined." Comments such as the following crop up: Will you admit that so-and-so is true? Will you admit that such-and-such is false? After "admitting" that certain statements are either true or false (without thinking ahead to their consequences), one of the RE's may find himself committed to some conclusion he cannot live with.

How can we properly assess whether or not there are fallacies in the form of an argument? Most of us are inconsistent in much of our thinking as well as in what we verbalize. However, often there comes a time when it would give us genuine pleasure to clarify our thoughts. An RE might be really surprised when someone asks him to back up a conclusion he drew, such as "thus, I know that such-and-such is so." After giving careful thought to the matter, he might be even surprised himself at the way he organized the available evidence to back it up. He may wonder why he even got himself into that trap.

What does the RE really mean when he says define your terms? Does he mean that a dictionary should be consulted? Every senior RE knows that one must know the meanings of many words in order to even

use a dictionary. Moreover, if he looks up those words which define
a word, he eventually gets back to the original word; the process is
circular--the very fallacy he may wish to avoid in reasoning. Hence,
in any sound discussion, obviously we must assume we have a basic
vocabulary; in short, we must begin with some undefined words.

An RE might have some other thoughts. What did I really mean
when I agreed that a statement was true? I wasn't really concerned
with truth, whatever that is (refer again to Chapter Two); I was just
agreeing to put a tag labelled "true" on some statements and a tag
labelled "false" on other statements. [*Aside:* Truth or falsity of a
statement may be clearly understood by everybody or it may be arbitrarily assigned.]

With these preliminaries out of the way, it is timely to state that
in the remainder of this chapter we are concerned only with a very few
of the most elementary aspects of logical argument, after each RE
has agreed to label each simple statement in a series of such statements as being either true or false. To repeat and elaborate, we shall
be concerned with some of the elementary aspects of logic (in a not
completely conventional way). When certain simple statements are
tagged "true, " how should certain other statements, which are combinations of the simple statements, be tagged? We shall be concerned
with only selected aspects of a deductive system; we shall not touch
upon many topics which are commonly treated in essays on logic.
[*Aside:* In Chapter Eleven, we shall use certain laws of logic; we
shall use undefined words; we shall use common (English) words and
our undefined words to define other words; we shall make certain assumptions (actually unproved statements, often called axioms or pos-
tulates or premises); and we shall collect a group of theorems which
are true on the basis of the foregoing.]

In short, this chapter is concerned with a mere outline (for RE's)
of the essential nature of a basic tool called logic. It is focused on
some of, not all, the basic laws of logic. The discussion is limited,
in the main, to "rough analyses" in terms of "truth functions" and

"tautologies." Clearly, if you are a logician or have had an introduction to deductive argument, you know that a truth table analysis may not be adequate if the components of a compound statement have specified logical relationships. Hence, you can skip directly to Chapter Four, although you might enjoy playing with some of the action items in this chapter.

Sentences and Statements

It is well-known that a simple English sentence is a group of words, silent or verbal or written, which expresses one complete thought or feeling; moreover, most of us usually think in simple sentences.

Well-formed simple sentences, for our purposes, are usually free of such words as "and," "or," "implies," "but." We shall define such a well-formed simple declaration to be a *simple statement* (or proposition); in the main, we shall denote such simple statements by the letters p, q, r, and s. It seems natural, then, to define a *compound statement* as being composed of two or more simple statements connected by words called sentential connectives (really "sentence connectives"), or more simply, connectives (e.g., and, and/or, if ... then ...).

Assumptions

It is assumed for all discussions in this chapter that any statement is either true or false; it cannot be both true and false simultaneously. It is further assumed that we know "all about" simple statements; that simple statements need not be logically related; and that the truth or falsity of simple statements must be determined outside the field of logic and/or mathematics. (Clearly, for the purposes of this chapter, the words true and false are undefined.)

Since any simple statement must be either true or false (only two possibilities), if given n (number of) simple statements, then there must be 2^n combinations of possible truth values.

NEGATION OF A SINGLE SIMPLE STATEMENT

"Not"

Given a single simple statement, say, p; according to our assumptions, p can be tagged either true (T) or false (F), where T and F are called truth values. For purposes of illustration, let the simple statement "The duck is dead" be tagged true. Suppose we write "It is false that" in front of the statement p; now we have "It is false that the duck is dead." Clearly, we have changed a statement tagged true into a statement which would now be tagged false. By writing "It is false that" in front of a statement, we convert a true statement into a false statement or we convert a false statement into a true statement. This operation is called *taking the negation* of a given statement; to illustrate, to take the negation of p is symbolized by $\bar{p}$ (p-bar, read "not p"). Clearly, then, when p is true, $\bar{p}$ is false; when $\bar{p}$ is true, p is false. Note that this operation of negation applies to a single statement. It is convenient to indicate in tabular form explicitly how the labels T and F are to be assigned (Table 3-1).

Table 3-1

p	$\bar{p}$
T	F
F	T

ACTION ITEM

Entries in licensed qualifying stakes are required to "qualify" (for the qualifying stake)--by not having "won" in specified "licensed" (or member club) stakes.   Those entries who do win are disqualified from the qualifying stake.

Consider the following statements concerning a retriever, R:

a: R has won first in an open all-age (OAA) stake (which, for convenience here, includes limited all-age stake).

b: R has won second in an OAA stake.

c: R has won third in an OAA stake.

d: R has won fourth in an OAA stake.

e: R has won a JAM in an OAA stake.

f: R has won first in an amateur all-age (AAA) stake.

g: R has won second in an AAA stake.

h: R has won third in an AAA stake.

i: R has won fourth in an AAA stake.

k: R has won first in two qualifying stakes.

If we take the negation of each of the 10 foregoing statements, we have the following statements:

$$\bar{a}, \quad \bar{b}, \quad \bar{c}, \quad \bar{d}, \quad \bar{e}, \quad \bar{f}, \quad \bar{g}, \quad \bar{h}, \quad \bar{i}, \quad \text{and} \quad \bar{k}.$$

Convince yourself that in order for a retriever R to be eligible for the qualifying stake (to qualify for the qualifying stake), each and every one of the 10 foregoing negations $(\bar{a}, \quad \bar{b}, \quad \dots, \quad \bar{i}, \quad \bar{k})$ must be labelled true.

COMBINING SIMPLE STATEMENTS WITH
"AND" and "AND/OR"

Given two simple statements p and q as follows:

p: The number of retrievers is increasing.

q: Demand for training facilities is increasing.

Clearly, p can be labelled either true (T) or false (F); likewise, q can be tagged true (T) or false (F), where T and F are again called truth values.

Two simple statements can be combined into a third statement by means of two basic connectives: "and" and "and/or." This new third statement has a truth value which depends on the truth values of its components. Again, it will be convenient to use tables (truth tables) to define how the tags T and F are to be assigned to the new third statement.

"And"

Clearly, "and" is a *conjunction*; when we connect two statements by "and" we shall indicate this new statement symbolically as $p \wedge q$ (read "p and q"). The truth table is shown (Table 3-2) for using "and" to connect two statements, say,

  p: The number of retrievers is increasing.
  q: Demand for training facilities is increasing.

Table 3-2

p	q	$p \wedge q$
T	T	T
T	F	F
F	T	F
F	F	F

[The new (combined) compound statement $p \wedge q$ is read: "The number of retrievers is increasing *and* demand for training facilities is increasing."] Note that $p \wedge q$ is labelled true for the first row of the table since both statements p and q are labelled true; in the lower three rows of the table, at least one statement labelled false is involved in the combined statement; hence, $p \wedge q$ is labelled false.

Given the possible truth values of each of the n = 2 statements p
and q, there are 2^n or 4 possible combinations of truth values for
p and   q   to be considered in assigning a truth value to the new combined statement.

In passing, note that we shall not distinguish between p ∧ q and
q ∧ p. That is, we shall assign the same truth value to p ∧ q as to
q ∧ p.

N.B.--If p and   q are both labelled true, then (the combination
of p and   q) p ∧ q is labelled true; otherwise p ∧ q is labelled
false.

"And/Or"

When we connect two statements by "and/or" we shall indicate
this new statement symbolically as p ∨ q (read "p or q" for convenience, but understood to be the inclusive "or," identical to "and/
or"). If the new statement, p ∨ q is labelled true, this connective,
∨, asserts that at least one of the statements is labelled true; that is,
one or the other or both statements are labelled true. The truth table
for using ∨ ("or," meaning "and/or") to connect two statements
(such as the two below) is Table 3-3 .

p: Kube is a Labrador retriever.

q: The duck is dead.

Table 3-3

p	q	p ∨ q
T	T	T
T	F	T
F	T	T
F	F	F

Note that the new statement, p ∨ q, "Kube is a Labrador retriever *or* the duck is dead" has a truth value of F only when both p and q are labelled false (last row of Table 3-3). Routinely, we shall hang the same truth tag on p ∨ q as on q ∨ p.

"IF ... THEN ..." STATEMENTS

In addition to the operation of negation and the formation of state-ments by using the two basic connectives ("and" and "and/or"), peo-ple who try to think clearly make widespread use of conditional state-ments (and statements of implication). Sometimes the speaker or writer explicitly states the "if ... then ..." aspects of his discus-sion; at other times he merely assumes that his listener or reader is completely knowledgeable concerning conditional statements as well as implication.

Simple Conditional Statements

To elaborate, frequently we will encounter simple conditional statements of the type "If duck are plentiful, (then) I will go duck hunting." Such a statement is of the form "If p, then q," symbol-ized p → q. In this example we have

p: Duck are plentiful.

q: I will go duck hunting.

p → q: If duck are plentiful, then I will go duck hunting.

How shall we assign a truth value to p → q? Note that there are four possible combinations of truth values for p and q as shown in the truth table (Table 3-4). In the first line of the table, both p and q are labelled true, and it would appear plausible to label p → q as true. In the second line, p is labelled true and q false, and thus it would seem appropriate to label p → q false. However, in the third line, where p is labelled false, q is labelled true, and in the fourth line, where p is labelled false, q is labelled false, the fact that "Duck are not plentiful" does not suggest a truth value for p → q,

Table 3-4

p	q	p → q
T	T	T
T	F	F
F	T	?
F	F	?

whether q be true or false. So let us arbitrarily agree to label p → q true for both cases. The truth table is as follows (Table 3-5).

Table 3-5

p	q	p → q
T	T	T
T	F	F
F	T	T
F	F	T

N.B. -- The simple conditional p → q is labelled false only when p is labelled true and q is labelled false; otherwise, the simple conditional p → q is labelled true.

The simple conditional p → q can be worded in various ways, such as the following: If p, then q; p implies q; q, if p; q follows from p. Clearly note that when statements are substituted for the letters p and q in the simple conditional p → q, there may be no relationship between the two clauses; in fact, none is required in a simple conditional. [In the remainder of this chapter, the simple conditional is referred to merely as the conditional; the word simple is not explicitly written but it is implied.]

Converse

Given the conditional $p \to q$, a new statement can be obtained by interchanging the statements p and q. This new statement, $q \to p$, is called the *converse* of the given conditional. It is a serious error to confuse a statement with its converse; moreover, the converse of a true conditional may be true or it may be false. For example, "If I have two retrievers, then I have a couple of dogs." The statement as usually interpreted is true; the converse is false.

Equivalence

In terms of simple statements, it is convenient to write "p is *equivalent* to q" in shorthand, $p \leftrightarrow q$, to indicate the *equivalence* of the two statements, and define the truth values as shown in Table 3-6. Clearly note that when $p \leftrightarrow q$, $q \leftrightarrow p$.

Table 3-6

p	q	$p \leftrightarrow q$
T	T	T
T	F	F
F	T	F
F	F	T

Furthermore, referring again to earlier sections, we can write $(p \land q) \leftrightarrow (q \land p)$ (read "p and q is equivalent to q and p"); this follows from Table 3-6 because $p \land q$ has the same truth table as

RUFUS. From a color print in the author's private Pontchippi Collection. Engraved from a picture by Wm. Smith. Published by M. A. Pittman, Warwick Square, London, July 1, 1832.

THE OLD PONY. From an old color print (in the author's private Pontchippi Collection) engraved by E. Hacker from a painting by J. Bateman (not dated).

*Billy harnessed to his sulky, in the lane by the homeplace Nr.
Seneca, Oconee County, South Carolina, circa 1926.*

Because this book is written for senior RE's, most of whom are (or will become sooner than they may think) harmless old men, this story (which was told to the author when he was a boy with a goat) by an anonymous old man, is passed along by a man who is not yet, and never shall become, harmless.

GOIN ON DOWN THE ROAD

Goin down the road (in his goat cart); little boy sees a little girl on the sidewalk.

> *Whoa doat! Wanta go to ride today lil gurl?*
> *Yes.*
> *Get in lil gurl! Giddup doat!*

Goin on down the road.

> *Anything doin today lil gurl?*
> *No.*
> *Whoa doat! Get out lil gurl! Giddup doat!*

Goin on down the road; little boy sees another little girl.

> *Whoa doat! Hello! Wanta go to ride today lil gurl?*
> *Yes.*
> *Get in lil gurl! Giddup doat!*

Goin on down the road.

> *Anything doin today lil gurl?*
> *No.*
> *Whoa doat! Get out lil gurl! Giddup doat!*

Goin on down the road; little boy sees a third little girl.

> *Whoa doat! Hello lil gurl! Wanta go to ride today lil gurl?*
> *Yes.*
> *Get in lil gurl! Giddup doat!*

Goin on down the road.

> *Anything doin today lil gurl?*
> *Yes.*
> *Whoadoat! Getoutgurl! Giddupdoat!*

ENGLISH SETTER AND LABRADOR

An old signed print by G. Vernon Stokes in the author's private Pontchippi Collection.

q $\wedge$ p. Likewise, (p $\vee$ q) $\leftrightarrow$ (q $\vee$ p) (read "p or q is equivalent to q or p"). In fact, this technique can be used as a test for equivalence; merely check whether or not two statements have the same truth table.

Logical Implication

If a relationship exists between two statements, A and B, such that the second must be true if the first is true, then we say that the first, A, *logically implies* the second, B. This is the same as saying that the second follows as a logical consequence of the first. Many writers call the first statement (the *"if* statement") the hypothesis and the second statement (the *"then* statement") the conclusion. This may be symbolized by p $\Rightarrow$ q (read "p logically implies q"), where p and q are the respective statements.

Sufficient Condition

When a mathematician uses the phrase "A is a *sufficient condition* for B," he usually means A $\Rightarrow$ B. To elaborate, "p logically implies q" is a translation of "p is a sufficient condition for q," which means "If p occurs, q will also occur."

Necessary and/or Sufficient Conditions

The converse of p $\Rightarrow$ q is defined to be q $\Rightarrow$ p. If the two statements are combined, we have the following situation: p $\Rightarrow$ q (meaning that if p occurs, q will also occur, i.e., p logically implies q) and q $\Rightarrow$ p (meaning that if q occurs, p will also occur, i.e., q logically implies p). The combination of the statements, p $\Rightarrow$ q and its converse q $\Rightarrow$ p, dictate that p can occur *if and only if* q occurs (i.e., if p is true, then q is true and if p is false, then q is false). Thus, q is a necessary condition for p, in that p can occur if and only if q occurs. Hence, q is both a *necessary and sufficient condition* for p. Likewise, p is both a necessary and sufficient condition for q. For example, "I shall go duck hunting, if and only if, duck are plentiful." In this case we have both $p \Rightarrow q$ and $q \Rightarrow p$. Moreover, we are asserting that "p is a necessary and sufficient condition for q." Clearly then, $p \Leftrightarrow q$ means that any time duck are plentiful, I am going duck hunting--I shall let nothing interfere; and I shall not go duck hunting *unless* duck are plentiful.

The following example illustrates the case where p is a sufficient condition for q, but is not a necessary condition.

      p: The entry retrieves a decoy.

      q: The entry is eliminated from the stake.

Clearly, p is sufficient for q because it is mandatory that the entry be eliminated if he retrieves a decoy. However, p is not necessary for q because the entry may be eliminated for other reasons (e.g., "breaking").

Consider the following two statements:

      p: My dog won a place in the stake.

      q: My dog competed in each test in the stake.

Comment: q is a necessary condition for p; however, q is not a sufficient condition for p, because an entry must be ranked fourth or higher among all entries which compete in and complete each and every test.

ARGUMENTS

Given two or more statements called the premises and a single statement called the conclusion: The assertion that the conclusion follows from the premises is called an argument. If in fact the conclusion logically follows from the hypothesis (the premises), the argument is said to be valid; that is, the conjunction of the premises logically implies the conclusion and could be symbolized as $(p \wedge q) \Rightarrow r$.

Valid (Forms of) and Not Valid (Forms of) Arguments

Arguments can be divided into two classes, valid (forms of) arguments and fallacies [not valid (forms of) arguments]. Validity of an argument depends only on the form of the statements. Valid forms of arguments are often referred to as rules of inference.

N.B.--Validity of an argument does not depend on the truth values assigned to statements; neither does validity depend on the meaning of the statements. Nevertheless, we can test the validity of the forms of some arguments by means of truth tables.

In this section, we shall examine selected forms of argument, some of which are valid and some of which are fallacious. We shall classify an argument as valid (using a truth table) when no row of the table contains truth values of the premises labelled T and the conclusion labelled F. (*N.B.*: The premises of the argument may be combinations of simple statements.) In other words, in every case in which the premises are collectively true, the conclusion is also true.

Logically implies.--The statement p → q may be read "If p, then q." As shown earlier in Table 3-5, it is sometimes labelled true and sometimes labelled false. A statement A logically implies another statement B, A ⇒ B, only if the conditional statement A → B is always labelled true. That is, A → B must be a tautology (see definition below).

To elaborate, by adding some columns to a basic truth table, we can determine the truth value of a compound statement. In general, the "formula" of the compound statement will have a truth value which depends upon the truth values of the statements which are substituted for its letters. Nevertheless, there are selected formulas which result in a label "true" (for compound) statements when any statements whatsoever are substituted for their letters. Such formulas are called tautologies.

In developing the laws of logic, it is necessary to prove that certain formulas are tautologies. *Definition:* A tautology is a function (expression, formula) whose truth value, according to an extended truth table, is always labelled true.

A Valid Form

An example of a valid form of argument is as follows (for convenience call it Form V-1).

Form V-1:

$$p \rightarrow q$$

$$\underline{p}$$

$$\therefore q \quad .$$

[Form of stating arguments: First we shall state the premises, then draw a line, and then state the conclusion. Read the argument as follows: "If p, then q; p; therefore, q."] The two premises are p → q and p; the conclusion is q. In order to demonstrate that this form of argument is valid, we must show that the conjunction of the premises logically implies the conclusion; that is, $[(p \rightarrow q) \wedge p] \Rightarrow q$. In other words, we must show that the conditional $[(p \rightarrow q) \wedge p] \rightarrow q$ is labelled true for every combination of truth values for p and q (components of the premises). Note in Table 3-7 that the conditional [column (5)] is labelled true for every combination of truth values for p and q. Hence, $[(p \rightarrow q) \wedge p] \Rightarrow q$ and the form of the argument is valid. [Such a compound statement, $[(p \rightarrow q) \wedge p] \rightarrow q$, having this characteristic ("all values T" in the "main column") is called a tautology; moreover, as stated earlier, a valid form of argument in this context must be associated with a tautology.] In passing, note that the form

$$q \rightarrow p$$

$$\underline{q}$$

$$\therefore p$$

is analogous to Form V-1.

An Invalid Form

Carefully note that the following form of argument is not valid, call it NV-1.

Form NV-1:

Table 3-7

p	q	p → q	(p → q) ∧ p	[(p → q) ∧ p] → q
(1)	(2)	(3)	(4)	(5)
T	T	T	T	T
T	F	F	F	T
F	T	T	F	T
F	F	T	F	T

$$p → q$$
$$\underline{q\qquad}$$
$$\therefore p$$

Clearly, in Table 3-8, the conjunction of the premises does not logically imply the conclusion for all combinations of truth values; that is, for all combinations of truth values, [(p → q) ∧ q] → p is not labelled true. Explicitly, in the third line of the table, [(p → q) ∧ q] → p is labelled F; hence, it is not a tautology. To be a valid form of argument, recall that column (5) of this table must contain only T's.

Table 3-8

p	q	p → q	(p → q) ∧ q	[(p → q) ∧ q] → p
(1)	(2)	(3)	(4)	(5)
T	T	T	T	T
T	F	F	F	T
F	T	T	T	F
F	F	T	F	T

A Second Valid Form

Form V-2:

$$p \rightarrow q$$
$$\underline{\overline{q} \qquad}$$
$$\therefore \overline{p} \qquad .$$

Table 3-9 contains the proof that this is a valid form of argument. The right-most column (the "main column") of the table, column (7), contains only T's.

Table 3-9

p	q	p → q	$\overline{q}$	(p → q) ∧ $\overline{q}$	$\overline{p}$	[(p → q) ∧ $\overline{q}$] → $\overline{p}$
(1)	(2)	(3)	(4)	(5)	(6)	(7)
T	T	T	F	F	F	T
T	F	F	T	F	F	T
F	T	T	F	F	T	T
F	F	T	T	T	T	T

A Second Invalid Form

Form NV-2:

$$p \rightarrow q$$
$$\underline{\overline{p} \qquad}$$
$$\therefore \overline{q} \qquad .$$

Because Table 3-10 contains one row (the third) where the two premises (p → q and $\overline{p}$) are labelled T and the conclusion $\overline{q}$ is labelled F, the form of the argument is not valid.

Table 3-10

p	q	p → q	p̄	(p → q) ∧ p̄	q̄	[(p → q) ∧ p̄] → q̄
(1)	(2)	(3)	(4)	(5)	(6)	(7)
T	T	T	F	F	F	T
T	F	F	F	F	T	T
F	T	T	T	T	F	F
F	F	T	T	T	T	T

A Third Valid Form

Form V-3:

$$p \lor q$$
$$\underline{\bar{p}}$$
$$\therefore q \quad .$$

Column (6) (the main column) of Table 3-11 contains no F's; hence, the argument is valid.

Table 3-11

p	q	p ∨ q	p̄	(p ∨ q) ∧ p̄	[(p ∨ q) ∧ p̄] → q
(1)	(2)	(3)	(4)	(5)	(6)
T	T	T	F	F	T
T	F	T	F	F	T
F	T	T	T	T	T
F	F	F	T	F	T

N.B.--Note that the word "form" is often omitted. When we say that an argument is valid, we really mean the form of the argument is valid.

A Third Invalid Form

Form NV-3:

$$p \vee q$$
$$\underline{\quad p \quad}$$
$$\therefore \bar{q} \quad .$$

Proof that the form of this argument is not valid is shown in Table 3-12.

Table 3-12

p	q	p ∨ q	(p ∨ q) ∧ p	$\bar{q}$	[(p ∨ q) ∧ p] → $\bar{q}$
(1)	(2)	(3)	(4)	(5)	(6)
T	T	T	T	F	F
T	F	T	T	T	T
F	T	T	F	F	T
F	F	F	F	T	T

Other Forms

Clearly there are numerous other forms of argument, both valid forms and invalid forms.

ILLUSTRATIVE APPLICATIONS

At the outset, it might be worthwhile to display a "hurricane warning." The word "some" (the quantifier meaning at least one) gives trouble in logical arguments. Not only must one be on the alert, but he must not be tricked by such usage as the following:

Some retrievers have long hair.

My retriever has long hair.

My retriever is some retriever.

Let us now see how we may use our various types of statements and their truth tables to check the validity of certain (forms of) arguments. As indicated earlier, if an RE asserts that a statement (which we shall call "the conclusion") follows from other statements (called the suppositions or premises), we shall call this an argument. We have defined the form of the argument to be valid if the conjunction of the premises logically implies the conclusion.

As an example, consider the statements:

p: My dog will enter the championship stake.

q: My dog will win the championship stake.

If we take $p \to q$ and p as our premises and q as our conclusion, is the argument valid? The form of the argument is valid if

$$[(p \to q) \wedge p] \Rightarrow q,$$

that is, if $[(p \to q) \wedge p] \to q$ is labelled true for every possible combination of truth values of the components of the premises. The argument for this example may be verbalized as follows: "If my dog enters the championship stake, then my dog will win the stake. My dog will enter the championship stake. Therefore, my dog will win the championship stake." Table 3-5 may be enlarged as in Table 3-13 to provide the answer. The last column of Table 3-13 shows that the conditional, $[(p \to q) \wedge p] \to q$, is labelled true under all the possible "truth combinations" of (components of the) premises and conclusion. In our example, the form of the argument is valid whether p and q are true or not true, i.e., whether or not "my dog enters ... ," or "my dog wins ... ." The set of statements for this example is of the following form (which is one of the basic forms of valid arguments,

Table 3-13

p	q	p → q	(p → q) ∧ p	[(p → q) ∧ p] → q
T	T	T	T	T
T	F	F	F	T
F	T	T	F	T
F	F	T	F	T

namely Form V-1):

$$p \rightarrow q$$
$$\underline{p \qquad}$$
$$\therefore q \quad .$$

(For an RE presenting such an argument undoubtedly he would "think" along these lines and read "If the conditional p → q is true and p is true, therefore q is true.") [In the language of the logician, this is known as *modus ponens*. Some writers also call it the "rule of detachment."]

Frost, running order, and probability.--Given the following statements for a licensed trial:

  q: I (prefer to) run late (in the morning).

  r: The probability of placing is greater.

Suppose an RE gives the argument

  q → r: If I run late then the probability of placing is greater.

  q: I run late.

∴ r: The probability of placing is greater.

The form of the argument is valid (Form V-1); hence,

$$[(q \rightarrow r) \wedge q] \Rightarrow r .$$

WATER DOG. From plate (facing p. 111) in John Scott, The Sportsman's Repository, London: Henry G. Bohn, 1845.

Commencement of a Cripple-Chase, after firing a Moof Shot into a Siege of Brent Geese & Sur-Wild Fowl.

London. Published by Longman & C.º 1844.

From plate (facing p. 462) in Lt. Col. Peter Hawker, Instructions to Young Sportsmen in all that Relates to Guns and Shooting (Fourth Edition), London: Longman and Co., 1844.

In other words, $[(q \to r) \wedge q]$ is a sufficient condition for r. Suppose another RE uses an argument of the following form:

$r \to q$: If the probability of placing is greater, then I run late.

r: The probability of placing is greater.

∴ q: I run late.

[*Aside*: In the foregoing, to emphasize the form of stating arguments, we have stated the premises, then drawn a line, and then stated the conclusion.] The form of the argument is valid (Form V-1); hence, $[(r \to q) \wedge r] \Rightarrow q$. Stated differently, $[(r \to q) \wedge r]$ is a sufficient condition for q.

For the next example, consider the following simple statements:

p: The animal is a retriever.

q: The animal has short hair.

r: The animal is a dog.

Suppose we formulate an argument in a form not stated earlier as follows:

$$p \to q$$
$$q \to r$$
$$\therefore p \to r.$$

The two conditionals making up the premises and the conditional composing the conclusion can be written out as follows:

Premises

$p \to q$: If the animal is a retriever, then the animal has short hair.

$q \to r$: If the animal has short hair, then the animal is a dog.

Conclusion

$p \to r$: If the animal is a retriever, then the animal is a dog.

Knowledge possessed by senior RE's concerning animals, dogs, and retrievers would undoubtedly lead them to tag the two premises false

(F) and the conclusion true (T).

For a valid form of argument we need to show that

$$[(p \rightarrow q) \wedge (q \rightarrow r)] \Rightarrow (p \rightarrow r).$$

At the risk of being objectionably redundant, we must show that

$$[(p \rightarrow q) \wedge (q \rightarrow r)] \rightarrow (p \rightarrow r)$$

is labelled true for every possible combination of truth values of the components of the premises. The right-most column of Table 3-14 shows that $[(p \rightarrow q) \wedge (q \rightarrow r)] \rightarrow (p \rightarrow r)$ is labelled true (T) for every possible truth value of the (components of the) premises; hence, the form of this argument is valid. (Some writers call this form of argument "law of the syllogism.")

Testing marking and/or memory.-- Some RE's assert that (1) memory cannot be tested by means of a single fall, and (2) multiple falls involve a test of both memory and marking ability. That is, the first fall that a retriever picks up is a test "mainly" of marking ability; the other retrieves test both marking ability and memory.

Given the following statements:

p: A retriever sees the fall (all the way to the "bottom").

q: A retriever's ability to mark is tested by the single fall.

Suppose that an RE presents an argument in the following form:

$$p \rightarrow q$$
$$\underline{\overline{p}}$$
$$\therefore \overline{q} \quad .$$

In English, his argument runs about as follows: If a retriever sees the fall, then his ability to mark is tested by the single fall. The retriever does not see the fall. Therefore, his ability to mark is not

Table 3-14

p	q	r	p → q	q → r	(p → q) ∧ (q → r)	p → r	[(p → q) ∧ (q → r)] → (p → r)
T	T	T	T	T	T	T	T
T	T	F	T	F	F	F	T
T	F	T	F	T	F	T	T
T	F	F	F	T	F	F	T
F	T	T	T	T	T	T	T
F	T	F	T	F	F	T	T
F	F	T	T	T	T	T	T
F	F	F	T	T	T	T	T

tested by the single fall. Even though the argument "sounds good," it is not of valid form (see Table 3-10). *Question:* From an intuitive point of view, why is the argument not valid?

Two licensed qualifying stakes, sponsored by clubs A and B, respectively, were held at the Bonnet Carré Spillway on successive days. Given two statements:

p: Wynk placed the first day.

q: Demo won an award the second day.

Given an argument of the form

$$p \lor q$$
$$\underline{\bar{p}}$$
$$\therefore q$$

which can be written out as follows:

$p \lor q$: Wynk placed the first day or Demo won an award the second day or Wynk placed the first day and Demo won an award the second day.

$\bar{p}$: It is false that Wynk placed the first day.

$\therefore$ q: Therefore, Demo won an award the second day.

The form of the argument is valid (refer to Table 3-11); hence,

$$[(p \lor q) \land \bar{p}] \Rightarrow q.$$

Given the following statements:

p: Game is food.

q: Man harvests food.

r: Man harvests game.

Consider an argument of the following form:

$$p \to q$$
$$\underline{\bar{r} \to \bar{q}}$$
$$\therefore \bar{r} \to \bar{p}.$$

From Table 3-15, it is clear that the foregoing form of argument is valid.

As a final example, given the following information:

    p: Kube is better than Demo.

    q: Demo is better than Wynk.

    r: Kube is better than Wynk.

In symbols, let R_1 = Kube, R_2 = Demo, and R_3 = Wynk, and the symbol > (greater than) stand for "is better than." Rewriting the foregoing three statements we have

    p: $R_1 > R_2$.

    q: $R_2 > R_3$.

    r: $R_1 > R_3$.

Suppose we formulate an argument as follows and label both premises true:

$$(p \wedge q) \to r \qquad \text{(true)}$$
$$\underline{\quad p \wedge q \quad} \qquad \text{(true)}$$
$$\therefore \ r \qquad\qquad .$$

We conclude that r is true because we used a valid form of argument, that is,

$$\{[(p \wedge q) \to r] \wedge (p \wedge q)\} \Rightarrow r$$

because

$$\{[(p \wedge q) \to r] \wedge (p \wedge q)\} \to r$$

is a tautology. [*Aside:* This is the form of argument used in the proof of Theorem 1 of Chapter Eleven.]

SUMMING UP

Some restricted aspects of logic have been examined in a cursory manner in this chapter. Even so, the discussion and examples indi-

Table 3-15

p	q	r	$\bar{p}$	$\bar{q}$	$\bar{r}$	$p \to q$	$\bar{r} \to \bar{q}$	$\bar{r} \to \bar{p}$	$(p \to q) \land (\bar{r} \to \bar{q})$	$[(p \to q) \land (\bar{r} \to \bar{q})] \to (\bar{r} \to \bar{p})$
T	T	T	F	F	F	T	T	T	T	T
T	T	F	F	F	T	T	F	F	F	T
T	F	T	F	T	F	F	T	T	F	T
T	F	F	F	T	T	F	T	F	F	T
F	T	T	T	F	F	T	T	T	T	T
F	T	F	T	F	T	T	F	T	F	T
F	F	T	T	T	F	T	T	T	T	T
F	F	F	T	T	T	T	T	T	T	T

cate clearly that it is the form of the argument and not necessarily the truth of the statements which make an argument valid. Most RE's will agree that valid reasoning from true premises is the only way to be sure of reaching true deductive conclusions--but this is not the only way. Over and beyond the foregoing, unless our reasoning is valid, the probability of getting reliable knowledge deductively is small. In general, however, we are interested in arriving at a true conclusion from true premises through a valid argument. After all, by definition, a sound argument is a valid form of argument with true premises. It seems, then, that in discussions with our colleagues, who are RE's, we face a difficult task. We must not only determine that the arguments are valid, but we must adopt only those conclusions (drawn from valid arguments) which are based on true premises (Table 3-16).

Table 3-16

Statements or premises	Deductive reasoning	Conclusion
T	Sound	T
T	Faulty	Unknown*
F	Not faulty	Unknown*
F	Faulty	Unknown*

*Unknown indicates that the conclusion may be either T or F.

Certainly by this time, a senior RE knows that he must "mind his p's and q's." Logical thought is not as easy as many suppose; moreover, if one asks too much of formal logic in a practical way, he may conclude that he has come up with logical nonsense due to the artificial nature of his testing device. Clearly, each RE must fit his own experiences into this brief and incomplete treatment of logical methods if he expects to have a useful framework through which to view the retriever game.

ACTION ITEMS

Convert to simple statements and write the following in shorthand.

Item 1.--If Kube is to win today, she is both capable and lucky.

Item 2.--If Kube is not lucky, something is sure to go wrong.

In the items below, select a form of argument. Write additional statements and/or modify the statements below so that you have a set of premises and a conclusion; then, determine if the form of your argument is valid (where applicable).

Item 3.--Retrievers: Given the three following statements:

Demand for trained retrievers is increasing.

Retrievers must be trained.

Training retrievers requires motivation.

Item 4.--Field Trials: Given the following two statements:

Retriever performance is tested in field trials.

Testing retriever performance motivates training.

Item 5.--Given the following simple statements:

p: Kube is a winner today.

q: Kube is capable today.

r: Kube is lucky today.

Item 6.--Given the following simple statements:

p: All RE's are reincarnated animals.

q: J is an RE.

r: J is a reincarnated animal.

Item 7.--Given the following n number of premises and the conclusion c. Think of an RE who fulfills your stereotype of a reincarnated jackass. Utilize the tools presented in this chapter to combine any combination of two premises with the conclusion in a form of argument of your own choosing. Establish whether or not the argument is valid.

Premises

p: He judges an open stake before he handles an open retriever.

q: He believes that accomplishments can be made in the field trial game by "politicking" (rather than by performance).

r: He brings an adding machine for convenience in adding up scores in trials he judges.

s: He wants to modify field trial procedures before he even knows the game.

t: He asks damnfool questions [which embarrass his colleagues (at a judging clinic)].

Conclusion

c: He is a reincarnated jackass.

Item 8.--Given the following simple statements:

p: All retriever trial judges are biased animals.

q: Reincarnated jackasses are biased animals.

r: All retriever trial judges are reincarnated jackasses.

Using the above simple statements, verbalize the following argument:

$$p \rightarrow q$$
$$\underline{q \rightarrow r}$$
$$\therefore p \rightarrow r.$$

Does your verbalization of this argument "make sense" to you? If not, rearrange in a more sensible form.

Item 9.--Given the following two premises and a conclusion, the problem is to formulate a valid argument:

Premises

p: Retriever enthusiasts (RE's) organize clubs.

q: Clubs sponsor field trials.

Conclusion

r: RE's sponsor field trials.

Item 10.-- The trial was over; the judges had a clear-cut winner and the other three places settled. The judges were going over the entries which had completed the trial but were unplaced. Number 54 (Kube) was in this group.

        p: Kube competed in each series.

        q: Kube did a workmanlike job in each series.

        r: Kube was awarded a JAM.

Suppose the following argument is presented:

$$q \rightarrow p$$
$$\underline{r \rightarrow q}$$
$$\therefore q \rightarrow r.$$

First verbalize the argument; then determine if the form is valid.

Item 11.-- Consider an example using logical implication. We shall begin with a false hypothesis, p, use valid reasoning, and arrive at a true conclusion, q; thus demonstrating p logically implies q, that is, that $p \Rightarrow q$ is true (T). Consider the assertion, "If 9 = 5, then 1 = 1." Clearly, p is defined to be "9 = 5" and q is defined to be "1 = 1." In high school we learned that when equals are divided by equals, the results are equal. Under the hypothesis p, 9 = 5; so we can divide both sides of this equation by 9 or 5 or one side by 9 and the other side by 5 and maintain equality.

    Starting again,

$$\text{if} \quad 9 = 5$$
$$\text{then} \quad 1 = 1$$
$$\text{because} \quad \frac{9}{9} = \frac{5}{5}.$$

Discuss.

Item 12.-- Select two competent "five-point" judges. Have them set up a test. Have some handlers and their retrievers try the test.

Select two performances that appear to be fairly evenly matched. Request the judges to set forth an argument independently why one performance is better than the other. Record the arguments. Use the procedures set forth in this chapter to determine whether or not the forms of the arguments are valid. Were the premises true in the sense that you would be willing to hang the label true on them? Discuss.

Item 13. -- Reference *Rules and Procedures for Retriever Trials:* Examine selected statements from these materials. Do you find logical inconsistencies? Discuss.

Item 14. -- Reference *Standing Recommendations of the Retriever Advisory Committee:* Examine selected statements from these materials. Are all simple statements unmistakably clear? Do you find logical inconsistencies? Discuss.

Quote from Lewis Carroll (Charles Lutwidge Dodgson) [1832-1898]

"Contrariwise," continued Tweedledee, "if it was so, it might be; and if it were so, it would be; but as it isn't, it ain't. That's logic."

A pittance of practice may be worth a tome of theory.

NOTES TO CHAPTER THREE

It is a purpose of these notes to explicitly indicate incompleteness of this chapter (although the extent of the incompleteness is not specified). As stated earlier, no attempt was made to provide a self-contained primer of logical thought. For instance, assistance of Venn diagrams (see Chapters Four and Eleven) has not been called upon to establish the validity of an argument. A second illustration of omission: methods of proof, as such, have not been treated.

More importantly, take as an example, the principle of substitution, applicable to variables as well as to statements; the basic rules have not been explored. In this form of argument, sometimes called the "law of substitution," a specific value may be substituted for a variable. For example:

Premises

    (Variable)   p: All retrievers are dogs.

    (Specific value) q: Wynk is a retriever.

Conclusion

                      r: Wynk is a dog.

This form of argument produces a true statement (valid argument) whenever the premise (p) is true for all values of the variable.

However, when p is not true for all values of the variable, the conclusion is not necessarily true. For example, given

Premises

    p: Some retrievers are short-haired.

    q: Wynk is a retriever.

Conclusion

    r: Wynk is short-haired.

Premise q is true; however, premise p is not "all inclusive," and, hence, the conclusion r is false in this case. [Wynk does not have short hair; he is a flat-coated retriever.] Carefully observe that no truth table is presented.

Many statements (as shown in the foregoing) contain words which mean how much or how many; these may be implicitly or explicitly stated, but in logic they must be considered explicitly. Some examples are as follows: the universal quantifier, *all*; the existential quantifier, *some*--meaning "at least

A PROFITABLE BREED OF DOGS

(Flat-coated retriever, "Langside Chief." Winner of first prize and championship for retrievers at Cruft's
Dog Show, 1902.) From a color print (dated 1902) in the author's private Pontchippi Collection.

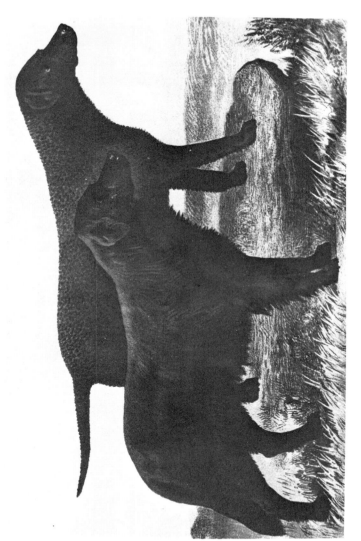

RETRIEVERS

Wavy-coated (left): "Dusk," the property of Mr. S. E. Shirley, J.P., M.P. Mr. Shirley (1844-1904) established the Kennel Club (1873) and was largely responsible for "fixing" the wavycoat and the flatcoat. Curly-coated (right): "Toby," the property of Mr. W. A. How. From an old color print (Vincent Brooks Day & Sons, Lith.) in the author's private Pontchippi Collection.

NEWFOUNDLAND, "LEO"

(The property of Mr. S. W. Wildman, late Mr. Howard Mapplebeck's.) From a color print in the author's private Pontchippi Collection. Original painting by W. E. M.; print by Cassell, Petter, Galpin & Co. Lith.,London.

IRISH WATER SPANIEL, "CAPTAIN"

(The property of Mr. Hugh Beaver.) From an old color print of the portrait by R. S. Moseley in the author's private Pontchippi Collection. (Printed by Cassell, Petter, Galpin & Co. Lith., London.)

one." Additionally, such phrases as "for all," "for each," and "for every" are used interchangeably in logic. Moreover, in logic, "for some" has the same meaning as "there is a" or "there is at least one." Clearly, these topics have not been extensively treated here.

Finally, as further illustrations of the incompleteness of this chapter, we have not treated methods of taking negations extensively enough. Explicitly, we have not even shown that $p \lor (\overline{p})$ is a tautology. We have not even taken the negation of $[p \land (\overline{p})]$ and then proved that the resulting proposition is a tautology; in fact, this tautology is the well-known "law of the excluded middle." This chapter is incomplete in other respects ... .

BLINDERS: "They say" retrievers don't whine if they wear them! But, then neither can we mark!

[Idea suggested by an article by Leonard Crawley, "Blinkers for a whining Labrador," *The Field*, January 8, 1970, page 51.]

INSTANT PUDDIN'

INSTANT
JUDGE??

INSTANT GRITS

Even a retriever needs training!

SHOOTING.   PLATE I.

Going Out

From a color print in the author's private Pontchippi Collection.   Engraved by T. Sutherland from a painting by
D. Wolstenholme.   Published by R. Ackermann,   101 Strand, London, May 1, 1823.

SHOOTING. PLATE II.

Game Found

From a color print in the author's private Pontchippi Collection. Engraved by T. Sutherland from a painting by D. Wolstenholme. Published by R. Ackermann, 101 Strand, London, May 1, 1823.

SHOOTING.   PLATE III.

Dogs Brought the Game and Reloading

From a color print in the author's private Pontchippi Collection.   Engraved by   T. Sutherland   from a painting by
D. Wolstenholme.   Published by R. Ackermann,   101 Strand, London, May 1, 1823.

SHOOTING. PLATE IV.

Refreshing

From a color print in the author's private Pontchippi Collection. Engraved by T. Sutherland from a painting by
D. Wolstenholme. Published by R. Ackermann, 101 Strand, London, May 1, 1823.

CHAPTER FOUR

IDEAL JUDGE

At this writing, probably no two (actual) experienced RE's or judges would agree on every detailed specification for an ideal judge. The foregoing notwithstanding, I am suggesting that any person who judges would profit by struggling through the mental exercise of preparing a set of specifications for his ideal judge. In short, I am asserting that each and every person who dares to judge requires a standard. Hence, in spite of the fact that such an undertaking borders on a philosophical inquiry and clearly involves values, I think it is worthwhile to make a start toward formulating a working standard or model of the ideal judge (see Chapter Seven for further comments concerning models). Inasmuch as no such individual actually exists, moderate departures from the conditions specified will not be expected to give rise to serious difficulties.

IDEAL JUDGE, $\mathcal{J}$

When a branch of knowledge makes repeated use of a definition, concept, or phrase, a symbol may be invented to represent the concept or phrase; in other words, it is worthwhile to write the subject matter in shorthand. In the language of symbolism, the first letter of a word is often used to represent a number. In this discussion, I have chosen to let a symbol represent a model. By writing the letter J in "foundry script" typeface in this book, I have explicitly assigned special meaning to this first letter of the word judge.

Definition of $\mathcal{J}$.--The symbol $\mathcal{J}$ refers to a theoretical model of the idealized (nonexistent) judge of American retriever trials.

Shifting concept. -- Many aspects of the concept of ideal judge $\mathcal{G}$ of retriever trials are expected to change not only as the retriever game changes, but along with other changes in America and the world. The foregoing notwithstanding, how could we, at this point in time, write the actual, complete, realistic specifications for our ideal judge?

I shall assume that it is not a feasible or practical task for you or for me; moreover, I shall assume that if the individual details could be explicitly stated, the ideal combinations of these detailed specifications would remain unknown. Clearly then, we shall be concerned here with only the most obvious and elementary theoretical aspects of the problem under very heavy implicit assumptions.

As a start, we could outline aspects of the model of our ideal judge in a number of ways, say, in the form of an essay, in terms of the probability of certain well-defined events, in terms of sets, by means of Venn diagrams, even in terms of the over-simplified graphic presentation often referred to as a profile, and in other ways. To suggest how this knotty problem might be approached, it is convenient to begin by illustrating elementary aspects of the methods known as sets and Venn diagrams.

General Comments on Sets

A collection of objects or things of any type will be called a set. For example, all five-point open judges as of January 1, 1963, would constitute a set and each member of this group would be called either a member or an element of the set.

[*Aside:* Other examples of sets may be worthwhile.

A set of camping cook pots which can be stuffed and nested together: frying pan, coffee boiler, 4 plates, and 4 cups (10 members or elements of the set); a set of camouflage clothing composed of cap, head net, jacket, and trousers (four elements); a set (an eight-member set) of game bird glasses: greenwing teal, Canada goose, canvasback, pheasant, mallard, pintail, widgeon, and quail; a set of U.S.

Mint Federal Duck Stamps, 1934 to 1967 (34 members); a set of colored prints entitled "shooting" and illustrating dove, duck, pheasant, and quail (four elements); a set of ceramic upland game birds consisting of mourning dove, cock quail, hen quail (three elements).]

The number of elements in a set can be either finite or infinite (e. g., the set of positive integers). If the set contains no elements it will be called an empty set and denoted by φ (lower case Greek letter phi). Sets may be specified in either of two ways, the *roster* method or the *descriptive* method. In the roster method all elements of the set are listed and enclosed in braces, e.g., the set consisting of the first three letters of the English alphabet {a, b, c} where the symbol { } is read "the set of." (Note that small letters are used in this case to name the members of the set.) In the descriptive method, a rule is given by which it can be determined whether or not an object is an element of the set. This was the case for the set of five-point judges mentioned above.

Two sets A and B are said to be equal if and only if they have the same elements (this is equivalent to saying that there are two names for the same set). Set A is said to be a subset of set B if all the elements of set A are also elements of set B. (Note that capital letters were used to name the sets.) If we wish to consider various subsets of a particular set (collection of objects) we will call this particular set the universe (short title for universal set) and denote it by U.

Now consider three operations on subsets of U:

(1) If A is a subset of U, then the complement of A (denoted by A') is the set of all elements of U which are not elements of A.

If A and B are any two subsets of U, then

(2) the *intersection* of A and B (denoted by A ∩ B) is the set of elements which belong to both A and B. (Read the symbol ∩ as "intersection." Read A ∩ B as "the intersection of A and B.") Note that any two sets have an intersection.

(3) The *union* of A and B (denoted by A ∪ B) is the set of elements that belong to either A or B or both (read the symbol ∪ as "union"; read A ∪ B as "union of A and B"). Note that any two sets have a union.

Comment on Venn Diagrams

These operations may be shown clearly by means of Venn diagrams. A rectangle will be drawn to represent the universal set U and circles will be drawn within the rectangle to represent the subsets A and B. We note that A ∩ A′ = φ and A ∪ A′ = U. If we denote

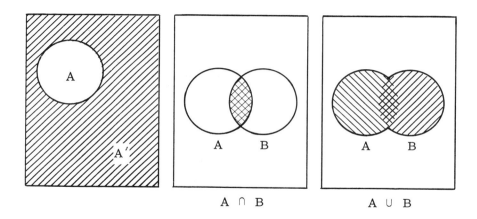

A ∩ B   A ∪ B

the number of elements in a set, say, set A, by n(A) (read "n of A") we can easily deduce the following relations by using Venn diagrams:

(a) n(A ∪ B) = n(A) + n(B) − n(A ∩ B), where n(A ∩ B) is the number of elements which belong to both sets A and B and n(A ∪ B) is the number which belong either to set A or set B or both. The subtraction is necessary in order that the elements common to both sets A and B do not get counted twice. If n(A ∩ B) = 0, that is, if A ∩ B = φ, we say that A and B are mutually exclusive (or disjoint) sets.

(b) n(A ∩ B′) = n(A) − n(A ∩ B) = number of elements in A which are not also elements of B.

(c) $n(A \cap B') + n(A' \cap B)$ = $n(A \cup B) - n(A \cap B)$ = $n(A) +$ $n(B) - 2n(A \cap B)$ = number of elements that belong to one set or the other but not to both.

The operations of intersection and union can be easily extended to three or more subsets since the operations, when applied to any two subsets, yield a single subset--actually a new set.

One Criterion of $\mathscr{J}$ in Terms of Sets

Let the universal set U be the set of all attributes (of interest) of our ideal judge $\mathscr{J}$. Further, denote these "important" attributes of interest as a_i and for purposes of this discussion, let i = 1, 2, ..., 9; hence we have a_1, a_2, a_3, a_4, a_5, a_6, a_7, a_8, and a_9. Continuing, let

$$U = \{a_1, a_2, a_3, a_4, a_5, a_6, a_7, a_8, a_9\}$$

be the universal set, and more conveniently, let

$$U = \{1, 2, 3, 4, 5, 6, 7, 8, 9\}.$$

Now consider the subsets of U given by

$$F = \{1, 2, 3, 6, 9\}, \quad G = \{4, 5, 6, 8\},$$
$$H = \{6, 8, 9\}, \quad I = \{7\}.$$

By applying the definition and operations stated earlier, the complements of F, G, H, and I are as follows:

$$F' = \{4, 5, 7, 8\},$$
$$G' = \{1, 2, 3, 7, 9\},$$
$$H' = \{1, 2, 3, 4, 5, 7\},$$
$$I' = \{1, 2, 3, 4, 5, 6, 8, 9\}.$$

The unions are given by

$$(F \cup G) = \{1,\ 2,\ 3,\ 4,\ 5,\ 6,\ 8,\ 9\},$$
$$(F \cup H) = \{1,\ 2,\ 3,\ 6,\ 8,\ 9\},$$
$$(F \cup I) = \{1,\ 2,\ 3,\ 6,\ 7,\ 9\},$$
$$(G \cup H) = \{4,\ 5,\ 6,\ 8,\ 9\},$$
$$(G \cup I) = \{4,\ 5,\ 6,\ 7,\ 8\},$$
$$(H \cup I) = \{6,\ 7,\ 8,\ 9\}.$$

The intersections follow:

$$(F \cap G) = \{6\},$$
$$(F \cap H) = \{6,\ 9\},$$
$$(F \cap I) = \varphi,$$
$$(G \cap H) = \{6,\ 8\},$$
$$(G \cap I) = \varphi,$$
$$(H \cap I) = \varphi.$$

Clearly, additional complements, unions, and intersections of these sets can be formed. For example,

$$(F \cup I) \cup (G \cup H) = \{1,\ 2,\ 3,\ 4,\ 5,\ 6,\ 7,\ 8,\ 9\}$$
$$= U,$$
$$(F \cap G) \cap H = \{6\},$$

and there are many others.

Criteria.--Suppose that we state that one criterion (in this model) of our ideal judge $\mathcal{J}$ is the attributes included in the largest number of intersections of our basic subsets. Obviously, attribute 6, really a_6, must be included.

Venn Diagrams

Pictorially, the attribute a_6 stands out clearly in Figure 4-1 (clearly it is R_1).

If a_1 is an object contained in a set F, it is convenient to write $a_1 \in F$ as shorthand for "a_1 is an element of F" (where $\in$ is the lower case Greek epsilon). In general, for any element, say x, we

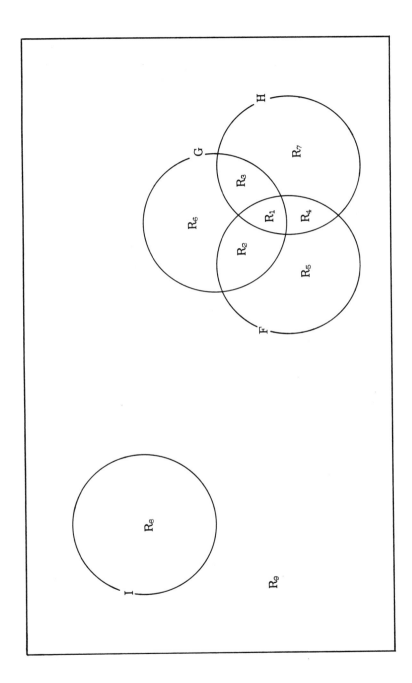

Figure 4-1. -- Venn diagram indicating nine non-overlapping regions for discussion.

can write $x \in F$ (x is an element of F or x belongs to F) or when x is not an element of F, we can write $x \notin F$.

Using our four basic subsets, the nine non-overlapping regions R_j $(j = 1, 2, \ldots, 9)$ of Figure 4-1 correspond to the nine possibilities for any element $x \in U$ as follows:

R_1 $x \in F$ and $x \in G$ and $x \in H$

      $x \in (F \cap G \cap H)$

R_2 $x \in F$ and $x \in G$ and $x \notin H$

      $x \in (F \cap G \cap H')$

R_3 $x \in G$ and $x \in H$ and $x \notin F$

      $x \in (G \cap H \cap F')$

R_4 $x \in F$ and $x \in H$ and $x \notin G$

      $x \in (F \cap H \cap G')$

R_5 $x \in F$ and $x \notin G$ and $x \notin H$

      $x \in (F \cap G' \cap H')$

R_6 $x \in G$ and $x \notin F$ and $x \notin H$

      $x \in (G \cap F' \cap H')$

R_7 $x \in H$ and $x \notin F$ and $x \notin G$

      $x \in (H \cap F' \cap G')$

R_8 $x \in I$ and $x \notin F$ and $x \notin G$ and $x \notin H$

R_9 $x \notin F$ and $x \notin G$ and $x \notin H$ and $x \notin I$.

From Figure 4-1 and the explicit description in terms of set notation, there remains no doubt that we want $\mathscr{J}$ to have attribute a_8.

Clearly, these methods can be extended to specify the attributes desired in the ideal judge, $\mathscr{J}$.

In Terms of a Profile

Without much doubt, we shall want specifications, measurements, which will predict well what our judge will do in a licensed stake. Indeed, we want multiple measurements on this individual. Furthermore, we might prefer to retain the identity of each measure until we integrate them to make the decision:

this is our ideal judge

versus

this is not our ideal judge.

We would like to measure with high reliability, to discriminate well between our "candidates" for the ideal judge, and measure aspects of behavior related to judging retriever trials as well as aspects uncorrelated in the population of candidates for ideal judge.

Now suppose that we assume away problems of unreliability and invalidity and attempt to operationally conceptualize the ideal judge in terms of an over-simplified graphic presentation, the profile. Further, suppose that we would like our ideal judge to surpass 9 out of 10 (or 95 out of 100, or even 99 out of 100) eight-point judges (where one might with some justification assume that all candidates for our ideal judge must be obtained from this population of eight-point judges) with regard to measurements on certain attributes which we think are important. For convenience in the remainder of this discussion, suppose that we settle on the ninety-fifth percentile; that is, out of 100 eight-point candidates selected strictly at random, we shall expect our ideal judge to be "better than" 95 of those candidates with regard to the individual attributes a_i, where $i = 1, 2, \ldots, k$, $k + 1, \ldots, n$. [*Aside:* As stated earlier, the collection of attributes that I select would undoubtedly differ from yours, not only with regard to content, but also number and importance (rank).] Now if we disregard the problem of combining these a_i, and invoke some well-known assumptions, we can suggest our model in terms of some selected specifications of our ideal judge $\mathscr{J}$ by means of the profile shown symbolically in Figure 4-2. Explicitly note that "normal probability paper" is used on the vertical scale.

MY IDEAL JUDGE, $\mathscr{J}$

In order to clarify my own thinking, I have described my ideal judge in terms of all five methods mentioned earlier. For the purposes of this book, I shall present my concept of $\mathscr{J}$ in the form of an essay (Appendix B) with all its ambiguities and shortcomings.

A pittance of practice may be worth a tome of theory.

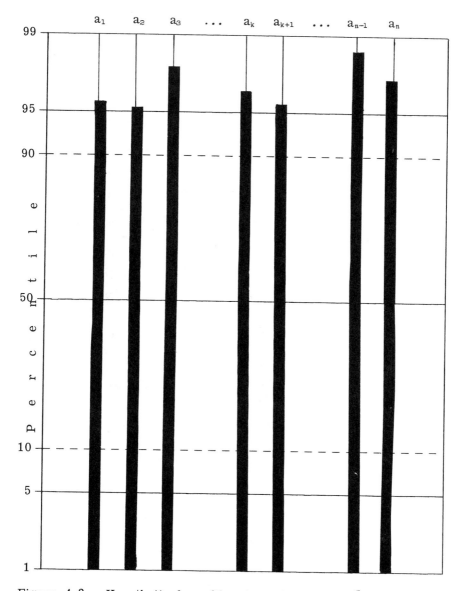

Figure 4-2. --Hypothetical profile of an ideal judge $\mathscr{J}$ of American retriever field trials.

"Ol' Mac. He hisse'f alone dared to do what he thought was best for the game. He did what he wanted to do. He didn't ask nobody!"

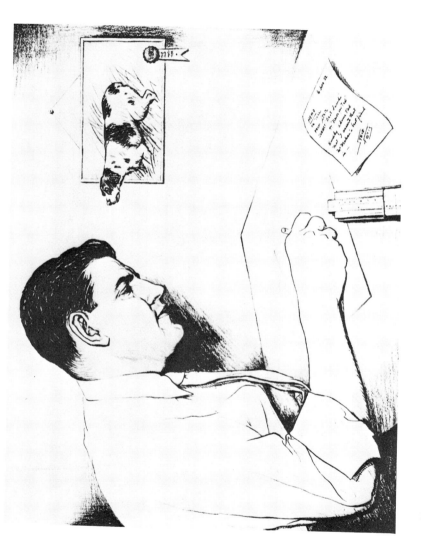

From a pencil sketch of the author and Tex, the Brittany, by (and a gift from) Stephen W. Fotis, 1952.

In a book "gone to the dogs" that contains pictures of H.M. the Queen, this one picture is devoted to His Honor, Mr. President. Group picture including the author (arrow) by Richard N. Corliss, The Independence Examiner, August 8, 1959.

CHAPTER FIVE

THE DRAWING

The field trial premium list issued by a host retriever club in the United States contains statements essentially as follows: ... entries will close with the field trial secretary at a specified address, date, and time. Drawing will take place at ... a specified address, date, and time. Furthermore, a set of rules applying to retriever field trials contains the statement which follows: "In stakes for retrievers the order of running shall be decided by lot at the draw, dogs worked by the same person or belonging to the same owner being separated when possible. ... The drawing may be arranged so that all bitches are drawn after all dogs." Since the noun "lot" may mean an object used in deciding a matter by chance, it is assumed that the above statement implies that the "running order" is to be determined by some randomizing device, by chance.

Randomization

Randomization is the impersonal, objective, mechanical process of arranging a series of (numbered) objects in random order (undefined in this book). The process is used in the drawing to prevent the favoring or handicapping of an entry, owner, or handler; and the process is used for other reasons. Subjective assignment of entries to the running order is not permissible in well-conducted drawings; there must be an element of randomization.

Haphazard versus random. -- A haphazard method of drawing cannot be substituted for a strictly random method under any circumstances; a randomizing device is mandatory. Furthermore, it is well-known that a common method of writing numbers on slips of paper, then "drawing numbers out of a hat" is a poor and inadequate randomizing device.

Randomly Generated Numbers

For convenience in preparing a randomized running order, tables of random sampling numbers can be used. These tables of so-called random numbers are produced by some sort of random digit generator. If one made a table of randomly generated digits from 0 to 9, "in the long run" one would expect the relative frequency of occurrence for each of the 10 digits to be the same; that is, equal to 0.1 for each digit. One would expect the numbers to have other characteristics of randomness also. There are many types of random digit generators, one of which makes use of ordered pairs.

Ordered pairs.--Within a pair of objects, oftentimes it is convenient to distinguish the first object from the second object. When such a distinction is made, the two objects are called an ordered pair. If the first object is denoted A and the second object is denoted B, the ordered pair is written (A, B). The ordered pair is enclosed in parentheses and a comma separates the first and second elements.

In a rectangular coordinate system, the ordered pair (x, y) represents a point in the plane under consideration. If $x = 4$ and $y = 7$, it is well-known that the ordered pair indicating the point (4, 7) is not the same as the ordered pair indicating the point (7, 4). Order counts; order is important in an ordered pair.

Ordered pair indicating shoe size.-- In the United States, it is a widespread practice to indicate shoe size by a pair of entries composed of a number followed by a letter such as $6\frac{1}{2}$ B. Suppose that retriever enthusiast McMahan is interested in purchasing a pair of boots. He has good evidence that he requires a size of $11\frac{1}{2}$ EE. He consults a catalog of a boot manufacturer and selects the type of boot he desires. On the page illustrating his boots of choice he notes that the sizes available are indicated by "x" in a table such as the one which follows:

	7	$7\frac{1}{2}$	8	$8\frac{1}{2}$	9	$9\frac{1}{2}$	10	$10\frac{1}{2}$	11	$11\frac{1}{2}$	12	$12\frac{1}{2}$	13
A					x	x	x	x	x	x	x	x	x
B			x	x	x	x	x	x	x	x	x	x	x
C	x	x	x	x	x	x	x	x	x	x	x	x	x
D	x	x	x	x	x	x	x	x	x	x	x	x	x
E	x	x	x	x	x	x	x	x	x	x	x	x	x
EE	x	x	x	x	x	x	x	x	x	x	x		

At the top of the table, there is a column labelled $11\frac{1}{2}$; on the left margin of the table, the last row is labelled EE. The intersection of the column (vertical strip) $11\frac{1}{2}$ and the row (horizontal strip) EE contains an x; this indicates that the desired pair of boots is available in the required size, $11\frac{1}{2}$ EE.

As indicated earlier, the mathematician has a somewhat different, but conventional, way of writing this; he calls it an ordered pair. He would write it as follows:

$$(11\tfrac{1}{2}, \text{ EE}),$$

where the first entry is a numeral and the second entry is a letter (a pair of letters in this case). He refers to this as an ordered pair where he separates the first entry from the second by means of a comma, and he encloses the pair in parentheses.

Note clearly that if we agree to use the ordered pair for shoe size of (numerals, letter(s)), we cannot reverse the order; that is, we cannot write (EE, $11\frac{1}{2}$). We must follow the order agreed upon.

Ordered pair indicating tract on a map.--In the example of shoe size, the first entry of the ordered pair was a numeral, the second entry was one or more letters. Obviously, this is not the only convention; in *other circumstances*, one could place the letter in the first

position and place the numeral in the second position. To illustrate,
periodically for many years, New Orleans Public Service Incorporated
(NOPSI) has issued a *Transit Guide and Street Map of New Orleans*. On
a map dated May, 1963 , certain locations are referenced by letters
and numbers, for example, the 1500-acre City Park where I have
trained retrievers and bird dogs for years was referenced as F-5,
E-5, E-6 (see cross-hatched areas of Figure 5-1). Pontchippi-on-
Canal is about 3   miles from the Harrison Avenue entrance to City
Park; using NOPSI notation, I would reference Pontchippi-on-Canal
as E-4 (see the solid black area of Figure 5-1). On the NOPSI map,
the letter is found in the side borders; it indicates a horizontal strip
across the map. The numeral is found in the top and bottom borders;
a numeral identifies a vertical section (strip) on the map. Following
the convention specified earlier, the mathematician would write the
ordered pair E-4 as   (E, 4). To elaborate further, as indicated in
Figure 5-1, the map has been divided into 11 horizontal strips and
17 vertical strips; each one of these 187 subdivisions can be identified by an ordered pair (letter, numeral), for example, (E, 4) as
shown in the foregoing.

If we focus on Figure 5-1 and use the ordered pair (letter, numeral), the first entry is a letter chosen from the set, say,

$$L \; = \; \{A, \; B, \; C, \; D, \; E, \; F, \; G, \; H, \; I, \; J, \; K\} \; ,$$

and the second entry is a numeral chosen from the set, say,

$$N \; = \; \{1, \; 2, \; 3, \; 4, \; 5, \; 6, \; 7, \; 8, \; 9, \; 10, \; 11, \; 12, \; 13, \; 14, \; 15, \; 16, \; 17\} \; .$$

[In Chapter Four, we agreed to call a collection of objects or
things of any type a set, the symbol { } is read "the set of." For
further discussion of the concept of set, see Technical Note 8-2 .]

For use with the NOPSI map, we agreed on the ordered pair (letter, numeral); hence, we cannot use (numeral, letter).

Kube with the professor in "City Park," 1969.

Pontchippi Shooting Brake (Morris Minor, 1963), with two-wheel mobile kennel designed and built (on the front end of a 1962 Volkswagen) by C. A. McMahan, Esq. (**Aside:** *Jack P. Strong and I made two trips, 1961 and 1965, to the British Isles together. Dr. Strong spent 1962-1963 in London; he acted as my agent, purchased the Morris, and had it shipped to me.)*

Nineteen-sixty-five Pontchippi Shooting Brake (Buick) with (roof carrier and) mobile kennel.

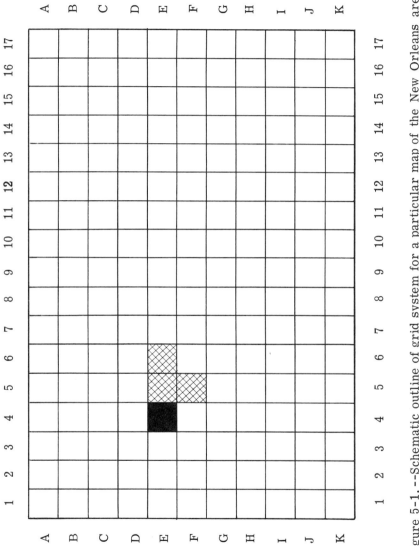

Figure 5-1.--Schematic outline of grid system for a particular map of the New Orleans area.

[Note that ordered pairs are referred to as *ordered* pairs rather than simply as pairs because the *order* of the entries is meaningful. Suppose a map were prepared using numerals for both horizontal and vertical strips. Pontchippi-on-Canal would then be located at the intersection of points (5, 4) instead of (E, 4). Obviously, the reference (4, 5) would not be the location of Pontchippi-on-Canal.]

Ordered pair, two tosses of a coin. -- If a coin is tossed twice and if H represents heads and T represents tails, the outcome can be represented as one of the ordered pairs (H, H), (H, T), (T, H), (T, T). It is understood that the first element of the ordered pair indicates the result of the first toss and the second element indicates the outcome of the second toss.

Random digit generators. --One of the simplest random digit generators is as follows: Toss a coin and then roll a die; this will produce an ordered pair; 12 ordered pairs can be produced using this method. Discard the 2 ordered pairs where the 6 appears on the die. Assign digits to the ordered pairs as shown in Table 5-1. As an illustration, suppose the coin shows a head and the die shows a 5 (H, 5); then the experiment has generated the random digit 4 .

As another illustration of a random digit generator, use can be made of two dice, say, one red and the other one white. Place the two dice in a cup, shake thoroughly, and roll. If the red die shows even, that is, 2, 4, or 6, consider that a head (H) has occurred; if the red die shows odd, that is, 1, 3, 5, consider that a tail (T) has occurred. Now observe the number face-up on the white die. This will produce an ordered pair; 12 ordered pairs can be produced using this method. Discard the 2 ordered pairs where the 6 appears on the white die. Assign digits to the ordered pairs as shown in Table 5-2. As an illustration, suppose the red die shows a 4 and the white die shows a 1 (H, 1); then the experiment has generated the random digit 0 .

Random numbers. --Random numbers is a short title for randomly generated numbers. A particular group or table (set) of random num-

Table 5-1.--Correspondence between ordered pairs (coin, die) and random digits

Ordered pair (coin, die)	Random digit
(H, 1)	0
(H, 2)	1
(H, 3)	2
(H, 4)	3
(H, 5)	4
(T, 1)	5
(T, 2)	6
(T, 3)	7
(T, 4)	8
(T, 5)	9

Table 5-2.--Correspondence between ordered pairs (red die, white die) and random digits

Ordered pair (red die, white die)	Random digit
(2 or 4 or 6, 1)	0
(2 or 4 or 6, 2)	1
(2 or 4 or 6, 3)	2
(2 or 4 or 6, 4)	3
(2 or 4 or 6, 5)	4
(1 or 3 or 5, 1)	5
(1 or 3 or 5, 2)	6
(1 or 3 or 5, 3)	7
(1 or 3 or 5, 4)	8
(1 or 3 or 5, 5)	9

bers (digits) is neither random nor not random *per se;* a group of digits is labelled random digits or random numbers because of the random
physical process which generated the numbers. The numbers in Table
5-3 were generated by a random process; hence, Table 5-3 is called
a table of random numbers.

It is ridiculously easy to randomize by using a table of random
numbers; however, to prepare detailed directions may make the method appear cumbersome since it may take much less time to do a randomization than to write about the process.

A Procedure for Drawing by Using a Table of Random Numbers

Suppose that nine handlers of retrievers meet for a training session where each handler has one and only one retriever. Further suppose that these handlers decide to run in a strictly randomized order.
Hence, the task is to arrange the nine retrievers in a strictly random
order.

Step one.--List the 9 retrievers by name and assign each retriever an identification number, 1, 2, and so on, to 9 as is shown
in the worksheet below.

Name of retriever	Identification number
Bias	1
Bob	2
Dash	3
Demo	4
Fara	5
Kube	6
Tex-S	7
Top	8
Weesie	9

Table 5-3.--Random digits, obviously tabulated in widely spaced, single columns for convenience

Line number	Column number																
	1	2	3	4	5	6	7	8	9	10	11	12	13	14	15	16	17
001	8	7	3	9	1	7	9	0	8	7	6	1	9	7	9	6	4
002	0	8	3	8	2	4	8	7	0	4	7	9	2	2	9	8	2
003	5	9	1	9	7	6	4	1	1	2	5	7	1	8	4	5	5
004	7	9	8	7	4	4	5	5	9	6	5	5	1	0	9	0	8
005	1	3	1	6	3	0	9	8	3	6	1	9	2	8	6	1	4
006	3	2	0	3	1	6	7	3	4	9	9	7	9	2	8	1	8
007	9	6	0	5	8	4	4	9	0	1	5	4	4	6	7	8	2
008	0	6	6	6	2	7	9	3	1	6	0	3	4	0	3	0	3
009	7	7	1	4	6	9	6	4	3	1	9	9	0	9	6	1	7
010	1	2	9	5	6	6	0	5	4	8	1	8	4	8	3	3	7
011	7	0	2	0	1	7	7	1	4	5	8	3	8	3	9	4	3
012	1	2	2	1	8	4	7	9	0	6	0	9	2	8	6	3	2
013	2	5	1	9	4	6	6	3	6	9	6	5	1	3	1	6	5
014	2	8	7	6	4	3	9	9	6	4	1	0	6	9	4	5	1
015	1	3	9	6	4	3	2	1	9	0	0	5	4	3	3	2	8
016	9	2	7	9	2	2	9	9	0	0	2	0	5	6	5	9	5
017	0	9	5	3	5	8	2	9	6	6	1	7	5	3	8	3	1
018	9	0	7	2	5	1	8	3	2	2	1	2	8	2	9	3	5
019	1	0	3	7	6	6	9	9	6	3	9	7	6	8	6	4	4
020	0	7	2	1	2	1	6	0	4	6	4	4	2	8	1	0	2
021	3	8	0	5	3	7	3	5	6	0	5	7	0	9	7	7	8
022	7	2	9	1	6	4	8	7	6	0	4	3	1	1	4	8	0
023	1	3	6	4	6	8	5	7	6	0	8	9	2	7	2	2	9
024	1	6	4	2	1	5	2	8	6	7	0	7	5	3	6	6	3
025	7	1	4	9	1	1	4	2	3	8	7	8	7	0	3	6	4
026	5	0	7	8	9	8	2	5	2	9	8	8	1	2	6	9	5
027	0	0	8	3	6	8	0	2	9	3	6	8	1	2	3	3	9
028	2	2	8	2	6	2	4	6	0	9	6	8	0	7	6	4	0
029	9	7	1	3	9	7	0	8	4	4	7	1	3	6	7	2	9
030	9	2	9	8	1	6	9	7	0	6	2	2	0	0	4	6	4
031	4	4	8	5	1	6	7	4	2	5	6	3	0	8	1	1	9

(Continued)

Table 5-3. --(Continued) Random digits, obviously tabulated in widely spaced, single columns for convenience

Line number	Column number																
	1	2	3	4	5	6	7	8	9	10	11	12	13	14	15	16	17
032	6	7	8	2	2	5	0	8	9	1	3	7	8	1	4	7	8
033	8	9	3	9	9	0	7	2	7	8	8	1	4	0	5	3	5
034	0	0	8	9	3	9	5	2	3	0	6	9	3	7	6	5	1
035	3	6	7	4	5	6	5	2	7	9	1	0	7	1	5	3	9
036	0	2	8	0	9	5	1	5	9	5	3	5	0	9	1	6	2
037	3	6	6	0	4	7	6	5	7	1	8	7	0	8	2	6	5
038	0	2	0	6	0	9	9	0	0	3	8	6	9	4	9	4	5
039	4	1	8	0	6	7	2	2	5	2	3	0	0	7	7	9	4
040	5	4	2	4	5	2	6	7	0	7	2	3	8	6	1	1	8
041	1	4	8	5	3	9	6	5	8	6	6	0	4	4	9	3	2
042	6	8	4	8	3	7	2	9	8	6	0	1	0	3	8	8	5
043	7	8	1	5	9	0	5	6	8	8	0	9	0	9	7	6	1
044	7	4	7	3	4	5	9	0	8	5	8	3	1	6	5	0	0
045	0	8	0	2	3	8	1	1	3	4	1	8	5	3	6	3	6
046	3	1	4	9	9	5	4	3	7	7	5	1	9	3	6	3	7
047	3	6	5	9	4	5	6	9	4	4	5	2	5	8	5	5	9
048	9	4	5	0	3	4	8	9	9	3	0	6	7	3	4	8	3
049	8	4	8	0	0	9	3	6	8	5	0	3	3	3	9	3	9
050	4	3	6	8	3	8	7	8	9	2	3	5	6	5	2	8	5
051	9	8	8	1	7	3	0	0	6	9	2	7	2	2	8	5	7
052	6	1	5	4	0	8	1	5	4	6	6	0	4	8	5	9	9
053	5	9	1	0	5	1	7	6	0	2	1	5	8	7	6	4	6
054	9	2	1	2	9	4	0	2	7	7	7	1	7	8	8	7	2
055	1	0	7	5	2	7	0	4	6	9	4	9	3	3	4	1	4
056	3	3	3	0	2	1	4	6	3	9	9	0	2	1	1	5	0
057	6	8	6	9	5	8	7	7	6	3	3	2	3	1	5	3	1
058	3	7	5	6	9	0	5	6	1	4	5	7	2	5	3	3	3
059	0	6	5	3	9	4	4	4	7	9	3	2	5	2	2	4	9
060	1	8	1	5	5	5	9	9	4	2	2	1	9	2	9	0	6
061	0	8	4	0	5	4	7	4	2	8	7	3	9	0	3	2	2
062	5	4	9	5	9	4	3	2	1	0	1	6	5	9	2	1	9

(Continued)

Table 5-3.--(Continued) Random digits, obviously tabulated in widely spaced, single columns for convenience

Line number	Column number																
	1	2	3	4	5	6	7	8	9	10	11	12	13	14	15	16	17
063	0	9	7	4	3	5	3	9	3	4	9	1	8	9	9	9	9
064	6	8	6	0	4	8	8	1	2	4	4	7	2	0	9	9	8
065	6	8	0	2	4	1	0	3	4	2	8	8	3	1	7	5	6
066	8	6	2	5	5	0	3	8	8	6	1	8	8	7	8	3	2
067	4	4	3	0	4	0	3	1	9	6	2	4	2	6	3	4	2
068	1	1	8	7	6	8	0	7	3	0	4	4	7	0	2	6	8
069	1	1	0	3	6	6	0	6	3	0	1	7	8	8	2	6	4
070	0	9	4	9	9	9	0	3	6	3	2	9	2	9	3	8	3
071	8	5	9	9	5	5	2	8	8	0	8	1	1	8	3	5	3
072	8	4	9	9	9	3	9	5	6	5	1	7	7	0	9	8	1
073	9	1	2	9	3	2	8	3	5	7	5	1	5	5	2	7	4
074	2	5	6	2	3	4	6	0	1	2	0	0	3	6	5	4	2
075	7	4	6	1	0	1	5	9	2	9	8	1	8	5	8	0	5
076	1	3	9	6	9	7	9	0	0	7	6	9	0	0	8	0	3
077	6	8	5	1	0	9	7	2	4	4	5	8	7	4	5	0	5
078	7	7	3	2	2	5	5	3	0	2	8	1	2	1	6	7	3
079	2	2	0	9	9	8	8	3	1	5	7	3	1	4	3	4	1
080	7	5	2	8	7	9	5	5	1	8	8	2	5	6	2	4	9
081	1	4	5	0	2	0	6	6	0	8	3	3	2	1	4	6	8
082	7	3	6	1	3	8	8	7	9	5	5	1	3	9	8	2	4
083	0	3	4	5	9	3	3	8	0	7	0	6	7	4	8	2	5
084	1	9	2	8	8	2	3	6	9	6	4	4	0	1	5	6	7
085	3	6	6	8	6	8	6	2	1	8	9	5	2	0	1	6	0
086	7	3	1	2	5	2	4	2	2	6	9	8	3	1	8	4	7
087	7	5	3	6	1	7	1	3	1	1	4	6	9	0	1	3	7
088	7	9	3	6	6	0	2	2	3	3	1	1	1	9	1	9	6
089	1	3	7	0	6	5	0	4	0	8	5	0	9	0	1	3	3
090	3	2	9	0	6	0	7	1	9	7	3	8	7	8	0	6	9
091	1	7	9	3	9	3	4	9	9	0	4	4	9	7	4	0	2
092	6	4	2	3	5	6	2	2	4	8	2	4	7	3	5	3	3
093	4	9	7	7	7	3	9	0	7	8	5	5	2	1	0	5	5

(Continued)

RETRIEVER THEORY

Table 5-3. --(Continued) Random digits, obviously tabulated in widely spaced, single columns for convenience

Line number	Column number																
	1	2	3	4	5	6	7	8	9	10	11	12	13	14	15	16	17
094	3	7	8	4	9	6	1	8	7	1	8	5	3	8	4	8	4
095	1	2	8	2	2	2	9	6	4	8	3	4	5	9	1	9	9
096	6	5	4	3	1	4	8	5	3	0	2	5	3	9	2	7	3
097	9	2	5	9	1	5	8	0	9	7	9	1	6	5	1	1	9
098	3	0	5	0	5	0	9	3	5	5	7	1	1	7	5	9	9
099	2	9	4	5	0	6	1	2	2	2	0	3	8	0	0	6	0
100	3	8	3	4	2	9	8	1	9	0	2	4	6	5	0	6	1
101	5	6	4	2	1	3	1	4	3	8	1	5	0	6	9	9	8
102	2	4	3	4	0	4	6	4	6	5	7	9	7	7	4	0	6
103	4	3	9	5	9	2	0	6	1	3	0	3	7	0	4	2	0
104	7	3	6	4	0	7	5	1	8	7	2	9	5	6	2	0	5
105	7	3	4	6	5	3	7	7	4	0	5	3	5	9	7	9	7
106	4	0	2	5	5	4	5	6	3	0	6	7	9	5	8	6	2
107	1	4	8	1	7	8	3	8	6	9	6	3	2	6	4	5	5
108	4	2	7	2	3	3	5	8	1	9	1	9	9	7	9	2	1
109	7	5	4	8	9	1	3	9	6	6	0	5	3	7	5	2	9
110	4	9	2	2	9	3	6	5	9	3	5	4	2	4	4	6	6
111	5	1	0	8	0	4	9	8	0	3	8	8	5	4	2	3	8
112	5	5	4	5	8	7	1	9	6	9	3	4	0	8	6	8	0
113	3	3	8	7	5	5	5	1	3	4	6	1	8	4	5	0	4
114	6	8	2	4	2	2	7	6	0	6	2	8	0	3	2	5	8
115	1	7	9	4	7	2	7	4	9	4	1	2	5	4	7	2	5
116	6	1	8	1	9	5	9	9	0	6	6	9	9	6	1	6	8
117	9	7	2	1	5	8	4	8	2	3	8	4	2	3	5	0	9
118	0	7	8	3	4	4	1	4	5	3	5	2	2	2	3	2	8
119	8	2	5	2	4	8	3	5	0	7	0	1	3	4	8	8	2
120	0	8	7	9	3	1	9	9	8	7	1	7	7	2	0	6	9
121	1	5	4	4	6	1	0	7	1	0	1	8	5	4	5	8	3
122	3	1	3	4	7	3	3	4	5	6	8	1	9	9	7	8	3
123	8	7	5	9	6	3	4	9	3	9	0	9	2	2	2	5	0
124	0	1	6	3	5	8	3	6	7	0	1	5	2	1	8	0	7

(Continued)

Table 5-3.--(Continued) Random digits, obviously tabulated in widely spaced, single columns for convenience

Line number	Column number																
	1	2	3	4	5	6	7	8	9	10	11	12	13	14	15	16	17
125	5	3	8	8	4	4	4	0	7	2	3	1	5	1	2	8	3
126	4	3	7	9	7	0	2	7	9	6	4	7	0	6	7	5	3
127	5	9	7	6	0	9	4	7	3	5	3	2	4	6	2	4	4
128	4	0	2	2	4	3	9	6	4	8	6	5	2	2	7	9	2
129	1	5	8	5	4	3	1	9	9	9	5	8	1	2	2	3	5
130	5	9	4	9	9	6	2	2	0	8	2	3	7	2	6	6	8
131	6	2	7	5	2	5	2	9	7	0	9	1	5	6	1	0	7
132	2	0	0	2	4	1	2	2	7	4	3	2	7	4	3	9	3
133	0	3	6	1	6	2	3	8	9	8	3	0	1	4	8	9	0
134	9	1	8	7	3	9	0	9	7	0	4	6	0	0	9	9	2
135	5	6	3	8	6	3	7	6	7	6	0	8	5	1	6	9	4
136	3	3	1	6	6	5	6	3	6	9	7	9	6	4	7	8	5
137	9	3	9	5	8	2	4	8	7	5	8	5	9	5	8	3	1
138	3	9	4	6	9	8	0	5	0	4	2	0	5	0	7	5	6
139	9	5	5	8	6	3	1	2	9	1	6	9	8	3	5	5	6
140	1	7	4	0	9	0	1	4	0	1	6	1	5	0	5	3	8
141	1	6	0	3	6	4	3	2	5	7	9	7	5	3	7	7	0
142	2	3	5	4	4	4	4	0	5	4	3	8	2	1	0	2	5
143	5	7	0	2	2	9	3	4	4	2	4	8	7	3	1	9	8
144	1	8	5	9	9	2	4	0	9	8	2	2	5	2	1	3	1
145	6	3	2	8	3	7	8	9	7	8	6	8	7	0	4	8	7
146	8	5	4	0	5	8	1	7	0	4	1	5	7	6	6	8	6
147	5	6	6	4	0	0	5	0	3	4	7	1	2	2	8	8	7
148	2	4	5	7	6	0	0	7	7	4	3	2	8	9	7	1	4
149	8	2	0	3	8	0	4	5	8	5	5	4	3	6	4	7	0
150	0	1	5	0	2	3	4	5	9	6	3	9	7	2	2	3	4
151	9	3	5	9	8	0	9	1	5	0	6	9	0	2	3	1	5
152	4	4	5	9	2	2	4	6	9	0	6	0	3	6	7	2	5
153	7	2	6	8	4	8	1	9	3	6	4	5	3	8	3	1	0
154	7	5	6	2	3	2	6	2	1	9	9	3	3	1	2	6	2
155	0	4	2	4	8	3	1	6	2	8	1	9	2	3	9	9	5

(Continued)

Table 5-3. --(Continued) Random digits, obviously tabulated in widely spaced, single columns for convenience

Line number	Column number																
	1	2	3	4	5	6	7	8	9	10	11	12	13	14	15	16	17
156	0	7	8	5	8	9	5	6	3	9	3	4	2	4	2	6	6
157	4	0	9	0	7	4	1	2	1	6	8	7	3	4	7	4	9
158	7	3	3	1	6	3	5	5	1	0	6	4	8	5	2	3	3
159	3	8	8	0	4	9	4	9	9	3	0	2	5	7	0	1	0
160	6	4	4	5	0	8	7	1	0	0	3	1	6	6	8	0	4
161	9	2	1	4	0	4	4	4	8	3	3	6	2	2	9	8	8
162	5	1	8	3	9	3	0	6	1	6	5	3	9	3	5	3	3
163	4	1	0	4	6	0	8	8	2	3	8	3	8	0	5	6	0
164	3	1	8	3	6	4	9	3	7	2	3	3	4	3	7	3	3
165	5	5	6	7	2	4	1	7	8	3	8	3	7	1	0	6	9
166	0	7	5	9	9	9	1	0	0	5	5	3	0	3	1	9	8
167	0	4	0	6	3	2	5	1	4	1	9	6	3	2	1	6	7
168	9	5	2	0	0	7	1	7	4	1	4	8	6	0	4	5	4
169	2	9	2	9	7	8	2	0	1	4	7	7	3	6	6	5	3
170	7	8	7	5	1	0	9	0	4	0	1	9	7	2	8	9	6
171	8	6	7	6	6	0	8	4	9	7	5	6	0	9	7	6	1
172	8	0	9	9	2	0	1	7	2	3	3	7	0	6	4	1	3
173	4	8	4	4	8	3	3	5	1	9	3	8	3	2	2	0	0
174	3	1	0	2	2	0	5	4	2	1	4	4	9	2	3	0	1
175	2	8	2	4	6	2	5	9	4	1	0	6	2	6	7	8	5
176	1	9	0	2	9	8	2	7	0	3	2	7	0	8	3	5	5
177	5	9	9	8	9	2	3	3	0	9	1	5	1	1	2	5	6
178	5	9	4	3	8	3	7	3	9	5	9	3	7	3	9	4	7
179	0	8	8	4	7	9	5	8	7	9	9	8	1	4	2	9	2
180	1	1	4	1	0	4	2	0	7	8	5	0	3	4	7	7	4
181	6	7	9	8	3	3	4	3	5	4	3	2	9	5	2	3	0
182	4	9	8	9	4	9	7	3	4	8	4	9	3	7	0	8	6
183	3	2	4	4	7	8	1	0	7	3	6	8	2	6	8	8	9
184	1	0	3	0	4	4	3	0	1	7	6	1	3	2	9	1	7
185	1	2	9	5	4	3	1	0	9	5	8	3	8	3	5	2	0
186	3	7	2	5	9	0	3	2	7	7	5	9	4	0	5	7	5

(Continued)

Table 5-3. --(Continued) Random digits, obviously tabulated in widely spaced, single columns for convenience

Line number	Column number																
	1	2	3	4	5	6	7	8	9	10	11	12	13	14	15	16	17
187	7	4	6	3	8	4	0	9	9	8	8	4	5	3	7	6	9
188	9	5	7	0	2	4	7	8	8	4	7	1	7	1	0	1	0
189	0	3	7	6	8	9	8	6	3	4	4	6	8	3	1	1	2
190	0	4	7	6	2	2	7	5	6	7	0	7	0	2	1	4	0
191	3	6	1	1	1	7	8	9	1	6	0	6	6	0	4	0	1
192	0	7	7	7	0	8	1	7	9	5	0	9	4	6	6	5	6
193	1	3	0	3	4	0	9	5	4	2	7	4	2	2	8	7	6
194	5	8	5	0	2	0	1	8	9	7	4	0	6	9	7	0	5
195	6	4	9	1	2	0	4	5	1	5	4	4	8	6	4	2	5
196	6	8	8	1	7	3	6	6	7	6	6	6	1	2	2	6	4
197	3	0	0	6	4	0	9	8	7	8	2	9	5	2	3	2	6
198	1	1	2	2	5	2	9	3	2	1	2	1	6	6	7	6	6
199	5	9	6	0	1	8	1	3	3	1	6	1	7	8	3	3	1
200	7	6	1	4	4	2	0	6	5	6	6	7	3	1	2	5	6
201	9	5	7	2	0	3	9	4	0	8	4	0	4	3	9	9	1
202	9	6	4	3	2	9	5	1	6	1	3	3	9	4	2	2	2
203	0	1	2	1	0	4	1	2	1	6	9	5	8	4	7	8	3
204	6	8	0	3	5	3	3	0	5	5	3	9	6	5	2	7	5
205	7	3	1	5	9	9	8	7	4	5	6	4	6	7	0	3	9
206	6	9	5	5	5	8	0	4	9	0	0	8	1	6	8	7	6
207	2	6	4	6	5	4	8	2	2	7	3	6	9	2	9	5	6
208	1	7	2	5	8	7	9	9	9	9	1	6	5	5	6	9	4
209	9	1	4	5	4	6	7	4	6	2	8	2	5	3	0	1	4
210	1	6	0	8	9	8	0	3	0	1	0	8	5	2	4	8	9
211	6	6	4	5	4	8	8	4	8	1	4	1	2	1	4	8	9
212	9	7	4	8	0	5	3	8	0	4	2	2	4	5	9	9	9
213	8	3	9	6	1	5	7	2	6	6	3	9	9	9	6	3	7
214	4	2	3	1	1	3	3	6	6	4	1	2	7	6	5	3	4
215	2	8	1	7	4	8	4	7	0	7	4	0	3	0	2	7	5
216	2	4	3	5	8	8	2	3	7	5	5	9	4	3	3	9	4
217	9	1	1	2	6	0	5	5	0	4	5	8	0	9	0	0	2

(Continued)

RETRIEVER THEORY

Table 5-3.--(Concluded) Random digits, obviously tabulated in widely spaced, single columns for convenience

Line number	Column number																
	1	2	3	4	5	6	7	8	9	10	11	12	13	14	15	16	17
218	1	8	5	6	8	6	8	3	9	3	7	0	4	7	5	4	0
219	0	7	0	1	6	3	0	5	4	6	6	0	8	5	4	3	6
220	4	8	6	4	4	6	9	5	0	7	2	2	4	3	4	3	8
221	0	2	2	0	5	6	5	8	8	1	2	8	0	9	7	1	0
222	4	9	3	6	0	7	6	2	9	2	8	1	7	7	9	6	2
223	2	4	9	1	0	9	3	2	4	2	7	2	3	8	2	7	3
224	6	1	3	6	0	2	5	1	2	6	6	1	5	0	9	1	5
225	9	5	2	6	9	7	3	4	3	4	2	6	7	5	1	3	5
226	1	2	9	5	7	3	2	5	7	7	5	2	7	4	7	7	3
227	1	1	5	5	6	4	0	8	8	4	1	4	5	3	8	9	7
228	0	3	8	4	2	1	9	9	3	5	9	8	9	4	0	7	0
229	4	3	0	9	3	1	4	4	9	8	2	6	7	1	3	0	4
230	0	7	7	6	2	6	7	3	3	6	3	1	9	3	2	2	2
231	2	9	3	1	7	2	3	7	0	4	5	7	3	1	3	3	9
232	3	2	9	7	5	3	3	9	2	6	3	1	3	1	9	3	8
233	7	3	9	3	0	2	6	0	9	7	7	0	7	6	6	6	1
234	7	6	8	9	0	3	2	3	7	7	9	3	3	3	4	9	9
235	9	7	9	1	9	7	3	4	3	1	2	9	0	6	0	7	9
236	7	9	4	7	2	9	1	0	9	1	5	3	4	6	1	2	9
237	8	8	1	9	9	5	2	2	8	9	1	1	0	3	6	6	5
238	4	7	9	9	9	1	4	2	8	1	7	2	9	3	9	5	9
239	9	2	7	3	6	9	0	5	4	8	2	2	2	3	6	8	1
240	9	2	3	4	0	9	9	0	9	9	4	8	3	4	7	1	5
241	7	8	4	7	9	8	1	2	2	5	9	9	7	0	5	8	6
242	1	0	7	9	1	9	9	3	2	4	5	7	1	0	3	6	5
243	9	3	8	7	3	6	9	7	6	4	6	3	2	8	2	6	2
244	6	9	7	0	4	0	3	9	3	6	8	9	6	4	2	8	8

Step two.--Blindly select a starting place with the eraser of your pencil on one of the pages of random numbers of Table 5-3; follow columns of digits in serpentine fashion

until 9 different numbers in the range from 1 to 9 are obtained; ignore 0 and numbers which you have selected. For convenience, an excerpt of a table of random numbers is shown below. Assume that

Eraser fell at the tip of the arrow; start there and follow down the column .... .

2	4	3	0	2	4	2	2	0	0
5	6	6	1	6	9	8	0	1	0
1	5	1	2	9	3	4	2	9	5
2	7	6	0	0	6	8	5	5	8
6	8	8	5	4	0	9	3	7	9
0	1	3	5	4	1	1	4	7	0
5	7	4	7	4	9	9	6	1	3
5	5	3	4	3	6	3	7	8	8
2	7	2	2	5	7	7	6	7	6
0	6	1	7	9	8	1	4	4	8
4	8	1	3	0	5	0	9	3	0
2	4	9	3	8	2	3	5	7	0
9	7	9	0	3	4	2	4	7	3
2	3	9	6	1	8	4	3	4	7

you blindly selected the starting place as shown in the worksheet. It is clear that the first number drawn is 9; hence, Weesie becomes number 1 in the running order. Suppose that the next random number is 3, then Dash is number 2 (second) in the running order. Suppose that 6 is drawn next; then Kube runs third in the training session.

Suppose that the next number is 0; skip it in this particular drawing. Suppose that 1 is drawn next; then Bias runs fourth today. Suppose that 9 is drawn next; skip it, because 9 has already been drawn. Suppose that 6 is drawn next; again skip since 6 has already been drawn. Suppose that 7 is drawn next; assign Tex-S position 5 in the running order. Suppose that the next number drawn is 8; Top would be assigned position 6 in the training session. If 5 is drawn next, Fara would run seventh. If 2 is the next random number drawn, Bob would run eighth. Obviously, Demo would run last, and it should be noted clearly that he too was assigned to this position by a strictly random process.

A way of writing. -- It will be convenient throughout this book to use shorthand; for example, H, the first letter of h̲eads has already been used in this chapter; likewise T, the first letter of t̲ails was used. To illustrate further, rather than list each retriever by name, we could identify Bias as R_1 where R is the first letter of r̲etriever and the subscript "1" is used like an adjective (refer again to worksheet indicating identification number). Bob would be R_2, and Dash R_3. Rather than list all the other retrievers, we could use three dots,..., where the first dot means "and," the second dot "so," and the third dot "on." Then we could list the last retriever, Weesie, as R_9. In short, the original list of the 9 retrievers could be indicated by

$$R_1, \quad R_2, \quad R_3, \quad \ldots, \quad R_9.$$

In many situations it will be convenient to refer to retriever i, the ith retriever, as R_i, where i is merely a general index. In this case, i takes on the values i = 1, 2, ..., 9. Thus, in notation, the running order determined by a strictly random process could be written as follows:

$$R_9, \quad R_3, \quad R_6, \quad R_1, \quad R_7, \quad R_8, \quad R_5, \quad R_2, \quad R_4.$$

After the running order has been prepared, it cannot be labelled random; however, it can be said that it was prepared by a randomizing process. Furthermore, it is not relative to the problem at the moment whether or not the randomized running order can be explicitly followed at the training session or trial.

Comment: It is common practice, with enough exceptions to confuse a reader, to use the first letter of a word as a symbol. For example, rather than use R for retriever, one might use E, the first letter of entry, and use more than one subscript as we shall demonstrate later.

A slightly more involved procedure for drawing by using a table of random numbers.--It is convenient in a trial for a handler who has more than one entry to have entries of other handlers interspersed between his entries (it is also specified in a set of rules that this be done when possible). With this restriction in mind, suppose there are 12 retrievers entered in a picnic trial as follows: One handler has 4 retrievers entered, a second handler has 3, a third handler has 2, and each of 3 handlers has 1 retriever entered. This is in sharp contrast to the previous illustration where each handler had one and only one retriever entered. The retrievers entered could be listed as follows: Handler one, retriever one; handler one, retriever two; handler one, retriever three; handler one, retriever four; handler two, retriever one; ... ; handler six, retriever one.

Since it is convenient to write in shorthand, suppose that we let R_{he} stand for retriever number e of handler number h. In tabular form, retrievers entered in this trial might be indicated as shown in the following worksheet. Inspect this worksheet along with Figure 5-2 and note that four groups or "blocks" identified temporarily as B'_i (read B-prime sub-i) have been constructed where the entries of each handler who has more than one retriever entered compose a block, and where each entry of handlers with only a single retriever has been grouped with other such entries to form a block. If there had been many handlers, each with a single retriever to handle, we might have

Name		Temporary block or group, B'_i	Longhand	Shorthand, R_{he}
Handler	Retriever			
B.B.	Bias	B'_1	Handler one, retriever one	R_{11}
B.B.	Bob		Handler one, retriever two (that is, the second entry of this handler called "one")	R_{12}
B.B.	Dash		Handler one, retriever three	R_{13}
B.B.	Data		Handler one, retriever four	R_{14}
K.C.	Demo	B'_2	Handler two, retriever one	R_{21}
K.C.	Duchess		Handler two, retriever two	R_{22}
K.C.	Fara		Handler two, retriever three	R_{23}
C.W.	Joe	B'_3	Handler three, retriever one	R_{31}
C.W.	Kube		Handler three, retriever two	R_{32}
D.J.	Top	B'_4	Handler four, retriever one	R_{41}
W.S.	Tex-R		Handler five, retriever one	R_{51}
A.H.	Tex-S		Handler six, retriever one	R_{61}

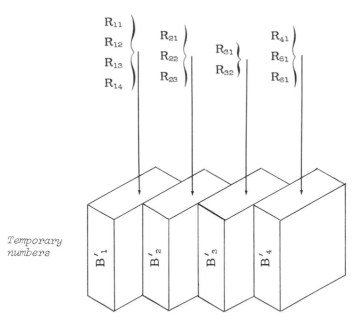

Figure 5-2. --Schematic illustration of temporary block assignments,
6 handlers, 12 retrievers.

utilized more than one group; that is, we might have used two or more
blocks as will be shown in generalized form later.

Again refer to Figure 5-2 which is a schematic illustration where
four (file) boxes, representing blocks, are utilized. Note that each
set of retrievers of a handler with multiple entries has been assigned
to a separate box (to a block); the three sets of retrievers where each
set belongs to a handler with multiple entries, occupy the first three
boxes. Inspect the symbols for the retrievers of box B'_1, and note
that the subscript $h = 1$ remains constant for each of the 4 retrievers of handler one; but note that the subscript e varies from 1 to
4, because this handler has 4 retrievers, each of which must be
identified. Reference B'_2, where the symbols for the 3 retrievers
for handler two all have $h = 2$, and e varies from 1 to 3. Reference B'_3 and note that for handler three $h = 3$ and e goes from
1 to 2.

The 3 single entries have been grouped together (blocked) and assigned to box (block) 4 denoted B'_4; note here that, in contrast to the 3 previous blocks, h varies from 4 to 6 and that e remains constant, remains equal to one (e = 1), because each handler has only 1 retriever.

Randomly assign permanent numbers to blocks. -- Again blindly select a starting place on a page of random digits of Table 5-3 with the eraser of your pencil; again follow columns of digits in serpentine fashion until 4 different numbers in the required range, from 1 to 4 are obtained; ignore 0 and numbers larger than 4. The 4 random numbers are the permanent numbers denoted B_1 of the blocks. For example, if you draw the number 4 first, temporary block 4 becomes permanent block 1; if the second random number is 2, temporary block 2 becomes permanent block 2; if the third random number is 1, temporary block 1 becomes permanent block 3; and, in view of the 3 random numbers already drawn, obviously, temporary block 3 becomes permanent block 4. The resulting permanent block assignments are shown schematically in Figure 5-3 as well as in the following worksheet. Inspect both the figure and worksheet and note that as a result of randomization, retrievers composing block B'_4 were switched from fourth position to first position, hence, B_1; retrievers in block B'_2 remained in second position, hence, B_2; retrievers in B'_1 became block B_3; and retrievers in block B'_3 became block B_4.

Reference the worksheet following Figure 5-3. --Because the blocks have been randomly and permanently assigned, the next step is to randomize within blocks. Refer again to the worksheet.

Refer to B_1. --Inspection of the R_{he} of block B_1 indicates that e is constant since each handler has only one retriever. Hence, we must randomize the handlers h, where h = 4, 5, or 6. Acting accordingly, we shall consult the table of random numbers in the range 4 to 6; the first random number selected is to be assigned first position within block 1, that is, number 1; say 6 is drawn from the

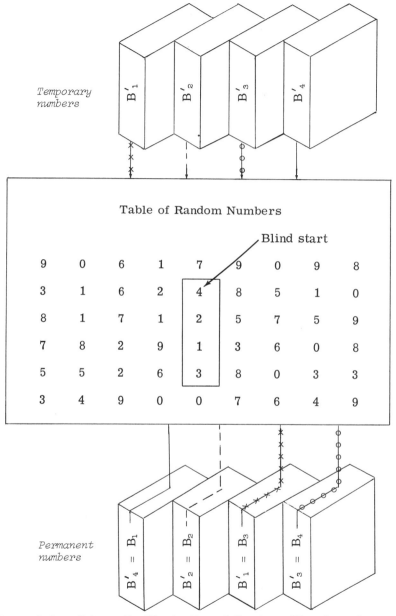

Figure 5-3.--Schematic illustration of the transition from temporary block numbers B'_1, through a table of random numbers to permanent block numbers B_1, 6 handlers, 12 retrievers, omitting symbolism R_{he} for convenience.

Permanent block, B_i	Shorthand, R_{he}
B_1	R_{41}
	R_{51}
	R_{61}
B_2	R_{21}
	R_{22}
	R_{23}
B_3	R_{11}
	R_{12}
	R_{13}
	R_{14}
B_4	R_{31}
	R_{32}

table; then R_{61}, where $h = 6$ is assigned number 1; the second random number in the range of 4 to 6, omitting 6, determines position 2, say 4 is drawn, then 4 is given position 2; that is, R_{41}, where $h = 4$ is given number 2; obviously, R_{51} takes position 3 and it should be noted that this position was assigned randomly also. Hence, the order is as follows for block B_1:

$$R_{61} \text{ is } 1, \quad R_{41} \text{ is } 2, \text{ and } R_{51} \text{ is } 3.$$

Refer to B_2.--We note that $h = 2$ does not vary in block B_2 since this is handler two and he has multiple retrievers entered. As a consequence, we shall randomize on e where e ranges from 1 to 3. Hence, we shall consult the table of random numbers in the range 1 to 3; the first random number selected is to be given first position in block B_2, say 1 is drawn; then R_{21}, where $e = 1$, is given number 1 in block $B = 2$; the second random number drawn, say

3, is given position 2; then R_{23}, where e = 3, is assigned 2; finally R_{22}, where e = 2, is given position 3 in block B_2. Hence, the order is as follows in block B_2:

R_{21} is 1, R_{23} is 2, and R_{22} is 3.

Refer to B_3.--In this block, inspection of the R_{he} indicates that h = 1 remains constant since these are the retrievers of handler one; hence, we shall randomize on e where e = 1, ... , 4. Consult the table of random numbers in the range 1 to 4; disregard digits 5, 6, ... , 9, 0; the first random number drawn is to be given first position in block B_3; say 4 is drawn, then R_{14}, where e = 4, is given position 1 in block B_3; if 2 is drawn next from the table of random numbers, R_{12}, where e = 2, is assigned position 2 in block B_3; if 3 is drawn next from the table of random numbers (skipping 4 and 2), then R_{13}, where e = 3, takes third position in block B_3; finally R_{11}, where e = 1, is assigned fourth position in block B_3. Hence, the positions in the running order corresponding to each retriever are as follows for block B_3:

R_{14} is 1, R_{12} is 2, R_{13} is 3, and R_{11} is 4.

Refer to B_4.--Again by inspection, we must randomize on e since h remains constant at h = 3. Consult the table of random numbers in the range 1 to 2; the first random number drawn is to be given first position in block B_4; if 2 is drawn, R_{32}, where e = 2, takes first position in block B_4; obviously, R_{31}, where e = 1, takes second position and the retrievers and corresponding positions in the running order are as follows for block B_4:

R_{32} is 1 and R_{31} is 2.

The retrievers with permanent block numbers and permanent order within blocks are shown in the worksheet below:

Permanent block, B_i (1)	R_{he} (2)	Permanent number within block (3)
B_1	R_{61}	1
	R_{41}	2
	R_{51}	3
B_2	R_{21}	1
	R_{23}	2
	R_{22}	3
B_3	R_{14}	1
	R_{12}	2
	R_{13}	3
	R_{11}	4
B_4	R_{32}	1
	R_{31}	2

Temporary running order. -- In order to prepare the temporary running order, list the first retriever in each block sequentially from block to block; next list the second retriever (if any) in each block sequentially; then list the third retriever in each block sequentially omitting any blocks that have been emptied, ... Following this procedure, the randomized temporary running order will be as follows: R_{61}, R_{21}, R_{14}, R_{32}, and back to block B_1, R_{41}, R_{23}, R_{12}, R_{31}, and back to block B_1, R_{51}, R_{22}, R_{13}, and since blocks B_4, B_1, and B_2 are empty, R_{11}. Inspection of the running order indicates that handler one will have to follow himself, that is, R_{11} follows R_{13}; however, this will rarely occur when preparing a running order for a licensed trial. By further inspection, it is clear that this can be remedied by assigning retriever R_{11} randomly to any one of the six positions indicated by X below:

$$X, \ R_{61}, \ X, \ R_{21}, \ R_{14}, \ R_{32}, \ X, \ R_{41},$$
$$X, \ R_{23}, \ R_{12}, \ R_{31}, \ X, \ R_{51}, \ X, \ R_{22}, \ R_{13}.$$

To repeat, X indicates a position where R_{11} could be assigned and handler number one not have to follow himself. Hence, number the X's from 1 to 6, say X_1, X_2, X_3, X_4, X_5, and X_6. (In passing, note that we have used X_i, where i = 1, 2, ..., 6.) Consult a table of random numbers in the range 1 to 6; the first random number selected indicates the position in the running order for R_{11}, say 3 is drawn from the table of random numbers. Then R_{11} would run in fifth position (that is, replace X_3) and the final randomized running order to appear in the program would be as follows:

$$R_{61}, \ R_{21}, \ R_{14}, \ R_{32}, \ R_{11}, \ R_{41},$$
$$R_{23}, \ R_{12}, \ R_{31}, \ R_{51}, \ R_{22}, \ R_{13}.$$

ORDER OF RUNNING FORMALIZED

With the two previous examples as background, it is worthwhile to re-examine the entire (randomized) drawing procedure in detail as well as to change the notation slightly. In this presentation, it is assumed that "owner" is synonymous with "person," and implies "handler" in this context. In other words, the discussion which follows disregards owner unless he is a handler.

General Procedure for Preparing the Running Order

If a handler has more than one entry, consider his multiple entries as a group called a block. In addition, where handlers have a single entry only, combine these single entries into one or more blocks (groups).

[*Aside: A further comment on symbolism and notation.*--As stated at the beginning of Chapter Four, when a branch of knowledge makes repeated use of a definition, concept, or phrase, a symbol may be invented to represent the concept or phrase; as indicated previously, it is convenient to write the subject matter in shorthand. In this book, the material is often stated symbolically since results stated "in letters" are amenable to several tests to which a problem "in numbers" is not amenable at all. In the language of symbolism, the first letter of a word is often used to represent a number; moreover, capital letters may be assigned a meaning which differs from a lower case letter. In the material which follows, note in particular that R is the first letter of ṟetriever, h is the first letter of ḥandler, e is the first letter of ẹntry, n is the first letter of ṉumber, m is the first letter of ṃaximum, b is the first letter of ḅlock, and s is the first letter of ṣmallest.]

In the previous example,

$$B'_t = \text{temporary block number}$$
$$B_t = \text{permanent block number}$$
$$R_{he} = \text{the } e^{th} \text{ entry of handler } h.$$

Now let

n_h = number of entries of handler h, so that e takes on values from 1 to n_h

H = total number of different handlers; hence, h takes on values from 1 to H

N = total number of entries, so that $n_1 + n_2 + \ldots + n_H = N$

k = number of handlers with a single entry

and

H − k = number of handlers with more than one entry.

Also let m and m′ be the two largest values of n_h with m′ ≤ m (read "m-prime is equal to or less than m"). That is, m is the maximum number of entries handled by a single handler. Thus,

$$n_h \leq m \text{ for } h = 1, 2, \ldots, H.$$

If s denotes the smallest integer equal to or greater than k/m, then

$$b = s + H - k,$$

where b is the number of blocks. In view of the above, i takes on values from 1 to b.

A DETAILED EXPLANATION

Case m ≤ k

This is the usual case in preparing a randomized running order for a particular stake in a licensed trial.

Step one.-- Clip together the multiple entries of each of the H − k handlers who have more than one entry; you will have H − k groups of entries. On each and every entry form, write an appropriate R_{he}. A listing of the R_{he} would appear as follows (where we are reserving the numbers 1 through k for handlers with a single entry):

$$R_{k+1,1}, \quad R_{k+1,2}, \quad \cdots, \quad R_{k+1, n_{k+1}} \tag{1}$$
$$R_{k+2,1}, \quad R_{k+2,2}, \quad \cdots, \quad R_{k+2, n_{k+2}}$$
$$\vdots \qquad \vdots \qquad \vdots \qquad \vdots$$
$$R_{H-k,1}, \quad R_{H-k,2}, \quad \cdots, \quad R_{H-k, n_{H-k}}.$$

Aside on notation.-- The dots of expression (1) do not imply that e is greater than 2; if e = 2, then expression (1) becomes

$$R_{k+1,1}, \quad R_{k+1,2}.$$

Step two.-- On each of the k forms where each of the k handlers had a single entry, write the appropriate R_{he} where e takes on the value "1" and h goes from 1 to k. Hence, a listing of the R_{he} (limited to those with one and only one entry) would appear as follows:

$$R_{11}, \quad R_{21}, \quad R_{31}, \quad \ldots, \quad R_{k1}. \tag{2}$$

Another aside on notation. -- Again the dots do not imply that k is greater than 3; if k = 2, then expression (2) becomes R_{11}, R_{21} or if k = 1, merely R_{11}.

Step three, assigning of temporary block numbers, B'_i. -- Since s denotes the smallest integer equal to or greater than k/m, then the k entries of handlers with a single entry will be divided into s blocks. Hence, the total number of blocks will be

$$b = s + H - k.$$

If we let the entries of each handler with multiple entries compose a block, there will be H − k blocks with temporary numbers

$$B'_1, \quad B'_2, \quad \ldots, \quad B'_{H-k}.$$

In addition, there will be s blocks made up of groupings of "single entries" with temporary numbers

$$B'_{H-k+1}, \quad B'_{H-k+2}, \quad \ldots, \quad B'_{H-k+s}.$$

Step four. -- Randomly assign permanent numbers B_i to blocks, where i goes from i = 1, 2, ..., H − k + s.

Step five. -- For permanent blocks which are composed of multiple entries of a single handler, that is, where h remains constant within a block B_i, randomize on e.

For permanent blocks composed of groups of entries of handlers with a single entry, that is, where e = 1 remains constant within a block B_i, randomize on h within blocks.

Now the results up to this point can be summarized in a table such as the worksheet which follows:

Permanent block, i (1)	R_{he} (2)	Permanent number assigned randomly within block i (3)
1	R_{he}	1 2 . . .
2	R_{he}	1 2 . . .
. . .	. . .	. . .
H − k + s	R_{he}	1 2 . . .

Printing the program. -- Now let E_{ij} denote the jth entry in the ith block of the previous worksheet with

$$i = 1, 2, \ldots, b$$

and

$$j = 1, 2, \ldots, n_i,$$

where n_i is the number of entries in the ith block and

$$n_i \leq m . \tag{3}$$

More on notation.-- Note that E is the first letter of entry. The subscripts i and j have no numerical significance; they are similar to adjectives. Eq. (3) indicates that the number of entries in any block number i must be equal to or less than m, the maximum number of entries handled by a single handler. Further note that i refers to block number, not to handler number.

The order of running which is to be printed in the program will be

$$E_{11}, \quad E_{21}, \quad \ldots, \quad E_{b1}, \quad E_{22}, \quad E_{23}, \quad \ldots, \quad E_{b2},$$
and so on,

where there is one-to-one correspondence between each E_{ij} and R_{he} through a table of random numbers. Obviously, you will publish information on each R_{he} using the associated E_{ij} for order only.

Case m > k

[*Aside on notation:* read "m greater than k."]

If $m \geq m'$ (read "m equal to or greater than m-prime"), say $m - m' = d$,   then d additional randomizations may be made to insure that no handler will have to follow himself. For example, on page 86 where m = 4, m' = 3,

$$m - m' = 1;$$

hence, only one random number was required (see page 93).

If bitches are to be run separately from dogs, the entire randomizing procedure should be performed once for dogs, then again for bitches.

Example.--At a spring licensed trial which I judged in   1966,   39 derby entries were listed in the program; these 39 entries were handled by 24 different handlers. One handler had 6 entries, 1 handler had 4 entries, 2 handlers had 3 entries each, 3 handlers had 2 entries each, and the other 17 handlers were listed as having a single entry only. This illustrates the usual case where m ≤ k.

Consider the problem of assigning these entries randomly, where dogs are not separated from bitches, with the restriction that no handler should succeed himself in the published running order. This restriction, that no handler should succeed himself in the published running order, may be violated in the tentative listing if any handler has more entries than the number of handlers with single entries, i.e., when m > k. This is not the case here and it seldom happens in preparing for licensed trials; however, if it does occur, randomize essentially as suggested and at the conclusion, inspect the results and make slight adjustments randomly as necessary; in other words, follow the procedure which was demonstrated for the "picnic trial" involving 12 retrievers.

In this example,

N = 39 entries

H = 24 handlers

k = 17 handlers with a single entry

m = 6 maximum number of entries handled by a single handler.

Since

$$\frac{k}{m} = \frac{17}{6} = 2\tfrac{5}{6}, \quad \text{then} \quad s = 3.$$

Hence,

$$b = s + H - k$$
$$b = 3 + 24 - 17$$
$$b = 10.$$

If the club desires to run bitches after dogs, separate the entries into two groups, dogs and bitches. In most cases, the number of dogs will be greater than the number of bitches. Set the entries of bitches aside; prepare the running order of bitches after the running order of dogs has been completed. The procedure which follows can be used for all entries or for dogs and then for bitches.

The purpose of the next two steps is to assign each entry to a block where the number of entries per block may vary from one to m, the maximum number of entries entered by a single handler in this stake.

Step one.--For the 7 handlers with multiple entries (totalling 22 retrievers), let the entries of each such handler compose a separate block. Note that there will be 7 blocks. On each of the 22 entry forms, write the appropriate R_{he}.

Step two.--Identify all entries which are entered by a specified handler who has no other entries in this particular stake; to elaborate, note that we are referring to a group constructed by repeatedly combining "the sole entry of a single handler." Write an appropriate R_{he} on each of the 17 forms. In addition, number each entry form from 1 to k, explicitly from 1 to 17. Next, divide these k entries into s blocks, where the number per block is equal to or less than the largest number of entries m entered by a single handler in this stake (explicitly note that this handler's entries are not being considered at the moment). Since k = 17 and one handler had 6 entries, m = 6, assign block sizes of 6 as far as possible; hence, 3 blocks are needed, say blocks 8 and 9 might be assigned 6 entries each, and block 10 might be assigned 5 entries.

Step three.--Assign temporary block numbers B'_i, where i = 1 to 7 for entries of handlers with multiple entries, and i = 8 to 10 for combined entries of handlers with single entries. To illustrate for this example, each block might now contain the following number of entries:

Temporary block number, B'_i	1	2	3	4	5	6	7	8	9	10
Corresponding number of entries	6	4	3	3	2	2	2	6	6	5

Step four. -- Arrange the blocks in random order by using Table 5-4 and renumber them; that is, assign a permanent number B_i from 1 to 10. To elaborate, in the present case there are 10 blocks temporarily numbered 1 through 10. In consulting the table of random numbers, 2 digits must be used (hence, Table 5-4), since 10 contains 2 digits; you will be seeking the numbers 01, 02, 03, ... , 09, 10. The first random number drawn between 01 and 10 becomes block number 1 and is given the permanent number 1 (B_1), the second random number drawn becomes block number 2 and is permanently numbered 2 (B_2), and so on to the last block drawn.

Step five. -- Randomize on e for the entries within each of the 7 blocks which is composed of multiple entries of a single handler (where h remains constant within a block B_i). For blocks of size 2, only the numbers 1 and 2 will be used for randomization; for blocks of size 3, only the numbers 1, 2, and 3 will be used for randomization; and so on.

Comment on Tables 5-3 and 5-4: Table 5-4 was prepared to emphasize that the desired random numbers were composed of two digits. Obviously, Table 5-3 would be completely satisfactory if two columns were consulted simultaneously. For this step, step five, I would use Table 5-3.

For permanent blocks composed of groups of entries of handlers with a single entry (where e = 1 remains constant within a block B_i) randomize on h within blocks.

Printing the program. --Now that the entries have been rearranged randomly within blocks, the procedure for preparing the running order to be printed in the program is as follows:

1. Block 1, entry in first position, E_{11}
2. Block 2, entry in first position, E_{21}
3. Block 3, entry in first position, E_{31}

RETRIEVER THEORY

Table 5-4.--Random digits tabulated in columns-of-two for convenience

Line number	Column number									
	1	2	3	4	5	6	7	8	9	10
001	30	27	31	17	16	24	85	97	60	28
002	19	14	89	47	62	12	34	93	13	00
003	75	39	49	64	50	55	36	88	51	65
004	66	81	01	92	02	33	73	10	23	26
005	54	78	58	22	41	74	76	04	99	57
006	03	63	95	83	68	37	77	96	20	71
007	94	15	18	43	21	67	53	82	11	79
008	46	72	32	42	52	61	44	05	59	90
009	86	25	80	09	87	98	08	45	70	69
010	35	29	38	91	48	07	56	84	40	06
011	71	07	37	73	54	75	50	91	17	32
012	48	67	41	52	77	93	10	59	14	05
013	29	58	45	31	25	86	61	40	70	51
014	12	02	60	55	99	23	57	87	82	94
015	97	83	63	88	22	69	27	76	64	11
016	36	90	84	19	65	68	38	42	47	89
017	18	06	34	20	49	21	46	96	13	28
018	62	35	03	16	01	74	04	44	56	09
019	26	33	43	39	08	00	66	30	92	15
020	81	78	80	24	95	72	53	98	79	85
021	56	75	77	47	76	49	26	65	62	11
022	13	70	78	85	20	16	98	99	50	51
023	07	45	25	22	63	35	91	39	15	06
024	81	24	03	84	61	60	94	34	18	54
025	12	41	17	57	28	08	88	30	80	74
026	43	69	79	55	00	52	72	97	89	32
027	92	73	96	93	36	58	29	86	01	53
028	09	83	05	68	23	14	27	46	40	19
029	66	33	64	95	67	71	42	87	02	48
030	21	37	82	90	59	44	10	38	31	04
031	02	94	97	71	45	00	85	83	74	52

(Continued)

Table 5-4.--(Continued) Random digits tabulated in columns-of-two for convenience

Line number	Column number									
	1	2	3	4	5	6	7	8	9	10
032	11	26	73	77	30	23	66	76	82	57
033	21	64	24	65	17	46	27	16	98	08
034	51	22	03	49	62	53	28	01	40	78
035	96	34	43	58	37	59	91	31	72	38
036	25	35	39	92	44	79	87	75	15	06
037	04	67	20	84	99	86	93	54	56	18
038	89	14	55	63	41	81	80	07	05	42
039	09	88	95	32	90	33	47	19	61	29
040	10	50	70	69	12	60	13	36	48	68
041	96	05	83	63	60	14	66	92	27	91
042	26	75	74	29	90	50	53	67	10	11
043	03	80	84	71	68	88	46	09	57	17
044	40	18	58	16	82	78	97	85	06	21
045	81	07	42	49	52	64	51	48	02	13
046	00	87	56	86	34	79	01	22	39	89
047	59	12	23	08	47	98	28	76	94	41
048	19	54	62	31	65	15	38	20	24	04
049	25	37	32	95	33	55	93	30	77	70
050	73	69	72	35	99	61	45	44	43	36
051	00	87	11	88	24	44	07	14	81	79
052	19	61	08	34	63	20	54	90	84	04
053	86	71	22	47	83	26	28	70	59	72
054	45	35	46	91	10	67	89	75	49	77
055	85	73	64	05	42	36	53	37	68	15
056	50	58	82	09	76	32	31	78	18	16
057	98	03	95	94	97	40	27	92	43	80
058	06	48	21	60	30	38	56	39	69	57
059	41	01	13	99	23	52	33	74	66	51
060	12	96	29	17	62	25	65	02	93	55
061	22	93	21	17	33	29	92	34	23	72
062	60	00	96	37	61	54	28	70	25	53

(Continued)

Table 5-4.--(Continued) Random digits tabulated in columns-of-two for convenience

Line number	Column number									
	1	2	3	4	5	6	7	8	9	10
063	71	46	36	11	66	77	87	67	74	26
064	80	27	35	91	12	52	30	64	43	20
065	94	24	75	05	62	78	04	95	82	15
066	81	83	51	39	58	48	41	79	02	63
067	86	90	16	40	31	38	07	42	69	57
068	84	73	55	10	88	89	14	03	08	50
069	68	85	97	98	65	56	18	09	47	99
070	59	13	76	44	49	45	32	01	06	19
071	36	73	48	97	34	74	63	10	01	49
072	96	17	72	78	40	00	47	64	88	71
073	30	92	37	55	62	19	09	80	42	18
074	22	60	82	35	76	70	95	58	79	81
075	28	68	41	38	27	51	25	46	98	53
076	54	56	90	89	87	99	85	67	45	04
077	31	83	02	57	29	26	77	21	91	84
078	14	15	08	05	86	03	33	59	66	69
079	13	43	93	23	44	07	06	12	32	52
080	20	16	50	65	75	11	39	24	61	94
081	65	56	67	21	99	09	79	38	43	84
082	23	87	26	50	53	45	04	24	15	49
083	78	20	06	47	76	98	92	48	17	73
084	71	14	34	08	46	22	27	57	88	68
085	02	59	12	96	37	36	82	75	35	31
086	93	77	60	44	91	83	86	01	18	03
087	97	41	07	29	30	72	05	11	52	95
088	70	90	61	66	28	39	33	81	13	58
089	94	10	00	19	89	16	32	62	80	55
090	25	40	85	63	51	74	54	42	69	64
091	22	06	86	69	27	41	37	28	98	52
092	84	47	31	80	82	51	08	76	94	30
093	79	53	57	17	72	56	20	95	93	01

(Continued)

Table 5-4. --(Continued) Random digits tabulated in columns-of-two for convenience

Line number	Column number									
	1	2	3	4	5	6	7	8	9	10
094	85	23	13	21	15	34	97	32	39	60
095	03	35	55	46	42	24	50	11	62	70
096	40	58	74	12	05	75	78	63	18	09
097	71	48	68	59	88	73	66	64	00	25
098	61	81	19	96	91	33	92	89	77	99
099	44	04	54	02	67	38	65	26	90	45
100	16	14	07	36	10	29	83	43	87	49
101	57	93	87	36	62	38	43	71	53	92
102	65	02	55	17	11	05	33	37	80	84
103	54	44	56	72	83	82	32	85	01	34
104	35	78	27	88	70	12	59	28	09	03
105	99	29	96	69	23	66	14	45	94	61
106	89	16	39	10	08	49	46	04	15	24
107	76	60	81	73	63	58	74	90	25	40
108	13	00	06	75	30	64	31	21	48	19
109	68	86	47	50	18	79	67	41	97	52
110	98	26	20	22	07	42	77	95	51	91
111	96	67	05	91	78	87	89	33	68	36
112	55	54	70	49	12	93	38	31	16	86
113	52	60	95	81	92	90	20	27	23	98
114	65	63	50	74	28	03	64	08	84	22
115	94	53	46	75	82	47	72	18	71	24
116	62	37	15	76	58	85	99	77	80	51
117	48	11	14	10	25	09	21	04	26	56
118	40	42	29	61	39	32	66	00	02	59
119	35	01	73	83	44	30	19	41	88	13
120	34	45	79	06	17	07	69	57	43	97
121	44	97	67	36	05	93	59	41	52	53
122	14	24	04	63	27	26	49	66	15	29
123	92	33	09	50	46	81	11	79	43	99
124	95	13	01	68	03	19	45	61	94	91

(Continued)

Table 5-4.--(Continued) Random digits tabulated in columns-of-two for convenience

Line number	Column number									
	1	2	3	4	5	6	7	8	9	10
125	28	73	88	00	56	48	08	70	65	20
126	25	16	80	51	02	83	69	96	76	58
127	23	38	75	57	47	86	34	42	10	98
128	31	87	64	39	85	21	78	07	71	12
129	77	90	40	72	84	32	22	37	18	06
130	62	89	74	55	30	35	82	54	17	60
131	40	09	81	50	02	24	35	83	66	74
132	84	33	59	86	46	64	95	78	54	75
133	36	49	57	72	19	42	17	01	51	27
134	89	91	52	97	73	93	61	69	87	13
135	56	28	15	21	20	00	88	68	94	62
136	92	32	04	11	45	96	53	63	79	18
137	70	41	98	80	58	31	26	14	34	67
138	85	37	12	65	38	39	03	30	48	60
139	90	08	22	06	23	47	25	76	43	55
140	99	71	16	44	77	07	29	82	05	10
141	24	06	07	12	64	36	63	92	56	95
142	10	81	38	61	21	59	73	09	37	78
143	11	16	20	49	98	80	82	85	43	96
144	65	86	08	02	03	84	48	77	66	33
145	93	41	75	15	87	46	90	67	18	29
146	13	79	35	99	62	58	23	17	00	97
147	39	60	72	31	69	26	94	05	45	76
148	25	32	22	30	89	19	68	40	70	47
149	04	50	88	51	55	52	14	28	53	74
150	83	71	44	27	91	01	57	42	54	34
151	88	36	67	81	73	65	51	21	22	78
152	12	76	08	26	45	25	05	37	83	74
153	48	09	71	57	56	84	52	11	20	68
154	13	63	50	10	58	02	01	91	00	55
155	59	82	23	89	34	30	98	69	72	53

(Continued)

Table 5-4.--(Continued) Random digits tabulated in columns-of-two for convenience

Line number	Column number									
	1	2	3	4	5	6	7	8	9	10
156	40	19	49	38	66	06	39	62	15	96
157	03	32	07	04	77	99	18	29	16	28
158	64	24	87	70	47	33	41	94	90	95
159	54	93	97	75	79	35	17	14	80	43
160	86	61	46	60	31	42	27	44	85	92
161	15	58	82	78	41	84	03	92	19	97
162	00	30	70	64	36	22	38	65	98	39
163	32	49	80	57	62	66	86	17	79	88
164	72	28	23	99	50	59	06	85	69	96
165	07	87	21	11	48	93	91	71	18	47
166	05	54	35	81	16	24	13	94	26	45
167	31	61	76	67	08	43	27	29	95	68
168	04	63	12	90	89	33	37	75	83	14
169	20	25	55	02	09	42	60	73	40	52
170	46	56	34	44	53	74	10	01	51	77
171	23	79	20	41	02	95	03	15	00	56
172	17	44	29	21	10	76	45	70	80	05
173	11	26	74	82	24	58	01	52	96	06
174	25	57	33	36	30	55	68	75	04	12
175	73	87	78	71	18	27	59	53	16	34
176	86	51	13	65	88	83	28	38	46	31
177	97	93	77	09	40	49	37	22	72	43
178	64	92	98	89	63	91	85	47	07	67
179	84	54	08	90	60	48	19	61	66	35
180	81	69	62	14	99	50	39	42	94	32
181	51	04	35	65	02	80	45	15	27	28
182	64	74	61	25	93	46	44	49	68	76
183	33	20	75	42	32	17	90	53	73	34
184	29	37	91	22	14	56	72	92	96	06
185	60	47	43	85	69	52	41	84	21	13
186	58	81	11	83	40	82	48	38	12	67

(Continued)

Table 5-4.--(Concluded) Random digits tabulated in columns-of-two for convenience

Line number	Column number									
	1	2	3	4	5	6	7	8	9	10
187	66	16	71	77	07	94	62	59	01	19
188	39	99	86	05	24	97	23	70	87	55
189	79	10	98	18	57	54	08	88	31	30
190	36	63	09	26	78	03	95	89	50	00
191	06	58	77	25	71	96	40	26	39	46
192	99	82	91	32	87	12	22	89	01	44
193	21	83	76	38	35	33	13	73	74	45
194	98	37	88	29	54	90	09	14	56	61
195	19	11	53	36	28	55	95	60	00	47
196	27	10	62	92	85	72	64	43	68	02
197	30	20	24	23	57	80	93	18	50	48
198	67	97	69	81	66	86	51	05	42	31
199	78	84	41	94	34	07	79	17	03	16
200	49	52	04	59	75	08	70	65	63	15

10. Block 10, entry in first position, $E_{10,1}$.

Now return to block number 1.

11. Block 1, entry in second position, E_{12}

12. Block 2, entry in second position, E_{22}

13. Block 3, entry in second position, E_{32}

.

.

.

20. Block 10, entry in second position, $E_{10,2}$.

(Note that a comma has been added for clarity, namely, 10, 2.) All blocks with only two entries are now empty; hence, skip them on the next round. Go back to block number 1; if it is empty, skip it and go to the next block which has an entry which has not been assigned to the running order. Continue until all entries are assigned.

Furnish the printer information on each R_{he} in the random order shown by the corresponding E_{ij}.

ACTION ITEMS

Item 1.--Devise practical procedures for conducting field trials which require dogs to come to the line essentially as drawn (assume that the drawing is conducted by a strictly random process).

Item 2.--As stated elsewhere herein, preliminary studies led me to hypothesize that running order was related to the probability of placing in an open stake. In 1967, a colleague and I designed a pilot study, wrote a protocol, and prepared a form (see next page) to collect data retrospectively with the intention of attacking the following question: During the period 1964-1966, was the order of running associated with the probability of placing in a licensed open stake? On December 29, 1967, I wrote a letter, ... , to which, according to my records, no written reply was ever received. I discussed the matter by telephone; and we even went to New York City in February, 1968, to pursue the matter further. In short, ... it was an abort!

(CAMcM--1967)

FOR RESEARCH PURPOSES ONLY

OPEN STAKE ONLY

Column	Code	Item
		NAME OF CLUB: _____

	_____ _____ _____	DATE OF TRIAL
		  Day
		  Month
		  Year

	_____	TOTAL NUMBER OF ENTRIES

	_____ _____ _____ _____	(PRINTED) PROGRAM NUMBERS OF ENTRIES AWARDED PLACES:
		  First
		    (1) Male (2) Female
		  Second
		    (1) Male (2) Female
		  Third
		    (1) Male (2) Female
		  Fourth
		    (1) Male (2) Female

	_____ _____ _____ _____ _____ _____ _____ _____ _____	(PRINTED) PROGRAM NUMBERS OF ENTRIES AWARDED JAM'S:
		  (1) Male (2) Female
		  (1) Male (2) Female
		  (1) Male (2) Female
		  (1) Male (2) Female
		  (1) Male (2) Female
		  (1) Male (2) Female
		  (1) Male (2) Female
		  (1) Male (2) Female
		  (1) Male (2) Female

		WERE FEMALES RUN LAST? (1) YES (2) NO
		IF YES, BLOCK NUMBERS OF FEMALES: _____

Checked by: _____   Prepared by: _____

    (Date): _____   (Date): _____

Action,   needed research: The basic question does need to be answered with a well-designed prospective study. Someone (else) must have enough "political finesse, " and be willing to exercise it, to negotiate and execute such a project.

Item 3.--Operational definition: Order of running is considered important in the two championship stakes.   *Comment (on evidence):* Even if he survives the stake, 10 or more series, retriever number one does not run first (in a championship stake) in each and every series.   Are there implications here for open stakes in particular? Discuss.

Oh,   Shurr-rrr,   Mac!

A pittance of practice may be worth a tome of theory.

NOTES TO CHAPTER FIVE

Names of Dogs and Bitches

Each name used for purposes of illustration in this book belonged to a personally owned dog-friend who, with but one exception, earned its keep as a hunter; furthermore, names of the "too many" animals which did not meet standards for quality work have been carefully excluded.

I named my first dog "Weesie"; she was a "brown all-southern water spaniel" who arrived at my home (covered with fleas and 6 weeks old) on a hot September day in 1926; I was 12 years old and in the eighth grade at the time. She turned out to be an excellent ratter; speak the word "rats!" and her ears went up--she was ready for action. Just to make the record explicitly clear, rat-killing was a minor field sport for the rural teen-age boy before the days of poison and pest-exterminating companies. In addition, Weesie "treed" squirrels and "jumped" and caught rabbits. Old photographs remind me that she would "sit-up," and climb a ladder and even fetch a thrown ball, a fallen dove, or a shot quail. I hadn't learned the term "mark a fall" at the time.

Fara was my first bird dog, an orange and white English setter bitch whelped in April, 1936; she was 6 weeks of age when she was given to me. She developed into a first-class bird dog; just how good she really was I didn't realize until I tried to replace her.

Dash was a dark red cocker male who hunted hard, and thoroughly enjoyed it; furthermore, he brought me my first ribbon in 1939.

Tex-S was a black and white English setter male; he was the first dog I owned that produced a field trial record. This must have been about 1940 since Tex was just coming into his prime as a 3-year-old when I was called to "active duty" in the fall of 1941.

Top was a handsome lemon and white pointer male; he was whelped in 1942 and I purchased him as a puppy. He was sired by a son of Muscle Shoals' Jake and turned out to be not only a real gentleman, but also a beautiful, high-headed, merry-tailed (in fact, I had the tip of his tail amputated because he kept it "raw" as a result of whipping briars), fast, wide-ranging bird-finder. He was among the very best of my many dog-friends, partially due, no doubt,

112

WEESIE

Holding a pipe, about 1927 or 1928.

A YOUNG ANIMAL TRAINER

The author with his goat, Billy, circa 1925. After training young calves to pull a wagon, I trained Bill to pull a cart, to gee and haw, to lie down on command, to walk on his hind legs, to "kneel and pray," to "shake hands," ... , to seek (be "it") in games of "hide and seek" among the aisles of a cotton warehouse, and to perform other feats.

FIELD DOG STUD BOOK REGISTRATION

McMAHAN'S LUCKIE PENNIE (256623)
NAME AND NUMBER

November 28, 1936
DATE WHELPED

White, black and ticked
COLOR

OWNER OF RECORD

. C. A. McMahan

Blue Ridge

. Ga.

English Setter Bitch
BREED AND SEX

Racketeer Don (225666)
SIRE

Miller's Pocono Dotty (247939)
DAM

DATE OF ISSUE

March 6, 1937

THE AMERICAN FIELD PUBLISHING COMPANY
INCORPORATED
1881

Certificate for the first gundog McMahan registered.

DIXIE

An English setter bitch puppy and litter mate to Pennie, with the author, spring, 1937.

DUCHESS

A Brittany spaniel, with Jerry and Mac, beside the 1941 car (Oldsmobile), 1944.

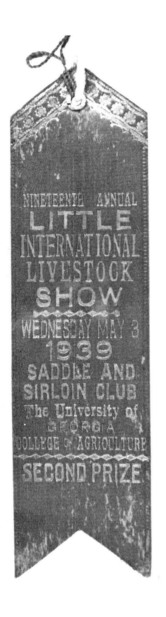

Exhibitor

Name _C a Mc Ilham_

№ 28

19 20 21 22 23

A cocker named Dash (1939).

Top with the author and Jerry, 1942.

Top (the pointer) and Patsy (the Brittany), with Jerry and the author, 1944 (note side-by-side, 16-gauge, Lefever).

I purchased Top as a puppy from his breeder Jas. C. Foster, Jr., the owner of "Triple Champion" Muscle Shoals' Jake (Top's grandsire), and the author of 20th Century Dog Breeding, San Antonio, The Naylor Company, 1939. In 1956, Alex and I spent a pleasant half-day with Mr. Foster at his loft of racing pigeon; Mr. Foster autographed my (then 17-year-old) copy of his book and it is now in my private Pontchippi Library.

Top, pointing quail, 1944.

Duchess and seven puppies in a temporary enclosure, Athens, Georgia, 1946.

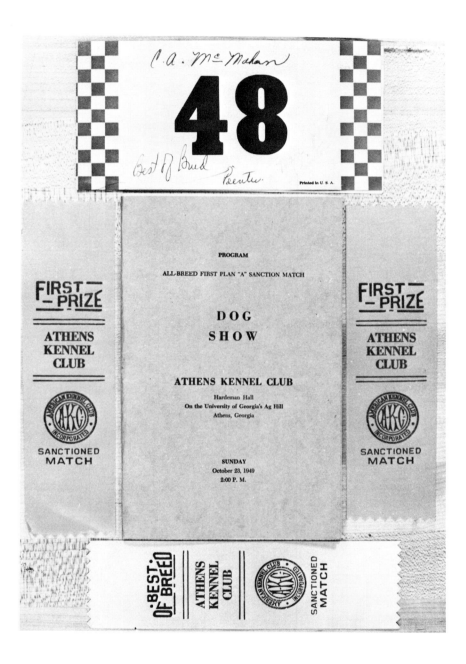

A pointer named Tim (1949).

QUAIL DOGS

Two first-rate walking shooting dogs (Brittanies), Bob (left) and Tex, with the author in the boot of the "fifty Buick," 1953.

TEX

Honoring his bracemate, 1953.

to the fact that someone else gave him lots of experience on birds (to a south-
erner, "birds" is synonomous with quail) for me during the "war years"
when I was otherwise occupied.

Unusual gundogs or ahead of my time.--As I reflect, it seems to me that I
have always been interested in unusual gundogs. In the late 1930's, along
with setters and pointers, I bred and hunted cocker spaniels on quail and used
them in the dove field.

When I was in the army during Hitler's war, I purchased three Brittany
spaniels: a dog in 1942, a bitch in 1943, and then another bitch, Duchess
(a litter mate to the first bitch). When I arrived home from the Philippines
in February of 1946, I bred Duchess; seven pups were whelped. Then along
came Tex-R (a really great liver and white Brittany male) in 1949. ... [It
was not until 1968 that Brittany fans got around to organizing the "Brittany
Spaniel Club of Louisiana" (see page 12, section two, *The Times-Picayune*,
New Orleans, Louisiana, Wednesday Morning, May 15, 1968).]

In short, there is a rich history associated with each and every name
used in this book. Some of the history is written in official records, while
friends of long-standing have first-hand knowledge concerning unofficial activities. There will be other comments to follow.

Excerpt From a Michigan Newspaper (Circa 1939)

Tex-S was the first field trial winner that I owned. The report of his
sale to me is described in the excerpt which follows:

> Fred B. "Abe" Martin scored a grand slam by piloting all three
> of his English Setters into the win column. He took first place in the
> puppy stake with Beau Jack, only five months old, and had the satis-
> faction of seeing his pup make a solid find, an unusual feat with the
> wily pheasant.
>
> Martin's Beau Tex, took second in the puppy stake, while Beau
> Reau beat out a classy field to take first in the derby.
>
> Martin's winners were sired by Shenvalee Sport, nationally
> known winner of 15 trials, who is also the sire of several other
> winners. Beau Reau and Beau Tex were recently sold by Martin to
> C. A. McMahan, Monroe, Ga., and Ralph Thomas of Detroit, well
> known sportsmen.

Weights of Dogs and Bitches

See Table 5-N-1.

Table 5-N-1.--Weight in pounds of four dogs and three bitches (a beagle and six retrievers), kennelled at Pontchippi-on-Canal, Friday, December 5, 1969

Kennel name, sex, breed	Approximate age	Weight in pounds			Estimated amount above or below specified animal's ideal weight‡
		Gross+	McMahan alone	Net of specified animal	
Chance, male, flatcoat	6 months	219	163	56	0
Choice, male, flatcoat	6 months	212	163	49	0
Demo, male, Labrador	$6\frac{1}{2}$ years	224	163	61	-10
Hankie, female, beagle	$11\frac{3}{4}$ years	183	163	20	0
Kube, female, Labrador	$11\frac{3}{4}$ years	244	163	81	+ 6
Wave, female, flatcoat	$3\frac{1}{2}$ years	235	163	72	+10
Wynk, male, flatcoat	$3\frac{1}{2}$ years	220	163	57	0

+ McMahan, in field trial attire, call it "Uniform F," holding specified animal in his arms and using usual bathroom scale.

‡ Amount in pounds; ideal weight is estimated in terms of general appearance and physical condition.

The author playing in the water with Wave and Wynk close to the "very gates" of the Spillway, 1966.

Hankie with Doc in the ... Spillway, 1966 or 1967.

Pontchippi Choice and Pontchippi Chance (flatcoat, M), age 7 weeks, held aloft by their breeder-owner-trainer-handler McMahan, 1969.

Three generations of retrievers at Pontchippi, 1969. From left to right: Digit, bitch sired by Demo; Demo; Kube, dam of Demo.

All-Breed Dog Show

BATON ROUGE
KENNEL CLUB, Inc.

(American Kennel Club Licensed)

ONE-DAY UNBENCHED

SHOW

Ryan Airport Field Gymnasium
Ryan Airport - Baton Rouge, La.

Sunday, February 22, 1959

Catalog—Price $1.00

Alex (arrow) and Hankie.

CHAPTER SIX

THE TRIPLE MARK

In private conversations, in small group discussions, as well as in panel discussions at judging conferences, I have been impressed with the muddled thinking concerning the (marked) triple. If you ask a question about the triple, no doubt a reply will follow; even if you ask a series of questions, undoubtedly a series of replies will follow. Note that I carefully avoided using the word *answer* in the previous sentence. These replies appear to reflect not only illogical but circular reasoning. Moreover, these muddled replies stem not only from novice judges who have judged (say) three qualifying stakes and, hence, know everything, but also from selected judges and selected handlers of national stature who know that they don't know all the answers.

After devoting considerable effort toward gaining a little insight into "the triple," I seem to discern a root of this illogical thinking. In short, and as a few experienced field trial men know, the triple involves highly variable and slightly complex phenomena.

It is the purpose of this chapter to barely outline a theoretical framework for considering the triple. In fact, for purposes of simplification, this chapter is limited, in the main, to the marked land triple on pheasant. It should be obvious that with slight modification, the methods and theory apply to the triple in general.

SETTING UP THE TEST

As was forcefully pointed out in the first two chapters and in Appendix A, it is assumed that the judges themselves have trained retrievers "all the way," that they know retrievers thoroughly, know how to exploit wind and terrain, know that "angle of flight" makes a difference, and are otherwise thoroughly competent and experienced in adjudicating all-age stakes. Beginning with these assumptions, discussion of the problem of setting up the triple is approached from the point of view of the judges, then from the point of view of the retriever picking up the "birds."

Use of three fliers is beyond the scope of this discussion. The problem is attacked from the point of view of judges who prefer to use one live bird in a test. The reader should carefully note, however, that examination and analysis of the problem is the same whether one flier or two fliers are utilized.

Assumptions Required

1.   Three locations in the field are used and these fixed locations are designated as 1, 2, and 3. These three locations are assumed to be fixed even if the judges "move the line" periodically. For convenience of discussion, the locations are numbered from left to right or clockwise as follows:

Location 2

Location 1   Location 3

(the "line")
Retriever-Handler

[*Opinion:* Note that this assumption reflects my biased opinion, namely, that in a triple, rarely should two birds be thrown from the same location (including a boat) at great distance from the line. *Justification:* It is my hypothesis that judges are "few and far between" who have enough experience and skill to combine distance of the falls from the line with angles of the throws to produce a genuinely sound test in such a circumstance (when two of three marks are "fired" from a single location).]

2. One live pheasant and two dead pheasant (or one dead and two live) are to be used.

3. Birds of either sex (hens or cocks) may be used at each location.

Symbolism: Utilize the following notation.

1. Let H denote a live hen, and h denote a dead hen.

2. Let C denote a live cock, and c a dead cock.

3. Let Hch indicate that a live hen was used at the first location, a dead cock at the second location, and a dead hen at the third location. To elaborate, the first letter indicates location 1, ..., and the third letter indicates location 3, as shown schematically below:

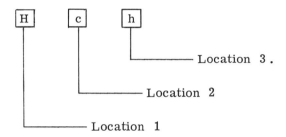

Similarly, ccC indicates that three cocks were used, with the live one being shot at the third location. Obviously, all other arrangements can be written by utilizing this scheme.

4. Let i, j, k, in the symbol

$$_{ijk}Hch,$$

indicate the order of firing (the order of throwing the marks). That is, let i = order of firing location 1, j = order of firing location 2, and k = order of firing location 3. Thus,

$$_{312}Hch, \tag{1}$$

indicates that a dead cock was thrown first at the second location, then a dead hen was thrown next at the third location, and lastly, a live hen was shot at the first location.

To elaborate, (the position of) i corresponds to the first location and the value of i tells in what order in the firing sequence the "first location was fired." A similar explanation can be made for j and k.

5.   Let ℓmn, in the symbol

$$_{ijk}Hch_{\ell mn},$$

indicate the order in which the birds were picked up.

Judges' Count of the Possibilities

If one live and two dead birds are used there are four possibilities in which (say) a live hen may be used at the first location, namely,

$$Hch, \qquad Hhc, \qquad Hhh, \qquad Hcc.$$

Whereas the live hen may also be used at any 1 of the 2 other locations, namely,

$$cHh, \qquad hHc, \qquad hHh, \qquad cHc,$$
$$chH, \qquad hcH, \qquad hhH, \qquad ccH,$$

there are 12 possibilities using a live hen with 2 other dead birds. Likewise, if 1 live cock is used we get 12 possibilities. Thus, we have 24 possible ways to set the test using 1 live pheasant and 2 dead pheasant at 3 locations.

There are 3! or 6 possible arrangements for the order of firing.

Notation: 3! is read "three-factorial"; it means the product of $1 \times 2 \times 3$. The symbol n! is read "n-factorial"; n! is defined as follows:

n! = 1 × 2 × 3 × ... × (n − 2) × (n − 1) × n.

Furthermore, zero factorial is defined to be equal to one; 0! = 1. It is conventional to write

$$3! = 3 \times 2 \times 1$$
$$3! = 6.$$

Permutations.--Each different order or arrangement in a line of a group of objects is called a permutation. In firing a triple, order is important; order "counts" in permutations.

There are 3! = 6 possible arrangements (permutations) for the order of firing, namely,

123,   132,   213,   231,   312,   321;

there are, in all, 24 × 6 = 144 possible ways of setting up the land triple on pheasant. These 144 ways are shown in Table 6-1. Column headings indicate three important aspects of the table: SN/W denotes the serial number of way of setting up the test; L-FS denotes location-firing sequence; and L-B denotes location and type of bird. For example, serial number 017 indicates

312   Hch,

which has the same meaning as expression (1) given earlier.

ACTION ITEM

Land triple simplified.--Suppose that a judge assumes that the observed performance of a retriever in a trial is a sample of all possible performances of that retriever (see section entitled "Inference, Population, and Sample" later in this chapter). Further suppose that the judge would like to observe a random sample of the performances of each retriever; more correctly, performance on a marked land

Table 6-1. --Listing of all possible ways of setting up a (marked land) triple on pheasant considering three locations, one live and two dead pheasant, cocks or hens, shot in any order

Serial number of way	Location-firing sequence	Location-type of bird	Serial number of way	Location-firing sequence	Location-type of bird
SN/W	L-FS	L-B	SN/W	L-FS	L-B
001	123	H h h	023	312	H c c
002	132	H h h	024	321	H c c
003	213	H h h	025	123	h H h
004	231	H h h	026	132	h H h
005	312	H h h	027	213	h H h
006	321	H h h	028	231	h H h
007	123	H h c	029	312	h H h
008	132	H h c	030	321	h H h
009	213	H h c	031	123	h H c
010	231	H h c	032	132	h H c
011	312	H h c	033	213	h H c
012	321	H h c	034	231	h H c
013	123	H c h	035	312	h H c
014	132	H c h	036	321	h H c
015	213	H c h	037	123	c H h
016	231	H c h	038	132	c H h
017	312	H c h	039	213	c H h
018	321	H c h	040	231	c H h
019	123	H c c	041	312	c H h
020	132	H c c	042	321	c H h
021	213	H c c	043	123	c H c
022	231	H c c	044	132	c H c

(Continued)

Note: C = live cock; H = live hen; c = dead cock; h = dead hen; SN/W denotes serial number of way of setting up the test; L-FS denotes location-firing sequence; L-B denotes location and type of bird.

Table 6-1.--(Continued) Listing of all possible ways of setting up a (marked land) triple on pheasant considering three locations, one live and two dead pheasant, cocks or hens, shot in any order

SN/W	L-FS	L-B			SN/W	L-FS	L-B		
045	213	c	H	c	071	312	c	c	H
046	231	c	H	c	072	321	c	c	H
047	312	c	H	c	073	123	C	h	h
048	321	c	H	c	074	132	C	h	h
049	123	h	h	H	075	213	C	h	h
050	132	h	h	H	076	231	C	h	h
051	213	h	h	H	077	312	C	h	h
052	231	h	h	H	078	321	C	h	h
053	312	h	h	H	079	123	C	h	c
054	321	h	h	H	080	132	C	h	c
055	123	h	c	H	081	213	C	h	c
056	132	h	c	H	082	231	C	h	c
057	213	h	c	H	083	312	C	h	c
058	231	h	c	H	084	321	C	h	c
059	312	h	c	H	085	123	C	c	h
060	321	h	c	H	086	132	C	c	h
061	123	c	h	H	087	213	C	c	h
062	132	c	h	H	088	231	C	c	h
063	213	c	h	H	089	312	C	c	h
064	231	c	h	H	090	321	C	c	h
065	312	c	h	H	091	123	C	c	c
066	321	c	h	H	092	132	C	c	c
067	123	c	c	H	093	213	C	c	c
068	132	c	c	H	094	231	C	c	c
069	213	c	c	H	095	312	C	c	c
070	231	c	c	H	096	321	C	c	c

(Continued)

Table 6-1.--(Concluded) Listing of all possible ways of setting up a (marked land) triple on pheasant considering three locations, one live and two dead pheasant, cocks or hens, shot in any order

SN/W	L-FS	L-B	SN/W	L-FS	L-B
097	123	h C h	121	123	h h C
098	132	h C h	122	132	h h C
099	213	h C h	123	213	h h C
100	231	h C h	124	231	h h C
101	312	h C h	125	312	h h C
102	321	h C h	126	321	h h C
103	123	h C c	127	123	h c C
104	132	h C c	128	132	h c C
105	213	h C c	129	213	h c C
106	231	h C c	130	231	h c C
107	312	h C c	131	312	h c C
108	321	h C c	132	321	h c C
109	123	c C h	133	123	c h C
110	132	c C h	134	132	c h C
111	213	c C h	135	213	c h C
112	231	c C h	136	231	c h C
113	312	c C h	137	312	c h C
114	321	c C h	138	321	c h C
115	123	c C c	139	123	c c C
116	132	c C c	140	132	c c C
117	213	c C c	141	213	c c C
118	231	c C c	142	231	c c C
119	312	c C c	143	312	c c C
120	321	c C c	144	321	c c C

triple selected at random.

If a judge thinks that a dead pheasant is a dead pheasant regardless of sex, he can set up a triple in six ways (see worksheet below),
where C = live cock, H = live hen, and ph = dead pheasant regardless of sex.

| "Way" number | Location | | |
for location	1	2	3
1	H	ph	ph
2	ph	H	ph
3	ph	ph	H
4	C	ph	ph
5	ph	C	ph
6	ph	ph	C

Of course there are 3 ! orders of firing (see unnumbered, untitled table on the following page). Clearly, under these restrictions,
there are 36 ways of setting up the land triple.

After a judge has used all his knowledge, skill, judgment, and art
in selecting the location, ... , he can select his test and firing order
randomly by rolling a die. First, roll a die for the sex and location
of the live bird; second, roll a die for the order of firing.

Example. -- Suppose the first roll of the die turns up a 3 , the live
bird, a hen (H), will be shot from location 3 (see way number 3
in the foregoing worksheet for location). Further suppose that a 5

"Way" number for order of firing	Location		
	1	2	3
1	1	2	3
2	1	3	2
3	2	1	3
4	2	3	1
5	3	1	2
6	3	2	1

turns up on the second roll of the die (see "way" number 5 of order of firing, above); the order of firing will be as follows: A dead pheasant is "shot" first at location 2; the live hen is shot second from location 3; and a dead pheasant is shot last at location 1.

In order to show the relationship of the foregoing to earlier discussions, suppose the judge feels that there is a difference in using a dead hen and a dead cock.

After a choice is made for the live bird (H or C) and a choice is made for the location (1, 2, or 3) there remain 2 distinct dead birds (h or c) to use in 2 distinct locations. This permits the judge further choice in $2^2 = 4$ ways (where the exponent 2 is the number of locations and the base 2 is the number of choices of birds) of selecting the dead birds and the locations after a live bird and location have been chosen. Whereas considering no difference in a dead hen and a dead cock led to $6 \times 3! = 36$ ways, now we have $6 \times 2^2 \times 3! = 144$ ways (as shown in Table 6-1).

Another example.--Suppose there were 3 types of dead birds (say, a dead cock pheasant, a dead hen pheasant, and a dead duck--not a drake) to choose from, we would have $6 \times 3^2 \times 3! = 324$ possibilities.

Discuss the possibilities for setting up "a quadruple."

PICKING UP THE MARKS

After the birds are down, a retriever can pick them up in $3! = 6$ possible ways, namely,

$$123, \quad 132, \quad 213, \quad 231, \quad 312, \quad 321.$$

Combining these 6 ways of picking up the pheasant with the 144 ways of setting up the test gives

$$6 \times 144 = 864$$

possible ways of completing the land test involving three marked pheasant.

Expanding expression (1),

$$_{312}\text{Hch}_{132} \tag{2}$$

indicates that the live hen which was shot last (third in the order) at the first location was retrieved first, the dead cock at the second location which was the first bird down ("fired first") was picked up last, while the dead hen at the third location which was the second bird thrown was picked up second.

In short, the retriever picked up the "wing birds," then the long one down the middle last. In particular, the last bird down was a flier on the left and he picked her up first, then he picked up the dead hen on the right, and finally he made the "long" retrieve of the dead cock.

The 864 ways of completing the triple are listed in Table 6-2. The first column indicates a convenient three-digit identification number (ID number). Entries of the second column are of the form xxx-x where the first three digits refer to the serial number of way (SN/W) of Table 6-1 and the digit following the hyphen (-) provides a permutation number (for one of the six permutations which a "retriever selects" in picking up the pheasant) within SN/W; hence, it is labelled "permutation number within way," denoted PN within way. Again, location-firing sequence is indicated by L-FS and location-bird by L-B. The column headed L-PS denotes location-pickup sequence.

To illustrate, the symbol used in expression (2) was as follows:

$$_{312}Hch_{132}$$

which can be written

$$312 \quad Hch \quad 132.$$

This way of completing the test was assigned ID number 098 in Table 6-2. Its permutation number within way (PN within way) is 017-2 which means that this way of completing the test is considered the second way (permutation) of 6 ways of picking up the birds for way 017 of setting up the test (from Table 6-1).

INFERENCE, POPULATION, AND SAMPLE

It is assumed that judges of all-age stakes would like to "reward" retrievers who have the ability to perform well under varying conditions and circumstances. It is further assumed that judges explicitly recognize that in any given trial they can obtain only a sample of a retriever's performance and capability.

As was shown earlier, there are 144 ways of setting up a land triple at 3 locations taking into consideration cocks or hens, live or dead, and firing order. These 144 ways can be thought of as the

Table 6-2.--Listing of all 864 possible ways of picking up a marked land triple on pheasant, where birds were shot at three locations in any order, one live and two dead pheasant, either cocks or hens

Identi-fication number	Permutation number within way	Location-firing sequence	Location-type of bird	Location-pickup sequence
ID number	PN within way	L-FS	L-B	L-PS
001	001-1	123	H h h	123
002	001-2	123	H h h	132
003	001-3	123	H h h	213
004	001-4	123	H h h	231
005	001-5	123	H h h	312
006	001-6	123	H h h	321
007	002-1	132	H h h	123
008	002-2	132	H h h	132
009	002-3	132	H h h	213
010	002-4	132	H h h	231
011	002-5	132	H h h	312
012	002-6	132	H h h	321
013	003-1	213	H h h	123
014	003-2	213	H h h	132
015	003-3	213	H h h	213
016	003-4	213	H h h	231
017	003-5	213	H h h	312
018	003-6	213	H h h	321
019	004-1	231	H h h	123
020	004-2	231	H h h	132
021	004-3	231	H h h	213
022	004-4	231	H h h	231
023	004-5	231	H h h	312
024	004-6	231	H h h	321
025	005-1	312	H h h	123
026	005-2	312	H h h	132
027	005-3	312	H h h	213
028	005-4	312	H h h	231
029	005-5	312	H h h	312
030	005-6	312	H h h	321

(Continued)

Note: C = live cock; H = live hen; c = dead cock; h = dead hen; ID number = identification number; PN within way denotes permutation number within way (from Table 6-1); L-FS denotes location-firing sequence; L-B denotes location and type of bird; and L-PS denotes location-pickup sequence.

Table 6-2.--(Continued) Listing of all 864 possible ways of picking up a marked land triple on pheasant, where birds were shot at three locations in any order, one live and two dead pheasant, either cocks or hens

ID number	PN within way	L-FS	L-B			L-PS
031	006-1	321	H	h	h	123
032	006-2	321	H	h	h	132
033	006-3	321	H	h	h	213
034	006-4	321	H	h	h	231
035	006-5	321	H	h	h	312
036	006-6	321	H	h	h	321
037	007-1	123	H	h	c	123
038	007-2	123	H	h	c	132
039	007-3	123	H	h	c	213
040	007-4	123	H	h	c	231
041	007-5	123	H	h	c	312
042	007-6	123	H	h	c	321
043	008-1	132	H	h	c	123
044	008-2	132	H	h	c	132
045	008-3	132	H	h	c	213
046	008-4	132	H	h	c	231
047	008-5	132	H	h	c	312
048	008-6	132	H	h	c	321
049	009-1	213	H	h	c	123
050	009-2	213	H	h	c	132
051	009-3	213	H	h	c	213
052	009-4	213	H	h	c	231
053	009-5	213	H	h	c	312
054	009-6	213	H	h	c	321
055	010-1	231	H	h	c	123
056	010-2	231	H	h	c	132
057	010-3	231	H	h	c	213
058	010-4	231	H	h	c	231
059	010-5	231	H	h	c	312
060	010-6	231	H	h	c	321
061	011-1	312	H	h	c	123
062	011-2	312	H	h	c	132
063	011-3	312	H	h	c	213
064	011-4	312	H	h	c	231
065	011-5	312	H	h	c	312
066	011-6	312	H	h	c	321
067	012-1	321	H	h	c	123
068	012-2	321	H	h	c	132
069	012-3	321	H	h	c	213

(Continued)

Table 6-2.--(Continued) Listing of all 864 possible ways of picking up a marked land triple on pheasant, where birds were shot at three locations in any order, one live and two dead pheasant, either cocks or hens

ID number	PN within way	L-FS	L-B			L-PS
070	012-4	321	H	h	c	231
071	012-5	321	H	h	c	312
072	012-6	321	H	h	c	321
073	013-1	123	H	c	h	123
074	013-2	123	H	c	h	132
075	013-3	123	H	c	h	213
076	013-4	123	H	c	h	231
077	013-5	123	H	c	h	312
078	013-6	123	H	c	h	321
079	014-1	132	H	c	h	123
080	014-2	132	H	c	h	132
081	014-3	132	H	c	h	213
082	014-4	132	H	c	h	231
083	014-5	132	H	c	h	312
084	014-6	132	H	c	h	321
085	015-1	213	H	c	h	123
086	015-2	213	H	c	h	132
087	015-3	213	H	c	h	213
088	015-4	213	H	c	h	231
089	015-5	213	H	c	h	312
090	015-6	213	H	c	h	321
091	016-1	231	H	c	h	123
092	016-2	231	H	c	h	132
093	016-3	231	H	c	h	213
094	016-4	231	H	c	h	231
095	016-5	231	H	c	h	312
096	016-6	231	H	c	h	321
097	017-1	312	H	c	h	123
098	017-2	312	H	c	h	132
099	017-3	312	H	c	h	213
100	017-4	312	H	c	h	231
101	017-5	312	H	c	h	312
102	017-6	312	H	c	h	321
103	018-1	321	H	c	h	123
104	018-2	321	H	c	h	132
105	018-3	321	H	c	h	213
106	018-4	321	H	c	h	231
107	018-5	321	H	c	h	312
108	018-6	321	H	c	h	321

(Continued)

Table 6-2.--(Continued) Listing of all 864 possible ways of picking
up a marked land triple on pheasant, where birds were
shot at three locations in any order, one live and two
dead pheasant, either cocks or hens

ID number	PN within way	L-FS	L-B	L-PS
109	019-1	123	H c c	123
110	019-2	123	H c c	132
111	019-3	123	H c c	213
112	019-4	123	H c c	231
113	019-5	123	H c c	312
114	019-6	123	H c c	321
115	020-1	132	H c c	123
116	020-2	132	H c c	132
117	020-3	132	H c c	213
118	020-4	132	H c c	231
119	020-5	132	H c c	312
120	020-6	132	H c c	321
121	021-1	213	H c c	123
122	021-2	213	H c c	132
123	021-3	213	H c c	213
124	021-4	213	H c c	231
125	021-5	213	H c c	312
126	021-6	213	H c c	321
127	022-1	231	H c c	123
128	022-2	231	H c c	132
129	022-3	231	H c c	213
130	022-4	231	H c c	231
131	022-5	231	H c c	312
132	022-6	231	H c c	321
133	023-1	312	H c c	123
134	023-2	312	H c c	132
135	023-3	312	H c c	213
136	023-4	312	H c c	231
137	023-5	312	H c c	312
138	023-6	312	H c c	321
139	024-1	321	H c c	123
140	024-2	321	H c c	132
141	024-3	321	H c c	213
142	024-4	321	H c c	231
143	024-5	321	H c c	312
144	024-6	321	H c c	321
145	025-1	123	h H h	123
146	025-2	123	h H h	132
147	025-3	123	h H h	213

(Continued)

Table 6-2.--(Continued) Listing of all 864 possible ways of picking
up a marked land triple on pheasant, where birds were
shot at three locations in any order, one live and two
dead pheasant, either cocks or hens

ID number	PN within way	L-FS	L-B	L-PS
148	025-4	123	h H h	231
149	025-5	123	h H h	312
150	025-6	123	h H h	321
151	026-1	132	h H h	123
152	026-2	132	h H h	132
153	026-3	132	h H h	213
154	026-4	132	h H h	231
155	026-5	132	h H h	312
156	026-6	132	h H h	321
157	027-1	213	h H h	123
158	027-2	213	h H h	132
159	027-3	213	h H h	213
160	027-4	213	h H h	231
161	027-5	213	h H h	312
162	027-6	213	h H h	321
163	028-1	231	h H h	123
164	028-2	231	h H h	132
165	028-3	231	h H h	213
166	028-4	231	h H h	231
167	028-5	231	h H h	312
168	028-6	231	h H h	321
169	029-1	312	h H h	123
170	029-2	312	h H h	132
171	029-3	312	h H h	213
172	029-4	312	h H h	231
173	029-5	312	h H h	312
174	029-6	312	h H h	321
175	030-1	321	h H h	123
176	030-2	321	h H h	132
177	030-3	321	h H h	213
178	030-4	321	h H h	231
179	030-5	321	h H h	312
180	030-6	321	h H h	321
181	031-1	123	h H c	123
182	031-2	123	h H c	132
183	031-3	123	h H c	213
184	031-4	123	h H c	231
185	031-5	123	h H c	312
186	031-6	123	h H c	321

(Continued)

Table 6-2.--(Continued) Listing of all 864 possible ways of picking up a marked land triple on pheasant, where birds were shot at three locations in any order, one live and two dead pheasant, either cocks or hens

ID number	PN within way	L-FS	L-B			L-PS
187	032-1	132	h	H	c	123
188	032-2	132	h	H	c	132
189	032-3	132	h	H	c	213
190	032-4	132	h	H	c	231
191	032-5	132	h	H	c	312
192	032-6	132	h	H	c	321
193	033-1	213	h	H	c	123
194	033-2	213	h	H	c	132
195	033-3	213	h	H	c	213
196	033-4	213	h	H	c	231
197	033-5	213	h	H	c	312
198	033-6	213	h	H	c	321
199	034-1	231	h	H	c	123
200	034-2	231	h	H	c	132
201	034-3	231	h	H	c	213
202	034-4	231	h	H	c	231
203	034-5	231	h	H	c	312
204	034-6	231	h	H	c	321
205	035-1	312	h	H	c	123
206	035-2	312	h	H	c	132
207	035-3	312	h	H	c	213
208	035-4	312	h	H	c	231
209	035-5	312	h	H	c	312
210	035-6	312	h	H	c	321
211	036-1	321	h	H	c	123
212	036-2	321	h	H	c	132
213	036-3	321	h	H	c	213
214	036-4	321	h	H	c	231
215	036-5	321	h	H	c	312
216	036-6	321	h	H	c	321
217	037-1	123	c	H	h	123
218	037-2	123	c	H	h	132
219	037-3	123	c	H	h	213
220	037-4	123	c	H	h	231
221	037-5	123	c	H	h	312
222	037-6	123	c	H	h	321
223	038-1	132	c	H	h	123
224	038-2	132	c	H	h	132
225	038-3	132	c	H	h	213

(Continued)

Table 6-2.--(Continued) Listing of all 864 possible ways of picking up a marked land triple on pheasant, where birds were shot at three locations in any order, one live and two dead pheasant, either cocks or hens

ID number	PN within way	L-FS	L-B			L-PS
226	038-4	132	c	H	h	231
227	038-5	132	c	H	h	312
228	038-6	132	c	H	h	321
229	039-1	213	c	H	h	123
230	039-2	213	c	H	h	132
231	039-3	213	c	H	h	213
232	039-4	213	c	H	h	231
233	039-5	213	c	H	h	312
234	039-6	213	c	H	h	321
235	040-1	231	c	H	h	123
236	040-2	231	c	H	h	132
237	040-3	231	c	H	h	213
238	040-4	231	c	H	h	231
239	040-5	231	c	H	h	312
240	040-6	231	c	H	h	321
241	041-1	312	c	H	h	123
242	041-2	312	c	H	h	132
243	041-3	312	c	H	h	213
244	041-4	312	c	H	h	231
245	041-5	312	c	H	h	312
246	041-6	312	c	H	h	321
247	042-1	321	c	H	h	123
248	042-2	321	c	H	h	132
249	042-3	321	c	H	h	213
250	042-4	321	c	H	h	231
251	042-5	321	c	H	h	312
252	042-6	321	c	H	h	321
253	043-1	123	c	H	c	123
254	043-2	123	c	H	c	132
255	043-3	123	c	H	c	213
256	043-4	123	c	H	c	231
257	043-5	123	c	H	c	312
258	043-6	123	c	H	c	321
259	044-1	132	c	H	c	123
260	044-2	132	c	H	c	132
261	044-3	132	c	H	c	213
262	044-4	132	c	H	c	231
263	044-5	132	c	H	c	312
264	044-6	132	c	H	c	321

(Continued)

Table 6-2.--(Continued) Listing of all 864 possible ways of picking up a marked land triple on pheasant, where birds were shot at three locations in any order, one live and two dead pheasant, either cocks or hens

ID number	PN within way	L-FS	L-B			L-PS
265	045-1	213	c	H	c	123
266	045-2	213	c	H	c	132
267	045-3	213	c	H	c	213
268	045-4	213	c	H	c	231
269	045-5	213	c	H	c	312
270	045-6	213	c	H	c	321
271	046-1	231	c	H	c	123
272	046-2	231	c	H	c	132
273	046-3	231	c	H	c	213
274	046-4	231	c	H	c	231
275	046-5	231	c	H	c	312
276	046-6	231	c	H	c	321
277	047-1	312	c	H	c	123
278	047-2	312	c	H	c	132
279	047-3	312	c	H	c	213
280	047-4	312	c	H	c	231
281	047-5	312	c	H	c	312
282	047-6	312	c	H	c	321
283	048-1	321	c	H	c	123
284	048-2	321	c	H	c	132
285	048-3	321	c	H	c	213
286	048-4	321	c	H	c	231
287	048-5	321	c	H	c	312
288	048-6	321	c	H	c	321
289	049-1	123	h	h	H	123
290	049-2	123	h	h	H	132
291	049-3	123	h	h	H	213
292	049-4	123	h	h	H	231
293	049-5	123	h	h	H	312
294	049-6	123	h	h	H	321
295	050-1	132	h	h	H	123
296	050-2	132	h	h	H	132
297	050-3	132	h	h	H	213
298	050-4	132	h	h	H	231
299	050-5	132	h	h	H	312
300	050-6	132	h	h	H	321
301	051-1	213	h	h	H	123
302	051-2	213	h	h	H	132
303	051-3	213	h	h	H	213

(Continued)

Table 6-2. --(Continued) Listing of all 864 possible ways of picking
          up a marked land triple on pheasant, where birds were
          shot at three locations in any order, one live and two
          dead pheasant, either cocks or hens

ID number	PN within way	L-FS	L-B	L-PS
304	051-4	213	h h H	231
305	051-5	213	h h H	312
306	051-6	213	h h H	321
307	052-1	231	h h H	123
308	052-2	231	h h H	132
309	052-3	231	h h H	213
310	052-4	231	h h H	231
311	052-5	231	h h H	312
312	052-6	231	h h H	321
313	053-1	312	h h H	123
314	053-2	312	h h H	132
315	053-3	312	h h H	213
316	053-4	312	h h H	231
317	053-5	312	h h H	312
318	053-6	312	h h H	321
319	054-1	321	h h H	123
320	054-2	321	h h H	132
321	054-3	321	h h H	213
322	054-4	321	h h H	231
323	054-5	321	h h H	312
324	054-6	321	h h H	321
325	055-1	123	h c H	123
326	055-2	123	h c H	132
327	055-3	123	h c H	213
328	055-4	123	h c H	231
329	055-5	123	h c H	312
330	055-6	123	h c H	321
331	056-1	132	h c H	123
332	056-2	132	h c H	132
333	056-3	132	h c H	213
334	056-4	132	h c H	231
335	056-5	132	h c H	312
336	056-6	132	h c H	321
337	057-1	213	h c H	123
338	057-2	213	h c H	132
339	057-3	213	h c H	213
340	057-4	213	h c H	231
341	057-5	213	h c H	312
342	057-6	213	h c H	321

(Continued)

Table 6-2.--(Continued) Listing of all 864 possible ways of picking up a marked land triple on pheasant, where birds were shot at three locations in any order, one live and two dead pheasant, either cocks or hens

ID number	PN within way	L-FS	L-B			L-PS
343	058-1	231	h	c	H	123
344	058-2	231	h	c	H	132
345	058-3	231	h	c	H	213
346	058-4	231	h	c	H	231
347	058-5	231	h	c	H	312
348	058-6	231	h	c	H	321
349	059-1	312	h	c	H	123
350	059-2	312	h	c	H	132
351	059-3	312	h	c	H	213
352	059-4	312	h	c	H	231
353	059-5	312	h	c	H	312
354	059-6	312	h	c	H	321
355	060-1	321	h	c	H	123
356	060-2	321	h	c	H	132
357	060-3	321	h	c	H	213
358	060-4	321	h	c	H	231
359	060-5	321	h	c	H	312
360	060-6	321	h	c	H	321
361	061-1	123	c	h	H	123
362	061-2	123	c	h	H	132
363	061-3	123	c	h	H	213
364	061-4	123	c	h	H	231
365	061-5	123	c	h	H	312
366	061-6	123	c	h	H	321
367	062-1	132	c	h	H	123
368	062-2	132	c	h	H	132
369	062-3	132	c	h	H	213
370	062-4	132	c	h	H	231
371	062-5	132	c	h	H	312
372	062-6	132	c	h	H	321
373	063-1	213	c	h	H	123
374	063-2	213	c	h	H	132
375	063-3	213	c	h	H	213
376	063-4	213	c	h	H	231
377	063-5	213	c	h	H	312
378	063-6	213	c	h	H	321
379	064-1	231	c	h	H	123
380	064-2	231	c	h	H	132
381	064-3	231	c	h	H	213

(Continued)

Table 6-2.--(Continued) Listing of all 864 possible ways of picking up a marked land triple on pheasant, where birds were shot at three locations in any order, one live and two dead pheasant, either cocks or hens

ID number	PN within way	L-FS	L-B	L-PS
382	064-4	231	c h H	231
383	064-5	231	c h H	312
384	064-6	231	c h H	321
385	065-1	312	c h H	123
386	065-2	312	c h H	132
387	065-3	312	c h H	213
388	065-4	312	c h H	231
389	065-5	312	c h H	312
390	065-6	312	c h H	321
391	066-1	321	c h H	123
392	066-2	321	c h H	132
393	066-3	321	c h H	213
394	066-4	321	c h H	231
395	066-5	321	c h H	312
396	066-6	321	c h H	321
397	067-1	123	c c H	123
398	067-2	123	c c H	132
399	067-3	123	c c H	213
400	067-4	123	c c H	231
401	067-5	123	c c H	312
402	067-6	123	c c H	321
403	068-1	132	c c H	123
404	068-2	132	c c H	132
405	068-3	132	c c H	213
406	068-4	132	c c H	231
407	068-5	132	c c H	312
408	068-6	132	c c H	321
409	069-1	213	c c H	123
410	069-2	213	c c H	132
411	069-3	213	c c H	213
412	069-4	213	c c H	231
413	069-5	213	c c H	312
414	069-6	213	c c H	321
415	070-1	231	c c H	123
416	070-2	231	c c H	132
417	070-3	231	c c H	213
418	070-4	231	c c H	231
419	070-5	231	c c H	312
420	070-6	231	c c H	321

(Continued)

Table 6-2.--(Continued) Listing of all 864 possible ways of picking up a marked land triple on pheasant, where birds were shot at three locations in any order, one live and two dead pheasant, either cocks or hens

ID number	PN within way	L-FS	L-B			L-PS
421	071-1	312	c	c	H	123
422	071-2	312	c	c	H	132
423	071-3	312	c	c	H	213
424	071-4	312	c	c	H	231
425	071-5	312	c	c	H	312
426	071-6	312	c	c	H	321
427	072-1	321	c	c	H	123
428	072-2	321	c	c	H	132
429	072-3	321	c	c	H	213
430	072-4	321	c	c	H	231
431	072-5	321	c	c	H	312
432	072-6	321	c	c	H	321
433	073-1	123	C	h	h	123
434	073-2	123	C	h	h	132
435	073-3	123	C	h	h	213
436	073-4	123	C	h	h	231
437	073-5	123	C	h	h	312
438	073-6	123	C	h	h	321
439	074-1	132	C	h	h	123
440	074-2	132	C	h	h	132
441	074-3	132	C	h	h	213
442	074-4	132	C	h	h	231
443	074-5	132	C	h	h	312
444	074-6	132	C	h	h	321
445	075-1	213	C	h	h	123
446	075-2	213	C	h	h	132
447	075-3	213	C	h	h	213
448	075-4	213	C	h	h	231
449	075-5	213	C	h	h	312
450	075-6	213	C	h	h	321
451	076-1	231	C	h	h	123
452	076-2	231	C	h	h	132
453	076-3	231	C	h	h	213
454	076-4	231	C	h	h	231
455	076-5	231	C	h	h	312
456	076-6	231	C	h	h	321
457	077-1	312	C	h	h	123
458	077-2	312	C	h	h	132
459	077-3	312	C	h	h	213

(Continued)

Table 6-2.--(Continued) Listing of all 864 possible ways of picking
up a marked land triple on pheasant, where birds were
shot at three locations in any order, one live and two
dead pheasant, either cocks or hens

ID number	PN within way	L-FS	L-B	L-PS
460	077-4	312	C h h	231
461	077-5	312	C h h	312
462	077-6	312	C h h	321
463	078-1	321	C h h	123
464	078-2	321	C h h	132
465	078-3	321	C h h	213
466	078-4	321	C h h	231
467	078-5	321	C h h	312
468	078-6	321	C h h	321
469	079-1	123	C h c	123
470	079-2	123	C h c	132
471	079-3	123	C h c	213
472	079-4	123	C h c	231
473	079-5	123	C h c	312
474	079-6	123	C h c	321
475	080-1	132	C h c	123
476	080-2	132	C h c	132
477	080-3	132	C h c	213
478	080-4	132	C h c	231
479	080-5	132	C h c	312
480	080-6	132	C h c	321
481	081-1	213	C h c	123
482	081-2	213	C h c	132
483	081-3	213	C h c	213
484	081-4	213	C h c	231
485	081-5	213	C h c	312
486	081-6	213	C h c	321
487	082-1	231	C h c	123
488	082-2	231	C h c	132
489	082-3	231	C h c	213
490	082-4	231	C h c	231
491	082-5	231	C h c	312
492	082-6	231	C h c	321
493	083-1	312	C h c	123
494	083-2	312	C h c	132
495	083-3	312	C h c	213
496	083-4	312	C h c	231
497	083-5	312	C h c	312
498	083-6	312	C h c	321

(Continued)

Table 6-2.--(Continued) Listing of all 864 possible ways of picking up a marked land triple on pheasant, where birds were shot at three locations in any order, one live and two dead pheasant, either cocks or hens

ID number	PN within way	L-FS	L-B			L-PS
499	084-1	321	C	h	c	123
500	084-2	321	C	h	c	132
501	084-3	321	C	h	c	213
502	084-4	321	C	h	c	231
503	084-5	321	C	h	c	312
504	084-6	321	C	h	c	321
505	085-1	123	C	c	h	123
506	085-2	123	C	c	h	132
507	085-3	123	C	c	h	213
508	085-4	123	C	c	h	231
509	085-5	123	C	c	h	312
510	085-6	123	C	c	h	321
511	086-1	132	C	c	h	123
512	086-2	132	C	c	h	132
513	086-3	132	C	c	h	213
514	086-4	132	C	c	h	231
515	086-5	132	C	c	h	312
516	086-6	132	C	c	h	321
517	087-1	213	C	c	h	123
518	087-2	213	C	c	h	132
519	087-3	213	C	c	h	213
520	087-4	213	C	c	h	231
521	087-5	213	C	c	h	312
522	087-6	213	C	c	h	321
523	088-1	231	C	c	h	123
524	088-2	231	C	c	h	132
525	088-3	231	C	c	h	213
526	088-4	231	C	c	h	231
527	088-5	231	C	c	h	312
528	088-6	231	C	c	h	321
529	089-1	312	C	c	h	123
530	089-2	312	C	c	h	132
531	089-3	312	C	c	h	213
532	089-4	312	C	c	h	231
533	089-5	312	C	c	h	312
534	089-6	312	C	c	h	321
535	090-1	321	C	c	h	123
536	090-2	321	C	c	h	132
537	090-3	321	C	c	h	213

(Continued)

Table 6-2.--(Continued) Listing of all 864 possible ways of picking up a marked land triple on pheasant, where birds were shot at three locations in any order, one live and two dead pheasant, either cocks or hens

ID number	PN within way	L-FS	L-B			L-PS
538	090-4	321	C	c	h	231
539	090-5	321	C	c	h	312
540	090-6	321	C	c	h	321
541	091-1	123	C	c	c	123
542	091-2	123	C	c	c	132
543	091-3	123	C	c	c	213
544	091-4	123	C	c	c	231
545	091-5	123	C	c	c	312
546	091-6	123	C	c	c	321
547	092-1	132	C	c	c	123
548	092-2	132	C	c	c	132
549	092-3	132	C	c	c	213
550	092-4	132	C	c	c	231
551	092-5	132	C	c	c	312
552	092-6	132	C	c	c	321
553	093-1	213	C	c	c	123
554	093-2	213	C	c	c	132
555	093-3	213	C	c	c	213
556	093-4	213	C	c	c	231
557	093-5	213	C	c	c	312
558	093-6	213	C	c	c	321
559	094-1	231	C	c	c	123
560	094-2	231	C	c	c	132
561	094-3	231	C	c	c	213
562	094-4	231	C	c	c	231
563	094-5	231	C	c	c	312
564	094-6	231	C	c	c	321
565	095-1	312	C	c	c	123
566	095-2	312	C	c	c	132
567	095-3	312	C	c	c	213
568	095-4	312	C	c	c	231
569	095-5	312	C	c	c	312
570	095-6	312	C	c	c	321
571	096-1	321	C	c	c	123
572	096-2	321	C	c	c	132
573	096-3	321	C	c	c	213
574	096-4	321	C	c	c	231
575	096-5	321	C	c	c	312
576	096-6	321	C	c	c	321

(Continued)

Table 6-2.--(Continued) Listing of all 864 possible ways of picking up a marked land triple on pheasant, where birds were shot at three locations in any order, one live and two dead pheasant, either cocks or hens

ID number	PN within way	L-FS	L-B			L-PS
577	097-1	123	h	C	h	123
578	097-2	123	h	C	h	132
579	097-3	123	h	C	h	213
580	097-4	123	h	C	h	231
581	097-5	123	h	C	h	312
582	097-6	123	h	C	h	321
583	098-1	132	h	C	h	123
584	098-2	132	h	C	h	132
585	098-3	132	h	C	h	213
586	098-4	132	h	C	h	231
587	098-5	132	h	C	h	312
588	098-6	132	h	C	h	321
589	099-1	213	h	C	h	123
590	099-2	213	h	C	h	132
591	099-3	213	h	C	h	213
592	099-4	213	h	C	h	231
593	099-5	213	h	C	h	312
594	099-6	213	h	C	h	321
595	100-1	231	h	C	h	123
596	100-2	231	h	C	h	132
597	100-3	231	h	C	h	213
598	100-4	231	h	C	h	231
599	100-5	231	h	C	h	312
600	100-6	231	h	C	h	321
601	101-1	312	h	C	h	123
602	101-2	312	h	C	h	132
603	101-3	312	h	C	h	213
604	101-4	312	h	C	h	231
605	101-5	312	h	C	h	312
606	101-6	312	h	C	h	321
607	102-1	321	h	C	h	123
608	102-2	321	h	C	h	132
609	102-3	321	h	C	h	213
610	102-4	321	h	C	h	231
611	102-5	321	h	C	h	312
612	102-6	321	h	C	h	321
613	103-1	123	h	C	c	123
614	103-2	123	h	C	c	132
615	103-3	123	h	C	c	213

(Continued)

Table 6-2.--(Continued) Listing of all 864 possible ways of picking up a marked land triple on pheasant, where birds were shot at three locations in any order, one live and two dead pheasant, either cocks or hens

ID number	PN within way	L-FS	L-B	L-PS
616	103-4	123	h C c	231
617	103-5	123	h C c	312
618	103-6	123	h C c	321
619	104-1	132	h C c	123
620	104-2	132	h C c	132
621	104-3	132	h C c	213
622	104-4	132	h C c	231
623	104-5	132	h C c	312
624	104-6	132	h C c	321
625	105-1	213	h C c	123
626	105-2	213	h C c	132
627	105-3	213	h C c	213
628	105-4	213	h C c	231
629	105-5	213	h C c	312
630	105-6	213	h C c	321
631	106-1	231	h C c	123
632	106-2	231	h C c	132
633	106-3	231	h C c	213
634	106-4	231	h C c	231
635	106-5	231	h C c	312
636	106-6	231	h C c	321
637	107-1	312	h C c	123
638	107-2	312	h C c	132
639	107-3	312	h C c	213
640	107-4	312	h C c	231
641	107-5	312	h C c	312
642	107-6	312	h C c	321
643	108-1	321	h C c	123
644	108-2	321	h C c	132
645	108-3	321	h C c	213
646	108-4	321	h C c	231
647	108-5	321	h C c	312
648	108-6	321	h C c	321
649	109-1	123	c C h	123
650	109-2	123	c C h	132
651	109-3	123	c C h	213
652	109-4	123	c C h	231
653	109-5	123	c C h	312
654	109-6	123	c C h	321

(Continued)

Table 6-2.--(Continued) Listing of all 864 possible ways of picking up a marked land triple on pheasant, where birds were shot at three locations in any order, one live and two dead pheasant, either cocks or hens

ID number	PN within way	L-FS	L-B			L-PS
655	110-1	132	c	C	h	123
656	110-2	132	c	C	h	132
657	110-3	132	c	C	h	213
658	110-4	132	c	C	h	231
659	110-5	132	c	C	h	312
660	110-6	132	c	C	h	321
661	111-1	213	c	C	h	123
662	111-2	213	c	C	h	132
663	111-3	213	c	C	h	213
664	111-4	213	c	C	h	231
665	111-5	213	c	C	h	312
666	111-6	213	c	C	h	321
667	112-1	231	c	C	h	123
668	112-2	231	c	C	h	132
669	112-3	231	c	C	h	213
670	112-4	231	c	C	h	231
671	112-5	231	c	C	h	312
672	112-6	231	c	C	h	321
673	113-1	312	c	C	h	123
674	113-2	312	c	C	h	132
675	113-3	312	c	C	h	213
676	113-4	312	c	C	h	231
677	113-5	312	c	C	h	312
678	113-6	312	c	C	h	321
679	114-1	321	c	C	h	123
680	114-2	321	c	C	h	132
681	114-3	321	c	C	h	213
682	114-4	321	c	C	h	231
683	114-5	321	c	C	h	312
684	114-6	321	c	C	h	321
685	115-1	123	c	C	c	123
686	115-2	123	c	C	c	132
687	115-3	123	c	C	c	213
688	115-4	123	c	C	c	231
689	115-5	123	c	C	c	312
690	115-6	123	c	C	c	321
691	116-1	132	c	C	c	123
692	116-2	132	c	C	c	132
693	116-3	132	c	C	c	213

(Continued)

Table 6-2.--(Continued) Listing of all 864 possible ways of picking
       up a marked land triple on pheasant, where birds were
       shot at three locations in any order, one live and two
       dead pheasant, either cocks or hens

ID number	PN within way	L-FS	L-B			L-PS
694	116-4	132	c	C	c	231
695	116-5	132	c	C	c	312
696	116-6	132	c	C	c	321
697	117-1	213	c	C	c	123
698	117-2	213	c	C	c	132
699	117-3	213	c	C	c	213
700	117-4	213	c	C	c	231
701	117-5	213	c	C	c	312
702	117-6	213	c	C	c	321
703	118-1	231	c	C	c	123
704	118-2	231	c	C	c	132
705	118-3	231	c	C	c	213
706	118-4	231	c	C	c	231
707	118-5	231	c	C	c	312
708	118-6	231	c	C	c	321
709	119-1	312	c	C	c	123
710	119-2	312	c	C	c	132
711	119-3	312	c	C	c	213
712	119-4	312	c	C	c	231
713	119-5	312	c	C	c	312
714	119-6	312	c	C	c	321
715	120-1	321	c	C	c	123
716	120-2	321	c	C	c	132
717	120-3	321	c	C	c	213
718	120-4	321	c	C	c	231
719	120-5	321	c	C	c	312
720	120-6	321	c	C	c	321
721	121-1	123	h	h	C	123
722	121-2	123	h	h	C	132
723	121-3	123	h	h	C	213
724	121-4	123	h	h	C	231
725	121-5	123	h	h	C	312
726	121-6	123	h	h	C	321
727	122-1	132	h	h	C	123
728	122-2	132	h	h	C	132
729	122-3	132	h	h	C	213
730	122-4	132	h	h	C	231
731	122-5	132	h	h	C	312
732	122-6	132	h	h	C	321

(Continued)

Table 6-2.--(Continued) Listing of all 864 possible ways of picking
up a marked land triple on pheasant, where birds were
shot at three locations in any order, one live and two
dead pheasant, either cocks or hens

ID number	PN within way	L-FS	L-B			L-PS
733	123-1	213	h	h	C	123
734	123-2	213	h	h	C	132
735	123-3	213	h	h	C	213
736	123-4	213	h	h	C	231
737	123-5	213	h	h	C	312
738	123-6	213	h	h	C	321
739	124-1	231	h	h	C	123
740	124-2	231	h	h	C	132
741	124-3	231	h	h	C	213
742	124-4	231	h	h	C	231
743	124-5	231	h	h	C	312
744	124-6	231	h	h	C	321
745	125-1	312	h	h	C	123
746	125-2	312	h	h	C	132
747	125-3	312	h	h	C	213
748	125-4	312	h	h	C	231
749	125-5	312	h	h	C	312
750	125-6	312	h	h	C	321
751	126-1	321	h	h	C	123
752	126-2	321	h	h	C	132
753	126-3	321	h	h	C	213
754	126-4	321	h	h	C	231
755	126-5	321	h	h	C	312
756	126-6	321	h	h	C	321
757	127-1	123	h	c	C	123
758	127-2	123	h	c	C	132
759	127-3	123	h	c	C	213
760	127-4	123	h	c	C	231
761	127-5	123	h	c	C	312
762	127-6	123	h	c	C	321
763	128-1	132	h	c	C	123
764	128-2	132	h	c	C	132
765	128-3	132	h	c	C	213
766	128-4	132	h	c	C	231
767	128-5	132	h	c	C	312
768	128-6	132	h	c	C	321
769	129-1	213	h	c	C	123
770	129-2	213	h	c	C	132
771	129-3	213	h	c	C	213

(Continued)

Table 6-2.--(Continued) Listing of all 864 possible ways of picking
up a marked land triple on pheasant, where birds were
shot at three locations in any order, one live and two
dead pheasant, either cocks or hens

ID number	PN within way	L-FS	L-B			L-PS
772	129-4	213	h	c	C	231
773	129-5	213	h	c	C	312
774	129-6	213	h	c	C	321
775	130-1	231	h	c	C	123
776	130-2	231	h	c	C	132
777	130-3	231	h	c	C	213
778	130-4	231	h	c	C	231
779	130-5	231	h	c	C	312
780	130-6	231	h	c	C	321
781	131-1	312	h	c	C	123
782	131-2	312	h	c	C	132
783	131-3	312	h	c	C	213
784	131-4	312	h	c	C	231
785	131-5	312	h	c	C	312
786	131-6	312	h	c	C	321
787	132-1	321	h	c	C	123
788	132-2	321	h	c	C	132
789	132-3	321	h	c	C	213
790	132-4	321	h	c	C	231
791	132-5	321	h	c	C	312
792	132-6	321	h	c	C	321
793	133-1	123	c	h	C	123
794	133-2	123	c	h	C	132
795	133-3	123	c	h	C	213
796	133-4	123	c	h	C	231
797	133-5	123	c	h	C	312
798	133-6	123	c	h	C	321
799	134-1	132	c	h	C	123
800	134-2	132	c	h	C	132
801	134-3	132	c	h	C	213
802	134-4	132	c	h	C	231
803	134-5	132	c	h	C	312
804	134-6	132	c	h	C	321
805	135-1	213	c	h	C	123
806	135-2	213	c	h	C	132
807	135-3	213	c	h	C	213
808	135-4	213	c	h	C	231
809	135-5	213	c	h	C	312
810	135-6	213	c	h	C	321

(Continued)

Table 6-2.--(Continued) Listing of all 864 possible ways of picking up a marked land triple on pheasant, where birds were shot at three locations in any order, one live and two dead pheasant, either cocks or hens

ID number	PN within way	L-FS	L-B			L-PS
811	136-1	231	c	h	C	123
812	136-2	231	c	h	C	132
813	136-3	231	c	h	C	213
814	136-4	231	c	h	C	231
815	136-5	231	c	h	C	312
816	136-6	231	c	h	C	321
817	137-1	312	c	h	C	123
818	137-2	312	c	h	C	132
819	137-3	312	c	h	C	213
820	137-4	312	c	h	C	231
821	137-5	312	c	h	C	312
822	137-6	312	c	h	C	321
823	138-1	321	c	h	C	123
824	138-2	321	c	h	C	132
825	138-3	321	c	h	C	213
826	138-4	321	c	h	C	231
827	138-5	321	c	h	C	312
828	138-6	321	c	h	C	321
829	139-1	123	c	c	C	123
830	139-2	123	c	c	C	132
831	139-3	123	c	c	C	213
832	139-4	123	c	c	C	231
833	139-5	123	c	c	C	312
834	139-6	123	c	c	C	321
835	140-1	132	c	c	C	123
836	140-2	132	c	c	C	132
837	140-3	132	c	c	C	213
838	140-4	132	c	c	C	231
839	140-5	132	c	c	C	312
840	140-6	132	c	c	C	321
841	141-1	213	c	c	C	123
842	141-2	213	c	c	C	132
843	141-3	213	c	c	C	213
844	141-4	213	c	c	C	231
845	141-5	213	c	c	C	312
846	141-6	213	c	c	C	321
847	142-1	231	c	c	C	123
848	142-2	231	c	c	C	132
849	142-3	231	c	c	C	213

(Continued)

Table 6-2.--(Concluded) Listing of all 864 possible ways of picking
up a marked land triple on pheasant, where birds were
shot at three locations in any order, one live and two
dead pheasant, either cocks or hens

ID number	PN within way	L-FS	L-B	L-PS
850	142-4	231	c c C	231
851	142-5	231	c c C	312
852	142-6	231	c c C	321
853	143-1	312	c c C	123
854	143-2	312	c c C	132
855	143-3	312	c c C	213
856	143-4	312	c c C	231
857	143-5	312	c c C	312
858	143-6	312	c c C	321
859	144-1	321	c c C	123
860	144-2	321	c c C	132
861	144-3	321	c c C	213
862	144-4	321	c c C	231
863	144-5	321	c c C	312
864	144-6	321	c c C	321

"population of ways of setting up the land triple"; also, this group of ways can be thought of as the listing of all possible ways of setting up the land triple, often called a "sampling frame."

Continuum of difficulty.--Some handlers and judges assume that "a flier is a flier"; sex of the bird is of little or no import. Others think that a cock may create more of a temptation to break or attract more attention and, thus, cause a retriever to be more likely not to remember another mark. Many would agree that a "flier" is more attractive than a dead bird to most all-age retrievers. Retriever handlers and judges seem to think that certain orders of throwing the marks increase the difficulty of the test. I have opinions concerning difficulty of various combinations, but I have not investigated the matter in detail. In fact, it would take considerable effort to consolidate the opinions of veteran field-trialers, even if they had an opinion, as to the order of difficulty of the 144 ways for setting up the triple. For example, if one selected at random only 9 of the 144 ways in order to clarify his own thinking or to obtain opinions of others as to degree of difficulty, one could compare the difficulty of each way with the difficulty of each of the other 8 ways. In approaching such a problem, I find it less tedious to group the ways into sets of three, called *triads*. Furthermore, by identifying *circular triads*, one can determine whether a handler or judge really has an opinion on relative difficulty of ways of setting up the test or is merely reasoning in a circle. To illustrate the meaning of circular triads, suppose that you have a group of three ways, call them U, V, and W (a triad), of setting up the triple. For the moment, let the symbol "greater than" (>) be read in this context as "is more difficult than." If a judge asserts that way U of setting up the test is most difficult, and say W is least difficult, then we could write the triad in rank order as

$$U > V > W.$$

From this ranking we know that when we make comparisons in pairs,

PHEASANT SHOOTING. II.   LA CHASSE AUX FAISANS.

Number 12 (of 25 in one of "the rarest of all" series of sporting prints). Imprinted Sam.ˡ Howitt dd., Edw.ᵈ Orme Excudit., W. M. Craig & H. Merke sculp. From a color print (in the author's private Pontchippi Collection) published July 1, 1807, by Edw.ᵈ Orme, Printseller to the King, Engraver & Publisher, Bond Street, the corner of Brook Street, London.

Hankie with Alex, Pontchippi-on-Canal, June, 1970.

U > V, V > W, and U > W. If, however, in the examination of a dozen such triads the judge makes a ranking such as

$$U > V > W > U,$$

we shall say that the triad is inconsistent or circular. [Clearly the ranking could be reversed and the "less than" symbol (<) used and read in this context as "is less difficult than."] Obviously, the larger the number of circular triads a judge generates, the more inconsistent is his ranking procedure. I have made some preliminary investigations and it appears that retriever enthusiasts (RE's) encounter trouble in ranking ways as to difficulty; in short, RE's assert that they can rank, but often they cannot.

Illustration of ranking concerning difficulty (utilizing triads).-- There are 72 ways of setting up the triple using a live cock pheasant and 2 dead pheasant. I randomly selected 9 of these 72 ways of setting up the triple, namely, 3 ways from the 24 ways using the live cock at location 1, ... , and 3 ways from the 24 ways using the live cock at location 3. Then I combined these 9 ways into 12 "well-chosen" sets of 3 (triads), using each way 4 times. By using this method, the ways can be ranked as to difficulty if a judge can actually distinguish a noticeable difference in difficulty among the 9 ways. Moreover, as mentioned earlier, circular reasoning can be identified although I shall not discuss in detail how to isolate circular reasoning; however, psychometric and statistical literature detail the methods. Furthermore, I shall outline only "hammer and tong" methods for ranking the ways as to difficulty (again, there are more elegant methods described elsewhere).

The 12 triads, which obviously were prepared randomly within the restrictions specified, follow on the next 12 pages; the answers (the items marked with an x) should be disregarded for the moment. Questions such as the following come to mind: Can a judge distinguish a noticeable difference in degree of difficulty within each triad? Can

Consider the three ways of setting up a triple shown on this page. If possible, select the way which appears most difficult; then select the way which appears least difficult; obviously, the remaining way will be intermediate. If there is no noticeable difference in difficulty, check "can't tell." Do not turn back to this page.

Number		Degree of difficulty
086A	c-3 C-1 Flier h-2 Retriever-Handler	Most difficult ( ) Intermediate (x) Least difficult ( ) Can't tell ( )
106B	C-3 Flier h-2 c-1 Retriever-Handler	Most difficult ( ) Intermediate ( ) Least difficult (x) Can't tell ( )
125C	h-1 h-3 C-2 Flier Retriever-Handler	Most difficult (x) Intermediate ( ) Least difficult ( ) Can't tell ( )

Consider the three ways of setting up a triple shown on this page. If possible, select the way which appears most difficult; then select the way which appears least difficult; obviously, the remaining way will be intermediate. If there is no noticeable difference in difficulty, check "can't tell." Do not turn back to this page.

Number		Degree of difficulty
078D	h-2 C-3 Flier h-1 Retriever-Handler	Most difficult ( ) Intermediate (x) Least difficult ( ) Can't tell ( )
133E	h-2 c-1 C-3 Flier Retriever-Handler	Most difficult ( ) Intermediate ( ) Least difficult (x) Can't tell ( )
117F	C-1 Flier c-2 c-3 Retriever-Handler	Most difficult (x) Intermediate ( ) Least difficult ( ) Can't tell ( )

Consider the three ways of setting up a triple shown on this page. If possible, select the way which appears most difficult; then select the way which appears least difficult; obviously, the remaining way will be intermediate. If there is no noticeable difference in difficulty, check "can't tell." Do not turn back to this page.

Number		Degree of difficulty
140G	c-3 c-1 C-2 Flier Retriever-Handler	Most difficult ( ) Intermediate (x) Least difficult ( ) Can't tell ( )
100H	C-3 Flier h-2 h-1 Retriever-Handler	Most difficult ( ) Intermediate ( ) Least difficult (x) Can't tell ( )
095J	c-1 C-3 Flier c-2 Retriever-Handler	Most difficult (x) Intermediate ( ) Least difficult ( ) Can't tell ( )

Consider the three ways of setting up a triple shown on this page. If possible, select the way which appears most difficult; then select the way which appears least difficult; obviously, the remaining way will be intermediate. If there is no noticeable difference in difficulty, check "can't tell." Do not turn back to this page.

Number		Degree of difficulty
086A	c-3 C-1 Flier h-2 Retriever-Handler	Most difficult ( ) Intermediate (x) Least difficult ( ) Can't tell ( )
078D	h-2 C-3 Flier h-1 Retriever-Handler	Most difficult ( ) Intermediate ( ) Least difficult (x) Can't tell ( )
140G	c-3 c-1 C-2 Flier Retriever-Handler	Most difficult (x) Intermediate ( ) Least difficult ( ) Can't tell ( )

Consider the three ways of setting up a triple shown on this page. If possible, select the way which appears most difficult; then select the way which appears least difficult; obviously, the remaining way will be intermediate. If there is no noticeable difference in difficulty, check "can't tell." Do not turn back to this page.

Number		Degree of difficulty
106B	C-3 Flier h-2 c-1 Retriever-Handler	Most difficult ( ) Intermediate (x) Least difficult ( ) Can't tell ( )
133E	h-2 c-1 C-3 Flier Retriever-Handler	Most difficult ( ) Intermediate ( ) Least difficult (x) Can't tell ( )
100H	C-3 Flier h-2 h-1 Retriever-Handler	Most difficult (x) Intermediate ( ) Least difficult ( ) Can't tell ( )

Consider the three ways of setting up a triple shown on this page. If possible, select the way which appears most difficult; then select the way which appears least difficult; obviously, the remaining way will be intermediate. If there is no noticeable difference in difficulty, check "can't tell." Do not turn back to this page.

Number		Degree of difficulty
125C	h-1	Most difficult (x)
		Intermediate ( )
	h-3 C-2 Flier	Least difficult ( )
		Can't tell ( )
	Retriever-Handler	
117F	C-1 Flier	Most difficult ( )
		Intermediate (x)
	c-2 c-3	Least difficult ( )
		Can't tell ( )
	Retriever-Handler	
095J	c-1	Most difficult ( )
		Intermediate ( )
	C-3 Flier c-2	Least difficult (x)
		Can't tell ( )
	Retriever-Handler	

Consider the three ways of setting up a triple shown on this page. If possible, select the way which appears most difficult; then select the way which appears least difficult; obviously, the remaining way will be intermediate. If there is no noticeable difference in difficulty, check "can't tell." Do not turn back to this page.

Number		Degree of difficulty
086A	c-3 C-1 Flier h-2 Retriever-Handler	Most difficult (x) Intermediate ( ) Least difficult ( ) Can't tell ( )
133E	h-2 c-1 C-3 Flier Retriever-Handler	Most difficult ( ) Intermediate ( ) Least difficult (x) Can't tell ( )
095J	c-1 C-3 Flier c-2 Retriever-Handler	Most difficult ( ) Intermediate (x) Least difficult ( ) Can't tell ( )

Consider the three ways of setting up a triple shown on this page. If possible, select the way which appears most difficult; then select the way which appears least difficult; obviously, the remaining way will be intermediate. If there is no noticeable difference in difficulty, check "can't tell." Do not turn back to this page.

Number		Degree of difficulty
106B	C-3 Flier h-2 c-1 Retriever-Handler	Most difficult ( ) Intermediate ( ) Least difficult (x) Can't tell ( )
117F	C-1 Flier c-2 c-3 Retriever-Handler	Most difficult ( ) Intermediate (x) Least difficult ( ) Can't tell ( )
140G	c-3 c-1 C-2 Flier Retriever-Handler	Most difficult (x) Intermediate ( ) Least difficult ( ) Can't tell ( )

Consider the three ways of setting up a triple shown on this page. If possible, select the way which appears most difficult; then select the way which appears least difficult; obviously, the remaining way will be intermediate. If there is no noticeable difference in difficulty, check "can't tell." Do not turn back to this page.

Number		Degree of difficulty
125C	h-1 h-3 C-2 Flier Retriever-Handler	Most difficult (x) Intermediate ( ) Least difficult ( ) Can't tell ( )
078D	h-2 C-3 h-1 Flier Retriever-Handler	Most difficult ( ) Intermediate ( ) Least difficult (x) Can't tell ( )
100H	C-3 Flier h-2 h-1 Retriever-Handler	Most difficult ( ) Intermediate (x) Least difficult ( ) Can't tell ( )

Consider the three ways of setting up a triple shown on this page. If possible, select the way which appears most difficult; then select the way which appears least difficult; obviously, the remaining way will be intermediate. If there is no noticeable difference in difficulty, check "can't tell." Do not turn back to this page.

Number			Degree of difficulty
117F		C-1 Flier	Most difficult ( )
			Intermediate ( )
	c-2	c-3	Least difficult (x)
			Can't tell ( )
		Retriever-Handler	
100H		C-3 Flier	Most difficult ( )
			Intermediate (x)
	h-2	h-1	Least difficult ( )
			Can't tell ( )
		Retriever-Handler	
086A		c-3	Most difficult (x)
			Intermediate ( )
	C-1 Flier	h-2	Least difficult ( )
			Can't tell ( )
		Retriever-Handler	

Consider the three ways of setting up a triple shown on this page. If possible, select the way which appears most difficult; then select the way which appears least difficult; obviously, the remaining way will be intermediate. If there is no noticeable difference in difficulty, check "can't tell." Do not turn back to this page.

Number		Degree of difficulty
078D	h-2	
		Most difficult ( )
		Intermediate ( )
	C-3 Flier h-1	
		Least difficult (x)
		Can't tell ( )
	Retriever-Handler	
095J	c-1	
		Most difficult (x)
		Intermediate ( )
	C-3 Flier c-2	
		Least difficult ( )
		Can't tell ( )
	Retriever-Handler	
106B	C-3 Flier	
		Most difficult ( )
		Intermediate (x)
	h-2 c-1	
		Least difficult ( )
		Can't tell ( )
	Retriever-Handler	

Consider the three ways of setting up a triple shown on this page. If possible, select the way which appears most difficult; then select the way which appears least difficult; obviously, the remaining way will be intermediate. If there is no noticeable difference in difficulty, check "can't tell." Do not turn back to this page.

Number		Degree of difficulty
133E	h-2 c-1 C-3 Flier Retriever-Handler	Most difficult ( ) Intermediate ( ) Least difficult (x) Can't tell ( )
140G	c-3 c-1 C-2 Flier Retriever-Handler	Most difficult ( ) Intermediate (x) Least difficult ( ) Can't tell ( )
125C	h-1 h-3 C-2 Flier Retriever-Handler	Most difficult (x) Intermediate ( ) Least difficult ( ) Can't tell ( )

a judge consistently distinguish which way is more difficult when compared with every other way, where the ways are considered in pairs
(pair or paired comparisons)?

   As an alternative to the use of one flier only, one could use two
fliers. In fact, as stated earlier, since analysis of the triple as presented here is the same as that for two fliers and one dead bird, the
reader could use the procedures outlined here to prepare his own triads using either one or two fliers. If you do investigate the problem,
undoubtedly you will quickly discover what your capabilities and opinions really are as compared with what you thought they were; also,
you will verify for yourself that many of our colleagues make assertions based on circular reasoning. In dealing with a colleague who
insists that he must see the background, the skyline, the light, the
terrain, the cover, in order to assess the difficulty of a test, kindly
suggest that he make any assumptions whatsoever concerning these
factors, but require him to carefully state these assumptions explicitly in writing. If he continues to procrastinate, accompany him to
the field, let him set the tests himself, and then let him proceed to
rank the ways as to difficulty according to firing order and type of
bird. A few such experiences will convince you that even some of our
most renowned judges often reason in circles.

   Analyzing the performance of a particular judge.--In order to rank
the ways as to difficulty one could compare every way with every other
way; say, assign a score of 1 each time a specified way is judged
more difficult than another given way; then assign a score of 0 when
it is less difficult. One could utilize a worksheet such as Table 6-3,
where the symbol > (greater than) is again read in this context as
"more difficult than." The results tabulated here were obtained from
the 12 previous triads, and represent the opinion of an experienced
field trial judge. For my convenience, the judge was "forced" to
make a choice; he was not allowed to check "can't tell." In Table
6-3, the nine "ways" evaluated are denoted by letters: A, B, ... ,
H, J. The total score for way A is denoted ΣA (read "sum A,"

Table 6-3.--Worksheet for summarizing paired comparisons

A	>	B	=	1	D > A = 0	G > A = 1
A	>	C	=	0	D > B = 0	G > B = 1
A	>	D	=	1	D > C = 0	G > C = 0
A	>	E	=	1	D > E = 1	G > D = 1
A	>	F	=	1	D > F = 0	G > E = 1
A	>	G	=	0	D > G = 0	G > F = 1
A	>	H	=	1	D > H = 0	G > H = 1
A	>	J	=	1	D > J = 0	G > J = 0

$\Sigma A = 6$ $\Sigma D = 1$ $\Sigma G = 6$

B	>	A	=	0	E > A = 0	H > A = 0
B	>	C	=	0	E > B = 0	H > B = 1
B	>	D	=	1	E > C = 0	H > C = 0
B	>	E	=	1	E > D = 0	H > D = 1
B	>	F	=	0	E > F = 0	H > E = 1
B	>	G	=	0	E > G = 0	H > F = 1
B	>	H	=	0	E > H = 0	H > G = 0
B	>	J	=	0	E > J = 0	H > J = 0

$\Sigma B = 2$ $\Sigma E = 0$ $\Sigma H = 4$

C	>	A	=	1	F > A = 0	J > A = 0
C	>	B	=	1	F > B = 1	J > B = 1
C	>	D	=	1	F > C = 0	J > C = 0
C	>	E	=	1	F > D = 1	J > D = 1
C	>	F	=	1	F > E = 1	J > E = 1
C	>	G	=	1	F > G = 0	J > F = 0
C	>	H	=	1	F > H = 0	J > G = 1
C	>	J	=	1	F > J = 1	J > H = 1

$\Sigma C = 8$ $\Sigma F = 4$ $\Sigma J = 5$

where Σ is the capital Greek letter sigma); the score for way B is denoted ΣB; ... ; and the score for way J is denoted ΣJ. (Note that I deliberately chose not to use the letter I.) Inspection of the worksheet indicates that this judge thought that way C was the most difficult of the nine ways, and way E least difficult.

Further inspection of the worksheet (Table 6-3) indicates that this judge could not "distinguish" between A and G or between F and H. For convenience in ranking, we can decide those positions randomly; hence, I shall take action as if this judge ranked the tests as follows on a scale from least difficult (easiest) to most difficult:

E (easiest), D, B, F, H, J, A, G, and C (most difficult).

Then we can prepare a tabulation using a format such as the one which follows, where the rank order established above is utilized.

Way (row)	Way (column)								
	E	D	B	F	H	J	A	G	C
E									
D									
B									
F									
H									
J									
A									
G									
C									

Next, using such a format and the data of Table 6-3, we can prepare Table 6-4 by making two entries for each pair of ways as follows: When the column way is reported as "more difficult" as compared with the row way, enter a 1 in the corresponding cell of the table; when the column way is reported as "less difficult," enter a 0 in the proper cell. This amounts to two entries for each pair of ways although as a tabulation technique, it is convenient to make only one entry at a single inspection of a pair. Results of the performance of our distinguished judge clearly indicate that he did some circular reasoning; if he had generated no circular triads, all entries above the diagonal would have been "1's" and all entries below the diagonal would have been "0's." In short, it is intuitively clear that even though our judge was not perfect, he did demonstrate considerable consistency in his judgments. In fact, taking proper precaution, analysis of his degree of consistency can be extended to include "tests of significance," but I shall leave that to the properly motivated and technically competent reader.

Sampling

As a judge, ideally in a particular trial, I would like to have information regarding how each retriever would perform on each and every 1 of the 144 ways of setting up the triple, but, obviously, that is impossible. Judges must draw a sample, usually of size 1 (although a small percentage of the entries may be tested on 2 land triples in the course of a trial); that is, the judges must set the test up in only 1 of the 144 possible ways, and make judgments or inferences based on performance on this single sample (of ways of setting up the triple) of size 1.

Throughout this book, the idea of evaluating sampling processes is involved. There is nothing particularly mysterious about a sample, because sampling is life itself; however, the judges do not evaluate a single sample when they draw an inference from a sample. The judges are able to make inferences from a single sample because they

Table 6-4.--Worksheet summarizing paired comparisons collected by means of triads

Way (row)	Way (column)								
	E	D	B	F	H	J	A	G	C
E		1	1	1	1	1	1	1	1
D	0		1	1	1	1	1	1	1
B	0	0		1	1	1	1	1	1
F	0	0	0		1	0	1	1	1
H	0	0	0	0		1	1	1	1
J	0	0	0	1	0		1	0	1
A	0	0	0	0	0	0		1	1
G	0	0	0	0	0	1	0		1
C	0	0	0	0	0	0	0	0	

have knowledge (or should have) of the process by which the single sample was drawn.

Again, throughout this book, it is assumed that in the applied situation, both estimates and decisions have to be made on the basis of inadequate information, on information obtained from samples. In fact, it is one purpose of this treatise to illustrate how it is possible to utilize limited information in combination with the mathematics of uncertainty to specify the risk of making erroneous estimates and reaching incorrect conclusions. Such risks can be specified validly only if the observations (limited information) have been "well-collected."

Because it is not known how nonrandom samples behave, and because a vast body of theory does exist based on probability sampling, we shall use only random (probability) sampling. We begin by defining a simple random sample.

Simple random sample.--A definition of (simple) random sample is as follows: If each item (potential observation) in a population has an equal chance of being chosen for the sample, the sample is called a (simple) random sample.

RANDOMIZATION

In all judging which I do, I prefer to generate some probabilities-- do some randomizing. To elaborate, first I make use of all the knowledge and skill which I possess to set up a test; then, for elements of the test for which I haven't a preference--don't know which way is the most difficult, and the like--I let the decision be made by means of a randomizing device.

For example, some of the 144 ways of setting up the triple seem (to me) to be easier than other ways (although sometimes I have difficulty supporting my case); I group those ways of similar difficulty and then select one way randomly. There are some ways that I think are more difficult than others; I group these so-called difficult ways together and select one randomly. If I thought each of the 144 ways was equal in difficulty, I would be perfectly willing, in fact prefer, to select one way strictly at random (from the 144 ways).

A THEORETICAL BUT IMPRACTICAL APPROACH

Day Prior to the Trial

It is possible that the two judges could select at least two, and preferably three, tentative areas for the land triple; furthermore, it is possible that details of the test up to and including location of the line, angle of "flight" of the birds, location of the gallery, the gunners, and the like, could be considered for each area. It is assumed that the judges will use all their skills and knowledge in setting up the test, to include an explicit statement to each other of what each expects a (particular way of setting up the) test to demonstrate ("prove").

The two judges, in conference with field trial marshals, stewards, committee, or all three, could agree on the types of birds to be used; then they could decide on what locations and order of firing appear to be of equal difficulty and in the range of difficulty that they think they prefer.

Random selection of the area. --If, say, three areas were tentatively selected, the judges could number the areas from 1 to 3; by consulting Table 5-3 in the range 1 to 3, a number could be selected randomly; then the land triple could be run at that location. Obviously, the above decision would be made "early" (and in the presence of a marshal or steward) so that key supporting personnel would be properly and adequately informed.

Day of the Trial

Selection of the test. --In the simplest case, suppose for theoretical purposes (keep in mind that this is not a cook-book) that birds of both types were plentiful, that the judges assumed that all 144 ways of setting up the test were of equal difficulty. The judges could refer to any table of random numbers or explicitly to Table 6-5, where random numbers have been conveniently tabulated in groups of three. Since there are 144 ways of setting up the marked land triple on pheasant after an area has been chosen, the judges would consult Table 6-5 in the range 001 to 144. Suppose that number 123 is drawn; then (referring to Table 6-1) the test would be run as follows:

$$_{213}hhC ;$$

explicitly, a dead hen "shot" first at location 2, a dead hen "shot" second at location 1, and a live cock shot third (last) at location 3.

Under the assumption that limitations had been placed on birds to be shot, the judges could consult Table 6-5, or some other table of random numbers, until a test using the specified type(s) of bird(s) first turns up.

RETRIEVER AND PHEASANT

An old print from a painting by Richard Ansdell (engraved by R. Dudensing), in the author's private Pontchippi Collection.

SETTER. From plate (facing p. 123) in John Scott, The Sportsman's Repository, London: Henry G. Bohn, 1845.

Table 6-5.--Random digits, obviously tabulated in groups of three for convenience

Line number	Column number									
	1	2	3	4	5	6	7	8	9	10
001	147	620	476	784	499	618	445	031	479	897
002	503	593	346	638	203	768	766	381	074	076
003	042	952	585	341	142	632	465	950	460	573
004	059	823	513	247	167	882	362	791	105	097
005	753	613	900	564	648	874	763	674	521	492
006	974	435	616	940	024	045	304	556	754	155
007	906	996	729	429	280	668	119	397	433	207
008	132	838	508	963	961	377	747	319	914	307
009	217	081	621	925	554	491	557	793	872	184
010	858	478	571	863	483	467	094	096	804	053
011	657	991	551	659	330	518	927	441	336	039
012	881	343	091	419	981	842	126	490	477	825
013	646	383	935	266	849	876	334	360	606	327
014	661	401	453	984	440	331	515	592	295	245
015	965	185	145	806	200	356	136	244	886	273
016	487	432	635	408	289	534	347	727	238	236
017	231	050	025	692	154	189	216	124	275	220
018	310	495	246	315	297	210	494	077	255	269
019	279	691	830	100	982	051	160	190	514	800
020	316	811	723	509	379	774	404	501	737	110
021	192	061	836	201	604	149	470	466	627	382
022	797	741	628	634	732	983	536	088	864	073
023	655	522	910	075	303	386	658	820	358	416
024	431	437	636	788	860	724	697	043	798	920
025	344	667	939	590	957	717	619	365	235	594
026	068	451	997	591	964	670	835	034	249	008
027	355	818	908	206	104	644	274	288	600	150
028	962	271	353	298	588	436	610	540	462	780
029	622	745	260	846	917	463	296	611	267	904
030	817	580	058	637	391	420	078	915	195	809
031	035	178	680	560	281	239	461	350	041	400

(Continued)

Table 6-5.--(Continued) Random digits, obviously tabulated in groups of three for convenience

Line number	Column number									
	1	2	3	4	5	6	7	8	9	10
032	146	525	624	482	787	998	576	060	064	221
033	721	027	749	617	040	869	989	652	570	268
034	411	527	577	166	287	735	485	389	884	137
035	262	827	205	208	837	905	750	177	647	253
036	845	549	323	065	710	643	951	427	545	500
037	502	129	148	277	421	528	676	309	878	748
038	328	392	767	888	302	762	689	575	923	662
039	532	700	390	714	067	756	090	535	263	426
040	759	901	764	405	550	985	172	682	893	930
041	544	569	993	049	848	833	321	322	681	450
042	337	070	683	639	752	306	497	425	734	037
043	118	684	812	877	349	529	834	225	170	448
044	879	000	311	883	230	250	021	651	831	122
045	972	538	693	810	695	403	844	388	862	169
046	672	948	828	958	960	293	986	599	366	707
047	803	584	808	702	867	496	776	679	134	313
048	698	455	372	369	839	792	605	969	773	852
049	625	191	028	561	157	690	151	222	458	018
050	765	850	841	135	385	348	612	832	819	709
051	789	861	988	464	660	924	052	444	380	294
052	016	164	511	153	449	156	943	968	099	902
053	418	233	713	770	801	143	055	209	123	378
054	586	799	572	782	669	977	098	367	873	089
055	128	003	080	907	489	036	224	885	526	486
056	559	892	181	106	880	183	678	442	510	722
057	423	896	447	999	840	843	701	995	769	434
058	547	677	010	937	001	290	663	023	493	054
059	739	740	019	248	653	933	188	699	898	579
060	731	944	959	498	875	558	326	543	688	086
061	114	022	871	241	335	338	530	941	214	694
062	108	589	361	505	066	484	069	488	251	013

(Continued)

Table 6-5. --(Continued) Random digits, obviously tabulated in groups of three for convenience

Line number	Column number									
	1	2	3	4	5	6	7	8	9	10
063	751	649	175	980	301	726	300	516	259	312
064	705	523	202	030	746	176	779	417	829	308
065	138	340	158	954	913	854	329	211	083	607
066	596	687	240	587	285	919	171	472	807	140
067	531	777	095	387	471	072	254	116	125	332
068	970	786	029	413	903	949	519	237	226	102
069	517	953	506	084	393	223	601	165	733	736
070	866	928	399	109	609	144	686	541	583	929
071	566	127	092	675	229	711	215	728	410	299
072	967	113	608	504	087	719	044	345	243	890
073	265	375	057	785	394	552	182	117	376	038
074	352	062	916	475	822	603	847	548	826	708
075	563	546	595	771	011	704	656	047	758	261
076	938	623	180	992	204	414	162	396	934	626
077	173	761	286	232	112	725	368	412	772	824
078	480	046	339	115	966	186	270	533	578	629
079	650	520	730	857	459	582	567	870	351	802
080	320	921	373	006	909	457	318	278	602	942
081	696	641	159	371	032	473	282	712	645	562
082	017	111	198	085	894	994	305	947	673	234
083	936	257	161	720	918	537	438	889	004	778
084	945	973	738	002	168	005	979	743	815	990
085	654	424	409	512	868	671	474	354	794	071
086	026	374	760	805	193	615	755	197	325	555
087	033	174	775	007	009	987	258	131	614	212
088	685	507	856	015	415	865	130	581	264	370
089	439	256	703	597	152	020	121	783	715	227
090	446	665	012	082	481	395	398	469	242	706
091	932	048	218	133	795	796	141	063	317	219
092	452	853	228	402	946	922	107	213	139	931
093	664	103	814	744	196	790	716	899	333	276

(Continued)

Table 6-5.--(Continued) Random digits, obviously tabulated in groups of three for convenience

Line number	Column number									
	1	2	3	4	5	6	7	8	9	10
094	976	314	272	956	252	813	456	975	454	079
095	430	642	978	384	553	912	443	359	816	163
096	056	093	640	283	821	407	895	342	179	524
097	539	565	911	542	757	887	324	406	926	120
098	187	364	101	357	199	568	971	781	574	422
099	631	718	955	666	633	194	598	742	468	284
100	291	891	855	859	363	630	014	428	851	292
101	938	235	264	945	059	038	478	461	690	903
102	279	439	396	077	401	790	001	241	399	577
103	571	842	392	559	793	333	844	257	110	606
104	138	460	101	004	345	369	064	615	721	733
105	611	069	902	982	630	043	154	769	431	742
106	540	298	623	355	028	998	631	743	208	858
107	111	048	574	386	366	364	296	334	157	499
108	915	179	035	718	500	735	826	121	149	568
109	150	536	375	218	017	276	604	453	103	838
110	243	897	009	496	995	068	734	237	174	085
111	836	481	388	754	978	457	132	418	622	698
112	824	456	348	597	765	229	039	032	791	344
113	205	961	426	999	815	143	450	979	065	075
114	105	261	343	061	748	419	325	899	107	966
115	370	227	207	831	909	535	792	825	134	661
116	436	784	833	956	222	299	560	402	088	363
117	879	680	616	900	782	943	537	374	055	830
118	919	997	864	191	144	524	585	382	420	625
119	701	211	634	099	139	049	865	871	471	603
120	488	321	022	459	829	649	026	338	129	408
121	474	654	773	804	963	195	130	693	234	210
122	353	827	783	968	592	183	247	040	545	816
123	608	533	034	543	010	679	119	594	394	311
124	980	932	293	531	505	562	244	609	610	184

(Continued)

Table 6-5.--(Continued) Random digits, obviously tabulated in groups of three for convenience

Line number	Column number									
	1	2	3	4	5	6	7	8	9	10
125	986	253	002	434	983	981	514	033	313	224
126	249	702	581	669	613	030	135	575	618	000
127	744	696	629	076	410	292	840	406	051	225
128	060	989	192	458	925	720	632	674	185	487
129	578	626	876	050	448	274	483	166	201	684
130	315	799	644	272	351	808	397	564	324	857
131	265	447	737	417	589	905	541	215	413	556
132	663	510	664	695	959	528	573	214	100	529
133	976	177	563	464	841	148	969	360	125	209
134	503	350	341	860	405	939	530	756	569	689
135	685	627	073	640	676	691	586	175	554	312
136	429	162	817	926	732	428	284	778	657	335
137	036	542	071	788	960	781	806	852	062	513
138	760	486	730	739	357	112	491	818	291	768
139	648	755	601	352	805	593	714	362	972	095
140	874	411	443	310	206	020	381	482	675	502
141	044	287	706	677	747	848	216	843	807	888
142	515	188	182	847	067	665	522	705	892	671
143	384	837	379	906	304	595	490	318	254	599
144	518	965	104	987	637	437	988	263	190	952
145	422	203	758	231	859	189	692	974	323	699
146	332	990	786	181	252	813	086	921	497	466
147	659	951	913	122	255	811	798	161	872	954
148	641	794	223	639	238	438	277	280	485	169
149	646	441	158	889	442	686	523	647	591	761
150	320	724	367	469	774	015	726	868	710	193
151	853	025	329	607	307	832	163	349	678	797
152	412	880	547	140	941	916	703	152	047	106
153	583	019	731	507	221	446	128	877	658	395
154	126	949	233	347	912	751	072	171	092	421
155	845	400	109	940	975	893	300	089	473	141

(Continued)

Table 6-5. --(Continued) Random digits, obviously tabulated in groups of three for convenience

Line number	Column number									
	1	2	3	4	5	6	7	8	9	10
156	354	495	985	757	996	275	011	553	516	809
157	736	176	898	173	633	555	766	467	054	142
158	014	346	380	081	719	108	407	006	588	628
159	167	361	854	455	923	226	286	946	200	314
160	358	752	780	894	425	862	590	094	271	725
161	452	617	463	643	316	527	819	170	546	662
162	186	713	521	476	282	090	653	596	023	297
163	239	435	576	777	937	479	614	598	137	550
164	294	202	572	303	728	558	385	666	924	901
165	145	509	964	745	337	194	723	917	393	544
166	372	551	172	927	151	834	432	083	232	302
167	525	929	021	746	681	820	127	391	164	508
168	770	950	935	390	712	638	091	908	398	180
169	383	024	650	933	046	260	319	958	934	771
170	306	212	131	278	971	371	947	948	087	711
171	289	045	498	115	849	683	700	187	283	936
172	764	116	931	451	930	058	715	082	356	196
173	012	113	896	492	821	789	763	053	697	619
174	146	168	074	262	910	197	430	031	259	066
175	387	440	493	359	738	561	342	993	124	475
176	532	114	922	886	250	427	772	570	823	566
177	973	977	579	336	219	810	870	160	042	330
178	767	093	873	228	013	779	285	470	891	248
179	270	875	694	098	750	587	136	217	489	056
180	708	433	147	846	198	673	368	992	269	741
181	861	749	403	548	895	994	416	883	729	376
182	415	984	839	133	759	920	236	856	501	800
183	722	851	656	835	717	155	326	373	159	802
184	918	814	288	914	290	080	785	097	123	801
185	378	991	642	029	251	584	887	468	454	863
186	519	308	672	753	120	309	567	636	423	776

(Continued)

Table 6-5. -- (Concluded) Random digits, obviously tabulated in groups of three
for convenience

Line number	Column number									
	1	2	3	4	5	6	7	8	9	10
187	667	582	539	620	660	444	256	727	063	655
188	331	204	796	295	365	538	052	078	003	621
189	118	866	305	199	651	246	957	602	258	890
190	600	465	117	740	268	377	389	213	007	878
191	328	612	668	911	812	153	018	472	962	102
192	016	534	795	414	079	869	565	041	005	506
193	424	027	340	281	504	480	245	645	942	240
194	580	008	967	477	904	273	775	322	787	970
195	409	855	084	267	670	762	156	867	220	317
196	882	605	462	526	822	928	301	624	552	850
197	178	549	057	517	907	327	512	242	803	707
198	404	449	557	885	704	682	266	635	070	037
199	716	494	230	884	484	520	944	165	652	339
200	828	688	709	953	955	511	881	687	096	445

Under the assumption of unequal difficulty of ways, the ways of equal difficulty could be grouped, and one of the ways selected at random.

DISCUSSION

The procedures of randomly selecting both an area and a way of setting up the test are just two precautions in our attempt to provide an unbiased method for bringing the best retrievers to the top over the long run. In years to come I suspect that retriever enthusiasts will demand that randomization procedures be applied to other aspects of the field trial game.

These procedures enable judges to make an inference about the performance of a specified group of retrievers regarding the factors considered in the triple. Furthermore, this method protects judges from selecting an area or permutation which might possibly favor or hinder a particular "type" of retriever, handler, or owner. In addition, it provides a protective device to keep one judge from dominating the pair. Moreover, it accomplishes other functions which will not be detailed here.

I have consistently used modifications of these methods throughout my judging career. Occasionally, colleagues have reported comments made by mutual acquaintances who have "run" in trials which I have judged. When I get a report that it was a "typical McMahan trial," and that such a comment had been uttered with the "proper overtones," I wonder ... ; now you know why. How could it be ... when it contained random elements? Field-trialers with whom I have been privileged to judge will recall that on occasion I have "used persuasive powers" for particular birds fired in a particular order; now you know that the randomization came out that way, and I was trying to follow "the book." Some handlers do "keep a book" on the types of tests that particular judges like; I ... to think about the problem(s) a handler must have in drawing patterns of McMahan's tests which have been based on random numbers.

SUMMING UP

In short, I am proposing that judges utilize every ounce of experience and good judgment at their disposal in setting up tests; this is mandatory. Then, within that framework, when they actually do not know or cannot distinguish one area or one way as being better or more difficult than another, decide the exact area of the test, the type of bird, and the order of firing by some randomizing device.

ACTION ITEMS

Item 1.--By this time, a reader might wonder why angle of flight (or angle of throw) has not been explicitly discussed in considering the triple. *Assertion:* No additional insight into the number of ways of setting up the triple mark is provided by considering angle of flight. To elaborate, and be absurd *in finitum* , using a magnetic compass, one set of judges could specify direction of the throw in terms of degrees; another set of judges could use degrees and minutes; and yet another set could use degrees, minutes, and seconds; ... . In view of "the innumerable angles" suggested above, clearly, angle of flight must be disregarded in this presentation. (However, a reader could select a very few well-chosen angles and make his own computations.)

Now suppose that two judges require three different gun locations, and are willing to shoot pheasant to fall on land or water, to shoot duck to fall on land or water, to use any combination of duck and pheasant, live or dead, cock or hen, drake or duck. In short, given the following information:

Number of locations: 3

Type of game: 2 (duck or pheasant)

Status of "bird": 2 (live or dead)

Sex of bird: 2 (male or female)

Type of terrain: 2 (land or water)

Firing order: 3 ! = 6 .

Explicitly note that these judges are willing to use one live bird and two dead birds, or two live and one dead, or three live birds, or three dead birds.

Thus, at each of the three locations a choice can be made of the following: type of game, status of bird, sex of bird, and type of terrain. Whence, at each location we have $2 \times 2 \times 2 \times 2 = 2^4 = 16$ ways to select these factors for the triple. Because the selection can be made independently at each location, we then have $16 \times 16 \times 16 = 4,096$ ways to set up the triple before firing. Now inasmuch as there are $3 ! = 6$ orders of firing, we have $6 \times 4,096 = 24,576$ ways in all of setting up this triple mark.

Picking up.--Verify that, again, there are $3 !$ ways of retrieving these marks; hence, there are $24,576 \times 6 = 147,456$ ways of setting up and picking up the triple mark.

Item 2.--Continuing the main stream of thought (from item 1) regarding setting up the triple mark, suppose that the judges are willing to shoot (throw) two birds from one location.

There are two choices for type of terrain (2 ways). There are now two choices for location at which two birds will be used (2 ways).

Now, let's look at the "one bird location," where there are eight ways: There are two choices of sex (male or female, 2); there are two choices for type of game (duck or pheasant, 2); and there are two choices for status of bird (live or dead, 2). Hence, $2 \times 2 \times 2 = 8$.

At the "two bird location," for convenience, designate birds as bird A and bird B. For A and for B there are $2 \times 2 \times 2$ (sex, game type, status) $= 8$ possibilities. Thus, there are $8 \times 8 = 64$ ways of selecting the two birds A and B. However, in 8 of these 64 cases the two birds are of the same sex, same game type, and same status of live or dead and, hence, they are indistinguishable to the retriever. This situation affects the count when order of firing is considered. With only two locations, there are three orders of firing, say, α, β, γ, and call the locations "1" and "2"; e.g.,

$$\alpha : \quad 1, \quad 2, \quad 1$$
$$\beta : \quad 1, \quad 1, \quad 2$$
$$\gamma : \quad 2, \quad 1, \quad 1,$$

where the symbols α, β, and γ are the lower case Greek letters alpha, beta, and gamma, respectively. In firing orders β and γ we must be certain that the eight indistinguishable cases listed above do not get duplicated in the count.

With these hints, I leave it to the reader (as an exercise) to verify that there are $24,576 + 5,632 = 30,208$ ways of setting up (repeat, *setting up*) the marked triple under the conditions specified in action items 1 and 2.

Item 3.--Given type of game, status of bird, sex of bird, and type of terrain as specified in the two immediately preceding action items. As an academic exercise, suppose you allow all three birds to be shot from one location; compute the number of ways of setting up the triple mark.   *Hint:* Be careful that indistinguishable cases do not get duplicated in the count.

Item 4.--*Question:* Do you think that "our distinguished judge" who asserted that "there are a million ways to set up a triple" *really knew* what he was talking about? Discuss.

Item 5.--*For the interested RE:* Reference "well-chosen" sets of 3 (triads), ... , on page 151. In this context, well-chosen means that I used a 3×3 balanced lattice design with $t = 9$, $k = 3$, $r = 4$, $b = 12$, and $\lambda = 1$. For further discussion, see William G. Cochran and Gertrude M. Cox, *Experimental Designs*, second edition, New York: John Wiley and Sons, Inc., 1957, pp. 396-438.

A pittance of practice may be worth a tome of theory.

NOTES TO CHAPTER SIX

Suppose a young judge puts the following question to a more experienced judge: How do you go about estimating the variability among open retrievers in the time it takes (a retriever) to complete a marked triple? (Note that the focus of the question is on variability.) The senior judge may smile and reply: "Well, that depends ... ." He might want to ask the young judge a series of questions: Just what do you mean, how long does it take? For a given retriever, what's going to determine, say, when you (we) start the stopwatch? What's going to set the limit as to when the watch is to be stopped? In this framework, a senior judge might reply that obviously the time required for a retriever to "mark and pick up a triple" (or for a club to conduct a triple) depends on many variables. He might list a few important variables such as the following: distance from the line to the falls, direction and velocity of the wind, age of the retriever, weather, land or water series, cover and/or depth of the water, "club mechanics," location of the ready box, ... , difficulty in getting to the line, ... , quality of the birdboys and the gunners, ...

The question posed by the young judge is certainly of interest if for nothing more than for interest's sake; however, it is of theoretical importance in such a book as this one. Moreover, through the years I have found it fascinating to ask judges, and other experienced RE's, questions which motivate them to make predictions. It is my hypothesis that a judge's ability to predict is one operational measure of his "true knowledge" of the game. Additionally, estimates of time required for a test may be of practical importance.

To elaborate, in planning a test, in the instances reported herein a marked triple in an open stake, many judges find it helpful to make use of a retriever (a "set-up dog") that is capable of doing essentially "average open work." If a "pretty good estimate" of the average time required (by a "typical" open retriever) to complete a test can be obtained, then a "pretty good estimate" of the variability to be expected among other open retrievers can be calculated for the proposed series.

For many years, I have made observations (and analyses) on the time required for many aspects of retriever field trials (for elapsed time between combinations of events taken 2 at the time). The data collected suggest that better than 9 out of 10 open retrievers who complete a marked triple fall will complete within the average (mean) time (of all retrievers in that series) plus or minus 2/5 or 40 per cent of that average time. For example, suppose a set-up retriever leads a judge to estimate that a marked triple will require approximately 4 minutes (240 seconds) on the average for each retriever; clearly, (2/5)(240) = 96 seconds. Now (if our 240 seconds is a "good estimate") if we add 96 seconds to and subtract 96 seconds from 240 seconds, we obtain an interval estimate that extends from 144 seconds to 336 seconds, that is, from 2 minutes 24 seconds to 5 minutes 36 seconds (of course, such preciseness is not required in practice--a judge might estimate "two and a half to five and a half" minutes).

As a second example, suppose the set-up retriever leads a judge to estimate that 7 minutes will be required on the average per retriever on a water triple. Roughly, we shall expect more than 9 out of 10 open retrievers to complete the test in 7 ± (2/5)(7) minutes--7 ± 2.8 minutes, or in terms of seconds, 420 ± 168 seconds; that is, we shall expect 9 out of 10 open retrievers to take between 252 and 588 seconds, which is between 4 minutes 12 seconds and 9 minutes 48 seconds, to complete the test. To be safe, we might predict over the long run that about 95 per cent of the retrievers who complete the test would do so within, say, 4 to 10 minutes, with most performances requiring closer to 7 minutes.

I do not purport to present data to serve as standards for comparison; however, I shall present tables which illustrate the types of findings on which the foregoing rule of thumb was based. (Since time trends are not the focus of interest here, I shall limit the presentation to data collected in the fall of 1969.) Before examining the data, we do need to make some definitions.

Selected Definitions of Statistical Terms

As a vehicle for discussion, suppose we are given a sample of five observations in minutes (one observation on each of five different retrievers) on the time it takes a retriever to complete a triple mark (water) as follows: 4, 5, 6, 7, 8.

Let x_i denote a typical value in the sample and n denote the number of observations in the sample. The items in any sample may be represented by

$$x_1, \ x_2, \ \ldots, \ x_n,$$

where the subscripts serve as identification tags and the three dots are read "and so on." Matching the symbols with the preceding values, we get

$$x_1 = 4, \quad x_2 = 5, \quad \ldots, \quad x_5 = 8,$$

where $n = 5$.

Arithmetic mean. -- The arithmetic mean, represented by $\bar{x}$ (read "x-bar"), is the value computed by adding the individual values and dividing by the number of observations (this is the "common average"); e.g.,

$$\bar{x} = \frac{x_1 + x_2 + \ldots + x_n}{n}.$$

This equation can be written in condensed form as

$$\bar{x} = \frac{\Sigma x}{n},$$

where x stands for every item successively and Σx is read "sum of the x." [The symbol Σ (the capital Greek letter sigma) is the sign of summation which directs that all n observations (in this case) are to be added together.]

Applying the formula to the data of our example,

$$\bar{x} = \frac{4 + 5 + 6 + 7 + 8}{5} = \frac{30}{5}$$

$$\bar{x} = 6 \text{ minutes.}$$

Sample variance. -- The sample variance, denoted s^2, is defined as follows:

$$\text{Sample variance} = \frac{\text{sum of (deviations from the mean)}^2}{n - 1};$$

that is,

$$s^2 = \frac{\Sigma(x - \bar{x})^2}{n - 1}, \tag{1}$$

where again the sign of summation tells us to add up all the squared deviations from the mean.

In the present case, where $n = 5$, proceed as follows:

Deviations from $\overline{x}$	(Deviations from $\overline{x}$) squared
$x_1 - \overline{x} = 4 - 6 = -2$	$(x_1 - \overline{x})^2 = 4$
$x_2 - \overline{x} = 5 - 6 = -1$	$(x_2 - \overline{x})^2 = 1$
$x_3 - \overline{x} = 6 - 6 = 0$	$(x_3 - \overline{x})^2 = 0$
$x_4 - \overline{x} = 7 - 6 = 1$	$(x_4 - \overline{x})^2 = 1$
$x_5 - \overline{x} = 8 - 6 = 2$	$(x_5 - \overline{x})^2 = 4$
	$\Sigma(x - \overline{x})^2 = 10.$

The value 10, which is the

$$\Sigma(x - \overline{x})^2,$$

is called the sum of the squared deviations about the mean, in short, the sum of squares (ss). Consequently, from Eq. (1),

$$s^2 = \frac{10}{4} = 2.5 \text{ square minutes.}$$

This statistic s^2, called the variance, is a measure (in a sense) of how different the individual observations in the sample are from each other on the average; s^2 is in square units, square minutes in this example.

Sample standard deviation. -- The sample standard deviation is usually referred to as the standard deviation and is defined as follows:

$$\text{Standard deviation} = \sqrt{\frac{\text{sum of (deviations from the mean})^2}{n - 1}}.$$

Symbolically, let s represent the standard deviation:

$$s = \sqrt{\frac{\Sigma(x - \overline{x})^2}{n - 1}}.$$

Note that the standard deviation is the square root of the variance. Consequently,

$$s \;=\; \sqrt{s^2}\,.$$

Hence, in this example,

$$s \;=\; \sqrt{2.5} \;\approx\; 1.58 \text{ minutes.}$$

This statistic s, called the standard deviation, is (in a sense) a measure of how different the individual sample observations are from each other on the average; s is in the units of the original observations, minutes in this example, 1.58 minutes.

Coefficient of variation.--The coefficient of variation (CV) computed from the sample is defined as follows:

$$CV \;=\; \frac{s}{\overline{x}} \times 100\,. \tag{2}$$

The coefficient of variation is a measure of relative variation and has some theoretical as well as practical applications in the retriever field trial game.

In the worked example under consideration in this section, substituting in Eq. (2),

$$CV \;=\; \frac{1.58}{6} \times 100$$
$$CV \;\approx\; 26 \text{ per cent.}$$

Note that the coefficient of variation is meaningful only when the mean, $\overline{x}$, and the standard deviation, s, are also explicitly stated.

Range.--The difference between the largest measurement and the smallest measurement in a sample is called the range. For our sample of five observations,

$$\text{range} \;=\; 8 - 4 \;=\; 4 \text{ minutes.}$$

Percentiles.--Percentiles are the set of values which divides a total frequency into 100 equal parts. In particular, a specified percentile is a point in a distribution of values arrayed from low to high below which the specified percentage of the cases lies.

Median.--The median is the value which divides a series into two equal parts when the observations have been arranged in order from the lowest value to the highest value. It is also P_{50}, the fiftieth percentile. If there is an even number of observations, the average (mean) of the two central values is taken.

On the Importance of Variability

Many young single "handler-owner-trainer" types (for generality call one such individual H), when in New Orleans, inquire of me regarding the French Quarter. In such a framework, I shall fabricate an example to illustrate that a measure of central tendency (such as the mean) may provide a grossly inadequate description--might even be misleading.

Example of arithmetic mean.--There is an apartment in the French Quarter where 5 "blonds" dwell; the average age of these 5 blonds is 20 years.

Let $\bar{x}$ refer to the arithmetic mean, in this case $\bar{x} = 20$, and

$$x_1 \ = \ \text{age of blond number one}$$
$$x_2 \ = \ \text{age of blond number two}$$
$$x_3 \ = \ \text{age of blond number three}$$
$$x_4 \ = \ \text{age of blond number four}$$
$$x_5 \ = \ \text{age of blond number five.}$$

That is,

$$\bar{x} \ = \ \frac{\sum\limits_{i=1}^{5} x_i}{5} \ = \ \frac{100}{5} \ = \ 20 \ .$$

Example of a measure of spread.-- The actual ages (in years) are as follows:

$$x_1 \ = \ 1$$
$$x_2 \ = \ 2$$
$$x_3 \ = \ 3$$
$$x_4 \ = \ 4$$
$$x_5 \ = \ \underline{90}$$
$$\text{Total} \ = \ 100 \ .$$

$$\overline{x} \;=\; \frac{\sum\limits_{i=1}^{5} x_i}{5} \;=\; \frac{100}{5} \;=\; 20\,.$$

It should be obvious to H that this measure of central tendency is insufficient; H needs a measure of variability (spread). The range here is $90 - 1 = 89$. Undoubtedly, some particular H might have been thinking in terms of a range of about 4 years (or even smaller).

Variance for the actual ages. -- Recalling Eq. (1),

$$s^2 \;=\; \frac{\sum (x - \overline{x})^2}{n - 1}\,,$$

we proceed as follows to compute "a measure" of variability:

Deviations from $\overline{x}$	(Deviations from $\overline{x}$) squared
$x_1 - \overline{x} \;=\; 1 - 20 \;=\; -19$	$(x_1 - \overline{x})^2 \;=\; 361$
$x_2 - \overline{x} \;=\; 2 - 20 \;=\; -18$	$(x_2 - \overline{x})^2 \;=\; 324$
$x_3 - \overline{x} \;=\; 3 - 20 \;=\; -17$	$(x_3 - \overline{x})^2 \;=\; 289$
$x_4 - \overline{x} \;=\; 4 - 20 \;=\; -16$	$(x_4 - \overline{x})^2 \;=\; 256$
$x_5 - \overline{x} \;=\; 90 - 20 \;=\; 70$	$(x_5 - \overline{x})^2 \;=\; \underline{4,900}$
	$\sum (x - \overline{x})^2 \;=\; 6,130\,.$

Hence,

$$s^2 \;=\; \frac{6,130}{5 - 1} \;\approx\; 1,532\,;$$

$$s \;\approx\; 39.1\,.$$

The dream of H. --Suppose the ages of the blonds had been exactly those ages that H "inferred" (hoped), say, 18, 19, 20, 21, 22. Now $\overline{x} = 20$ but

$$s^2 \;=\; \frac{10}{4} \;=\; 2.5$$

and

$$s \;\approx\; 1.6\,.$$

Discussion. --The sample variance (or the standard deviation) is a measure of the variation of the observations within a sample; moreover, the variance depends on deviations from the mean. It follows that if each of the 5

"Steadying" Wynk on live free-living pigeon on the neutral ground at the edge of the French Quarter, 1970.

Doc in the '68 Shooting Brake at the corner of Esplanade and Bourbon (just barely caught in the French Quarter), 1970.

Pontchippi Shooting Brake, Model 68 (superstructure and kernels designed and built by the author). Note New Orleans ironwork on the balcony (the Spanish via the French) featuring passionflower.

Pontchippi Shooting Brake, Model 68, towing the mobile kennel (Model 63).

PONTCHIPPI SHOOTING BRAKE, MODEL 1957

At the National Amateur Championship Stake, Park Rapids, Minnesota, Saturday, June 24, 1961.

blonds had been exactly 20 years of age, each of the 5 deviations would have been 0; hence, the variance would have been 0. Nevertheless, by inspection of the calculations in this section, in particular, $s^2 = 2.5$ versus $s^2 = 1,532$, it is clear that with each measure of central tendency, we do need an accompanying measure of variability.

Some Illustrative Data

Now we are ready to examine some observations for one (particular) licensed open stake. In passing, it is worth noting that with all the distractions at a trial, it is not easy to collect "good" data.

In the licensed open stake under study (Table 6-N-1), the elapsed time for the first series was 3 hours 55 minutes and there were reported to be 45 actual "starters." The mean elapsed time (gross) over the series per starter was approximately 5 minutes 13 seconds; the mean elapsed time between event A and event B was 3 minutes 38 seconds. (See Chapter Seven for further discussion of "event.") The mean time between entries, when no retriever was on line, was the difference, or approximately 1 minute 35 seconds.

Recall that the coefficient of variation (CV) is defined as

$$CV = \frac{s}{\bar{x}} \times 100.$$

From Table 6-N-1, by transforming the mean of 3 minutes 38 seconds to 218 seconds, we verify that the

$$CV = \frac{48}{218} \times 100 \approx 22 \text{ per cent.}$$

Observe that the CV for this marked land triple is not far from 20 per cent.

I shall leave it to the reader to inspect Table 6-N-2 in detail. I do call attention to the CV for this marked water triple; it too is not far removed from 20 per cent, but it is less than 20 per cent. *Hypothesis:* In the manner that open stakes are usually conducted in America, the CV for the land triple would be expected to be larger than the CV for the water triple.

Do you now see the basis for the rule of thumb stated early in these notes? If you do, clearly you can develop your own rule of thumb based on your observations.

Table 6-N-1.--Elapsed time in minutes and seconds between arrival on the line (event A) and departure from the line (event B), and selected statistical measures, 41 performances on a marked land triple (pheasant, one live hen, two dead hens) in the first series of a licensed open stake, 1969

Observations (arrayed from low to high)		Frequency of occurrence	Cumulative frequency	Percentile (approximate)
Collected in minutes and seconds	Transformation to seconds for calculations			
2 : 25	145	1	1	2
2 : 30	150	1	2	5
2 : 41	161	2	4	10
2 : 45	165	1	5	12
2 : 49	169	1	6	15
2 : 56	176	1	7	17
2 : 59	179	1	8	20
3 : 00	180	1	9	22
3 : 06	186	2	11	27
3 : 08	188	1	12	29
3 : 09	189	1	13	32
3 : 11	191	1	14	34
3 : 13	193	1	15	37
3 : 15	195	1	16	39
3 : 17	197	1	17	41
3 : 18	198	1	18	44
3 : 23	203	1	19	46
3 : 25	205	2	21	51
3 : 26	206	1	22	54
3 : 35	215	1	23	56
3 : 41	221	1	24	59
3 : 42	222	2	26	63
3 : 54	234	1	27	66
3 : 55	235	1	28	68
3 : 57	237	1	29	71
3 : 59	239	1	30	73
4 : 00	240	1	31	76
4 : 05	245	1	32	78
4 : 11	251	1	33	80
4 : 17	257	1	34	83
4 : 20	260	1	35	85
4 : 30	270	1	36	88
4 : 31	271	1	37	90
4 : 48	288	1	38	93
4 : 55	297	1	39	95
5 : 09	309	1	40	98
6 : 25	385	1	41	100

Note.--Event A: Handler arrives with retriever at well-defined point near the line. Event B: Handler crosses well-defined "line of departure" after "his retriever" has been tested.

(Continued)

Table 6-N-1. --(Concluded) Elapsed time in minutes and seconds between arrival on the line (event A) and departure from the line (event
B), and selected statistical measures, 41 performances on
a marked land triple (pheasant, one live hen, two dead hens)
in the first series of a licensed open stake, 1969

Selected Statistical Measures

Mean	=	3 minutes	38 seconds
Median	=	3 minutes	25 seconds
Range	=	4 minutes	
Low	=	2 minutes	25 seconds
High	=	6 minutes	25 seconds
Variance	=	2,335 square seconds	
Standard deviation	=	48 seconds	
Coefficient of variation	=	22 per cent	

Reported number of starters: 45;
missed observations (observer error or failure to complete the test): 4.

Starting time (event A for first entry): 8:20 a.m.

Time series ended (event B for last entry): 12:15 p.m.

Elapsed time for the first series: 3 hours 55 minutes.

Description of cover: Pontchippi middling.

Estimated distances (where estimated means "paced off") from the line to
the falls: (1) 70 yards; (2) 70 yards; (3) 60-65 yards.

Comment: The percentile estimates are for rough guidance only; it is
well-known that there is little point in attempting to calculate values of percentile points when the number of observations is small. Moreover, different
formulas for calculating percentiles may yield different values.

Table 6-N-2.--Elapsed time in minutes and seconds between signal by judge
for first duck to be thrown (event C) and delivery to handler's
hand of third duck retrieved (event D), and selected statistical measures, 11 performances on a marked water triple
(shackled duck), with honoring, in the fourth series of a licensed open stake, 1969

| Observations (arrayed from low to high) | | Frequency of occurrence | Cumulative frequency | Percentile (approximate) |
Collected in minutes and seconds	Transformation to seconds for calculations			
6 : 23	383	1	1	9
6 : 55	415	1	2	18
7 : 21	441	1	3	27
7 : 29	449	1	4	36
7 : 41	461	1	5	45
7 : 42	462	1	6	55
7 : 44	464	1	7	64
7 : 57	477	1	8	73
8 : 57	537	1	9	82
9 : 04	544	1	10	91
11 : 18	678	1	11	100

Note.-- Event C: Judge signals for first duck to be thrown.   Event D:
Retriever delivers third duck to (handler's) hand.

Selected Statistical Measures

Mean	=	8 minutes 3 seconds
Median	=	7 minutes 42 seconds
Range	=	4 minutes 55 seconds
Low	=	6 minutes 23 seconds
High	=	11 minutes 18 seconds
Variance	=	6, 353 square seconds
Standard deviation	=	1 minute 20 seconds
Coefficient of variation	=	17 per cent

(Continued)

Table 6-N-2.--(Concluded) Elapsed time in minutes and seconds between signal by judge for first duck to be thrown (event C) and delivery
to handler's hand of third duck retrieved (event D), and selected statistical measures, 11 performances on a marked
water triple (shackled duck), with honoring, in the fourth
series of a licensed open stake, 1969

Number called back for the fourth series: 13 ;
    missed observations (observer error): 2 .

Starting time (event C for first entry): 11:34 a.m.

Time series ended (event D for last entry): 1:45 p.m.

Elapsed time for the fourth series: 2 hours 11 minutes.

[*A not-so-crude geographical description.*-- The test was "conducted
from a road." Gunners and birdboys were positioned at three locations.
Order of firing: The middle bird was thrown first ① ; the right-hand
bird was thrown second ② ; and the short duck to the left was thrown
last ③ .

It is convenient to let the point (spot) where the retriever sat on the line
be called L. Draw straight lines from L to each of the three falls (as well
as one to the left, parallel to the road). Clearly, L is the vertex of each of
these "rays."

A surveyor's instrument (theodolite with telescope mounted--transit),
rod, "150-foot" steel tape, were used to measure angles and selected distances; then the desired distances to the falls were estimated (calculated)
using trigonometric methods. Distances from the line (L) to the falls were
estimated (to the nearest yard) to be as follows: L to ① = 89; L to ② =
156; L to ③ = 34. Using the spot L as the vertex, angles were measured (to the nearest 5 minutes) as follows: Between the straight lines to
falls ① and ② , 30°35′; between the straight lines to falls ③ and ① ,
49°30′; between "the road" and the line to fall ③ , 33°00′. Appreciation
is expressed to AIB for "surveying assistance."]

On Confidence Intervals

Interval estimates are often used in everyday field trial discussions. For example, we don't ordinarily say that judge J-Bar is 55 years and 1 month old; we don't attempt to be that precise. Instead, we are more likely to speculate that J-Bar is over 50 but less than 60 years young. Another example, we don't even estimate the distance to a fall by a precise point estimate such as $85\frac{2}{3}$ yards because intuitively we think it would be incorrect; instead, we use a less precise estimate, an interval estimate, such as, say, between 75 and 100 yards which is more likely to be correct--to bracket the true distance. All of us know that each such estimate either brackets the true value or it fails to bracket the true value. In short, each such interval estimate is either right or wrong. The retriever judge who knows a little about probability and statistics has this advantage: Under certain circumstances, he can pretty well know his likelihood of error.

In addition, there is the problem of actually making measurements; to make precise (and accurate) measurements is not an easy task.

At this point, some assertions as background material to set the stage for what is to follow are in order. (1) No measuring instrument is perfect, not even a stopwatch in the hands of a qualified retriever field trial judge. (2) No retriever field trial judge can measure perfectly. (3) In addition, variability due to sampling procedures is expected.

Concoction and invention.--After wide-spread use of instant replay on television, I developed the PRPM (Pontchippi Retriever Performance Meter), obviously, under the trade mark Pontchippi. The PRPM enables an investigator (housed in a small highly mobile vehicle with half-track) with the use of computerized techniques and instant replay to repeatedly measure the performance of a retriever in the field. Even with such sophisticated equipment and advanced programming techniques, there remains some variability associated with repeatedly measuring the performance of a specified retriever in the field; nevertheless, measurement error is small by usual standards.

It follows, then, that even with PRPM, seldom will we estimate the true performance of a retriever in the field exactly; however, we should expect to bracket the true performance with high probability by subtracting a well-chosen amount from the reading on PRPM and adding a well-chosen amount to that reading. If we assume that each measurement is a random sample, and if we construct a confidence interval (CI) for each measurement, we can further assume that each such confidence interval is a random sample from a population of such confidence intervals, where 95 out of each 100 intervals bracket the value of the true performance.

"Wrong most of the time."-- In what sense is a good judge wrong most of the time?

Analogy.--Define a population of size N of only 4 observations, $x_1 = 2$, $x_2 = 3$, $x_3 = 5$, $x_4 = 6$. The mean of the population, μ (lower case Greek letter mu, true value, parameter) is equal to 4. Suppose we decide to draw all possible samples of size n = 2 from this population; employ random sampling with replacement where no two *samples* are alike. In this case there are $\binom{N}{n}$ + N possible samples; that is, $\binom{4}{2}$ + 4 = 6 + 4 = 10 possible samples that contain two members; namely, (2 , 3), (2 , 5), (2 , 6), (3 , 5), (3 , 6), (5 , 6), (2 , 2), (3 , 3), (5 , 5), (6 , 6) (see page 230).

[*Aside:* In simple random sampling with replacement where the order of the draw is considered as making a difference, there are N^n possible samples. In simple random sampling where any member of the population is allowed to appear only once in the sample, we designate this method of sampling as sampling without replacement. In simple random sampling without replacement, there are $\binom{N}{n}$ possible samples (see Chapter Seven, page 221).]

Suppose we attempt to estimate the population mean (the parameter), μ, from the arithmetic average, the sample mean $\bar{x}$, from each possible sample. The estimates are shown below.

ID number of sample	Composition of sample	Sample mean, $\bar{x}$
1	2 , 3	2.5
2	2 , 5	3.5
3	2 , 6	4.0
4	3 , 5	4.0
5	3 , 6	4.5
6	5 , 6	5.5
7	2 , 2	2.0
8	3 , 3	3.0
9	5 , 5	5.0
10	6 , 6	6.0

$$\Sigma\bar{x} = 40.0$$
$$\Sigma\bar{x}/10 = 4.0 = \bar{\bar{x}}$$

Note that the mean over all possible samples is equal to the population mean; in shorthand, $\bar{\bar{x}} = \mu = 4.0$ which verifies that the estimator $\bar{x}$ is un-biased--"gives the right answer over the long run" (over all possible samples). Now if we make a frequency distribution of $\bar{x}$, we have the following:

Value of $\overline{x}$	Frequency f
2.0	1
2.5	1
3.0	1
3.5	1
4.0	2
4.5	1
5.0	1
5.5	1
6.0	1
	10 .

Note that we estimated the true population mean, $\mu = 4$, exactly with only 2 samples out of 10; we made a "wrong" estimate with 80 per cent of our samples. This is what we mean when we say that a judge is "wrong most of the time" when he uses point estimates.

By inspection, we note that if we construct an interval (estimate) by adding and subtracting 1.5 from each sample mean, we will expect to bracket μ with about 4 samples out of 5 (with probability of 0.80). Our rule (*by inspection*) can be explicitly stated as follows:

$$\overline{x} \pm 1.5 .$$

The interval estimate of μ, constructed from each sample, is shown in tabular form on the following page.

Clearly, for any particular sample, if you say that the interval includes μ, you will be either right or wrong. Over the long run, you would expect that 80 per cent of your interval estimates would be correct; that is, you will be correct unless a 1 in 5 sample has been drawn.

Value of $\overline{x}$	Interval estimate of μ $\overline{x} \pm 1.5$	Brackets $\mu = 4.0$?
2.0	0.5-3.5	No
2.5	1.0-4.0	Yes
3.0	1.5-4.5	Yes
3.5	2.0-5.0	Yes
4.0	2.5-5.5	Yes
4.5	3.5-6.0	Yes
5.0	3.5-6.5	Yes
5.5	4.0-7.0	Yes
6.0	4.5-7.5	No

In practice, judges perform without knowledge of the population parameters. When they make confidence statements, in general, they do not know whether they are correct or not; they do know the probability they selected. In this book, we shall work at the 95 per cent level (although the foregoing worked example, for purposes of illustration, is at the 80 per cent level). The confidence statement is correct unless the sample is one of the divergent kind that occurs about 1 in 20 samples.

Estimation versus proving. -- Confidence intervals provide a method of stating "how close" the estimate may be to the quantity being estimated. Suppose that we are interested in the rates of climb of hen versus cock pheasant. One can make estimates by means of point estimates; however, I prefer interval estimates. Under well-known assumptions, if the intervals do not overlap, one can take action as if the rates of climb are truly different. Nevertheless, the foregoing does not prove, in the mathematical sense, that hen pheasant have a "quicker" rate of climb than cock. [*Aside:* As far as judging is concerned, there seems to be yet another use of the word prove. In these times, it is not enough to just take part; there seems to be a desire to *prove* something to someone. The latter seems to be true whether a judge is motivated by personal satisfaction, personal glory, or national prestige.]

[*Aside:* Also see Technical Note C-1 (the technical note to Appendix C); nevertheless, the general theory of confidence statements is used but not explicitly presented in this book; most elementary books in statistics give adequate presentations.]

On Marking

In a test involving multiple marked falls, how long must a "bird" be airborne in order for an open retriever to mark the fall (with high probability)?
Many experienced RE's will assert there is no generalized answer to the
question posed, and I agree. In fact, I make no attempt here to answer that
question; however, I intend to demonstrate that it is possible and practicable
to collect empirical data which could provide an approximate solution. The
foregoing notwithstanding, most judges prefer to provide the retriever with
the opportunity for a "good look" at a fall. What is practical to qualify as a
good look? I set as my goal a minimum of 3 seconds with small variability
among birds with regard to "time in the air."

Before the test dog runs, I ask the birdboys to make some practice
throws. By means of a stopwatch (as inconspicuously as practicable) I attempt to measure the time that the "bird" is in the air (how closely it approximates 3 seconds). I measure the time that the flier (if there is one) is
in the air when we are "obtaining dead birds" and when the test dog runs. I
must admit that I have to settle for less than 3 seconds in many series and,
always it seems, I have to contend with greater variability than I would like
during the trial.

Frequently, one observes an excellent performance when seemingly the
retriever didn't even see the fall; in contrast, a bird may remain airborne
for well over 3 seconds yet the retriever's performance be poor. In fact,
it is my hypothesis that the relative frequency of "excellent" retriever performances is associated with "average flight times" of the bird, and conversely, "poor" retriever performances occur relatively more often in conjunction with "extreme flight times"--both short and long.

More Illustrative Data

[Obviously, the data presented in these Notes to Chapter Six were collected on stakes which I did not judge.]

Observations were made on flying cocks that were shot in the first series
of a licensed trial (Table 6-N-3). The average observed time in the air was
less than 2.5 seconds with only 3 cocks approaching 3 seconds in the air.

Observed time in the air, two observers.--The observations reported in
Table 6-N-3 were made on 24 shot flying cocks by each of 2 observers.
Observer Alpha and observer Delta tied (recorded identical time intervals) on
5 cocks; observer Alpha was higher than observer Delta on 14 cocks; and

Table 6-N-3.--Elapsed time in seconds between release of live cock pheasant
           from hand of birdboy on upswing (event E) and shot cock hits
           ground initially (event F), and selected statistical measures,
           two independent observers, 24 shot cocks in first series of a
           licensed qualifying stake, 1969

Identification number of cock i and statistical measure	Observer code		Cock mean and over-all $\bar{x}$, s^2, and s
	Alpha	Delta	
1	1.8	2.1	1.95
2	2.6	2.6	2.60
3	2.2	2.1	2.15
4	2.1	2.1	2.10
5	2.4	2.4	2.40
6	3.0	2.8	2.90
7	2.0	1.9	1.95
8	2.4	2.5	2.45
9	2.4	2.5	2.45
10	2.7	2.4	2.55
11	2.6	2.3	2.45
12	2.2	2.1	2.15
13	2.3	2.5	2.40
14	2.6	2.3	2.45
15	2.9	2.5	2.70
16	2.4	2.1	2.25
17	3.1	2.9	3.00
18	2.4	2.1	2.25
19	2.5	2.3	2.40
20	2.3	2.3	2.30
21	2.6	2.7	2.65
22	2.7	2.7	2.70
23	2.7	2.5	2.60
24	3.1	2.8	2.95
$\bar{x}$	2.50	2.40	2.45
s^2	0.1087	0.0726	0.0915
s	0.33	0.27	0.30

(Continued)

Table 6-N-3.--(Concluded) Elapsed time in seconds between release of live cock pheasant from hand of birdboy on upswing (event E) and shot cock hits ground initially (event F), and selected statistical measures, two independent observers, 24 shot cocks in first series of a licensed qualifying stake, 1969

Note: Reference the last two rows of the "main" table, in particular the right-most column (the fourth column) where $s^2 = 0.0915$ and $s = 0.30$. Observe that these entries are not measures of variation of the entries in this column; instead, s^2 is the variance of all 48 observations; likewise, s is the standard deviation of all 48 observations.

One-Way Analysis of Variance (ANOVA)†

Source of variation	Degrees of freedom	Sum of squares	Mean square	F-ratio
Among cocks	23	3.7748	0.1641	7.50**
Between observers (on each cock)‡	24	0.5250	0.0219	
Total	47	4.2998	0.0915	

† For the methodology used here, see an elementary text in statistics.

** Statistically significant, $P < 0.01$ (see Chapter Seven).

‡ This measure is repeated on pages 202 and 203 under the heading "For lack of a better estimate of measurement error."

observer Delta recorded longer time in the air than observer Alpha on 5 cocks. Observer Alpha recorded approximately one-tenth of a second more (cock airborne longer) on the average (per cock) than observer Delta.

Now let's analyze a problem of measurement. This is a one-sample problem. Only one group of cocks has been observed; there is only one set of 24 "true times"--one "true airborne time" for each cock. However, 2 observations (estimates) have been reported on each cock. Even though the observers performed independently, clearly, the observation on cock i by Delta is not independent of the observation by Alpha on cock i. Hence, the sample can be considered to consist of the 24 observed differences d_i in "flying time," $d_i = x_\alpha - x_\Delta$, where x_α = observed time by observer Alpha on the ith cock and x_Δ = observed time by observer Delta on the same cock i. The question is as follows: Over the long run, do these two observers record the same (airborne) time on the average? In other words, is the mean of the differences zero? In still other words, do these two observers "measure the same on the average"?

For purposes of analysis in the simplest sort of way, focus on the differences; let

d_i = $x_\alpha - x_\Delta$, and retain the sign of the difference; let

$\overline{d}$ = mean of the differences (where sign is considered),

that is,

$$\overline{d} = \frac{\Sigma d_i}{n},$$

and

$$s_d^2 = \frac{\Sigma(d_i - \overline{d})^2}{n - 1}.$$

The standard error of the mean is

$$SE_{\overline{d}} = \frac{s_d}{\sqrt{n}}.$$

An appropriate test statistic is

$$T = t = \frac{\overline{d} - 0}{SE_{\overline{d}}}.$$

In this example,

$$d_1 \;=\; 1.8 \,-\, 2.1 \;=\; -0.3$$
$$d_2 \;=\; 2.6 \,-\, 2.6 \;=\; 0.0$$
$$\vdots \qquad\qquad \vdots \qquad\qquad \vdots$$
$$d_{24} \;=\; 3.1 \,-\, 2.8 \;=\; 0.3\,.$$

It turns out that $\bar{d} = 0.1042$, $s_d = 0.1853$, $n = 24$, $SE_{\bar{d}} = 0.0378$, observed $t = 2.75$. (For the methodology used here, see an elementary text
in statistics.)

Conclusion: We reject the hypothesis that Alpha and Delta "measure the
same on the average" ($P < 0.05$) (see Chapter Seven). Note clearly, however, that this apparently real variability between the two observers is confounded with variability due to the measuring instruments, the stopwatches.

For lack of a better estimate of measurement error.--The term measurement error may be used to describe the failure of repeated measurements by
the same method on the same material by the same observer to yield identical
results. When one observer is in the field equipped with only one stopwatch,
it is not easy for him to duplicate his measurements (observations) on a particular shot flying cock. Suppose he is willing to treat an observation on the
same cock (the ith cock) by one of his colleagues (using another watch) as if
it were his own repeated (blind, independent duplicate) observation. Then he
might assume for convenience that the failure of the two observations to be
the same would provide an estimate of measurement error. Making use of
the data from Table 6-N-3 again, he could compute the sum of squares for
"assumed measurement error" as follows:

$$\left[1.8 - \frac{1.8 + 2.1}{2}\right]^2 + \left[2.1 - \frac{1.8 + 2.1}{2}\right]^2$$
$$+ \left[2.6 - \frac{2.6 + 2.6}{2}\right]^2 + \left[2.6 - \frac{2.6 + 2.6}{2}\right]^2$$
$$+ \left[2.2 - \frac{2.2 + 2.1}{2}\right]^2 + \left[2.1 - \frac{2.2 + 2.1}{2}\right]^2$$
$$+ \left[\quad \cdots \quad\right]^2 + \quad \cdots$$
$$+ \left[3.1 - \frac{3.1 + 2.8}{2}\right]^2 + \left[2.8 - \frac{3.1 + 2.8}{2}\right]^2,$$

which is equal to 0.5250 square seconds. The mean square for "assumed measurement error" would be 0.0219 square seconds. The estimated standard deviation for assumed measurement error would be the $\sqrt{0.0219}$ or approximately 0.15 seconds. By well-known statistical assumptions, one could estimate that the true observation on a flying cock such as treated here would be expected to be in the interval [(the observation) ± 2(0.15)] in approximately 95 shot flying cocks out of 100.

Comment: Because observer Alpha and observer Delta (see earlier analysis) appeared to measure differently, one might suspect that this particular estimated measurement error may be a little large. Would you agree that a better estimate of the standard deviation for measurement error might be about one-tenth (0.1) of a second?

Example.-- Suppose observer Delta recorded that a flying shot cock was airborne for 2.5 seconds. Using the foregoing rule with s for measurement error equal to 0.15, we would estimate that the cock was really in the air somewhere between

$$2.5 \pm 2(0.15) = 2.5 \pm 0.3,$$

or between 2.2 seconds and 2.8 seconds.

Comment: In spite of the problems of measurement, it is clear from the ANOVA on the second page of Table 6-N-3 that these retrievers did not get equal "looks at" the cock in the air. In particular, note that the variability (mean square) among cocks (time airborne) is relatively large as compared to "assumed measurement error" (mean square between observers "within" each cock). In other words, it is clear that the time airborne among cocks is different in spite of errors in measuring. So what? Everybody will say they knew all this all the time! If you know of someone who has measured it before and published his results, please cite source (and date) so that motivated RE's can "share the knowledge." Of course, "it's obvious--after it's pointed out."

Additional Illustrative Data

Data obtained from licensed trials, in terms of both point estimates as observed (by a human--not a retriever) and interval estimates as computed, regarding the time that a "bird" is in the air, are presented in Tables 6-N-4, 6-N-5, and 6-N-6. Note the small percentage of "birds" that were observed

Table 6-N-4. --Frequency distribution and cumulative frequency distribution
of observations on elapsed time in seconds between release of
live hen pheasant from hand of birdboy on upswing (event E)
and shot hen hits ground initially (event F), and selected statistical measures, 44 shot hens in first series of a licensed
open stake, 1969

| Observed point estimate of elapsed time in seconds, x | Interval estimate+ x ± 2s | | Frequency | Cumulative frequency | Percentile (approximate) |
	if s = 0.15	if s = 0.1			
2.0	1.7-2.3	1.8-2.2	1	1	2
2.1	1.8-2.4	1.9-2.3	1	2	5
2.2	1.9-2.5	2.0-2.4	0	2	5
2.3	2.0-2.6	2.1-2.5	2	4	9
2.4	2.1-2.7	2.2-2.6	1	5	11
2.5	2.2-2.8	2.3-2.7	8	13	30
2.6	2.3-2.9	2.4-2.8	5	18	41
2.7	2.4-3.0	2.5-2.9	5	23	52
2.8	2.5-3.1	2.6-3.0	2	25	57
2.9	2.6-3.2	2.7-3.1	6	31	70
3.0	2.7-3.3	2.8-3.2	7	38	86
3.1	2.8-3.4	2.9-3.3	1	39	89
3.2	2.9-3.5	3.0-3.4	0	39	89
3.3	3.0-3.6	3.1-3.5	4	43	98
3.4	3.1-3.7	3.2-3.6	0	43	98
3.5	3.2-3.8	3.3-3.7	1	44	100

+ Approximate 95 per cent confidence interval estimate in seconds (1.96
from the normal distribution has been rounded to 2.00), where x is observed airborne time and s is estimated standard deviation for measurement
error.

Selected Statistical Measures

Mean	=	2.76	seconds
Median	=	2.70	seconds
Range	=	1.5	seconds
Low value	=	2.0	seconds
High value	=	3.5	seconds
Variance	=	0.1071	square seconds
Standard deviation (observations)	=	0.33	seconds
Coefficient of variation (observations)	=	11.9	per cent

Table 6-N-5. --Frequency distribution and cumulative frequency distribution of observations on elapsed time in seconds between release of dead hen pheasant from hand of birdboy on upswing (event E) and dead hen hits ground initially (event F), and selected statistical measures, 38 dead hens in first series of a licensed open stake, 1969

Observed point estimate of elapsed time in seconds, x	Interval estimate† x ± 2s		Frequency	Cumulative frequency	Percentile (approximate)
	if s = 0.15	if s = 0.1			
1.7	1.4-2.0	1.5-1.9	2	2	5
1.8	1.5-2.1	1.6-2.0	1	3	8
1.9	1.6-2.2	1.7-2.1	4	7	18
2.0	1.7-2.3	1.8-2.2	1	8	21
2.1	1.8-2.4	1.9-2.3	8	16	42
2.2	1.9-2.5	2.0-2.4	1	17	45
2.3	2.0-2.6	2.1-2.5	9	26	68
2.4	2.1-2.7	2.2-2.6	4	30	79
2.5	2.2-2.8	2.3-2.7	5	35	92
2.6	2.3-2.9	2.4-2.8	1	36	95
2.7	2.4-3.0	2.5-2.9	2	38	100

† Approximate 95 per cent confidence interval estimate in seconds (1.96 from the normal distribution has been rounded to 2.00), where x is observed airborne time and s is estimated standard deviation for measurement error.

Selected Statistical Measures

Mean	=	2.23	seconds
Median	=	2.30	seconds
Range	=	1.0	second
Low value	=	1.7	seconds
High value	=	2.7	seconds
Variance	=	0.0669	square seconds
Standard deviation (observations)	=	0.26	seconds
Coefficient of variation (observations)	=	11.6	per cent

Table 6-N-6.--Frequency distribution and cumulative frequency distribution of observations on elapsed time in seconds between release of shackled duck from hand of birdboy on upswing (event G) and shackled duck hits water (event H), and selected statistical measures, third marked fall in a water triple, 12 shackled duck in the fourth series of a licensed open stake, 1969

Observed point estimate of elapsed time in seconds, x	Interval estimate+ x ± 2s		Frequency	Cumulative frequency	Percentile (approximate)
	if s = 0.15	if s = 0.1			
2.1	1.8-2.4	1.9-2.3	1	1	8
2.2	1.9-2.5	2.0-2.4	0	1	8
2.3	2.0-2.6	2.1-2.5	2	3	25
2.4	2.1-2.7	2.2-2.6	0	3	25
2.5	2.2-2.8	2.3-2.7	3	6	50
2.6	2.3-2.9	2.4-2.8	1	7	58
2.7	2.4-3.0	2.5-2.9	2	9	75
2.8	2.5-3.1	2.6-3.0	0	9	75
2.9	2.6-3.2	2.7-3.1	1	10	83
3.0	2.7-3.3	2.8-3.2	0	10	83
3.1	2.8-3.4	2.9-3.3	1	11	92
3.2	2.9-3.5	3.0-3.4	1	12	100

+ Approximate 95 per cent confidence interval estimate in seconds (1.96 from the normal distribution has been rounded to 2.00), where x is observed airborne time and s is estimated standard deviation for measurement error.

Selected Statistical Measures

Mean	=	2.62 seconds
Median (interpolated value)	=	2.55 seconds
Range	=	1.1 seconds
Low value	=	2.1 seconds
High value	=	3.2 seconds
Variance	=	0.1070 square seconds
Standard deviation (observations)	=	0.33 seconds
Coefficient of variation (observations)	=	12.5 per cent

to be in the air for 3   seconds or more. Further note that the coefficient of variation (for time airborne) in all three tables is not far removed from   12 per cent.

Do pheasant fly higher in Alabama?--Given good birds, good weather, good birdboys, ... ,   good shots, and judges who care: Data presented in Table 6-N-7 indicate that (provided I clocked well) 95 per cent of birds can be "shown" for 3 or more seconds.   The fact remains that variability among birds (time shown) is great; however, the CV is again close to 12 per cent.

"VIEW FROM THE TOP"

Aerial view of Louisiana,   ... , and Alabama, flight-time.

Table 6-N-7. --Frequency distribution and cumulative frequency distribution
of observations on elapsed time in seconds (to nearest fifth)
between release of live hen pheasant from hand of birdboy on
upswing (event E) and shot hen hits ground initially (event F),
and selected statistical measures, 21 shot hens in fourth series of a licensed open stake, 1969

| Observed point estimate of elapsed time in seconds, x | Interval estimate† x ± 2s | | Frequency | Cumulative frequency | Percentile (approximate) |
	if s = 0.15	if s = 0.1			
2.8	2.5-3.1	2.6-3.0	1	1	5
3.0	2.7-3.3	2.8-3.2	0	1	5
3.2	2.9-3.5	3.0-3.4	2	3	14
3.4	3.1-3.7	3.2-3.6	3	6	29
3.6	3.3-3.9	3.4-3.8	6	12	57
3.8	3.5-4.1	3.6-4.0	3	15	71
4.0	3.7-4.3	3.8-4.2	3	18	86
4.2	3.9-4.5	4.0-4.4	0	18	86
4.4	4.1-4.7	4.2-4.6	2	20	95
4.6	4.3-4.9	4.4-4.8	0	20	95
4.8	4.5-5.1	4.6-5.0	1	21	100

† Approximate 95 per cent confidence interval estimate in seconds (1.96
from the normal distribution has been rounded to 2.00), where x is observed airborne time and s is estimated standard deviation for measurement
error.

Selected Statistical Measures

Mean	=	3.71	seconds
Median	=	3.6	seconds
Range	=	2.0	seconds
Low value	=	2.8	seconds
High value	=	4.8	seconds
Variance	=	0.2063	square seconds
Standard deviation (observations)	=	0.45	seconds
Coefficient of variation (observations)	=	12.2	per cent

CHAPTER SEVEN

RETRIEVER PROBABILITY

Many aspects of the modern retriever field trial game involve probability. The purpose of this chapter is to examine some of the most elementary topics of probability. The reader should fully realize that this chapter is merely a survey of the easiest methods of the mathematics of uncertainty. Numerous technical procedures and much useful terminology, such as "sample spaces" and "sets" are avoided (although the concept of sets is used in Chapters Five and Eight).

A basic assumption underlying the methods of probability is that the entire discussion is limited to "experiments" which can be repeated, either actually or conceptionally, many times under essentially the same conditions. In such a series of experiments, it is possible to observe the relative frequency with which certain well-defined events occur. When the relative frequency of an event is computed on observed phenomena in the real world, it is assumed that the value obtained approximates a "true number," an ideal number, called the probability of the event in a theoretical or probabilistic model, the latter being undefined for this discussion. It could be assumed that as the number of repetitions, called trials, of the experiment becomes large, the relative frequency of the event approaches (gets closer and closer to) the probability of the event; however, one can just as well think of probability as the relative frequency which applies to a large but finite (countable) number of trials (repetitions). After the concept of probability has been intuitively established, for many purposes it will be convenient to assume that the probability of an event is completely known and to make deductions under that assumption. In other words, the concern is with the two-way relationship between actual and theoretical results.

It is well-known that the outcome of a single trial of an experiment cannot be predicted exactly; if it could, it would be a demonstration, not an experiment. It is of value to know the relative frequency, a stable property, with which a particular result can be expected to occur in repeated trials under the same conditions.

Experiment

Any act that can be repeated under given conditions (essentially the same conditions) is called an experiment or a trial of the experiment.

Observations and Results

In planning an experiment, just as in judging the performance of a retriever, the investigator must select from the many possible observations that could be made what is to be observed. That is, an explicit decision must be made concerning what to observe. Furthermore, the investigator must be capable of listing all possible results of these observations, where each result is mutually exclusive of the others. Thus, on a single trial of the experiment, it must be possible for one and only one of the results to occur. For example, suppose that a trial of an experiment is defined as the observed performance of a retriever marking and retrieving a land triple on pheasant. Assuming perfect ability to measure, the judge makes the following decision after observing the performance of each entry (after each trial of the experiment): drop = D; confer with other judge concerning whether to call back or not = ? ; definitely call back = B. Obviously, if a judge preferred, he could use numbers, for example, drop = 0; discuss with the other judge about whether to call back or not = 1; definitely call back = 2. Theoretically, after the series each entry could be assigned to one and only one of the categories.

List of simple results or possible outcomes.-- All the different, non-overlapping, simple results make up the list of simple results or outcomes of an experiment. Note that these terms refer to all the different outcomes that can possibly happen when making a particular observation on one trial of an experiment.

Event. -- In contrast, event refers to that simple result or group of simple results (composite but still called event) which is of special interest, and whose relative frequency of occurrence or probability (long-run relative frequency) is to be computed. Thus, event can mean a collection of outcomes. Note, however, that when the experiment has been performed, event E (to give it a name) has occurred if the result is one of the outcomes which compose E ("E" is a short title for "event E"). Event E must be defined so that it can be determined without any doubt whether E has or has not occurred.

From the point of view of one judge at the end of a series, if a single judge uses the grading scheme suggested a bit earlier, four simple results must explicitly be considered as follows: (1) retriever fails to get the meat, is assigned a 0, and is dropped; (2) retriever gets the meat, is assigned a 1, and after discussion with the other judge, is dropped; (3) retriever gets the meat, is assigned a 1, and after discussion with the other judge, is called back; (4) retriever gets the meat in a workmanlike manner, is assigned a 2, and is called back. If we take the event of interest as called back, clearly it is composed of the simple results numbered (3) and (4).

Alternatively, if after extensive discussion, the judges could not agree on how to classify the retrievers assigned a 1, and hence, decided to call back all entries which got the meat, the event callback is then composed of the three (modified) simple results originally numbered (2), (3), and (4).

RELATIVE FREQUENCY

The relative frequency, R(E), of event E is defined by the equation

$$R(E) = \frac{n(E)}{N}, \tag{1}$$

where

$R(E)$ = relative frequency of event E,

N = number of times the experiment is performed,

$n(E)$ = number of times event E occurred out of N results.

[$R(E)$ is read "R of E," and $n(E)$ is read "n of E."]

Example.-- Two pennies are tossed and allowed to come to rest. Each penny is observed as to whether a head (H) or a tail (T) appeared. If the experiment is repeated (replicated) 600 times, what is the relative frequency with which both pennies turn up heads? This is an experiment since the act can be repeated under given conditions. The observation of interest is whether the pennies fall heads or tails; the concern is not with the height of the toss, the number of spins, whether or not they bounce, or with other observations that could be made. All possible outcomes of the experiment, all the possible ways that two pennies can land, are listed in Table 7-1. In this example,

Table 7-1.--All possible ways two pennies can fall

First penny	Second penny	Outcome
Head (H)	Head (H)	(H, H)
Head (H)	Tail (T)	(H, T)
Tail (T)	Head (H)	(T, H)
Tail (T)	Tail (T)	(T, T)

the simple results are HH (head on first penny and head on second penny), HT (head on first penny and tail on second penny), TH (tail on first penny and head on second penny), and TT (tail on first penny and tail on second penny). Note that these are ordered pairs. The interest in this example is focused on the event E "both pennies are heads, " that is, the ordered pair (H, H). It is clear that for any outcome of the experiment it can be determined whether this event E does or does not occur.

Two pennies were secured, a bright one and a tarnished one, and were tossed 600 times (Table 7-2). The total number of experiments

Table 7-2.--Outcomes of 600 tosses of two coins

Outcome	Number of experiments
HH	178
HT	145
TH	132
TT	145
Total	600

N is 600; the number of experiments in which event E occurred out of N results is n(E) or 178. Substituting in Eq. (1),

$$R(E) = \frac{178}{600}$$

$$R(E) \approx 0.2967.$$

[The symbol $\approx$ is read "is approximately equal to."]
Note that relative frequencies may be expressed as fractions or as decimals; it is more common to express relative frequencies as decimals. Relative frequencies (R) range from 0 to 1; symbolically, this might be written $0 \leq R \leq 1$. [This is read "R is greater than or equal to zero and less than or equal to one."]

Example.--Since before World War II, I have been interested in a dog food especially adapted for feeding sporting dogs in hot, humid areas of the deep South. In the research and development which led to Pontchippi Palatable Puppifood, "widely known" as P-Kube (PPP

or P^3), slight adjustment of some of the data yielded the hypothetical
values shown in Table 7-3 .

Table 7-3. --Assessment of condition of Pontchippi Palatable Puppifood (P-Kube) after 8 months, 2 preservatives

Condition of P-Kube	Preservative SJ	Preservative CI
Definitely useable	51	38
Spoiled	4	14
Total	55	52

Consider an experiment that consists of selecting and treating a
sack of P-Kube with SJ or without SJ (with CI), and then observing the number of sacks in which spoilage occurs in the first 8 months
after "treatment." The event E of interest is spoilage.   The relative frequency of event E is given by R(E) = n(E)/N . In this case
N = 107 which includes the 55 sacks of food in the SJ group and
the 52 sacks in the control group (CI). Since the total number spoil-
ing in the two groups (4 + 14) composes the event E , n(E) = 18:

$$R(E) = \frac{18}{107}$$
$$R(E) \approx 0.168 .$$

Example.--I secured 2 pint cartons; in 1 carton I placed 107
wooden beads (89 natural colored beads and 18 dark colored beads).
Each bead represented a sack of food in the P-Kube study of Table
7-3 . The dark colored beads represented the 18 sacks of food which
spoiled.

The experiment consisted of mixing the beads thoroughly, then,
holding the carton in such a position that I could not see into it, counting 55 beads and placing them in the other carton, and then observing

the number of dark colored beads (number of sacks of P-Kube which spoiled) in the sample of 55. With the assistance of some "friends," I repeated the experiment 1,120 times. Results of these experiments are shown in Table 7-4.

Table 7-4.--Frequency of sacks of spoiled food (dark colored beads) in an experiment which consisted of drawing samples of size n = 55, without replacement, from a population where $\pi = 18/107$

Number of sacks of spoiled food (number of dark colored beads) in samples of n = 55	Frequency
18	0
17	0
16	1
15	3
14	12
13	34
12	83
11	161
10	209
9	216
8	191
7	124
6	56
5	23
4	5
3	2
2	0
1	0
0	0
Total number of experiments	1,120

Note: The Greek letter π indicates the "true proportion" of dark colored beads (spoiled sacks of food) in the population.

If the event E is 14 or more spoiled sacks of P-Kube in the SJ group (that is, 14, 15, 16, 17, or 18 dark colored beads in the sample of 55 beads), what is the relative frequency of event E?

Solution: $R(E) = \frac{n(E)}{N}$; from Table 7-4,

$$R(E) = \frac{(12 + 3 + 1 + 0 + 0)}{1,120}$$

$$= \frac{16}{1,120} \approx 0.014, \text{ or}$$

$$R(E) < 0.02.$$

[Read the last line above as "R of E is less than 0.02."]

If the event E is 4 or fewer spoiled sacks of P-Kube (4, 3, 2, 1, or 0), what is the relative frequency of event E?

Solution: $R(E) = \frac{n(E)}{N}$; again, from Table 7-4,

$$= \frac{(5 + 2 + 0 + 0 + 0)}{1,120}$$

$$= \frac{7}{1,120} \approx 0.006, \text{ or}$$

$$R(E) < 0.01.$$

If the event E is 4 or fewer spoiled sacks of P-Kube or 14 or more spoiled sacks of P-Kube, what is the relative frequency of event E?

Solution: $R(E) = \frac{7 + 16}{1,120}$

$$= \frac{23}{1,120} \approx 0.021, \text{ or}$$

$$R(E) < 0.03, \text{ or,}$$

since the context is clear, $R < 0.03$.

Example.-- For some specified time period, suppose that we define any retriever who has been awarded a judges' award of merit or a "place" in an open stake of a licensed trial as an open retriever. Consider an experiment that consists of following a cohort, a large closed group, of open retrievers, say, 1,000, from the instant that each becomes an open retriever to the instant that each is separated from the open retriever group (by death or retirement or by some other criterion); in short, the experiment consists of observing the "survival" of a retriever in open stakes. The observation of interest is whether or not an individual retriever survives to a specified exact number of years after attaining open status (after entering the group of open retrievers). The results of such an experiment can be illustrated by means of a hypothetical follow-up study of 1,000 retrievers as shown in Table 7-5; it is assumed here that no retriever was lost from follow-up.

Table 7-5.--Selected data from a hypothetical follow-up study of 1,000 open retrievers

Year after attaining open status	Number "alive" on each anniversary (of 1,000 entries)
0	1,000
1	668
2	546
3	418
4	275
5	159
6	65
7	12
8	4
9	0

What is the relative frequency of surviving for 8 years in the open? In this case the total number of experiments N is equal to 1,000. The event E "survived to year 8" occurred n(E) or 4 times out of 1,000 trials. It follows from the definition of relative frequency,

$$R(E) = \frac{n(E)}{N}$$

$$= \frac{4}{1,000}$$

$$R(E) = 0.004 .$$

Thus, $0.001 < R(E) < 0.01$.

⌈Read the line above as "R of E is greater than 0.001 and less than 0.01."⌋ Because the context is clear, $0.001 < R < 0.01$.

To illustrate another idea with other data from Table 7-5, it is clear that the relative frequency of surviving from year 3 to year 4 is 275/418. Also, it is intuitively clear that

$$\left(\begin{array}{l}\text{R of surviving from}\\\text{year 3   to year 4}\end{array}\right) + \left(\begin{array}{l}\text{R of not surviving}\\\text{from year 3 to year 4}\end{array}\right) = 1.000.$$

Making use of elementary algebra,

$$\left(\begin{array}{l}\text{R of not surviving}\\\text{from year 3 to year 4}\end{array}\right) = 1.000 - \left(\begin{array}{l}\text{R of surviving from}\\\text{year 3 to year 4}\end{array}\right).$$

In this example,

$$\left(\begin{array}{l}\text{R of not surviving}\\\text{from year 3 to year 4}\end{array}\right) = 1.000 - \frac{275}{418}$$

$$\left(\begin{array}{l}\text{R of not surviving}\\\text{from year 3 to year 4}\end{array}\right) \approx 1.000 - 0.658$$

$$\left(\begin{array}{l}\text{R of not surviving}\\\text{from year 3 to year 4}\end{array}\right) \approx 0.342.$$

In other words, based on this experience, among each 3 open retrievers who survive 3 years, about 1 fails to survive the fourth year.

PROBABILITY

It is assumed that for certain experiments an "ideal" number exists which the relative frequency of event E approximates. That ideal number is called the probability of E, denoted $P(E)$. To elaborate on the concept of "ideal number," if one rolls an ordinary six-sided die, intuitively he expects each face to turn up in approximately one-sixth of the rolls. On the other hand, if the die is rolled a large number of times, each face probably will not turn up with relative fre-

The probability of "a single snowfall" of 4.5 inches or more during one calendar year in New Orleans is approximately 0.03. This picture (December 31, 1963) of 6356 Bellaire Drive is evidence that such rare events do occur. Should not judges expect rare events to occur with, say, $P \leq 0.05$? Further, should they be surprised when rare events do occur when they are judging?

Basis for the above probability statement: Records covering the period 1875-1969 were examined at the Weather Bureau, Environmental Science Services, United States Department of Commerce, 701 Loyola Avenue, New Orleans. Local Climatological Data, December, 1963, indicated 4.5 inches of snow on December 31, 1963. Moreover, during the 95-year period under study, such a "single snowfall" was exceeded in two calendar years (explicitly, in February, 1895, when 8.2 inches was recorded and in January, 1881, when 5.0 inches was recorded). Assuming that these data refer to "one big annual snowfall," the relative frequency of event E (a snowfall of 4.5 inches or greater in a calendar year) is 3/95 or approximately 0.03.

In contrast, the probability of a "measurable snow" is 9/95 or 0.09+ which is not a rare occurrence according to our definition. However, the probability of a snowfall of 1.3 inches (such as occurred in 1958) is a borderline rare occurrence; $P = 5/95$ or $P \approx 0.05$. Snowfalls of 1.3 inches or greater were recorded in 1881, 1895, 1899, 1958, and 1963. Additional measurable snows were recorded in 1879, 1897, 1935, and 1960.

Demo and Kube with the author at the foot of the levee, Pontchippi-on-Canal, New Year's Eve, 1963.

With four flat-coated retrievers, Chance, Choice, Wave and Wynk, at the foot of the levee, Easter, 1970.

quency of exactly one-sixth; thus one-sixth might not be the "true value" for this particular die. Nevertheless, if the physics of the problem is disregarded and if one transfers from the real world to the theoretical world, where it is assumed that a die is perfectly balanced, then each face should turn up in approximately one-sixth of the rolls. Under such assumptions "one-sixth" is what is meant by an ideal number.

It is also useful to think of relative frequency, based upon a large, finite number of trials, as probability. In other words, one would expect the relative frequency of event E, computed over a large number of trials, to closely approximate the probability of E; that is, $R(E) \approx P(E)$ when N is "large."

Example. -- Consider an experiment which consists of inspecting a large group of registration certificates of pure-bred dogs (United States) for the calendar years 1964 and 1965, and recording the event when the dog is classified as Labrador retriever. The number of experiments (registrations) N occurring in 1964-1965 was reported as 1,363,100; the event E "Labrador retriever" occurred n(E) or 22,710 times.

$$R(E) = \frac{n(E)}{N}$$

$$= \frac{22,710}{1,363,100}$$

$$R(E) \approx 0.0167 .$$

Since most people would agree that N is large in this example, it appears reasonable to expect that $P(E) \approx 0.017$, or this may be written in abbreviated form as $P \approx 0.017$ since it is unmistakably clear that P refers here to the probability of event E.

In other words, if you number the registration certificates of 1964 and 1965 and pull 1 certificate by a strictly random process, the probability is about 17 in 1,000 that you will draw a certificate where the breed is listed as Labrador retriever.

Models

Mechanical versus statistical models.--Refer again to Tables 7-3 and 7-4. Recall that the experiment consisted of drawing samples of size n = 55 without replacement from a population where π = 18/107. This experiment involved a model which utilized pint cartons and wooden beads; it was designed to simulate the experiment reported in Table 7-3 under the hypothesis that there was no difference in the two preservatives used. That is, the hunch was that the proportion of spoiled sacks of food was the same regardless of which preservative was used. Any so-called mathematical or statistical model, even a "mechanical" device or model, is an idealization which may involve many assumptions. If the investigator chooses the model correctly, he expects it to produce results which have some useful applications to the real situation.

In contrast to the mechanical model utilized above (cartons and beads), a mathematical or statistical model is an abstraction which enables the investigator to perform on paper (rather than with a mechanical device) what are equivalent to real experiments; he can calculate what would happen under certain assumed conditions. Furthermore, he can compute probabilities of complicated outcomes if the probabilities are known for those outcomes which are less complicated. For the most part, calculated probabilities apply to these idealized models only; it requires careful thought to determine if they apply to the real situation. Generally the relationship between theory and practice is complicated.

Statistical models.--Topics treated later indicate that a table which specifies the possible values which a chance variable can take on and which gives the corresponding relative frequencies or probabilities is called a probability distribution for the "parent population." Experience in applied statistics indicates that the approximate distribution of such a chance variable can be idealized by selection of a mathematical function chosen on the basis of theory or experience or both. Furthermore, a few such idealized distributions suffice as models for most practical problems. These idealized distributions serve as "knowns" or "standards" from which, theoretically, all possible samples can be drawn randomly. As a consequence, the variability of a specified statistic among random samples can be calculated from a sampling distribution. With this knowledge involving a model, wise decisions and good estimates of parameters may be made on the basis of the data collected by means of a single sample.

To be concrete about the concept of model, what might one select as an appropriate mathematical model for the experiments we carried out with the beads, the results of which are shown in Table 7-4? Be careful to note that concern at the moment is not with the original experiment, but with the one performed using beads where sampling was conducted without replacement and the concern is with integral values. What mathematical model will indicate the probability of obtaining a specified number of dark colored beads in a sample of 55 under the conditions specified (under the assumptions)?

Equally likely outcomes. -- In order to furnish a relatively uncomplicated model and yet illustrate one which is often used, it must be assumed that every possible sample of size 55 is as likely to be drawn (from the population of 107) as any other sample of that size. If this assumption is made, on the basis of both theory and experience it is asserted that the hypergeometric distribution is an appropriate model. A first step is to examine the general functional form. Hence, the general equation for the hypergeometric distribution involving one variable may be written (utilizing notation described later in the section on permutations and combinations)

$$P(X = x) = \frac{\binom{r}{x}\binom{N - r}{n - x}}{\binom{N}{n}}, \tag{2}$$

where

N = size of the population,
r = number of elements in a particular class A,

n = size of the sample,

x = number of items from class A observed in the sample.

Note that this idealized distribution or model depends upon three parameters, N, r, and n. In functional notation this might be written as

$$f(x, N, r, n) = P(X = x) = \frac{\binom{r}{x}\binom{N - r}{n - x}}{\binom{N}{n}}.$$

When parameters for this particular experiment, that is, when N = 107, r = 18, n = 55, are substituted in Eq. (2), this model becomes a special case of the general functional form. Hence, after substituting in Eq. (2), the probability that the hypergeometric random variable X takes on the value x, denoted by P(X = x), or that there are x number of dark colored beads (spoiled sacks, SS) in the sample of 55 is given by the equation

$$P(xSS) = \frac{\binom{18}{x}\binom{89}{55 - x}}{\binom{107}{55}}$$

which will be discussed in detail later. The probabilities are shown in Table 7-6.

Definition of Probability

In light of the example above, and for many purposes, it is convenient to define probability in terms of equally likely outcomes. The probability of event E is defined by the equation

$$P(E) = \frac{n}{N},$$

Table 7-6.--Probability that exactly x spoiled sacks of food (SS) occur in a sample of 55 from a population of 107, where $\pi = 18/107$ (hypergeometric probability distribution)

Number of spoiled sacks (SS), x	Probability $P(xSS) = \dfrac{\binom{18}{x}\binom{89}{55-x}}{\binom{107}{55}}$
0	0.00000 +
1	0.00001
2	0.00013
3	0.00101
4	0.00519
5	0.01903
6	0.05155
7	0.10562
8	0.16598
9	0.20158
10	0.18967
11	0.13794
12	0.07696
13	0.03250
14	0.01015
15	0.00226
16	0.00033
17	0.00003
18	0.00000 +

where

$P(E)$ =   probability of event E,

N =   total number of different equally likely out-
              comes of an experiment,

n =   number of outcomes (out of N) which corres-
              pond to the event E.

The reader should note carefully that n is included in N.

Example. -- It is well-known that for many families, retriever training and field trialing are family enterprises. For purposes of illustration, suppose that we have a large list of three-child families who
participate in the retriever field trial game. Now, assume that among
these "retriever-happy" families the number of boys equals the number of girls; explicitly, males (M) and females (F) have an equal
chance of being born and of surviving. Further suppose that an experiment consists of drawing one family at random and of observing
the sex of the children. What is the probability that all three children
are males?

Solution: Obviously, the first child can be either male or
female, the second child can be either male or female, and the third
child can be either male or female. Consequently, Table 7-7 contains all the different possible outcomes. The total number of outcomes N is eight; under the assumptions, each outcome is equally
likely. The event E "all three are males" is composed of the single
outcome MMM ; in this case, $n = 1$; thus, in this problem,

$$P(E) \;=\; \frac{n}{N}$$

$$=\; \frac{1}{8}$$

$$P(E) \;=\; 0.125\,.$$

The reader should note that in this example the relative frequency of
occurrence of a specified result was not observed. An ideal situation
was assumed, where the $P(\text{male}) = P(\text{female}) = 1/2$. The problem

Table 7-7.--Possible sex composition of three-child "retriever-happy" families according to order of child

First child	Second child	Third child	Outcome
M	M	M	MMM
M	M	F	MMF
M	F	M	MFM
M	F	F	MFF
F	M	M	FMM
F	M	F	FMF
F	F	M	FFM
F	F	F	FFF

was to compute the probability of a more complicated outcome.

Notation: The probability of any specified outcome or event is denoted "P(_____)," or alternatively "Pr(_____)," where the blank contains the name of the outcome or the event.

Example. -- Refer again to Table 7-7 which contains the sex of the children of three-child "retriever-happy" families, by place of child in the family. Assume that the eight cases are equally likely. The reader will find it worthwhile to verify the probability of each of the following events by explicitly writing down each outcome of the experiment that is included in each event along with its probability.

    (1) P(all three males) = 1/8 .

    (2) P(exactly two males) = 3/8 .

    (3) P(exactly one male)   = 3/8 .

    (4) P(at least one male) = 7/8 .

[*Hint:* The event "at least one male" is the complement of the event "none is male" (see page 243).]

    (5) P(at least two males) = 4/8 .

    (6) P(first child a male) = 4/8 .

    (7) P(more males than females) = 4/8 .

    (8) P(at least one male and one female) = 6/8 .

Odds

The ratio of the probability of an event occurring to the probability of the event not occurring is known as odds in favor of the event.
If the words are replaced by shorthand,

$$\text{(odds in favor of } E) \ = \ \frac{P(E)}{P(\overline{E})},$$

where $P(\overline{E})$ is the probability that event E does not occur.

Example.-- In the problem of the three-child "retriever-happy"
family, what are the odds in favor of three males ?

Solution: The probability of three males is one-eighth; hence,
$P(E) = 1/8$. The probability of there not being three males is seven-
eighths; that is, the probability of "not-E" (denoted by $\overline{E}$) is $P(\overline{E}) =$
$7/8$. Consequently,

$$\text{(odds in favor of } E) \ = \ \frac{1/8}{7/8} \ = \ \frac{1}{7}.$$

PERMUTATIONS AND COMBINATIONS

In the example of the three-child families, how does one know that
the total number of possible cases (outcomes) is eight? Permutations
and combinations provide answers to such questions since they deal
with the arrangement and grouping of objects.   They are useful in determining the total number of outcomes of an experiment as well as
the number of outcomes to be included in an event E.   As a consequence, they are useful in computing probabilities.   One must decide
from the nature of the problem whether permutations or combinations
are involved.   Order "counts" (order is important) in a permutation
while order does not "count" in a combination.

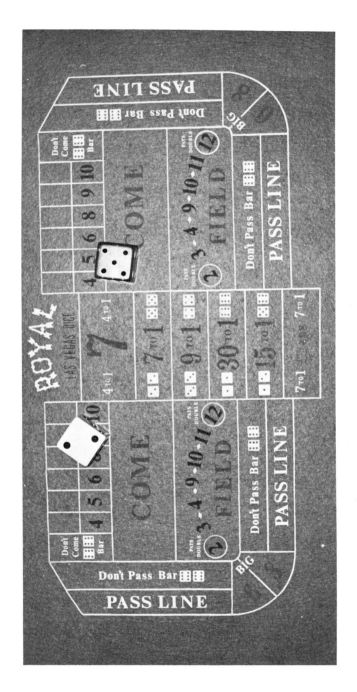

The smarter the clientele (the RE's) the closer the odds offered by the house (the judges) approach the true ones; the less they (the RE's) know, the greater the house percentage—the more the judges "out art-em."

THE PONTCHIPPI CASINO

Presents this Certificate to

Mr. Knowledgeable Retriever Enthusiast

Who is versed in the *gamblementals* of Retriever Field Trial Theory

and, hence, expert in the Game of Chance called "Field Trialing."

The hints which you have reaped on probability and odds are intended to enlighten you about the ways of chance and to enhance your pleasure. It is our sincere wish that you will "gamble only what you can afford to risk" in any trial and in so doing will enjoy a lifetime in our unique sport of sportsmen.

The Management
The **Pontchippi** Casino

A property of
CAMAC Enterprises

PONTCHIPPI

Trademark

Permutations

A permutation is each different ordering or arrangement in a line of a group of objects. To arrange a collection of objects in a definite order is to permute that collection of objects.

Multiplication rule. -- If a series of operations can be performed successively in a given number of ways, say, n_1 ways for the first operation, n_2 ways for the second operation, ... , and n_k ways for the kth operation, then the number of ways in which all the operations can be done together is the product of all the given ways, that is, $(n_1) \times (n_2) \times ... \times (n_k)$.

In the example which concerned three-child families, the first child could be either a male or a female, $n_1 = 2$; the second child could be either a male or a female, $n_2 = 2$; and the third child could be either male or female, $n_3 = 2$. Consequently, the total number of outcomes in three-child families is given by $n_1 \times n_2 \times n_3$ or $2 \times 2 \times 2 = 8$. The multiplication principle applies to situations where one operation can be performed, and then a second operation can be performed, and then another, and so on.

For convenience, another fundamental principle (the addition principle) which is used later is stated in this context.

Addition principle. -- Two events are said to be mutually exclusive when the occurrence of one of them excludes the occurrence of the other; e.g., if event E occurs, event F cannot occur; if event F occurs, event E cannot occur.

Example. -- For a specified retriever, if event E is "death" and event F is "survival," then these two events illustrate what is meant by two events being mutually exclusive. If E occurs, F cannot occur; if F occurs, E cannot occur.

Two operations can also be said to be mutually exclusive. Assume that two operations are mutually exclusive. If the first operation can be performed in m ways and the second operation in n ways, then one operation or the other can be performed in m + n ways.

Permutations of N things taken all together. -- The number of per-

mutations of N things (taken all together) is N! (read "N factorial"). N! is the product of all whole numbers from 1 to N, as
follows: $1 \times 2 \times 3 \times \ldots \times (N - 2) \times (N - 1) \times N$, or, as it is
usually written, $N \times (N - 1) \times (N - 2) \times \ldots \times 3 \times 2 \times 1$. As
particular examples,

$$5! \; = \; 5 \times 4 \times 3 \times 2 \times 1 \; = \; 120$$
$$4! \; = \; 4 \times 3 \times 2 \times 1 \; = \; 24$$
$$3! \; = \; 3 \times 2 \times 1 \; = \; 6$$
$$2! \; = \; 2 \times 1 \; = \; 2$$
$$1! \; = \; 1$$
$$0! \; = \; 1.$$

[Zero factorial is defined to be equal to one.]

Example. -- Consider an experiment in which a photographer is asked
to take a picture of 5 retrievers in a row. He could number the position of each retriever, from left to right, as 1, 2, ... , 5. In
fact, he could arrange the retrievers from left to right as follows: a
Chesapeake, a flatcoat, a golden, a black Labrador, and a yellow Labrador. If the photographer makes one picture, he will utilize only one
order (one arrangement). Obviously, he could have made the picture
in a different order. How many possible orders (arrangements) are
there?

Solution:

$$N! \; = \; 5! \; = \; 5 \times 4 \times 3 \times 2 \times 1$$
$$5! \; = \; 120 \text{ arrangements.}$$

To elaborate, any 1 of the 5 retrievers can be selected for the
first position on the left; the first position can be filled (occupied) in
any 1 of 5 different ways. For each of the 5 ways of filling the
first position, the second position can be filled (occupied) in 4 ways
(by any 1 of the 4 other retrievers). Then the first 2 positions

from the left can be filled in 20 ways. Any 1 of the 3 remaining retrievers can be assigned to the third (middle) position (3 ways); thus, for each of the 20 ways of filling the first 2 positions, there are 3 ways of filling the third position. The first 3 positions can be occupied in 60 ways. For each of the 60 ways of filling the first 3 positions, there are 2 ways of filling the fourth position. Thus, there are 120 ways of filling the first 4 positions. For each of the 120 ways of filling the first 4 positions, there is only 1 way of filling the fifth position; that is, there is only 1 retriever left to occupy the last position. Therefore, the 5 retrievers can be "arranged" for the photograph in 120 ways.

Permutations of N things taken n at a time. -- The problem here is to determine the total number of arrangements which can be made by choosing n distinct elements at a time from the total number N, and then ordering them in a line. The number of permutations of N things taken n at a time, repetition not allowed, is given by (the multiplication rule):

$$_NP_n = N(N - 1) \ldots (N - n + 1) = \frac{N!}{(N - n)!}.$$

Notation: In the above, $_NP_n$ indicates the number of permutations of N things taken n at a time. Furthermore, $_NP_N$ is used to denote the number of permutations of N things (the left subscript) taken N (the right subscript) at a time (all together). Note that $_NP_N$ is N! and $_NP_n$ is $N!/(N - n)!$.

Example. -- Suppose that a veterinarian has 5 treatments, A, B, C, D, and E. He would like to try all 5 treatments, combined 2 at a time, in all possible orders of application (arrangements).

Solution: N = 5 and n = 2.

$$_NP_n = N(N - 1) \ldots (N - n + 1)$$
$$_5P_2 = 5 \times 4 = 20.$$

Alternatively,

$$_N P_n = \frac{N!}{(N-n)!}$$

$$_5 P_2 = \frac{5!}{(5-2)!}$$

$$= \frac{5 \times 4 \times 3 \times 2 \times 1}{3 \times 2 \times 1}$$

$$_5 P_2 = 20 .$$

The 20 permutations of 5 things taken 2 at a time are written below:

AB, AC, AD, AE, BC, BD, BE, CD, CE, DE,

BA, CA, DA, EA, CB, DB, EB, DC, EC, ED.

Combinations

A group of things in a straight line without regard to order is known as a combination. In combinations, order is unimportant, order does not "count." Two combinations are different if one group has an object in it which the other group does not; two permutations are different even if they consist of the same objects, if the objects are in different order. The number of *combinations* of N different things taken n at a time is given by

$$\binom{N}{n} = \frac{N!}{n!(N-n)!} .$$

Also,

$$\binom{N}{n} = \frac{N(N-1) \ldots (N-n+1)}{n!} .$$

Example.-- An owner-handler has 5 retrievers in training; he takes 2 retrievers out for training at the time. How many combinations of 2 retrievers are there?

THE FIRST BIRD OF THE SEASON

An old print in the author's private Pontchippi Collection (appeared on page 585 of Harper's Weekly, September 12, 1868).

An oil painting by Sir Edwin Landseer, PRA (1802-1873), "possibly a forebear of the golden retriever." Photograph courtesy of The Field, Spink & Son Ltd., and the owner of the painting, Princess Lee Radziwill.

PTARMIGAN RETRIEVED

An oil painting by Maud Earl in the possession of James Buchanan & Co. Ltd. (Courtesy James Buchanan & Co. Ltd.)

WILD DUCK SHOOTING.
(From an ORIGINAL PAINTING by C. H. WEIGALL.)

From plate (facing p. 233) in Henry D. Miles (editor), The Book of Field Sports and Library of Veterinary Knowledge, *Volume I, London: Henry Lea, 1864.*

CHEASAPEAKE BAY DOG

Reproduced from plate (facing p. 145) in Joseph A. Graham, The Shooting Dog, *New York: The Macmillan Company, 1904 (in the author's private Pontchippi Library).*

Solution: Order does not count: N = 5 and n = 2 .

$$\binom{N}{n} = \frac{N!}{n!(N-n)!}$$

$$\binom{5}{2} = \frac{5!}{2!\,3!}$$

$$= \frac{5 \times 4 \times 3 \times 2 \times 1}{2 \times 1 \times 3 \times 2 \times 1}$$

$$\binom{5}{2} = 10 .$$

Alternatively,

$$\binom{N}{n} = \frac{N(N-1) \ldots (N-n+1)}{n!}$$

$$\binom{5}{2} = \frac{5 \times 4}{2 \times 1} = 10 .$$

The 10 combinations (pairs of retrievers) follow: AB, AC, AD, AE, BC, BD, BE, CD, CE, DE.

Example.-- If a combination of 2 retrievers is chosen at random in the immediately preceding example, what is the probability that retriever A will be chosen?

Solution: The event E of interest is retriever A. There are 10 equally likely outcomes, and retriever A (event E) appears in 4 of these outcomes. Let us agree to use the general formula, $P(E) = \frac{n}{N}$, where now N = 10 and n = 4; hence,

$$P(E) = \frac{4}{10}$$

$$P(E) = 0.4 .$$

What is the probability of retrievers A and B being chosen to be trained together?

Solution: N = 10 and n = 1; consequently,

$$P(E) \;=\; \frac{1}{10}$$

$$P(E) \;=\; 0.1\,.$$

Some Applications of Fundamental Principles

A retriever litter of 10.-- A friend of yours has bred his FTCh. bitch, a female that you admire greatly, to a male that you likewise admire greatly; this is the ideal mating in your opinion. Your friend, the breeder, carefully picks out (in a nonrandom manner) one pup that he would like to keep for himself, but he has confided "his pick" to no one. To be magnanimous, your friend comes to you and says that you can have the "pick of the litter," but that your selection must be made randomly. As you know so well, this does not mean to haphazardly pick a pup; this does not mean to look over the litter and select a pup; this means to select a pup by means of some randomizing device.

Accordingly, you secure 10 metal-rim tags and number them 0, 1, 2, ..., 9; this is a total of 10 digits. You attach one such numbered tag by means of a light string to each puppy. Then you all consult a table of random numbers. What is the probability that you select the same puppy that your breeder friend would like to keep?

Solution: Event E is "you select the same puppy that your friend has chosen."

$$P(E) \;=\; \frac{(\text{number of choices you make--one})}{(\text{total number of puppies in the litter})}$$

$$\;=\; \frac{1}{10}$$

$$P(E) \;=\; 0.1\,.$$

There are 4 yellow puppies and 6 black puppies in the litter. What is the probability of selecting a black puppy?

Solution: Let event E be "puppy selected is black."

$$P(E) \quad = \quad \frac{\text{(number of black puppies)}}{\text{(number of puppies in the litter)}}$$

$$= \quad \frac{6}{10}$$

$$P(E) \quad = \quad 0.6 .$$

What is the probability of selecting a yellow puppy?

Solution: Event E is "puppy selected is yellow."

$$P(E) \quad = \quad \frac{\text{(number of yellow puppies)}}{\text{(number of puppies in the litter)}}$$

$$= \quad \frac{4}{10}$$

$$P(E) \quad = \quad 0.4 .$$

"Old-time" Calcutta pool, retriever style.-- After the entries are in, the drawings made, and the program printed, the Calcutta pool opens with an "entry or retriever auction" in which those present, usually owners and retriever fans, bid for individual retrievers. The bid is for the privilege of "owning" a retriever for the ensuing trial. In trials beginning on Friday, the auction is usually held on Thursday night; when trials begin on Saturday, the auction is usually held on Friday night. After a certain percentage of the total "take" is siphoned off for the club treasury or other "worthwhile cause," the remainder is divided as follows: X per cent to the "owner" of the first place retriever; Y per cent to the "owner" of the second place retriever; Z per cent to the "owner" of the third place retriever; and W per cent to the "owner" of the fourth place retriever. Sometimes, the winning retriever "takes all" after the "cut for the house."

Suppose there are 35 entries in the derby of the trial which starts tomorrow. At the Calcutta tonight it is announced that a single prize will go to the "owner" of the winner. You are high bidder and "own" one retriever. Rather than wait for the results of the trial tomorrow, it is decided to determine the winner by randomly selecting 1 of the

35 derbies. What is the probability that if 1 retriever is selected
at random from the 35 it is the retriever you bid for and "won"?

    Solution: Let event E be "your retriever is the one se-
lected." From the above,

$$P(E) \;=\; \frac{1}{35} \;\approx\; 0.03 \,.$$

What is the probability that your retriever is not the one selected?
Thus, the question concerns the event "not E" (written $\overline{E}$). The
event E and event $\overline{E}$ exhaust the set of all possible outcomes, so

$$P(E) \,+\, P(\overline{E}) \;=\; 1;$$
$$P(\overline{E}) \;=\; 1 \,-\, P(E).$$

The P(E) is 1/35, and substituting,

$$P(\overline{E}) \;=\; 1 \,-\, \frac{1}{35}$$
$$P(\overline{E}) \;=\; \frac{34}{35} \,.$$

    Derby.--It is well-known that for most licensed trials 4, and
only 4, retrievers each receive a trophy in a particular stake. In a
derby stake tomorrow with an entry of 35, 4 retrievers will receive
a trophy and 31 will not. If each retriever has an equal chance of
winning the stake, what is the probability that if 1 retriever is selected at random from the 35 entries it will win a trophy tomorrow?

    Solution: Let event E be "winner of a trophy tomorrow."

$$P(E) \;=\; \frac{4}{35} \;\approx\; 0.11 \,.$$

Another way of arriving at this same result is to reason that the denominator is the number of ways that one can select 1 retriever out of 35 retrievers, $\binom{35}{1}$, and these are equally likely. For the numerator, some combinations satisfy the criteria that "this retriever will win a trophy tomorrow"; there are as many of these as there are ways of selecting 1 retriever out of 4 retrievers; hence,

$$P\left(\begin{array}{l}\text{a trophy winner}\\ \text{is drawn}\end{array}\right) = \frac{\binom{4}{1}}{\binom{35}{1}} = \frac{4}{35}$$

$$P \approx 0.11 .$$

What is the probability that a trophy winner is not drawn? Recall that

$$P(\overline{E}) = 1 - P(E); \text{ so,}$$

$$P(\overline{E}) = 1 - \frac{4}{35} \text{ (or } 1.00 - 0.11)$$

$$= \frac{31}{35}$$

$$P(\overline{E}) \approx 0.89 .$$

The term odds in favor of event E was defined earlier as

$$(\text{odds in favor of E}) = \frac{P(E)}{P(\overline{E})} ;$$

hence, for this example,

$$(\text{odds in favor of E}) = \frac{0.11}{0.89} \approx \frac{1}{8} .$$

Consequently, the odds are 1 to 8 in favor of E, drawing a trophy winner, or stated differently, 8 to 1 against drawing a trophy winner.

Qualifying. -- Four retrievers receive trophies in a qualifying stake also; again assume an entry of 35 in the qualifying stake.

This time, suppose that 2 retrievers are drawn randomly from the 35 entered in this stake. What is the probability that both retrievers win trophies tomorrow?

Solution: Let event E be "both retrievers win trophies tomorrow."

$$P(E) = \frac{\binom{4}{2}}{\binom{35}{2}}.$$

The denominator is the number of ways that 2 out of 35 retrievers $\binom{35}{2}$ can be selected and these are equally likely. The numerator is composed of the number of combinations that satisfy the criteria that "both retrievers are trophy winners tomorrow"; there are as many of these as there are ways of selecting 2 out of 4 retrievers; hence,

$$P\binom{2 \text{ trophy winners}}{\text{are drawn}} = \frac{\binom{4}{2}}{\binom{35}{2}}$$

$$= \frac{\frac{4!}{2!\,2!}}{\frac{35!}{2!\,33!}}$$

$$P\binom{2 \text{ trophy winners}}{\text{are drawn}} = \frac{6}{595}$$

$$P \approx \frac{1}{99}.$$

What is the probability that both retrievers are not trophy winners? That is, what is the probability that you do not get 2 trophies? Recall that

$$P(\overline{E}) = 1 - P(E)$$

$$= 1 - \frac{1}{99}$$

$$P(\overline{E}) = \frac{98}{99} \approx 0.99.$$

The odds are 1 to 98 in favor of E, drawing 2 trophy winners, since

$$\frac{\frac{1}{99}}{\frac{98}{99}} = \frac{1}{98}.$$

Open. -- Suppose that you "buy" 3 different open retrievers at the Calcutta, and there are 35 entries in the open stake which begins tomorrow morning. What is the probability that all 3 are trophy winners?

Solution: To review, the probability of event E "all 3 retrievers will win trophies in the open" is given by

$$P(E) = \frac{(\text{number of favorable outcomes})}{(\text{number of possible outcomes})}.$$

There are as many favorable outcomes as there are ways of selecting 3 retrievers out of 4 retrievers; hence, the numerator is given by $\binom{4}{3}$. There are as many possible outcomes as there are ways of selecting 3 retrievers out of 35 retrievers, or $\binom{35}{3}$ combinations of 3. Consequently,

$$P(E) = \frac{\binom{4}{3}}{\binom{35}{3}}$$

$$P(E) = \frac{\frac{4!}{3! \, 1!}}{\frac{35!}{3! \, 32!}}$$

$$= \frac{4}{6,545} \approx \frac{1}{1,636}$$

$$P(E) \approx 0.0006,$$

or about $\dfrac{6}{10,000}$.

What is the probability that all 3 retrievers drawn in the open stake do not win trophies? That is, what is the probability that you do not pick up 3 trophies? Again,

$$P(\overline{E}) = 1 - P(E)$$

$$= 1 - \frac{4}{6,545}$$

$$P(\overline{E}) = \frac{6,541}{6,545} \approx 0.9994,$$

or about $\dfrac{9,994}{10,000}$.

The odds in favor of E are equal to

$$\frac{\frac{4}{6,545}}{\frac{6,541}{6,545}}$$

$$(\text{odds in favor of } E) = \frac{4}{6,541} .$$

Amateur. -- Again suppose that there are 35 entries in the amateur and that the chance of any retriever entered winning a trophy on Sunday is equal to the chance of any other retriever entered. Further suppose that you go to a table of random numbers and select 4 numbers from 01 to 35; then you "bid" these 4 retrievers at the Calcutta. What is the probability that all 4 win trophies on Sunday?

Solution: The event E of interest is "all 4 retrievers will win trophies on Sunday." The number of favorable outcomes and the number of possible outcomes can be computed, so

$$P(E) \ = \ \frac{\text{(number of favorable outcomes)}}{\text{(number of possible outcomes)}} \cdot$$

There are as many favorable outcomes as there are ways of selecting 4 retrievers out of 4 retrievers, obviously, only 1 way, denoted $\binom{4}{4}$. There are as many possible outcomes as there are ways of selecting 4 retrievers out of 35 retrievers, or $\binom{35}{4}$ combinations of 4. Consequently,

$$P(E) \ = \ \frac{\binom{4}{4}}{\binom{35}{4}}$$

$$= \ \frac{\dfrac{4!}{4! \ 0!}}{\dfrac{35!}{4! \ 31!}}$$

$$= \ \frac{1}{52,360}$$

$$P(E) \ \approx \ 0.000019,$$

$$\text{or about} \ \frac{19}{1,000,000} \cdot$$

What is the probability that all 4 retrievers selected in the amateur stake do not win trophies? That is, what is the probability that you do not "take home" 4 trophies? As before,

$$P(\overline{E}) \ = \ 1 \ - \ P(E)$$

$$= \ 1 \ - \ \frac{1}{52,360}$$

$$= \ \frac{52,359}{52,360}$$

$$P(\overline{E}) \ \approx \ 0.99998.$$

Return to the qualifying.-- Recall that 2 retrievers were drawn randomly from 35 entered in the qualifying stake. Also recall that

$$P(2 \text{ trophy winners}) = \frac{\binom{4}{2}}{\binom{35}{2}}$$

$$= \frac{6}{595} \approx \frac{1}{99}$$

$$P \approx 0.01.$$

What is the probability that 1 wins a trophy and 1 does not?

Solution: The denominator remains the same as before; it is the number of ways that 2 retrievers out of 35 retrievers $\binom{35}{2}$ can be selected and these are equally likely.

Numerator.--Of the $\binom{35}{2}$ combinations, some satisfy the criteria "one is a trophy winner and one is not." One trophy winner from 4 can be selected in $\binom{4}{1}$ ways, and 1 nonwinner can be selected in $\binom{31}{1}$ ways. Applying the fundamental multiplication principle,

$$P(1 \text{ trophy winner and 1 nonwinner}) = \frac{\binom{4}{1}\binom{31}{1}}{\binom{35}{2}}$$

$$= \frac{124}{595}$$

$$P \approx 0.21.$$

What is the probability that at least 1 gets a trophy? That is, the probability that you take home either 1 or 2 trophies.

$$P\binom{2 \text{ trophy}}{\text{winners}} + P\binom{1 \text{ trophy winner}}{\text{and 1 nonwinner}} = \frac{6}{595} + \frac{124}{595}$$

$$= \frac{130}{595}$$

$$P \approx 0.22.$$

Furthermore, note that the event "at least one gets a trophy" is "the opposite" of the event "neither one gets a trophy." Hence,

$$P\left(\begin{array}{l}\text{at least one}\\\text{gets a trophy}\end{array}\right) + P\left(\begin{array}{l}\text{neither one gets}\\\text{a trophy}\end{array}\right) = 1.00.$$

What is the probability that you do not take home a trophy?

Solution:

$$
\begin{aligned}
P(\text{no trophy}) &= 1 - P(\text{at least one trophy})\\
&= 1 - 0.22\\
P(\text{no trophy}) &= 0.78.
\end{aligned}
$$

An alternative solution is as follows: Using the denominator of $\binom{35}{2}$, the numerator is the product of the number of combinations of no trophy winner $\binom{4}{0}$ and $\binom{31}{2}$ from the nonwinners. Thus,

$$
\begin{aligned}
P(\text{no trophy}) &= \frac{\binom{4}{0}\binom{31}{2}}{\binom{35}{2}}\\
&= \frac{(1)\,(465)}{595}\\
P(\text{no trophy}) &\approx 0.78 \text{ as before.}
\end{aligned}
$$

All cases have been exhausted.

$$P\left(\begin{array}{l}\text{2 trophy}\\\text{winners}\end{array}\right) + P\left(\begin{array}{l}\text{1 trophy winner}\\\text{and 1 nonwinner}\end{array}\right) + P(\text{no winner})$$
$$= 1.00.$$

Substituting,

$$
\begin{aligned}
0.01 + 0.21 + 0.78 &= 1.00\\
1.00 &= 1.00.
\end{aligned}
$$

INDEPENDENT EVENTS AND
COMPLEMENTARY EVENTS

Independent Events

Two or more events are said to be independent if the probability of occurrence of any of them is not affected by the occurrence of any other. In particular, two events E and F are independent if the probability of their joint occurrence, P(E and F), is equal to P(E) multiplied by P(F); that is, event E and event F are independent if

$$P(E \text{ and } F) = P(E) \times P(F).$$

The above is a definition. In non-technical language, this definition implies that these two events could not possibly have any relationship or influence upon each other. Events which are not independent are called dependent events.

Example of independent events. -- Earlier, an experiment was described in which two pennies were tossed. All possible outcomes of the "two-penny experiment" are as follows:

First penny	Second penny	Experimental outcome
H	H	(H, H)
H	T	(H, T)
T	H	(T, H)
T	T	(T, T)

There are four possible outcomes of the two-penny experiment, and it is reasonable to assume that they are equally likely. Thus, each outcome could be assigned probability one-fourth.

Let event E denote head (H) on first coin and event F denote head (H) on second coin. From the above list, it is clear that P(E and F) is equal to one-fourth. Most people would agree that the probability of event E "head on first coin" is equal to one-half and the probability of event F "head on second coin" is also equal to one-half. Then these two events are independent if, and only if,

$$P(E \text{ and } F) = P(E) \times P(F)$$
$$\frac{1}{4} = \frac{1}{2} \times \frac{1}{2}$$
$$\frac{1}{4} = \frac{1}{4}.$$

By definition, these two events are said to be independent.

Complementary Events

Earlier, it was noted that on an experimental trial one may let E be the event which may occur and $\overline{E}$ be the event that E does not occur; two such events are called complementary events. If E and $\overline{E}$ are complementary events, $P(E) + P(\overline{E}) = 1.00$. It follows immediately that $P(\overline{E}) = 1 - P(E)$.

Example. -- There are two old field champion retrievers (retired from competition), A and B, of the same age who are owned by different owners and kennelled in different cities. Given that the probability that each will be hospitalized in the next year is 0.1. Assume that the episodes of hospitalization are independent for these retrievers, and answer the following questions.

Question 1: What is the probability that both retrievers will be hospitalized during the next year?

Notation: Let A be the event "hospitalization of A"; let $\overline{A}$ indicate the event "A is not hospitalized"; let B denote the event "B is hospitalized," and $\overline{B}$ indicate the event "B is not hospitalized."

$$P(A \text{ and } B) = P(A) \times P(B)$$
$$= (0.1) \times (0.1)$$
$$P(A \text{ and } B) = 0.01.$$

Question 2: What is the probability that neither retriever is hospitalized? If the probability of A's being hospitalized, P(A), is equal to 0.1, the probability of his not being hospitalized is

$$P(\overline{A}) = 1 - P(A)$$
$$= 1.0 - 0.1$$
$$P(\overline{A}) = 0.9.$$

If the probability that B is hospitalized, P(B), is 0.1, the probability of his not being hospitalized is

$$P(\overline{B}) = 1 - P(B)$$
$$= 1.0 - 0.1$$
$$P(\overline{B}) = 0.9.$$

Hence,

$$P(\overline{A} \text{ and } \overline{B}) = P(\overline{A}) \times P(\overline{B})$$
$$= (0.9) \times (0.9)$$
$$P(\overline{A} \text{ and } \overline{B}) = 0.81.$$

Question 3: What is the probability of A's being hospitalized and B's not being hospitalized?

$$P(A \text{ and } \overline{B}) = P(A) \times P(\overline{B})$$
$$= (0.1) \times (0.9)$$
$$P(A \text{ and } \overline{B}) = 0.09.$$

Question 4: What is the probability of A's not being hospitalized and B's being hospitalized?

$$P(\overline{A} \text{ and } B) = P(\overline{A}) \times P(B)$$
$$= (0.9) \times (0.1)$$
$$P(\overline{A} \text{ and } B) = 0.09.$$

Note that all possible outcomes have been accounted for, in that

$$
\begin{aligned}
P(A \text{ and } B) &= 0.01 \\
P(\overline{A} \text{ and } \overline{B}) &= 0.81 \\
P(A \text{ and } \overline{B}) &= 0.09 \\
P(\overline{A} \text{ and } B) &= \underline{0.09} \\
\text{Total} \quad & 1.00 .
\end{aligned}
$$

Question 5: What is the probability that at least one of the retrievers is hospitalized? This means that one of the retrievers is hospitalized or that more than one (both in this case) may be hospitalized. Thus,

$$
P\left(\genfrac{}{}{0pt}{}{\text{at least one is}}{\text{hospitalized}}\right) = P(A \text{ and } B) + P(A \text{ and } \overline{B})
$$
$$
+ P(\overline{A} \text{ and } B)
$$
$$
= 0.01 + 0.09 + 0.09
$$
$$
P\left(\genfrac{}{}{0pt}{}{\text{at least one is}}{\text{hospitalized}}\right) = 0.19 .
$$

Additional Applications

Example. -- Given that the probabilities that Demo (D) and Kube (K) are called back after the second series are 0.7 and 0.9, respectively. Let D be event "D is called back," and $\overline{D}$ be event "D is not called back"; let K be event "K is called back," and $\overline{K}$ be event "K is not called back." Then, $P(D) = 0.7$, $P(\overline{D}) = 0.3$, $P(K) = 0.9$, $P(\overline{K}) = 0.1$. Assume that the calling back (or dropping) of D and K are independent events.

    1. What is the probability that both D and K are called back?

    2. What is the probability that both D and K are dropped?

    3. What is the probability that D is called back and K is dropped?

4. What is the probability that D is dropped and K is called back?

5. What is the probability that at least one is dropped?

6. What is the probability that at least one is called back?

Solution:

1. P(D and K) = 0.7 × 0.9 = 0.63
2. P($\overline{D}$ and $\overline{K}$) = 0.3 × 0.1 = 0.03
3. P(D and $\overline{K}$) = 0.7 × 0.1 = 0.07
4. P($\overline{D}$ and K) = 0.3 × 0.9 = 0.27

Total = 1.00

5. P$\left(\begin{matrix}\text{at least one}\\\text{is dropped}\end{matrix}\right)$ = P($\overline{D}$ and $\overline{K}$) + P(D and $\overline{K}$)

  　　　　　　　　　+ P($\overline{D}$ and K)

  　　　　　　　= 0.03 + 0.07 + 0.27

P$\left(\begin{matrix}\text{at least one}\\\text{is dropped}\end{matrix}\right)$ = 0.37 .

6. P$\left(\begin{matrix}\text{at least one is}\\\text{called back}\end{matrix}\right)$ = P(D and K) + P(D and $\overline{K}$)

  　　　　　　　　　+ P($\overline{D}$ and K)

  　　　　　　　= 0.63 + 0.07 + 0.27

P$\left(\begin{matrix}\text{at least one is}\\\text{called back}\end{matrix}\right)$ = 0.97 .

Example.-- A land triple is set up with two gunners and two bird-boys at each of three locations; one live bird and two dead birds are used. Reference the live bird: Each of two Guns, A and B, has probability of 0.8 of hitting a flying target. Assume independence and that each Gun fires only once.

1. What is the probability that both Guns will hit the pheasant?

2. What is the probability that neither will hit and, hence, there will be a "flyaway"?

3.   What is the probability that A will hit and B miss?

4.   What is the probability that A will miss and B hit?

5.   What is the probability that at least one will hit?

Solution: Let A and B respectively denote the events "Gun A hits" and "Gun B hits"; likewise, let $\overline{A}$ and $\overline{B}$ denote misses.

1. $P(A \text{ and } B)$ = $(0.8) \times (0.8)$ = 0.64

2. $P(\overline{A} \text{ and } \overline{B})$ = $(1.0 - 0.8) \times (1.0 - 0.8)$ = 0.04

3. $P(A \text{ and } \overline{B})$ = $(0.8) \times (0.2)$ = 0.16

4. $P(\overline{A} \text{ and } B)$ = $(0.2) \times (0.8)$ = 0.16

         Total   = 1.00

5. $P\left(\begin{array}{c}\text{at least one}\\\text{will hit}\end{array}\right)$ = $P(A \text{ and } B) + P(A \text{ and } \overline{B})$

                        + $P(\overline{A} \text{ and } B)$

            = $0.64 + 0.16 + 0.16$

$P\left(\begin{array}{c}\text{at least one}\\\text{will hit}\end{array}\right)$ = 0.96 .

Alternatively,

$P\left(\begin{array}{c}\text{at least one}\\\text{will hit}\end{array}\right)$ = $1.00 - P(\overline{A} \text{ and } \overline{B})$

            = $1.00 - 0.04$

$P\left(\begin{array}{c}\text{at least one}\\\text{will hit}\end{array}\right)$ = 0.96 .

Example. -- Given two retrievers Tex (T) and Wynk (W) with probabilities of dying during a specified period equal to one-third and two-fifths, respectively. Let T be event "T dies" and $\overline{T}$ be event "T does not die"; let W be event "W dies" and $\overline{W}$ be event "W does not die." Are the events T and W independent if the probabilities are as shown in Table 7-8?

Table 7-8.--Probabilities of event of dying for two retrievers

Event	Event		Sum
	T	$\overline{T}$	
W	2/15	4/15	2/5
$\overline{W}$	3/15	6/15	3/5
Sum	1/3	2/3	1.00

Solution: If two events are independent, then

$$P(E \ \text{and} \ F) \ = \ P(E) \times P(F).$$

Checking Table 7-8, for W and T to be independent,

$$P(W \ \text{and} \ T) \ \text{must equal} \ \frac{2}{5} \times \frac{1}{3} \ = \ \frac{2}{15};$$

this is true; hence, W and T are independent. Furthermore, it can be shown that three other pairs of events in the table are independent:

$$P(W \ \text{and} \ \overline{T}) \ \text{must equal} \ \frac{2}{5} \times \frac{2}{3}, \ \text{which holds;}$$

$$P(\overline{W} \ \text{and} \ T) \ \text{must equal} \ \frac{3}{5} \times \frac{1}{3}, \ \text{which holds;}$$

$$P(\overline{W} \ \text{and} \ \overline{T}) \ \text{must equal} \ \frac{3}{5} \times \frac{2}{3}, \ \text{which holds.}$$

Example.-- Given two retrievers Bob (B) and Fara (F) with probabilities of becoming field champions during a specified period of 0.5 and 0.7, respectively. Let B be event "B becomes a field champion," and $\overline{B}$ be event "B does not become a field champion"; let F be event "F becomes a field champion," and $\overline{F}$ be event "F does not become a field champion." Are the events B and F independent if the probabilities are as shown in Table 7-9?

Table 7-9. --Probabilities of event becoming field champion for two retrievers

Event	Event		Sum
	B	$\overline{B}$	
F	0.40	0.30	0.70
$\overline{F}$	0.10	0.20	0.30
Sum	0.50	0.50	1.00

Solution: In order for the two events B and F to be independent,

$$P(B \text{ and } F) = P(B) \times P(F).$$

Checking Table 7-9, for B and F to be independent, the P(B and
F) must equal 0.50 × 0.70, which is equal to 0.35; the (appropriate) entry in the table is 0.40, and because 0.35 is not equal to
0.40 the two events are not independent.

CONDITIONAL PROBABILITY

In many situations it is necessary to deal with subgroups or sub-
populations of outcomes of experiments. These subgroups of outcomes
are defined by additional conditions beyond those for the whole population of outcomes. Probabilities of the occurrence of events within
these subgroups are called conditional probabilities.

Initially, however, it is worthwhile to discuss marginal totals or
distributions. In Table 7-10 the columns have been numbered from
1 to 2; and the rows have been numbered from 1 to 3; these row
and column numbers are shown in parentheses.

Table 7-10.--Reported number of starters in the national championship stake, by sex and breed, 1956-1960

| Breed | Sex | | Total |
	Dog (1)	Bitch (2)	
Labrador (1)	176	30	206
Golden (2)	20	0	20
Chesapeake (3)	3	1	4
Total	199	31	230

Marginal Distributions

Marginal distribution of sex.-- The headings of the columns, in
combination with the column totals at the bottom of the table, furnish
the distribution of sex (by itself); in other words, breed is not considered. This is called a marginal distribution because it appears on
the margin of the table.

Example.-- Consider an experiment in which a retriever is selected
randomly and its sex observed. What is the probability that event E
"bitch" occurs? Assume that probabilities which can be computed
from Table 7-10 apply to the population from which the retriever was
selected.

Solution: Utilizing the marginal totals, the grand total, 230,
is the number of retrievers in the experiment; of these 230 retrievers, 31 were reported to be bitches. The probability of event E
"bitch" can be obtained by writing the solution in the form

$$P(E) = \frac{31}{230}$$

$$= 0.1348$$

$$P(E) \approx 0.13 .$$

Marginal distribution of breed.-- The row designations for breed, together with the row totals at the far right, give the distribution of breed (by itself). Again, this distribution is called a marginal distribution because it appears on the margin of the table.

Example.-- Consider an experiment in which a retriever is selected randomly and its breed observed. What is the probability that event F "Labrador" occurs? Assume that probabilities which can be computed from Table 7-10 apply to the population from which the retriever was selected.

Solution: The probability of event F "Labrador" is

$$P(F) = \frac{206}{230}$$
$$= 0.8957$$
$$P(F) \approx 0.90 .$$

These numbers were obtained from the marginal totals at the extreme right of the table.

Marginal distributions and the two examples immediately preceding.-- In summary and to repeat, the right-most column of the table (headed total) in combination with the numbered rows (headed breed), and the last (unnumbered) row labelled total in combination with numbered columns (headed sex) are called marginal distributions. The solutions of the two preceding examples involved the two marginal distributions separately.

Computing Conditional Probabilities

There was nothing new about the computations which were made in the two immediately preceding examples; however, suppose that one knew before the experiment that the particular retriever was a bitch. This is additional information, partial knowledge, and it should improve the estimate of the probability of selecting a retriever of a specified breed.

Example. -- What is the probability of event F "Labrador," given that the retriever is a bitch? Again, assume that probabilities which can be computed from Table 7-10 apply.

Solution: If the probability of event F, given event E, is denoted by P(F|E) [read "the probability of F given E"], the following equation,

$$P(F|E) \ = \ \frac{P(F \ and \ E)}{P(E)}, \tag{3}$$

can be used to answer the question. Eq. (4) says nothing more nor less than Eq. (3):

$$P(F|E) \ = \ \frac{\dfrac{(\text{number in } F \ and \ E)}{N}}{\dfrac{(\text{number in } E)}{N}}. \tag{4}$$

To be explicit, first calculate P(F and E). The number who are bitches and who are also Labradors (n) can be found at the intersection of row (1) and column (2) and is equal to 30; of course, N = 230. Consequently, the

$$P(F \ and \ E) \ = \ \frac{n}{N}$$

$$P(F \ and \ E) \ = \ \frac{30}{230}.$$

Next calculate the P(E) when n is the number who are bitches and N is the total number of equally likely outcomes (N = 230); thus,

$$P(E) \ = \ \frac{n}{N}$$

$$P(E) \ = \ \frac{31}{230}.$$

Copying Eq. (3) again,

$$P(F|E) = \frac{P(F \text{ and } E)}{P(E)},$$

and substituting,

$$P(F|E) = \frac{\frac{30}{230}}{\frac{31}{230}}$$

$$= \frac{30}{230} \times \frac{230}{31}$$

$$= \frac{30}{31}$$

$$P(F|E) = 0.9677$$

$$P(F|E) \approx 0.97.$$

Observe that the probability of F given E or $P(F|E)$ = 30/31 really means concentrating attention on the 31 retrievers of the subgroup "bitches" and computing the probability of a retriever being a Labrador if it belongs to this particular sex group.

Example. -- Find the probability that a retriever selected randomly from the group of *dogs* will be

    1.   a golden;

    2.   a Chesapeake;

    3.   a Labrador.

Again, assume that probabilities which can be computed from Table 7-10 apply to the population from which the retriever will be selected.

    Solution:

    1.   Let E be event "dog" and A be event "golden."

$$P(A|E) = \frac{P(A \text{ and } E)}{P(E)}.$$

Taking into account the subgroup "dogs,"

$$P(A|E) = \frac{20}{199}$$

$$= 0.1005$$

$$P(A|E) \approx 0.10.$$

In detail, taking into account the complete list of outcomes,

$$P(A|E) = \frac{\frac{20}{230}}{\frac{199}{230}}$$

$$= \frac{20}{230} \times \frac{230}{199}$$

$$P(A|E) = \frac{20}{199}$$

and again $$P(A|E) \approx 0.10.$$

2.   Again, let E be event "dog," and let B be event "Chesapeake."

$$P(B|E) = \frac{P(B \text{ and } E)}{P(E)}$$

$$= \frac{3}{199}$$

$$P(B|E) \approx 0.02.$$

3.   Again, let E be event "dog," and let C be event "Labrador."

$$P(C|E) = \frac{P(C \text{ and } E)}{P(E)}$$

$$= \frac{176}{199}$$

$$P(C|E) \approx 0.88.$$

The sum of the above three probabilities calculated in 1, 2, and 3 is

$$\frac{20}{199} + \frac{3}{199} + \frac{176}{199} = \frac{199}{199} = 1.00 .$$

This is as it should be because the three cases exhaust all retrievers whose sex was reported as dog. In passing, the reader should be careful to note that $P(E|F)$ is seldom the same as $P(E$ and $F)$.

DISCRETE RANDOM VARIABLES AND
PROBABILITY FUNCTIONS

A variable is a symbol like X, Y, or Z (a quantity) which may take on any one of a number of specified values; thus a variable, in contrast to a constant, is not restricted to a single value.

Discrete Random Variable

When the value of a variable is a number which is determined by the outcome of an experiment, the variable is called a random variable. The number of values which a random variable can take on depends upon the number of possible outcomes of the experiment. If the values of the random variable form a discrete collection (set) it is called a discrete random variable. Furthermore, a discrete random variable is understood to have an associated probability function stating how often the values are expected to occur.

Probability Function

A probability function can be shown by a table which indicates each possible value of the discrete random variable with its associated probability. Let Z (capital Z) be the discrete random variable, and let z_i (lower case z) refer to a value which the random variable can take on. The probability function of the random variable Z is displayed in Table 7-11. Note that each row of the table is really an ordered pair. If the elements of the table are written in line, each term within a bracket is an ordered pair, thus, $[z_1, f(z_1)]$, $[z_2, f(z_2)]$, ... , $[z_k, f(z_k)]$. As illustrated, a probability function can

Table 7-11.--Probability function

Number of ... , z	Probability $P(Z = z) = f(z)$
z_1	$f(z_1)$
z_2	$f(z_2)$
.	.
.	.
.	.
z_k	$f(z_k)$

be shown as ordered pairs; it could have been shown by a formula for $f(z)$; however, in this book, the probability function will be presented by means of a table in many situations.

Example.-- Two pennies are tossed and allowed to come to rest. Let the random variable Z represent the number of heads. Note that Z is a random variable in that the value of Z is a number determined by the outcome of an experiment. The probability function for "number of heads when two coins are tossed" is shown in Table 7-12 . Ordinarily, the table showing the probability function will be displayed in much less detail as illustrated in Table 7-13 .

Table 7-12.--Probability function shown in detail for number of heads in two-coin experiment

Number of heads, z	Probability $P(Z = z) = f(z)$
$z_1 = 0$	$P(Z_1 = 0) = f(z_1) = 1/4$
$z_2 = 1$	$P(Z_2 = 1) = f(z_2) = 2/4$
$z_3 = 2$	$P(Z_3 = 2) = f(z_3) = 1/4$

Notation: In order to distinguish between the random variable and one of its values, a capital letter is used for the random

Table 7-13.--Probability function for number of heads in two-coin experiment

Number of heads, z	Probability f(z)
0	1/4
1	1/2
2	1/4

variable and the small lower case letter is used for one of its values. In the above example, Z refers to the random variable and z_t refers to a value of the random variable.

Mathematical Expectation

In gambling, probability of an event is a good estimate of the proportion of the games in which the event is expected to occur in a long series of trials. Mathematical expectation is a good estimate of the average gain or loss in a long series of games of chance (trials). In fact, mathematical expectation is a weighted average, where each possible value of the random variable is weighted by the probability of its occurrence. It is a special type of summation.

Mean, population mean, expected value, expectation, and mathematical expectation. -- The mathematical expectation of a random variable is sometimes called the mean of the random variable; sometimes called the population mean, and is written using the small Greek letter μ (mu). Thus, for the random variable Z, $E(Z) = \mu_z$ [read E(Z) as "the mathematical expectation of Z"] and the subscript Z may be omitted when the context is clear.

"Expected value" and "expectation" are used as abbreviations for mathematical expectation. Be careful to note that the expected value may not occur frequently; in fact, it may be impossible for it to occur. It is merely the "long run average."

Example. -- An experiment consists of rolling a single fair die and observing the number of dots on the top face of the die. Let the random variable Z be the number of dots on the top face of the die. The probability function is shown in Table 7-14. To compute the mathematical expectation of the random variable E(Z), each possible value of the random variable is weighted by the probability of its occurrence. Consequently [from Table 7-14],

$$
\begin{aligned}
E(Z) &= 1 \times (1/6) + 2 \times (1/6) + 3 \times (1/6) + 4 \\
&\quad \times (1/6) + 5 \times (1/6) + 6 \times (1/6) \\
&= 1/6 + 2/6 + 3/6 + 4/6 + 5/6 + 6/6 \\
&= 21/6 \\
E(Z) &= 3.5 .
\end{aligned}
$$

Table 7-14. --Probability function for number of dots on the top face of a die

Number of dots, z	Probability f(z)
1	1/6
2	1/6
3	1/6
4	1/6
5	1/6
6	1/6

Note that the mathematical expectation, the value 3.5, cannot occur in any trial of the experiment; thus, it cannot occur often; in fact, in this particular case, it cannot be expected to occur at all. In this case, the $P[Z = E(Z)] = 0$.

To repeat, in shorthand, mathematical expectation of Z is denoted by $E(Z)$ (read "the mathematical expectation of Z" or "the expected value of Z"). The expected value of Z is given by the following equation:

$$E(Z) \quad = \quad z_1 \times f(z_1) \; + \; z_2 \times f(z_2) \; + \; \ldots \; + \; z_k \times f(z_k). \qquad (5)$$

When the summation sign is utilized, it becomes

$$E(Z) \quad = \quad \sum_{i=1}^{k} z_i \times f(z_i) \quad = \quad \sum_{i=1}^{k} z_i f(z_i) \; .$$

Example.-- The probability function for number of heads when two coins are tossed was given earlier and is repeated in Table 7-15.

Table 7-15.--Probability function (repeated) for number of heads in two-coin experiment

Number of heads, z	Probability $f(z)$
0	1/4
1	1/2
2	1/4

The mathematical expectation of the number of heads is computed by substituting in Eq. (5), so that

$$\begin{aligned} E(Z) \quad &= \quad 0 \times (1/4) \; + \; 1 \times (1/2) \; + \; 2 \times (1/4) \\ &= \quad 0 \; + \; 1/2 \; + \; 2/4 \\ E(Z) \quad &= \quad 1 \, . \end{aligned}$$

If one tosses two coins a great number of times, he expects to obtain one head "on the average," and that is exactly what $E(Z)$ indicates.

Example.-- Suppose you obtained two ordinary six-sided dice, one light colored, the other one dark. Let an experiment consist of throwing these two ordinary six-sided dice and observing the total score on their top faces. The possible results from this two-dice experiment are shown in Table 7-16. As an exercise, let us construct the list of all possible outcomes (sums) from the ordered pairs shown in Table 7-16; then display the probability function in an untitled table; and use Eq. (5) to find the mathematical expectation of the random variable.

Table 7-16. --Possible results of a two-dice experiment

Outcome		Light die (i)					
		1	2	3	4	5	6
Dark die (j)	1	(1, 1)	(2, 1)	(3, 1)	(4, 1)	(5, 1)	(6, 1)
	2	(1, 2)	(2, 2)	(3, 2)	(4, 2)	(5, 2)	(6, 2)
	3	(1, 3)	(2, 3)	(3, 3)	(4, 3)	(5, 3)	(6, 3)
	4	(1, 4)	(2, 4)	(3, 4)	(4, 4)	(5, 4)	(6, 4)
	5	(1, 5)	(2, 5)	(3, 5)	(4, 5)	(5, 5)	(6, 5)
	6	(1, 6)	(2, 6)	(3, 6)	(4, 6)	(5, 6)	(6, 6)

Solution: The listing of each sum (total score) from Table 7-16, row by row, is as follows:

2,	3,	4,	5,	6,	7
3,	4,	5,	6,	7,	8
4,	5,	6,	7,	8,	9
5,	6,	7,	8,	9,	10
6,	7,	8,	9,	10,	11
7,	8,	9,	10,	11,	12 .

The preceding listing yields the list of all possible outcomes (sums) as follows: 2, 3, 4, 5, 6, 7, 8, 9, 10, 11, 12. The probability function for total score on the top faces of the two dice follows in the unnumbered, untitled table.

Total number of dots, z	Probability $f(z)$
2	1/36
3	2/36
4	3/36
5	4/36
6	5/36
7	6/36
8	5/36
9	4/36
10	3/36
11	2/36
12	1/36

Copying Eq. (5)

$$E(Z) = z_1 \times f(z_1) + z_2 \times f(z_2) + \ldots + z_k \times f(z_k);$$

and substituting from the foregoing unnumbered table,

$$\begin{aligned}
E(Z) = \; & 2 \times 1/36 + 3 \times 2/36 + 4 \times 3/36 + 5 \\
& \times 4/36 + 6 \times 5/36 + 7 \times 6/36 + 8 \\
& \times 5/36 + 9 \times 4/36 + 10 \times 3/36 \\
& + 11 \times 2/36 + 12 \times 1/36
\end{aligned}$$

$$E(Z) \;=\; 2/36 \;+\; 6/36 \;+\; 12/36 \;+\; 20/36 \;+\; 30/36$$
$$+\; 42/36 \;+\; 40/36 \;+\; 36/36 \;+\; 30/36$$
$$+\; 22/36 \;+\; 12/36$$
$$=\; 252/36$$
$$E(Z) \;=\; 7 \,.$$

SAMPLING DISTRIBUTIONS, PROBABILITY FUNCTIONS, AND PROBABILITY DISTRIBUTIONS

In some aspects of the application of statistics the abstract idea of population and sample must be translated into a practical problem. The abstract idea involved is actually a mathematical model; as stated earlier, in order to be useful the model must agree closely with the practical problem.

At the risk of being redundant, sampling properties of statistics can be studied by means of mathematical statistics or by actually drawing samples, or by both methods. If samples are drawn, the mathematical model is determined by the method of sampling. One purpose of this section is to illustrate that the method of sampling determines the appropriate mathematical model.

If sampling is conducted with replacement from a two-class population (say, success or failure), an appropriate theoretical model is the binomial distribution. Note that the probability of success does not change from trial to trial when sampling with replacement. If sampling is conducted without replacement from a two-class population, the appropriate theoretical model is the hypergeometric distribution. Thus, in this section, a comparison is made of sampling with replacement and sampling without replacement; that is, a binomially distributed random variable is compared with a random variable which has a hypergeometric distribution.

Sampling Distribution of a Statistic

Population in the statistical sense is an abstract concept; it refers to a fixed body of numbers generated by the process of selection, classification or measurement, and recording of results. A sample is a subclass of the population and, thus, may vary from size one to the size of the entire population. A statistic characterizes a sample. Once a statistic is selected, the concept of population can be extended to all possible samples of a specified size, where each sample yields a value for the statistic. The (relative frequency) distribution of this "new population" is called the sampling distribution of the statistic for random samples of size n from the original population.

Illustration of a sampling distribution of a statistic computed from a two-class population. -- In an earlier section of this chapter, it was assumed that in retriever-happy families, males (M) and females (F) had an equal chance of being born and surviving. This implies that the true proportion, called π for convenience (not 3.1416, when used in this sense), of male children in the population of retriever-happy families is $\pi = 0.50$. Further, it was assumed that a large list of three-child retriever-happy families was available and that an experiment was conducted by randomly selecting a sample of one family from this list and observing the sex of each child.

If the random variable X is the number of males for each child observed, then X has two possible values; that is, if the child is male, X takes on the value $x_1 = 1$, and if the child is not male, X is $x_2 = 0$. (In other words, the random variable X takes on one of two values for each child observed depending on whether the child is male or female.) If the statistic of interest is T, the sample total (that is, the total number of male children in the family), then $T = \Sigma x$, where T can take on the values 0, 1, 2, or 3. Then utilizing Table 7-7, the sampling distribution of the statistic T for families of size three can be constructed (Table 7-17).

In general, in order to derive a sampling distribution, it is assumed that the population is completely known and that sampling is (simple) random; then by a deductive procedure based on probability theory, the sampling distribution of a statistic computed from all pos-

Table 7-17.--Sampling distribution of the number of males
in three-child retriever-happy families, assuming $\pi = 0.50$

Number of males in three-child families $T = \Sigma x$	Relative frequency or probability
3	1/8
2	3/8
1	3/8
0	1/8

sible samples of a specified size drawn from this population is derived.

From the above it is clear that in discussing a sampling distribution, the following three items must be specified: population, sample size, and statistic. Furthermore, a sampling distribution is comparable to a "known" in the field of chemistry. In applied research,
a sampling distribution is deduced from assumptions, but it should be
clear that "not just any" assumptions will suffice. Assumptions must
be made for the explicit purpose of testing whether or not they are
consistent with observed facts.

In statistical inference, not only are there many statistics but the
samples vary in size and the populations are large. By this time, the
reader must have realized how great the task would be to write down
the sampling distributions of several statistics using different sample
sizes for even a small population; the task is insurmountable for a
large population.

One possibility would be to approximate the sampling distribution
for a specified statistic by drawing many, many samples and recording the observed distribution, but this is not a practical method for
producing sampling distributions. A better solution is to make use of

mathematical methods involving "proven theorems" for which one must "pay a price"; these theorems are based upon assumptions and the price one pays is that he must assure himself that the assumptions have not been violated.

With these preliminary remarks out of the way, it is time to get acquainted with two of these theoretical sampling distributions, called probability distributions, namely, the binomial distribution and the hypergeometric distribution. The hypergeometric distribution has already been mentioned in connection with (mathematical) models. When a probability distribution is discussed, complete information is assumed; consequently, the discussion of these two distributions is entirely mathematical in nature. Practical methods for using probability distributions in making "wise decisions" and "good estimates" in the face of uncertainty are utilized elsewhere in this book.

Binomial Distribution

Binomial population.--Many experiments are concerned with two-class populations where a proportion π of the individuals have a specified characteristic and a proportion $1 - \pi$ of the individuals do not have it. If an individual has the characteristic, a score of 1 may be assigned; if an individual does not have the characteristic, the score of 0 may be assigned.

The mean of such a binomial population is equal to π; the variance of such a binomial population is equal to $\pi(1 - \pi)$. The remainder of this subsection concerns the binomial distribution which is a sampling distribution; take special care not to confuse it with the binomial population discussed in this particular paragraph.

Binomial distribution.--Binomial experiments can be thought of as being composed of repetitions of independent trials, where each trial has only two possible outcomes, success or failure, lived or died, one or zero, immune or not immune, dropped or called back, head or no head, ace or no ace, and the like. The number of successes X in n binomial trials, where each trial has probability of suc-

cess π, is called a binomial random variable. In shorthand, $X \stackrel{d}{=}$
$B(n,\ \pi)$. [Read "X is binomially distributed with n trials and with
probability of success π ." Note that X is a discrete random variable.]

A probability function with possible values x = 0, 1, ... , n,
and associated probabilities

$$P(X = x) \; = \; \binom{n}{x} \pi^x (1 - \pi)^{n-x} \tag{6}$$

is called a binomial probability function or the binomial distribution.
The function, Eq. (6), gives the probability that n (binomial) trials
with probabilities π for success and $1 - \pi$ for failure result in x
successes and $n - x$ failures. The parameters here are n and π.
In functional notation, this would be written as

$$f(x,\ \pi,\ n) \; = \; P(X = x) \; = \; \binom{n}{x} \pi^x (1 - \pi)^{n-x}.$$

Obviously, when this probability function is shown in table form, values for n, x, and π have to be explicitly shown.

Example.--An experiment consists of tossing a coin twice and of
observing the number of heads (successes). The task is to display the
binomial probability function in the form of a table.

This experiment qualifies as a binomial experiment since (1) the
number of trials is fixed, n = 2 ; (2) each trial has only two outcomes, say, head = success, tail = failure; (3) the probability of
success remains constant from trial to trial since it is assumed that
the probability of heads, $\pi = 0.5$, does not change from trial to trial
(if this were thought of in terms of sampling, this would be sampling
with replacement); (4) the coin was flipped twice, each flip having
"nothing to do" with the other flip, so each trial is independent.

The probability function of the number of heads, where $X \stackrel{d}{=}$
$B(2,\ 0.50)$, would appear in the usual form as shown in Table 7-18.

Table 7-18. --Probability function for number of heads

Value (number of heads), x	Probability, B(x; 2, 0.50)
0	$\binom{n}{x} \pi^x (1 - \pi)^{n-x}$ = $\binom{2}{0} (0.5)^0 (0.5)^2$ = 0.25
1	$\binom{n}{x} \pi^x (1 - \pi)^{n-x}$ = $\binom{2}{1} (0.5)^1 (0.5)^1$ = 0.50
2	$\binom{n}{x} \pi^x (1 - \pi)^{n-x}$ = $\binom{2}{2} (0.5)^2 (0.5)^0$ = 0.25

The label "binomial" comes about from the method of generation because the probabilities above are the terms in the binomial formula for the expansion of $[(1 - \pi) + \pi]^n$. That is, to refresh memories in terms of elementary algebra, let $a = 1 - \pi$, $b = \pi$, and $n = 2$. The expression $[(1 - \pi) + \pi]^n$ becomes

$$(a + b)^2 = a^2 + 2ab + b^2. \tag{7}$$

Recall that a^2 and b^2 are understood to have coefficients of one; thus, the right side of Eq. (7) becomes, when rewritten in slightly different form,

$$1aa + 2ab + 1bb. \tag{8}$$

Since $a = 0.5$ and $b = 0.5$, substituting in Eq. (8) leads to

$$1(0.5)(0.5) + 2(0.5)(0.5) + 1(0.5)(0.5),$$

and finally,

$$0.25 + 0.50 + 0.25$$

as shown above in Table 7-18 displaying the binomial probability function.

Selected binomial distributions.--Extensive tables have been published of the binomial distribution. In this book only two small tables are provided. Table 7-19 contains values for individual terms of n = 2 up to 10 for 7 values of π. Table 7-20 gives the probability of x or more successes, that is, cumulative probability of x or more successes for n = 2 through 10 for the same 7 values of π.

Individual terms.--Note that Table 7-19 carries values of π equal to 0.2, 0.3, 0.4, 0.5, 0.6, 0.7, and 0.8; if one desired, values of π for 0.6, 0.7, and 0.8 need not have been tabulated.

Example.--What is the probability of exactly 5 successes in a binomial experiment of 8 trials, if the probability of success on each trial is 0.4 ?

Solution: Read in Table 7-19 on row n = 8, x = 5, column π = 0.40, the value 0.124. To verify, compute by substituting in Eq. (6) as follows:

$$P(X = 5) = \binom{n}{x} \pi^x (1 - \pi)^{n-x}$$

$$= \binom{8}{5} (0.4)^5 (0.6)^3$$

$$= \frac{8!}{5!\,3!} (0.4)^5 (0.6)^3$$

$$= \frac{8 \times 7 \times 6 \times 5!}{5!\,3!} (0.01024)(0.216)$$

$$P(X = 5) = 56(0.00221184)$$
$$P(X = 5) \approx 0.124.$$

Cumulated terms.--Table 7-20 gives the probability of x or more successes.

Example.--If the probability of success is 0.4, what is the probability of 5 or more successes in 8 trials?

Solution: From Table 7-20 read row n = 8, x = 5, column π = 0.40, the value 0.174. As a check, compute

Table 7-19.--The probability that X = x for selected binomial distributions (n, π)

n	x	0.20	0.30	0.40	0.50	0.60	0.70	0.80
					π			
2	0	0.640	0.490	0.360	0.250	0.160	0.090	0.040
	1	0.320	0.420	0.480	0.500	0.480	0.420	0.320
	2	0.040	0.090	0.160	0.250	0.360	0.490	0.640
3	0	0.512	0.343	0.216	0.125	0.064	0.027	0.008
	1	0.384	0.441	0.432	0.375	0.288	0.189	0.096
	2	0.096	0.189	0.288	0.375	0.432	0.441	0.384
	3	0.008	0.027	0.064	0.125	0.216	0.343	0.512
4	0	0.410	0.240	0.130	0.062	0.026	0.008	0.002
	1	0.410	0.412	0.346	0.250	0.154	0.076	0.026
	2	0.154	0.265	0.346	0.375	0.346	0.265	0.154
	3	0.026	0.076	0.154	0.250	0.346	0.412	0.410
	4	0.002	0.008	0.026	0.062	0.130	0.240	0.410
5	0	0.328	0.168	0.078	0.031	0.010	0.002	0.000+
	1	0.410	0.360	0.259	0.156	0.077	0.028	0.006
	2	0.205	0.309	0.346	0.312	0.230	0.132	0.051
	3	0.051	0.132	0.230	0.312	0.346	0.309	0.205
	4	0.006	0.028	0.077	0.156	0.259	0.360	0.410
	5	0.000+	0.002	0.010	0.031	0.078	0.168	0.328
6	0	0.262	0.118	0.047	0.016	0.004	0.001	0.000+
	1	0.393	0.303	0.187	0.094	0.037	0.010	0.002
	2	0.246	0.324	0.311	0.234	0.138	0.060	0.015
	3	0.082	0.185	0.276	0.312	0.276	0.185	0.082
	4	0.015	0.060	0.138	0.234	0.311	0.324	0.246
	5	0.002	0.010	0.037	0.094	0.187	0.303	0.393
	6	0.000+	0.001	0.004	0.016	0.047	0.118	0.262

(Continued)

Table 7-19. --(Continued) The probability that X = x for selected binomial distributions (n, π)

n	x	π						
		0.20	0.30	0.40	0.50	0.60	0.70	0.80
7	0	0.210	0.082	0.028	0.008	0.002	0.000+	0.000+
	1	0.367	0.247	0.131	0.055	0.017	0.004	0.000+
	2	0.275	0.318	0.261	0.164	0.077	0.025	0.004
	3	0.115	0.227	0.290	0.273	0.194	0.097	0.029
	4	0.029	0.097	0.194	0.273	0.290	0.227	0.115
	5	0.004	0.025	0.077	0.164	0.261	0.318	0.275
	6	0.000+	0.004	0.017	0.055	0.131	0.247	0.367
	7	0.000+	0.000+	0.002	0.008	0.028	0.082	0.210
8	0	0.168	0.058	0.017	0.004	0.001	0.000+	0.000+
	1	0.336	0.198	0.090	0.031	0.008	0.001	0.000+
	2	0.294	0.296	0.209	0.109	0.041	0.010	0.001
	3	0.147	0.254	0.279	0.219	0.124	0.047	0.009
	4	0.046	0.136	0.232	0.273	0.232	0.136	0.046
	5	0.009	0.047	0.124	0.219	0.279	0.254	0.147
	6	0.001	0.010	0.041	0.109	0.209	0.296	0.294
	7	0.000+	0.001	0.008	0.031	0.090	0.198	0.336
	8	0.000+	0.000+	0.001	0.004	0.017	0.058	0.168
9	0	0.134	0.040	0.010	0.002	0.000+	0.000+	0.000+
	1	0.302	0.156	0.060	0.018	0.004	0.000+	0.000+
	2	0.302	0.267	0.161	0.070	0.021	0.004	0.000+
	3	0.176	0.267	0.251	0.164	0.074	0.021	0.003
	4	0.066	0.172	0.251	0.246	0.167	0.074	0.017
	5	0.017	0.074	0.167	0.246	0.251	0.172	0.066
	6	0.003	0.021	0.074	0.164	0.251	0.267	0.176
	7	0.000+	0.004	0.021	0.070	0.161	0.267	0.302
	8	0.000+	0.000+	0.004	0.018	0.060	0.156	0.302
	9	0.000+	0.000+	0.000+	0.002	0.010	0.040	0.134

(Continued)

Table 7-19.--(Concluded) The probability that X = x for selected binomial distributions (n, π)

n	x	π						
		0.20	0.30	0.40	0.50	0.60	0.70	0.80
10	0	0.107	0.028	0.006	0.001	0.000+	0.000+	0.000+
	1	0.268	0.121	0.040	0.010	0.002	0.000+	0.000+
	2	0.302	0.233	0.121	0.044	0.011	0.001	0.000+
	3	0.201	0.267	0.215	0.117	0.042	0.009	0.001
	4	0.088	0.200	0.251	0.205	0.111	0.037	0.006
	5	0.026	0.103	0.201	0.246	0.201	0.103	0.026
	6	0.006	0.037	0.111	0.205	0.251	0.200	0.088
	7	0.001	0.009	0.042	0.117	0.215	0.267	0.201
	8	0.000+	0.001	0.011	0.044	0.121	0.233	0.302
	9	0.000+	0.000+	0.002	0.010	0.040	0.121	0.268
	10	0.000+	0.000+	0.000+	0.001	0.006	0.028	0.107

Table 7-20.--The probability of x or more successes for selected binomial distributions (n, π)

n	x	π						
		0.20	0.30	0.40	0.50	0.60	0.70	0.80
2	0	1.000	1.000	1.000	1.000	1.000	1.000	1.000
	1	0.360	0.510	0.640	0.750	0.840	0.910	0.960
	2	0.040	0.090	0.160	0.250	0.360	0.490	0.640
3	0	1.000	1.000	1.000	1.000	1.000	1.000	1.000
	1	0.488	0.657	0.784	0.875	0.936	0.973	0.992
	2	0.104	0.216	0.352	0.500	0.648	0.784	0.896
	3	0.008	0.027	0.064	0.125	0.216	0.343	0.512
4	0	1.000	1.000	1.000	1.000	1.000	1.000	1.000
	1	0.590	0.760	0.870	0.938	0.974	0.992	0.998
	2	0.181	0.348	0.525	0.688	0.821	0.916	0.973
	3	0.027	0.084	0.179	0.312	0.475	0.652	0.819
	4	0.002	0.008	0.026	0.062	0.130	0.240	0.410
5	0	1.000	1.000	1.000	1.000	1.000	1.000	1.000
	1	0.672	0.832	0.922	0.969	0.990	0.998	1.000-
	2	0.263	0.472	0.663	0.812	0.913	0.969	0.993
	3	0.058	0.163	0.317	0.500	0.683	0.837	0.942
	4	0.007	0.031	0.087	0.188	0.337	0.528	0.737
	5	0.000+	0.002	0.010	0.031	0.078	0.168	0.328
6	0	1.000	1.000	1.000	1.000	1.000	1.000	1.000
	1	0.738	0.882	0.953	0.984	0.996	0.999	1.000-
	2	0.345	0.580	0.767	0.891	0.959	0.989	0.998
	3	0.099	0.256	0.456	0.656	0.821	0.930	0.983
	4	0.017	0.070	0.179	0.344	0.544	0.744	0.901
	5	0.002	0.011	0.041	0.109	0.233	0.420	0.655
	6	0.000+	0.001	0.004	0.016	0.047	0.118	0.262

(Continued)

Table 7-20.--(Continued) The probability of x or more successes for
selected binomial distributions (n, π)

n	x	π						
		0.20	0.30	0.40	0.50	0.60	0.70	0.80
7	0	1.000	1.000	1.000	1.000	1.000	1.000	1.000
	1	0.790	0.918	0.972	0.992	0.998	1.000-	1.000-
	2	0.423	0.671	0.841	0.938	0.981	0.996	1.000-
	3	0.148	0.353	0.580	0.773	0.904	0.971	0.995
	4	0.033	0.126	0.290	0.500	0.710	0.874	0.967
	5	0.005	0.029	0.096	0.227	0.420	0.647	0.852
	6	0.000+	0.004	0.019	0.062	0.159	0.329	0.577
	7	0.000+	0.000+	0.002	0.008	0.028	0.082	0.210
8	0	1.000	1.000	1.000	1.000	1.000	1.000	1.000
	1	0.832	0.942	0.983	0.996	0.999	1.000-	1.000-
	2	0.497	0.745	0.894	0.965	0.991	0.999	1.000-
	3	0.203	0.448	0.685	0.855	0.950	0.989	0.999
	4	0.056	0.194	0.406	0.637	0.826	0.942	0.990
	5	0.010	0.058	0.174	0.363	0.594	0.806	0.944
	6	0.001	0.011	0.050	0.145	0.315	0.552	0.797
	7	0.000+	0.001	0.009	0.035	0.106	0.255	0.503
	8	0.000+	0.000+	0.001	0.004	0.017	0.058	0.168
9	0	1.000	1.000	1.000	1.000	1.000	1.000	1.000
	1	0.866	0.960	0.990	0.998	1.000-	1.000-	1.000-
	2	0.564	0.804	0.929	0.980	0.996	1.000-	1.000-
	3	0.262	0.537	0.768	0.910	0.975	0.996	1.000-
	4	0.086	0.270	0.517	0.746	0.901	0.975	0.997
	5	0.020	0.099	0.267	0.500	0.733	0.901	0.980
	6	0.003	0.025	0.099	0.254	0.483	0.730	0.914
	7	0.000+	0.004	0.025	0.090	0.232	0.463	0.738
	8	0.000+	0.000+	0.004	0.020	0.071	0.196	0.436
	9	0.000+	0.000+	0.000+	0.002	0.010	0.040	0.134

(Continued)

Table 7-20.--(Concluded) The probability of x or more successes for selected binomial distributions (n, π)

n	x	π						
		0.20	0.30	0.40	0.50	0.60	0.70	0.80
10	0	1.000	1.000	1.000	1.000	1.000	1.000	1.000
	1	0.893	0.972	0.994	0.999	1.000-	1.000-	1.000-
	2	0.624	0.851	0.954	0.989	0.998	1.000-	1.000-
	3	0.322	0.617	0.833	0.945	0.988	0.998	1.000-
	4	0.121	0.350	0.618	0.828	0.945	0.989	0.999
	5	0.033	0.150	0.367	0.623	0.834	0.953	0.994
	6	0.006	0.047	0.166	0.377	0.633	0.850	0.967
	7	0.001	0.011	0.055	0.172	0.382	0.650	0.879
	8	0.000+	0.002	0.012	0.055	0.167	0.383	0.678
	9	0.000+	0.000+	0.002	0.011	0.046	0.149	0.376
	10	0.000+	0.000+	0.000+	0.001	0.006	0.028	0.107

$$P(X = 5) + P(X = 6) + P(X = 7) + P(X = 8).$$

The $P(X = 5)$ has already been computed, and continuing,

$$P(X = 6) = \frac{8!}{6! \, 2!} (0.4)^6 (0.6)^2 = 0.041,$$

$$P(X = 7) = \frac{8!}{7! \, 1!} (0.4)^7 (0.6)^1 = 0.008,$$

$$P(X = 8) = \frac{8!}{8! \, 0!} (0.4)^8 (0.6)^0 = 0.001.$$

Summarizing,

$$0.124 + 0.041 + 0.008 + 0.001 = 0.174,$$

which agrees with the tabulated value of 0.174.

Hypergeometric Distribution

In studying the binomial distribution, it was pointed out that the probability of success must remain constant from trial to trial; in terms of sampling in order to maintain π at a constant level, the sampling would have to be with replacement. Now the discussion turns to sampling without replacement.

Given a population of size N consisting of r elements with property A, and $N - r$ elements with property $\overline{A}$, the number of items X with property A in a random sample of size n is called a hypergeometric random variable. Note that the hypergeometric random variable is a discrete random variable. A probability function which gives the probability that a sample of n elements, drawn without replacement, will contain x elements with property A and $n - x$ elements with property $\overline{A}$ is called the hypergeometric distribution and is given by Eq. (9).

$$P(X = x) = \frac{\binom{r}{x}\binom{N-r}{n-x}}{\binom{N}{n}}. \tag{9}$$

Point and cumulative probabilities for the hypergeometric distribution for $N \leq 10$ are given in Table 7-21. In order to read the table, let

N = size of the population,

r = number of elements in class A,

n = size of the sample, and

x = the number of items from class A observed in the sample.

Example.--A veterinarian admits 10 sick retrievers to a study. Six of the retrievers have a mild case of disease D_1 and 4 of the retrievers have a severe case of disease D_1. What is the probability, or chance, of finding exactly 2 severe cases in a sample of 3 chosen at random from the group of sick retrievers?

Solution: When $N = 10$, $r = 4$, $n = 3$, $x = 2$, read from Table 7-21 the (point probability) value 0.300. This entry in the table can be verified by copying and substituting in Eq. (9) as follows:

$$P(X = x) = \frac{\binom{r}{x}\binom{N-r}{n-x}}{\binom{N}{n}}$$

$$P(X = 2) = \frac{\binom{4}{2}\binom{10-4}{3-2}}{\binom{10}{3}}$$

$$= \frac{\left(\frac{4!}{2!\,2!}\right)\left(\frac{6!}{1!\,5!}\right)}{\left(\frac{10!}{3!\,7!}\right)}$$

$$P(X = 2) = 0.300.$$

Table 7-21.--Hypergeometric point and cumulative probabilities for
N ≤ 10

N	r	n	x	Point probability	Cumulative probability
2	1	1	0	0.500000	0.500000
2	1	1	1	0.500000	1.000000
3	1	1	0	0.666667	0.666667
3	1	1	1	0.333333	1.000000
4	1	1	0	0.750000	0.750000
4	1	1	1	0.250000	1.000000
4	2	1	0	0.500000	0.500000
4	2	1	1	0.500000	1.000000
4	2	2	0	0.166667	0.166667
4	2	2	1	0.666667	0.833333
4	2	2	2	0.166667	1.000000
5	1	1	0	0.800000	0.800000
5	1	1	1	0.200000	1.000000
5	2	1	0	0.600000	0.600000
5	2	1	1	0.400000	1.000000
5	2	2	0	0.300000	0.300000
5	2	2	1	0.600000	0.900000
5	2	2	2	0.100000	1.000000
6	1	1	0	0.833333	0.833333
6	1	1	1	0.166667	1.000000
6	2	1	0	0.666667	0.666667
6	2	1	1	0.333333	1.000000
6	2	2	0	0.400000	0.400000
6	2	2	1	0.533333	0.933333
6	2	2	2	0.066667	1.000000
6	3	1	0	0.500000	0.500000
6	3	1	1	0.500000	1.000000
6	3	2	0	0.200000	0.200000

(Continued)

Table 7-21. --(Continued) Hypergeometric point and cumulative probabilities for N ≤ 10

N	r	n	x	Point probability	Cumulative probability
6	3	2	1	0.600000	0.800000
6	3	2	2	0.200000	1.000000
6	3	3	0	0.050000	0.050000
6	3	3	1	0.450000	0.500000
6	3	3	2	0.450000	0.950000
6	3	3	3	0.050000	1.000000
7	1	1	0	0.857143	0.857143
7	1	1	1	0.142857	1.000000
7	2	1	0	0.714286	0.714286
7	2	1	1	0.285714	1.000000
7	2	2	0	0.476190	0.476190
7	2	2	1	0.476190	0.952381
7	2	2	2	0.047619	1.000000
7	3	1	0	0.571429	0.571429
7	3	1	1	0.428571	1.000000
7	3	2	0	0.285714	0.285714
7	3	2	1	0.571429	0.857143
7	3	2	2	0.142857	1.000000
7	3	3	0	0.114286	0.114286
7	3	3	1	0.514286	0.628571
7	3	3	2	0.342857	0.971429
7	3	3	3	0.028571	1.000000
8	1	1	0	0.875000	0.875000
8	1	1	1	0.125000	1.000000
8	2	1	0	0.750000	0.750000
8	2	1	1	0.250000	1.000000
8	2	2	0	0.535714	0.535714
8	2	2	1	0.428571	0.964286

(Continued)

Table 7-21.--(Continued) Hypergeometric point and cumulative probabilities for $N \leq 10$

N	r	n	x	Point probability	Cumulative probability
8	2	2	2	0.035714	1.000000
8	3	1	0	0.625000	0.625000
8	3	1	1	0.375000	1.000000
8	3	2	0	0.357143	0.357143
8	3	2	1	0.535714	0.892857
8	3	2	2	0.107143	1.000000
8	3	3	0	0.178571	0.178571
8	3	3	1	0.535714	0.714286
8	3	3	2	0.267857	0.982143
8	3	3	3	0.017857	1.000000
8	4	1	0	0.500000	0.500000
8	4	1	1	0.500000	1.000000
8	4	2	0	0.214286	0.214286
8	4	2	1	0.571428	0.785714
8	4	2	2	0.214286	1.000000
8	4	3	0	0.071429	0.071429
8	4	3	1	0.428571	0.500000
8	4	3	2	0.428571	0.928571
8	4	3	3	0.071429	1.000000
8	4	4	0	0.014286	0.014286
8	4	4	1	0.228571	0.242857
8	4	4	2	0.514286	0.757143
8	4	4	3	0.228571	0.985714
8	4	4	4	0.014286	1.000000
9	1	1	0	0.888889	0.888889
9	1	1	1	0.111111	1.000000
9	2	1	0	0.777778	0.777778
9	2	1	1	0.222222	1.000000

(Continued)

Table 7-21.--(Continued) Hypergeometric point and cumulative probabilities for N ≤ 10

N	r	n	x	Point probability	Cumulative probability
9	2	2	0	0.583333	0.583333
9	2	2	1	0.388889	0.972222
9	2	2	2	0.027778	1.000000
9	3	1	0	0.666667	0.666667
9	3	1	1	0.333333	1.000000
9	3	2	0	0.416667	0.416667
9	3	2	1	0.500000	0.916667
9	3	2	2	0.083333	1.000000
9	3	3	0	0.238095	0.238095
9	3	3	1	0.535714	0.773810
9	3	3	2	0.214286	0.988095
9	3	3	3	0.011905	1.000000
9	4	1	0	0.555556	0.555556
9	4	1	1	0.444444	1.000000
9	4	2	0	0.277778	0.277778
9	4	2	1	0.555556	0.833333
9	4	2	2	0.166667	1.000000
9	4	3	0	0.119048	0.119048
9	4	3	1	0.476190	0.595238
9	4	3	2	0.357143	0.952381
9	4	3	3	0.047619	1.000000
9	4	4	0	0.039683	0.039683
9	4	4	1	0.317460	0.357143
9	4	4	2	0.476190	0.833333
9	4	4	3	0.158730	0.992063
9	4	4	4	0.007936	1.000000
10	1	1	0	0.900000	0.900000
10	1	1	1	0.100000	1.000000

(Continued)

Table 7-21.--(Continued) Hypergeometric point and cumulative probabilities for N ≤ 10

N	r	n	x	Point probability	Cumulative probability
10	2	1	0	0.800000	0.800000
10	2	1	1	0.200000	1.000000
10	2	2	0	0.622222	0.622222
10	2	2	1	0.355556	0.977778
10	2	2	2	0.022222	1.000000
10	3	1	0	0.700000	0.700000
10	3	1	1	0.300000	1.000000
10	3	2	0	0.466667	0.466667
10	3	2	1	0.466667	0.933333
10	3	2	2	0.066667	1.000000
10	3	3	0	0.291667	0.291667
10	3	3	1	0.525000	0.816667
10	3	3	2	0.175000	0.991667
10	3	3	3	0.008333	1.000000
10	4	1	0	0.600000	0.600000
10	4	1	1	0.400000	1.000000
10	4	2	0	0.333333	0.333333
10	4	2	1	0.533333	0.866667
10	4	2	2	0.133333	1.000000
10	4	3	0	0.166667	0.166667
10	4	3	1	0.500000	0.666667
10	4	3	2	0.300000	0.966667
10	4	3	3	0.033333	1.000000
10	4	4	0	0.071429	0.071429
10	4	4	1	0.380952	0.452381
10	4	4	2	0.428571	0.880952
10	4	4	3	0.114286	0.995238
10	4	4	4	0.004762	1.000000

(Continued)

Table 7-21.--(Concluded) Hypergeometric point and cumulative probabilities for N ≤ 10

N	r	n	x	Point probability	Cumulative probability
10	5	1	0	0.500000	0.500000
10	5	1	1	0.500000	1.000000
10	5	2	0	0.222222	0.222222
10	5	2	1	0.555556	0.777778
10	5	2	2	0.222222	1.000000
10	5	3	0	0.083333	0.083333
10	5	3	1	0.416667	0.500000
10	5	3	2	0.416667	0.916667
10	5	3	3	0.083333	1.000000
10	5	4	0	0.023810	0.023810
10	5	4	1	0.238095	0.261905
10	5	4	2	0.476190	0.738095
10	5	4	3	0.238095	0.976190
10	5	4	4	0.023810	1.000000
10	5	5	0	0.003968	0.003968
10	5	5	1	0.099206	0.103175
10	5	5	2	0.396825	0.500000
10	5	5	3	0.396825	0.896825
10	5	5	4	0.099206	0.996032
10	5	5	5	0.003968	1.000000

Hence, the probability is 0.3 that 2 of the severe cases would be randomly chosen in a sample of 3 .

OTHER APPLICATIONS

Test for Randomness

Inspection of the portion of the program indicating sex of entries for the derby stake of the ... Amateur Retriever Club, February, 1966, is puzzling. Sex of the entries in the order as listed in the program was as follows (where M = male and F = female):

M	M	M	M	M	M	M	M	M	M
M	M	M	M	M	M	M	M	M	F	M
M	F	F	F	F	F	F	F	F	F	F
M	M	M	M	M	M.				

It appears to me that a decision had been made to separate dogs and bitches, but the action was not followed through completely.

Reference the 10 females which appear together.--Further inspection of the program for these 10 females indicates that 2 females from the same litter were included in these 10 females.

Two litter sisters, obviously born 10-25-64(?) (although the program indicated otherwise), appear as entries number 28 and number 29 with a man and his wife as handlers. If the randomization process had been thorough, one would not expect these two entries to be "back-to-back."

In particular, 10 females can be arranged in 10! ways or 3,628,800 ways. The two sisters, female one, F_1, and female two, F_2, of the same litter (10-25-64(?)) could appear back-to-back in 9 back-to-back positions; obviously, for each of the 9 positions, F_1 could appear before F_2 or F_2 could appear before F_1. Consequently, they could appear back-to-back in 2(9) or 18 ways as follows:

Program number	24	25	26	27	28	29	30	31	32	33
	F_1	F_2								
	F_2	F_1								
		F_1	F_2							
		F_2	F_1							
			F_1	F_2						
			F_2	F_1						
				F_1	F_2					
				F_2	F_1					
					F_1	F_2				
					F_2	F_1				
						F_1	F_2			
						F_2	F_1			
							F_1	F_2		
							F_2	F_1		
								F_1	F_2	
								F_2	F_1	
									F_1	F_2
									F_2	F_1

Hence, the probability of 2 litter sisters being listed back-to-back in the group of 10 females which appeared together in the running order is

$$P \left(\begin{array}{c} \text{2 litter sisters being} \\ \text{listed back-to-back} \end{array} \right) = \frac{2(9)}{10!} = \frac{18}{3,628,800}$$

$$P \begin{pmatrix} 2 \text{ litter sisters being} \\ \text{listed back-to-back} \end{pmatrix} = \frac{1}{201,600}$$

$$P \begin{pmatrix} 2 \text{ litter sisters being} \\ \text{listed back-to-back} \end{pmatrix} \approx 0.00000496 .$$

Conclusion: Based on this evidence alone, I do not believe that the drawing by lot for running order was "well-conducted," although there are about 5 chances in 1,000,000 that it was.

Genetics and Conjecture

Many persons have inquired and I had wondered whether or not my black bitch by Cork "had yellow in her bloodlines." Hence, in the spring of 1963, I bred her to a yellow male.

Since black acts as dominant, the capital letter B is used to denote the gene that produces it; and since yellow ("red") is recessive to black, let the lower case letter b denote that gene. Assume cells from the yellow dog carry only b genes; he is "pure yellow"; he has no B genes. If the black bitch Kube is homozygous (pure black, no yellow), the possible combinations in the pups are as shown below. All the pups will be black, because B is dominant.

Dog	Bitch	
	B	B
b	bB	bB
b	bB	bB

If the bitch is heterozygous (has both black and yellow genes), the possible combinations in the pups are as follows:

Dog	Bitch	
	B	b
b	bB	bb
b	bB	bb

Hence, over many hundreds of puppies one would expect equal numbers of black and yellow puppies.

Even so, from the above, it is clear that the birth of one yellow
pup would "prove" that the bitch is heterozygous (is not pure black).
On the other hand, I can never know for sure that the bitch is homozygous.

From the 1963 mating, 13 pups were whelped, all black. If
Kube were heterozygous, the probability of this happening is $(1/2)^{13}$
or only $1/8,192$. Hence, I was pretty sure that she is homozygous
black, that she would never whelp a yellow puppy. As a further test,
I bred her to the same yellow male again late in 1964. This mating
resulted in 10 pups; again as predicted, all were black. If Kube were
heterozygous, the probability of this happening is $(1/2)^{10}$ or $1/1,024$.
The probability of getting 23 black pups from the 2 matings of bb
with Bb is

$$\frac{1}{8,192} \times \frac{1}{1,024} = \frac{1}{8,388,608} .$$

I am convinced that Kube is pure black, BB (homozygous) although I
shall never know "for sure."

Integrity, Variability, and Honest Mistakes (Once Upon
a Time)

In a small licensed qualifying stake, I happened to have personal
knowledge concerning the limited experience which both judges had

Five "future hopefuls" (ex Kube), Pontchippi, 1965 (photo by VPA).

The same five Labradors, 1965 (photo by VPA).

OLD DOG AND PUPPY

An old signed print by G. Vernon Stokes in the author's private Pontohippi Collection.

with retrievers. As one of the many studies which I have conducted regarding making judgments independently, I asked two persons who had judged licensed all-age stakes as well as one other person (the latter, in my opinion, had more "retriever knowledge" than either of the actual judges) to "gallery judge" the trial. In particular, I asked these three persons to independently give me the program numbers of the four entries which they thought should be awarded silver. These persons were not asked to place the entries.

Limitations.--Obviously, gallery judges are limited; they cannot see what really goes on at the line. If a handler hisses a dog, rattles a chain, or if the dog gets tangled in the decoys, obviously, these particular types of events as well as others may not be "seen or heard" by persons in the gallery.

At the end of the trial, these three gallery judges independently presented to me the numbers of four entries; in fact, they agreed as to the four entries which they thought should have been awarded trophies. Two entries (entries E and F) of a specified handler X were included in the lists. However, when the awards were made, the two entries (E and F) of this particular handler X each received a JAM; that is, two entries (entries C and D) of another handler Y placed above the two entries E and F.

Discussion of variability.--Neither entry E nor entry F had a performance which was "poor," and each entry had good style and manners; variability in the performances of these two entries was not great.

In contrast, entries C and D each had at least one "poor performance" on at least one test; the performances of C and D were not consistently good.

Comment: It would appear that the judges failed to consider variability.

Chain rattling.--Next, "pocket motions" were seen and a noise came from the direction of the handler of the winning entry when he was honoring on the line; several persons in the gallery, including the three gallery judges, made the inference that the noise stemmed from the rattling of a chain. In fact, the noise was so loud that a person sitting in a car near the line recorded it on a tape recorder. [How about that for a lie?] One might infer that this "chain rattling," if in fact it did stem from the rattling of a chain, was intended to keep the entry which turned out to be chosen the winner from breaking.

Comment: If one is to assume honesty on the part of these judges, one must also make the inference that each judge probably had impaired hearing.

Some probabilities. -- Recall that in most trials, places are not assigned independently by the two judges; it is a pooled effort. Eleven entries completed the trial. Ignoring the chain rattling episode, suppose that the judges were correct in placing the two top entries. What is the probability that they made the following error? Awarded silver to two entries (C and D) of handler Y, where both entries performed with great variability, in contrast to awarding silver to the two entries of handler X, namely, E and F, which had consistently fair-to-good performances.

Task. --Assume that 17 entries started the trial: N = 17. How do we formulate the problem in such a way as to discuss various aspects of it? That is, what questions do we really want answered here? Basically, we want a random model against which to evaluate the performances of the two sets of judges--a model for evaluating discussion of the problem.

Aspects Which Should be Explicitly Discussed.

1. The number of combinations of 4 trophy winners out of 17 entries is

$$\frac{N!}{n! \, (N - n)!} \;=\; \frac{17!}{4! \; 13!} \;=\; 2,380 \,.$$

Suppose that the group of 4 trophy winners had been selected randomly from the 17 entries without conducting any tests. There is 1 chance in 2,380 (1/2,380) that the 4 entries which were actually awarded trophies would have been the same 4 entries as the set selected by the random process.

2. All 11 entries which completed the trial were awarded ribbons. The number of combinations of 4 trophy winners out of the group of 11 is

$$\frac{11!}{4!\,7!} = 330.$$

There is 1 chance in 330 that the set of 4 entries which were actually awarded trophies is the same set of 4 which would have been selected by a strictly random process from the group which completed the trial.

3. The 4 actual trophy winners could have been arranged in 4! or 24 orders as shown in the unnumbered, untitled table on the following page, where the 4 actual trophy winners are called A, B, C, and D. Inspection of the table indicates that entries A and B could be awarded the first 2 places (first and second) in 4 out of 24 ways. Likewise, C and D could have been awarded the other 2 trophies (third place and fourth place) in 4 out of 24 ways.

4. Seven of the final 11 entries were awarded ribbons but no trophies (JAM's). The gallery judges expressed the opinion that 2 out of this 7 should have been awarded trophies. The number of combinations of 2 out of 7 is

$$\frac{7!}{2!\,5!} = 21.$$

5. (a) What is the probability that the 2 official judges independently assigned the 4 entries into the group to receive silver? (b) What is the probability that the 2 official judges independently assigned the same 4 places?

Permutation number	Place			
	First	Second	Third	Fourth
1	A	B	C	D
2	A	B	D	C
3	A	C	B	D
4	A	C	D	B
5	A	D	B	C
6	A	D	C	B
7	B	A	C	D
8	B	A	D	C
9	B	C	A	D
10	B	C	D	A
11	B	D	A	C
12	B	D	C	A
13	C	A	B	D
14	C	A	D	B
15	C	B	A	D
16	C	B	D	A
17	C	D	A	B
18	C	D	B	A
19	D	A	B	C
20	D	A	C	B
21	D	B	A	C
22	D	B	C	A
23	D	C	A	B
24	D	C	B	A

Solution: If assignments were made strictly at random,

(a) $\dfrac{1}{330} \times \dfrac{1}{330} = \dfrac{1}{108,900} = 0.000009$;

(b) $\dfrac{1}{11 \cdot 10 \cdot 9 \cdot 8} \times \dfrac{1}{11 \cdot 10 \cdot 9 \cdot 8}$

$\qquad = \left(\dfrac{1}{7,920}\right)^2 = \dfrac{1}{62,726,400}$

$\qquad = 0.000000016$.

6. (a) What is the probability that the 3 gallery judges independently selected the group of 4 entries to receive silver? (b) What is the probability that the 3 gallery judges independently assigned the same 4 places?

Solution: If assignments were made strictly at random,

(a) $\left(\dfrac{1}{330}\right)^3 = \dfrac{1}{35,937,000} = 0.000000028$;

(b) $\left(\dfrac{1}{7,920}\right)^3 = \dfrac{1}{496,793,088,000} = 2 \times 10^{-12}$.

7. What is the probability that the 2 official judges and the 3 gallery judges selected independently the same 4 entries to receive silver?

Solution: If selections were made by a randomizing device,

$$\dfrac{1}{108,900} \times \dfrac{1}{35,937,000} = \left(\dfrac{1}{330}\right)^5 = \dfrac{1}{39,135,393} \times 10^{-5}$$

$$= 25 \times 10^{-14} .$$

ACTION ITEM

Now every senior RE knows that places and JAM's are not assigned at random; so what? I leave it to the reader to spell out the implications.

Comment: After having carefully made observations on judges over a number of years, I can assure the reader that one can learn a great deal about a judge from analyses such as these.

Question: How did McMahan know that about me?   *Answer:* He didn't know for sure, but he certainly made an interesting inference.

A pittance of practice may be worth a tome of theory.

NOTES TO CHAPTER SEVEN

The purpose of this note is to demonstrate use of events, "if ... , then ..." statements, the "exclusive or, " and "calling shots in advance"; in addition, a purpose is to demonstrate that Venn diagrams do not always provide assistance in the solution of a problem (in short, to indicate relationships among chapters thus far).

In the exclusive sense, the word *or* can mean that only one of two or more alternatives is true. *Example:* After this series, my retriever will be called back *or* my retriever will be dropped.

As stated many times throughout this book, I like to "call my shots" in advance and state the associated probability.

Because clubs, as well as people, have "personalities," "club behavior" is predictable to a limited degree; the probability of this example's being generated was neither 0.00 nor 1.00.

Reference the following description of stakes, running order, and entry fees for an A.K.C. licensed field trial:

Open All-Age	8:00 A.M., Friday,	September 26,	... $25.00
Amateur All-Age	12:00 Noon, Saturday,	September 27,	... $25.00
Qualifying	8:00 A.M., Sunday,	September 28,	... $20.00
Derby	10:00 A.M., Saturday,	September 27,	... $20.00.

I reasoned that if I entered Wynk (who was more than 3 years old), certified "not qualified, " and submitted only $20.00 as entry fee, then it would be unambiguously clear in which stake he was to be entered. I sent in U.S. Postal Money Order number 7,497,259,536 for $20.00; I did not indicate in what stake Wynk should be entered; I left this to those at the drawing. *Prediction:* Wynk will not be entered, or I'll get a 'phone call the night of the drawing (September 18).

ACTION ITEMS

Item 1.--What is the probability that the stake intended was derby?

Item 2.--What is the probability that the stake intended was open or amateur?

Item 3.--What is the probability that the stake intended was qualifying?

The problem is explicitly stated in tabular form below, where events are identified by capital letters in parentheses.

Entry fee	Age of entry	
	Under 2 years (C)	2 years or older (D)
$20.00 (A)	Enter in derby or qualifying	Enter in qualifying
$25.00 (B)	Enter in amateur or open	Enter in amateur or open

Let

A denote the event of a $20.00 fee.

B denote the event of a $25.00 fee.

C denote the event that the entry is under 2 years of age.

D denote the event that the entry is 2 years of age or older.

E denote the event of entry in the derby stake.

F denote the event of entry in the qualifying stake.

G denote the event of entry in the amateur stake.

H denote the event of entry in the open stake.

The following statements can be made:

1. If A and C, then E or F (not inclusive or).

2. If A and D, then F.

3. If B and C, then G or H (not inclusive or).

4. If B and D, then G or H (not inclusive or).

That is, if the entry fee is $20.00 and the entry is 2 years of age or older, then the entry must be entered in the qualifying stake. Note that statements 1, 3, and 4 do not uniquely determine which stake for the entry. Also, note that using Venn diagrams does not clarify the situation. A cannot intersect B; C cannot intersect D; G and H cannot be distinguished.

Outcome.--On Thursday evening, September 18, I received a courteous and considerate telephone call from a person who stated that he was at the drawing and needed to know in which stake I wanted Wynk entered.

Could it be that those in charge of the drawing reasoned that if McMahan failed to indicate "stake," he may also have made an error in the amount of the entry fee he submitted? Discuss.

Item 4.--Suppose McMahan had sent entry fees in the amount of $70.00. What stakes would you infer that he intended? Also discuss for the following entry fees: $50.00; $45.00.

The preparation of this action item, the completion of the entry form (including the deliberate omission of "stake"), and the posting of the entry form and fee, were all duly witnessed. Further deponent sayeth not.

Item 5.--Another look: Let event M be "the retriever marked the fall well"; let event E be "the handler handled his retriever"; let event F be "the handler should have handled." In general, events E and F are not independent of events M or $\overline{M}$. Carefully consider the implications of the foregoing in relationship to the following statement: I'll give a retriever two mistakes; however, he may make both mistakes on the same bird, say, fail to mark and fail to handle. Discuss.

Item 6.--Newcomers to the retriever field trial game often have only limited time to devote to retriever activities. More often than not, they have limited kennel space and/or training facilities. Additionally, they have limited knowledge of the game. Nevertheless, after winning a couple of ribbons, they often become over-enthusiastic, obtain additional retrievers, and before they know it, they are over-dogged. What is the relative frequency of over-dogged RE's? Discuss.

Item 7.--In 1965, a colleague of mine served as field trial secretary at a picnic trial for the New Orleans Retriever Club. She took with her (to the field) a randomized running order, complete with blocks. She covered over the randomized order and chose a starting place for the first entry randomly. As soon as all entries were in hand, she uncovered the random numbers. According to well-chosen rules, she prepared the running order immediately; duplicated the "program"; and the trial commenced. All of this was accomplished with no additional time devoted to the randomization process on the trial grounds. Try this or some adaption (of your own) at your next club or picnic trial.

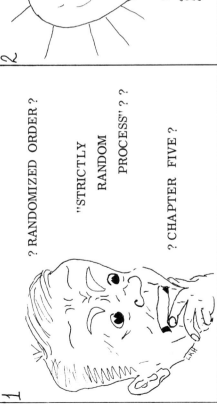

1

? RANDOMIZED ORDER ?

"STRICTLY

RANDOM

PROCESS" ? ?

? CHAPTER FIVE ?

2

3

Drawing by lot (strictly at random, *as McMahan says*) is easy! It really amounts to using several empty cigar boxes. Obtain one empty box for each handler with multiple entries. Get a few more boxes—determine how many more by dividing the number of handlers who have only one entry by the number of entries of the handler with the most entries. Take the handlers who each have one entry; divide them about equally among the "few more boxes."

4

Separate the handlers who have multiple entries each into his own cigar box. Randomize the entry forms within each of the boxes—those for single entry handlers and those for multiple entry handlers; then randomize the order of the boxes in a line. Choose one entry (form) from each box in sequence (say, from left to right), repeatedly (beginning with the left-most box containing entries each time). Make slight adjustment if needed—seldom necessary.

That's all, folks!

CHAPTER EIGHT

RETRIEVERSHIP EXPECTANCY

This chapter is concerned with the manpower pool of field trial retriever enthusiasts and the dogpower pool of open retrievers. In particular, it is concerned with (1) how long a retriever enthusiast can be expected to maintain membership in a particular American retriever club, and (2) how long an open retriever can be expected to maintain open retriever status in America.

One way of estimating the average "membership life" (or "average open working life" of a retriever) is by means of a tool called the "life table." The usual or standard life table is a demographic or actuarial device (really a bookkeeping device) for summarizing the "mortality experience" of a population or group during a specified period of time (usually a short period). The life-table technique has been applied widely--from estimating working life to estimating the "life of an automobile"; in fact, the life table is a useful tool for various sorts of follow-up studies.

Background Material on the Life Table

Even though the material of this chapter can probably be understood without examining the anatomy of a life table, a technical note is provided [Technical Note 8-1, "Selected Aspects of the Life-Table Method"] and I shall assume that the reader is familiar with it.

MEMBERSHIP LIFE EXPECTANCY

The membership of a retriever club may change year by year; it is well-known that members of retriever clubs (which sponsor field

trials) come and go. For illustration, suppose, for a particular retriever club, we concentrate on the year 1950, and examine membership rosters for 1949 and 1951 as well. In short, given three membership rosters of a retriever club as follows: membership, 1 January
1949; membership, 1 January 1950; and membership, 1 January
1951. Now inspect the roster for 1 January 1950; probably there
are names on the 1950 roster which were not on the roster for 1 January 1949; these are *accessions*, call them 1950 accessions. No
doubt some of these 1950 accessions were members of the club previous to 1950, but they had dropped out at least for the year 1949;
undoubtedly, some of the accessions for 1950 were members of the
club for the first time (truly new members) in 1950. If we compare
the 1950 roster with the 1951 roster, we shall probably find names
from the 1950 roster missing on the 1951 roster; we can call the
missing names *separations*. If we liked, separations could be classified as due to death or to other reason or reasons.

We shall go about finding out how long, on the average, a person
maintains membership in an American retriever (field trial) club by
using the life-table method. This method was chosen for good reason.
Explicitly, if we asked each member whose name appears on a current roster how long he had been a member, obviously our estimate
would be biased. [Why?] Moreover, we cannot interview all the separations, because some of them are probably dead and others probably cannot be located; some may even refuse to answer our questions.

Inasmuch as retriever field trial clubs are rather late-comers to
the American scene, to make a point, I shall make use of clubs devoted to American bird dog field trials.

Bird dog field trial devotees.--The American Field was established
in 1874; suppose that we obtained the membership roster of every
bird dog field trial club in the United States for 1874 and identified
the new members. Now if it were possible to determine for each and
every one of these new bird dog devotees the specific years each was
a member of a field trial club during his remaining lifetime, we could

A color print of a painting by A. Pope, Jr. (1880), in the author's private Pontchippi Collection.

SUSSEX SPANIEL RETRIEVING PHEASANT

An old signed print by G. Vernon Stokes in the author's private Pontchippi Collection.

construct a "cohort" membership life table (because it is reasonably certain that all of these devotees are no longer active members--1967). To elaborate, we could obtain the number of years that each new devotee of 1874 was a member of a club as long as he lived. By totalling the number of years of membership for each such devotee and dividing by the total number of new devotees on club membership rosters in 1874, an average expectation of "club membership life of new devotees" of 1874 could be calculated.

In shorthand, we can let the number of (whole) years that bird dog devotee number 1 was a member of a club be denoted BDD_1; the number of years (integer) that bird dog devotee number 2 was a member of a club would be denoted by BDD_2; ...; and the number of years (integer) that bird dog devotee number n was a member of a club would be denoted BDD_n. Also we can let the number of new bird dog devotees in 1874 be denoted by n. Clearly then, the average expectation of membership life, call it e_x, for these n new bird dog devotees of 1874 can be calculated as follows:

$$e_x = \frac{BDD_1 + BDD_2 + \ldots + BDD_n}{n}.$$

[*Aside:* Reference Technical Note 8-1: Because membership is usually for a complete year, say, for a calendar year, a person is assumed to be either on the roster on January 1 or he was dropped from the roster as of the immediately preceding December 31. Hence, the concept of curtate expectation of life, e_x, appears appropriate.] For most groups, the construction of such a table as described above is impracticable. Furthermore, the results would only have historical significance and would be of little use for predictive purposes. In lieu of such a table, it is preferred to calculate a "current" membership life table. In the preparation of a current table, it is conventional to apply an average attrition rate observed over a period of years to a hypothetical cohort, usually 1,000. Such a table answers the question of what membership life expectancy would be if the observed separation rates remained constant. Thus, unlike the cohort membership life table, no individual is actually "exposed" throughout his lifetime to the attrition rates used in a current table.

A knowledge of exposure to risk is mandatory before valid conclusions can be drawn concerning the experience of persons assigned to certain categories or marked by some characteristic. For example, survival is uncertain. Each of us is continually exposed to some chance of dying, but it is uncertain as to the exact day that death will occur even though it is certain that death will eventually occur. The degree of the uncertainty is the risk; probability measures that uncertainty or risk; in particular, the proportion dying is a quantitative measure of that risk and any particular value may be called a "mortality rate."

Membership in a retriever field trial club is uncertain. Instead of a mortality rate, we are concerned with a separation rate which, obviously, includes mortality but other causes as well.

Person-year.--In follow-up studies using the actuarial approach, the experience of each individual is utilized for the time he is actually under observation and for that time only. His experience in the study is transformed into person-years, where a person-year is defined as the experience of one person for one calendar year.

In computing exposed to risk in terms of person-years, care must be exercised that all possibilities are taken into account.

Length of membership life of American retriever enthusiasts.--Suppose that I had a list of all American retriever clubs which had been in continuous operation for the 9 years 1959-1967. Further suppose that I selected 10 clubs strictly at random from that list. If we had a membership roster as of January 1 for each club for each year, we would have 90 rosters. We could use these 90 rosters to estimate (within certain restrictions) the expected length of membership life in American retriever clubs. In short, we could make an inference concerning membership life of American retriever enthusiasts based on 9 years of experience.

Unfortunately, I do not have the foregoing data; I have limited data on one club only. As a consequence, the findings presented here are suggestive only, and clearly apply to members of one and only one club.

Hennepin County Amateur Retriever Club, Incorporated

One of the "strongest" retriever clubs that I belong to and have first-hand knowledge of is the Hennepin County Amateur Retriever Club, Incorporated (HCARC). Membership rosters were located for the years 1959, 1960, 1961, 1962, (not located for 1963), 1964, 1965, 1966, and 1967. I made certain estimates [see Technical Note 8-2, "Membership Life Expectancy"] to replace the missing data brought about by my failure to find the 1963 roster. Then, I computed a table of membership life expectancy for this club.

Data from the Rosters

A form was used to abstract data from the eight available rosters (Figure 8-1); cards were punched, estimates were made of the number of members in 1963 and numbers of "new members" for 1959, 1963, and 1964 (Technical Note 8-2); then each card was "corrected" and "updated" where required. Hence, data were available (within the limitations specified) just as though all nine rosters were in hand.

Continuous Membership Life

Initially, to simplify our problem, let's concentrate on members from the time they first appeared on our rosters until they first failed to appear on a subsequent roster. In other words, let's examine a lower limit, call it continuous membership life.

Recalling that the event of interest is first membership in HCARC, for purposes of follow-up, we shall concentrate on "new members" only for the 8 years, 1959-1966; this gives us a group of

$$\text{"71"} + 117 + 83 + 70 + \text{"70"} + \text{"39"} + 67 + 44 = 561$$

Membership-Life: HCARC , 1959-1967

Column number		
1- 4		Identification number
5-29		Record name as shown, omit punctuation

Year of membership (0) if absent (1) if present		Coded by	Checked by
30		1959		
31		1960		
32		1961		
33		1962		
34		1963		
35		1964		
36		1965		
37		1966		
38		1967		
79-80	85	Deck number		

Figure 8-1.--Form used to abstract data from available membership rosters for the Hennepin County Amateur Retriever Club, 1959-1967.

new members during the period.

New members, 1959 (71).-- As a first step, further concentrate on the 71 new members of 1959. For each of the 71 new members who was still a member in 1960, assign "1"; otherwise assign "0" because this member did not survive to the 1960 roster (1 year). Those who did not survive until 1960 are eliminated from further consideration because we are interested, for the moment, only in continuous membership from first entrance. For those remaining members (of the 71 in 1959) who were listed in 1960, assign a "1" if present in 1961; otherwise assign "0" because the member did not survive to the 1961 roster (1 year--from the 1960 roster to the 1961 roster). Continue the foregoing process (of examination and assignment) as follows: 1961 to 1962; 1962 to 1963; 1963 to 1964; 1964 to 1965; 1965 to 1966; and 1966 to 1967. To repeat again, explicitly for 1966-1967: Of the original 71 new members of 1959 (who appeared in all subsequent rosters 1960, 1961, 1962, 1963, 1964, 1965, 1966), assign a "1" if present in 1967; otherwise assign a "0."

New members, 1960 (117); ... ; new members, 1966 (44).--Repeat the foregoing process for the new members of each year, 1960, 1961, 1962, 1963, 1964, 1965, and 1966.

Now if we add all the "1's" of the 561 new members, we shall have the sum of the person-years of continuous membership, 917 person-years. If we divide this sum by 561, we have 1.63, which is an observed estimate of a lower limit of the average length of membership life since it represents only continuous membership.

The foregoing notwithstanding, we can obtain a better estimate of expected length of membership by using the life-table technique. We shall expect the life-table method to provide a larger number. [Why?]

Measurement of Continuous Survival After First Membership, HCARC

Results of examining the "complete data" from the nine rosters are shown in Table 8-1. The number of members entering the study,

Table 8-1.--Number of persons experiencing continuous membership in Hennepin County Amateur Retriever Club, Incorporated, for specified numbers of years after first joining the club, 1959-1967

Year entered	Number of members entering	Number remaining after specified elapsed number of years							
		1 year	2 years	3 years	4 years	5 years	6 years	7 years	8 years
(1)	(2)	(3)	(4)	(5)	(6)	(7)	(8)	(9)	(10)
1959	71	45	31	27	16	15	12	10	10
1960	117	71	54	31	28	22	17	15	---
1961	83	54	28	25	19	13	9	---	---
1962	70	63	19	14	10	7	---	---	---
1963	70	44	13	11	5	---	---	---	---
1964	39	34	26	21	---	---	---	---	---
1965	67	41	27	---	---	---	---	---	---
1966	44	30	---	---	---	---	---	---	---
Total	561	382	198	129	78	57	38	25	10

Note: Those members who entered, dropped out, and re-entered are included for their *first* (continuous) memberships only.

column (2), is shown by the year in which members entered, column (1). In addition, the numbers "alive" (meaning who continue membership uninterrupted) 1 year after first joining the club, column (3), 2 years after first joining, column (4), ... , and 8 years after first joining, column (10), are shown. Totals appear in the last row of the table; a total of 561 members entered the study (joined the club for "the first time"--as far as 8 rosters and our estimates indicate) during the years 1959-1966; the study terminated in 1967.

Computation of the probability of surviving.--Column (3) indicates that 382 members survived the first year after joining, where "survived" means "renewed their memberships"; thus, the relative frequency of survival from the date of first joining for 1 year after first joining is given by

$$R(\text{survival}) = \frac{\text{number who remain 1 year after first joining out of those new members who entered study (by first joining)}}{\text{number of members who entered study (new members)}}.$$

For discussion, let N be the number who entered the study and n_1 be the number out of N who remain 1 year later. Then the relative frequency of survival for 1 year, which for this example is treated as probability, is (in actuarial notation for probability of surviving) $p_0 = n_1/N$, where the subscript 0 indicates the date ("age of the follow-up period") of joining initially. Substituting the numbers at the bottom of column (2), Table 8-1, for N and at the bottom of column (3) for n_1,

$$p_0 = \frac{382}{561}$$

$$p_0 \approx 0.681.$$

Again, note the use of lower case p since actuarial notation is being used. Recall (from Chapter Seven) that the probability of dying (drop-ping out) is $q_x = 1 - p_x$; hence,

$$q_0 = 1 - 0.681$$
$$q_0 = 0.319 .$$

Thus, according to this experience, about 319 members of 1,000 "drop" (where drop means fail to renew their memberships) within 1 year after first joining the HCARC .

Probability of surviving the second year after initial membership. --
Of the n_1 who remain 1 year after first joining, the 30 who entered the study in 1966 were not observed during the second year. In other words, they were not exposed to the risk of "dropping out" under ob-servation in this study. Hence, the number of person-years observed (that is, exposed to the risk of dropping out under observation) the second year was $n_1 - 30$ or 352 . This concept of "exposed to risk" or "person-years of exposure" must always be taken into account in computing the survival rate. The probability of surviving the second year after first joining is

$$p_1 = \frac{n_2}{n_1 - 30} ,$$

where

> p_1 = probability of surviving from 1 year after (first) joining for 1 additional year (recall that the left subscript is understood to be "1" if it is omitted),
>
> n_2 = number who remain 2 years after joining, which is shown as a total in column (4).

Hence,

$$p_1 = \frac{198}{352}$$
$$p_1 \approx 0.562 .$$

Consequently,

$$q_1 = 1 - p_1$$
$$= 1 - 0.562$$
$$q_1 = 0.438 .$$

Probability of surviving the third year after initial membership, hereafter called joining for convenience.--Of n_2, that is, 198, who were still remaining 2 years after joining, the 27 persons who entered the study in 1965 were not observed for the third year after joining. They were not exposed to the risk of dropping out under ob - servation; as a consequence, they must be dropped for calculating the probability of surviving the third year after joining.

The probability of surviving the third year after joining in this study is

$$p_2 = \frac{n_3}{n_2 - 27} ,$$

where

n_3 = number who survived 3 years after joining, the total of column (5).

Substituting,

$$p_2 = \frac{129}{171}$$
$$p_2 \approx 0.754 .$$

As a consequence,

$$q_2 = 1 - 0.754$$
$$q_2 = 0.246 .$$

Probability of surviving the fourth year after joining.--In short-hand,

$$p_3 = \frac{n_4}{n_3 - \left[\begin{array}{l}\text{number observed } 3 \\ \text{years but not } 4 \text{ years}\end{array}\right]}.$$

Substituting from Table 8-1,

$$p_3 = \frac{78}{129 - 21}$$

$$= \frac{78}{108}$$

$$p_3 \approx 0.722;$$

and the complement,

$$q_3 = 1 - p_3$$
$$= 1 - 0.722$$
$$q_3 = 0.278.$$

Probability of surviving the fifth year after joining.--In actuarial symbols,

$$p_4 = \frac{n_5}{n_4 - \left[\begin{array}{l}\text{number observed } 4 \\ \text{years but not } 5 \text{ years}\end{array}\right]}.$$

From Table 8-1,

$$p_4 = \frac{57}{78 - 5}$$

$$= \frac{57}{73}$$

$$p_4 \approx 0.781.$$

The probability of dropping out after surviving 4 years, but before attaining the fifth anniversary of joining, is given by

$$q_4 = 1 - p_4$$
$$= 1 - 0.781$$
$$q_4 = 0.219 .$$

Probability of surviving the sixth year after joining.--Making use of Table 8-1, in even more abbreviated form,

$$p_5 = \frac{38}{57 - 7}$$
$$= \frac{38}{50}$$
$$p_5 = 0.760 .$$

The complement,

$$q_5 = 1 - 0.760$$
$$q_5 = 0.240 .$$

Probability of surviving the seventh year after joining.--Continuing,

$$p_6 = \frac{25}{38 - 9}$$
$$= \frac{25}{29}$$
$$p_6 \approx 0.862 .$$

Hence,

$$q_6 = 1 - 0.862$$
$$q_6 = 0.138 .$$

Probability of surviving the eighth year after joining.-- Continuing for the last year involved in this study,

$$p_7 = \frac{10}{25 - 15}$$

$$p_7 = 1.000 .$$

Clearly then, for this limited sample size,

$$q_7 = 0.000 .$$

Survivorship table.--By beginning with a radix equal to some arbitrary number, say, 1,000, the probability of failing to renew membership (dropping out) calculated in the foregoing paragraphs can be combined in the form of an abbreviated life table as in Table 8-2. [*Note:* No graduation procedure was used; reference McMahan.[1]]

From the ℓ_x column, it is clear that about 163/1,000 or 16.3 per cent of new members renew their memberships continuously for 5 years. In other words, the 5-year continuous membership rate (survival rate) for new members in this study was 16.3 per cent. Furthermore, we might reasonably expect to find about 1 of 9 members ($\ell_8/\ell_0 = 107/1,000$) who has 8 years of continuous experience after first joining this club.

Estimated curtate expectation of continuous membership after first joining.-- There are some rather serious methodological problems here, but we shall overlook them for convenience and assert that a lower estimate of continuous membership life for 8 years of experience (after first membership) can be computed from the following equation:

$$e_x = \frac{\ell_{x+1} + \ell_{x+2} + \ell_{x+3} + \ell_{x+4} + \ell_{x+5} + \ell_{x+6} + \ell_{x+7} + \ell_{x+8}}{\ell_x}$$

$$e_0 = \frac{681 + 383 + 289 + 209 + 163 + 124 + 107 + 107}{1,000}$$

$$e_0 \approx 2.063 \text{ years.}$$

A slightly more realistic estimate.--Obviously, some of the 561 new members of 1959-1966 dropped out and re-entered. The observed

Table 8-2. --Excerpts from a (continuous) membership life table based
upon 8 years of observation of new members (persons
who first joined), Hennepin County Amateur Retriever
Club, Incorporated, 1959-1967

Year after entrance	Probability of dropping out during each year	Number retaining continuous membership on each anniversary, of 1,000 new members (entrants)	Number dropping out during each year
x	q_x	ℓ_x	d_x
0	0.319	1,000	319
1	0.438	681	298
2	0.246	383	94
3	0.278	289	80
4	0.219	209	46
5	0.240	163	39
6	0.138	124	17
7	0.0	107	0
8	---	107	---

number of person-membership-years contributed by those who had
discontinuous membership was 50. Hence, if we add (unjustifiably)
50 to the 2,063 person-years of continuous (life-table) membership,
we get 2,113. Continuing, 2,113/1,000 = 2.1 years. Because, as
of 1967, there are some members in this club who were charter
members in 1943, 2.1 years is a slight underestimate.

Further comment on membership life expectancy and survival rates.--
Clearly, this membership life expectation does not reflect expected
productive work life. It is well-known that a very few dedicated RE's
carry the burden of a club and its activities. Nevertheless, these
survivorship rates do indicate the need for continued, vigorous re-
cruitment of "new blood." Moreover, these estimates do not reflect
retriever-happy families, for which only one name appears on a ros-

ter and major contributions are made by one or more other members of the family.

ACTION ITEMS

Item 1.-- Suppose that someone counted the names (each time a name appeared) in each roster from 1959-1967. He would find 2,488 names. Then suppose that he determined how many different individuals (different names) there were in these 9 rosters; he would count 810 different individuals. Further suppose that he made the following calculation:

$$\frac{2,488}{810} = 3.07.$$

Question: What does 3.07 mean?

Question: Why does one expect the life-table method to provide a more realistic estimate?

Item 2.--To that person or those persons who can locate a 1963 membership roster for HCARC: Replace the estimates in this study with known data; then re-calculate all probabilities and expectancies presented in this study of HCARC membership. Note how closely the "correct data" agree with the estimates presented here.

LENGTH OF WORKING LIFE FOR OPEN RETRIEVERS
IN THE UNITED STATES, 1954-1963

In order to determine the money value of a retriever, estimates are needed of the official duration of productive competitive life. It is a purpose of this section to construct tables of working life for retrievers taking into consideration accession into and attrition from the status of "open retriever."

Contrast this discussion of retriever working life with estimated membership life. Note carefully that I did not attempt to estimate expected working life of members, because I assert that many members "dead-head"--are really parasites or drones.

Definition of Open Retriever

Any retriever who was awarded a judges' award of merit (JAM) or who was placed in an open stake in a trial licensed by the American Kennel Club during the period January 1, 1954 through December 31, 1963, and whose name appeared on the annual listings of such retrievers published by *Field Trial News* is defined to be an open all-age retriever (for this study).

Problem

Analogous to the problem of estimating expected membership life, in order to accomplish the practical task of constructing a table of open working life, the probability of separation from the open working group must be estimated. A straight-forward estimate of this probability of separation may be obtained by means of a follow-up study. This can be accomplished by ascertaining the status of each open retriever on December 31 of each anniversary of the event of his classification as an open retriever.

Data

The source of the data for this study was the rosters entitled Open All-Age Placings published annually as of December 31 by *Field Trial News* for the calendar years 1954-1963, inclusive.

Limitations of the data.--Obvious duplication of information was deleted; however, no attempt was made to check for omissions. Variability due to spelling of names was adjusted when it was detected.

Terminology

Retriever-year of exposure.--In this follow-up study utilizing the actuarial approach, the experience of each retriever is utilized for the time the retriever is actually under observation and for that time only. A retriever's experience in the study is transformed into retriever-years of exposure, where a retriever-year is defined as the experience of one retriever for one calendar year.

Accessions to the working group of open retrievers.--For this study, a retriever could enter the open group but once each year; that is, when its name first appeared on the roster which had an "as of date" of December 31 for a specified year.

Separations from the working group of open retrievers.--For this study, a retriever could drop out of the open group only once each year, as of December 31. A retriever was considered as a separation if the retriever's name failed to appear on all subsequent rosters during the period of follow-up. This implies that a retriever which appeared on a roster for year t, but failed to appear on year $t + 1$, then appeared on the roster again at year $t + k$, would be considered an open retriever during year $t + 1$ and all other intervening years up to and including year $t + k$.

Complete expectation of open working life.-- The average number of complete years of future ribbon-getting life in the open (stake) for retrievers with x years in the open (stake) is called the expectation of open working life at age x.

Curtate expectation of open working life.--When it is assumed that all dropouts (separations) that occur in any year occur at the very instant at which that year begins, it leads to the so-called curtate expectation of open working life. Such a computation neglects the fractional parts of years lived by those retrievers who drop out in any year (see later discussion).

Table of Open Working Life

A table of working life follows, through successive ages, the experience of an initial cohort of, say, ℓw_0 open retrievers (in this study, $\ell w_0 = 1,000$). The table shows the attrition which might be expected if the observed rates remain unchanged; in addition, it indicates the average expectation of open working life. [See Technical Note 8-3, "Cohort Table of Open Working Life."]

Working Life-Table Functions

In order to emphasize working life, notation has been adopted using w; for the most part, this amounts to adding a w to earlier notation used in this chapter. Let

x = precise age in years (elapsed time since the retriever attained the status of open retriever) of the individuals in the group. The symbol (x) is used to represent an open retriever aged x.

ℓw_x = number in the open group at beginning of year (of age x).

pw_x = probability that (x) will remain in the open group for 1 year, to age x + 1.

qw_x = $1 - pw_x$ = probability of being separated from the group of open retrievers before the attainment of age x + 1.

If ℓw_x denotes the number of retrievers who according to the table of working life attain precise age x in any year of time, and if qw_x is the probability that (x) will be separated from the group between ages x and x + 1, it follows that

$$dw_x = (\ell w_x) \times (qw_x),$$

where dw_x is the number of separations.

Further let

Lw_x = $0.5 (\ell w_x + \ell w_{x+1})$. Note the capital L; this is really the number of retriever-years in the hypothetical open retriever group in the year of age x.

Tw_x = $\sum_{n=0}^{w} Lw_{x+n}$. Note the capital T and capital L; this is really the total number of retriever-years in the hypothetical open retriever group in the given year and all following years for retrievers in the open group at the exact year of age.

As a reminder, it should be clear that the expectation of open working life is merely a common average (an arithmetic mean), where the denominator is ℓw_x; and the number (in the numerator) is the sum of

> (those retrievers who obtained an open ribbon during the first calendar year after attaining known open retriever status)

> +   (those retrievers who obtained an open ribbon during the second calendar year after attaining known open retriever status)

> +   (those retrievers who obtained an open ribbon during the third calendar year after attaining known open retriever status)

> +   ...

> +   (those retrievers who obtained an open ribbon during calendar year ω--the Greek letter omega--after attaining known open retriever status).

If ew_x (read "e-double-u sub-x") denotes the curtate expectation of open working life, it follows from the above that

$$ew_x = \frac{\ell w_{x+1} + \ell w_{x+2} + \ell w_{x+3} + \ldots + \ell w_{\omega}}{\ell w_x} .$$

Measurement of Survival of Open Status

Results of examining the rosters (entitled Open All-Age Placings) for retrievers having been awarded a JAM or place are shown in Tables 8-3 and 8-4. Three retrievers of 567 had an observed (curtate) working life of 7 or more years. Results of follow-up for 8 years are shown in abbreviated (work) life-table form in Table 8-5. Estimated curtate retriever work life expectancy after attaining open status follows:

$$ew_0 = \frac{665 + 551 + 416 + 283 + 194 + 88 + 15 + 7}{1,000}$$

$$ew_0 = \frac{2,219}{1,000} = 2.22 .$$

Table 8-3. --Number of retrievers surviving for specified numbers of years after attaining open status, 567 retrievers, "licensed" American field trials, 1955-1963

Year entered study	Number of retrievers classified as attaining open status (entering study)	Number classified as maintaining open status on each anniversary							
		1956	1957	1958	1959	1960	1961	1962	1963
1955	65	45	40	29	23	17	7	2	1
1956	65	---	36	29	23	15	11	5	0
1957	69	---	---	55	45	34	20	14	7
1958	73	---	---	---	46	38	27	18	10
1959	60	---	---	---	---	41	36	28	20
1960	72	---	---	---	---	---	57	49	38
1961	80	---	---	---	---	---	---	48	35
1962	83	---	---	---	---	---	---	---	49

Table 8-4.--(Rearrangement of data in Table 8-3) Number of retrievers surviving for specified numbers of years after attaining open status, 567 retrievers, "licensed" American field trials, 1955-1963

Year entered study	Number of retrievers classified as attaining open status (entering study)	Number classified as maintaining open status on each anniversary							
		1 year	2 years	3 years	4 years	5 years	6 years	7 years	8 years
1955	65	45	40	29	23	17	7	2	1
1956	65	36	29	23	15	11	5	0	---
1957	69	55	45	34	20	14	7	---	---
1958	73	46	38	27	18	10	---	---	---
1959	60	41	36	28	20	---	---	---	---
1960	72	57	49	38	---	---	---	---	---
1961	80	48	35	---	---	---	---	---	---
1962	83	49	---	---	---	---	---	---	---
Total	567	377	272	179	96	52	19	2	1

Table 8-5.--Excerpts from a work life table based upon 8 years of observation of American retrievers attaining open status, 1955-1963

Year after attaining open status	Probability of maintaining (surviving) open status each year	Probability of losing open status in each year	Number retaining open status on each anniversary, of 1,000 open retrievers	Number dropping from open status during each year
x	pw_x	qw_x	ℓw_x	dw_x
0	0.665	0.335	1,000	335
1	0.829	0.171	665	114
2	0.755	0.245	551	135
3	0.681	0.319	416	133
4	0.684	0.316	283	89
5	0.452	0.548	194	106
6	0.167	0.833	88	73
7	0.500	0.500	15	8
8	0.000	1.000	7	7

Other estimates of open working life of the American retriever, by type of award, are shown in Table 8-6.

Table 8-6.--Estimated (curtate) American retriever open working life, from time of attaining open status, by type of award received, licensed American field trials, 1955-1963

Category with regard to awards received (all categories are not mutually exclusive)	Estimated curtate working life from date of qualification as an open retriever in approximate	
	years	months
All open retrievers	2.22	27
At least one first place	3.87	46
Fourth place or higher	2.90	35
Never placed first	1.04	12
Only judges' award of merit	0.48	6

Back in 1965, I supplied an abridged version of a somewhat similar analysis (giving complete retriever open work life expectancy based on a different time period) to my friend, the editor of *The Field*, and asked the following question: Are such estimates available for British retrievers? He assigned the article to a member of *The Field* staff, the renowned Mr. F. Warner Hill, whose article is reproduced herein with permission (Source: *The Field*, February 3, 1966, page 193).

A RETRIEVER'S LIFE

An American survey is compared to British experience, and some deductions made about durability

JOHN GRAUNT, an exceptional layman, crudely approximated a table for measuring human longevity in his *Natural and Political Observations Made Upon the Bills of Mortality*, published in 1662, and Halley was the first (1693) competent scientific person to publish a life table from fairly current data. Such are the observations of Dr. C. A. McMahan in the introduction to a paper on *The Length of Working Life for*

Open American Retrievers, from which many of my later quotations on the field-trial position in America emanate.

Dr. McMahan is an enthusiastic and experienced field trialler who in private life is Professor of Biostatistics at the New Orleans Medical School, and the whole of his script bears testimony to the precision and solidity of qualified American diction. He explains that, because retriever trials are not conducted on natural game in the United States for a variety of reasons, one might expect that American retrievers would have a greater average working life than retrievers in Great Britain, and estimates of the average duration of competitive life in open stakes can be obtained from tables of working life for retrievers, taking into consideration accession into and attrition from the status of 'open retriever.' He thinks that not only are such tables interesting, but that they may be of assistance in estimating the money value of a retriever.

The Professor, in arriving at his tables and averages, includes any retriever which was awarded a judges' award of merit, J.A.M., or which was placed in an open stake in a trial under A.K.C. rules during the period 1954-63, and one whose name appeared on the published listings of such retrievers is considered to be an open all-aged retriever.

To accomplish the practical task of constructing a table of open working life, the probability of separation from the open working group must be estimated. A straightforward estimate of this probability of separation was obtained by means of a follow-up study. That is, the status of each open retriever on the anniversary of the event of his classification as an open retriever was ascertained. By employing an actuarial method, the experience of each retriever was utilised for the time he was under observation, and for that time only. Each retriever's experience was transformed into retriever-years of exposure where a retriever-year means the experience of one retriever for one calendar year.

The expected or average number of complete years of future ribbon-getting life in the open stake from the date of award of the first open ribbon is called the complete expectation of open working life. On this basis the estimated complete working life from date of qualification as an open retriever in the various categories is: All open retrievers 32 months. At least one first place 49 months. Fourth place or higher 39 months, never placed 18 months, only judges' awards of merit 12 months, and only three retrievers out of 716 had an observed working life of seven or more years. The question is asked: 'Are such estimates available for British retrievers?' For reasons which I will explain the answer is 'No.'

Since the seventeenth century, it has been common practice to use life tables not only for measuring the average length of human life and average working life, but for estimating longevity of other things both animate and inanimate, from insects to light bulbs. As a layman I have found myself more in sympathy with the bionicists than the self-styled geneticists, and have always cast a wary eye on the statisticians, and I would quote an instance.

A statistical expert on the Ministry which I happened to serve, with a beautifully sharpened Venus H.P. pencil, covered a quarto sheet with meticulous arrangements proving that a corn merchant was in credit to the extent of a considerable number of such mundane things as corn sacks. His figures were almost incontrovertible until in desperation I suggested we visited the merchant and actually saw the sacks in question. Now an ex-member of the Big Five at Scotland Yard, appointed enforcement officer of Ministry regulations in the particular area, knew full well that the sacks in question, through neglect, had become rodent riddled and burnt. Ultimately the figures won and the merchant was credited with non-existent sacks.

Supporting the practical against the theoretical it is well known that animal breeders of a low level in scholarship have beaten the theorists in the provision of winners, and thus I suggest that the practical approach to gundog work in this country does not lend itself to comparison with the more artificial work of retrievers in America.

When I first visited America I believe it was possible to run a trial on our lines on Fisher's Island on more or less wild pheasants. However, with the growth of the trial movement, to ensure equality of opportunity, and because of the wide expanses involved, pheasants were obtained from game farms, and planted for the trials. They were placed in a sack and whirled rapidly round, and this was known as 'dizzying,' and they were then gently fed into cover, where they would remain for an indefinite period. Where water tests were concerned hand-released birds were flown toward waiting guns. In case of failure a dead bird was floated on a small raft to be retrieved. In the latest report I have read concerning retriever trials game farm birds are released to the guns, and only dead birds are retrieved. There is an umpire present and, in case of doubt, a call of 'no bird' is declared, just as we have an umpire in claybird shooting to decide whether a clay has been properly expelled from the trap.

This certainly does provide equality of opportunity, but puts a premium on marking and super-fast retrieving with few if any points for scenting powers. In our country the simple out and back retrieve, whilst gaining points for marking, pick-up and speed and style in delivery, carries no stake-winning virtue, for this is something expected of every competing retriever. Top points go for the collection of a runner, denied our American contestants. It should be within the powers of a handler or gun, generally speaking, to walk out and pick up a dead bird, and this often happens at a trial where birds lie out on grass and are easily visible. Where retrievers pursue their natural bent in retrieving game beyond the capability of the individual, the merit of each performance is assessed individually by the judge of the day.

We realise that a wounded bird will travel as far as it can through the tightest cover, and lie up in the most impenetrable thicket to be found. Thus our retrievers in the course of a trial are subject to a more wearing experience than their American counterparts. Thus it is realised that hotted-up retrievers are the stake winners in America, and, when speed fails, they finish in the charts as competitors. In this country I am afraid too much emphasis is laid on speed also, and this type of runner, when relegated to the ordinary shooting field, is apt, without a separate handler, to run wildly out of hand.

On the other hand, there are many judges who will appraise a dog on its genuine game-finding qualities, and put him up against the speedy automaton. This is shown through a glance at retriever awards over the past two seasons. In the card for last year's retriever championship appeared a dog born in 1957, and this meant that he had won an open stake eight years later. Still running well was another born the same year, whilst another to run creditably at the season's trials was born in 1954.

At this year's retriever championship in 19 runners the average birth year was 1961, creating an average of 48 months against the American average of 32 months. Out of these runners one was born as far back as 1959. These comparative figures can apply only if our retrievers were competing in their first season, and as this information is not available to me, then the figures constitute a matter of interest rather than accuracy.

In America, through the scarcity of wild game, the pure form of retriever work is of little worth after a dog's competition life has finished. They prefer dogs of the German shorthaired pointer, the Vizla, the Weimaraner, the Brittany spaniel type which are jacks of all trades. In Britain the genuine field-trial retriever, apart from the hotted-up professionally handled runner, when he loses the initial speed of youth can become a useful adjunct to the ordinary shoot for many years. Thus we create a dual life for the retriever, non-existent in America, comprising a field-trial life and a normal working life. These can be superimposed each on the other to the extent that my answer to Professor McMahan must be as first declared, that there can be no international.

If one should still be sought, I would suggest the field-trial life of an American-owned retriever is comparable only to the competitive life of a retriever in this country, which is run exclusively at gundog working tests, and not at trials.

As to the value of a working retriever, in my opinion no table or chart could be of any assistance. It has been proved in this country that a beaten animal in many forms of competition will often achieve a much greater figure when sold than its victor. In a few months' time I shall be undertaking a tour of American shows, and it was originally suggested I should judge at field trials also. On second thoughts the sponsors, becoming aware of my approach to gundog work, consider it better that I attend the trials as a spectator, with perhaps judging appointments when I have assimilated the American outlook.

F.W.H.

[*Note:* The pictures published in this article are reproduced (with captions) on the following page.]

REFERENCE

1. McMahan, C. A.   *Life Tables for the Population of Georgia, by Color, Residence, and Sex, 1950-1951,* Atlanta: Georgia Department of Public Health, 1955.

A pittance of practice may be worth a tome of theory.

THE LABRADOR. Lord Rank's F.T.Ch. Scotney Crickleybarrow Pebble, the most consistent Field Trial winner of recent years, has kept his form over four successive seasons.

THE GOLDEN RETRIEVER. Mrs. Joan Hendley's Ch. Samdor Nimble Nick, ran in field trials in 1956. Ten years later he has still been working, having won more than 30 awards (apart from show prizes) in the meantime.

IRISH WATER SPANIEL PICKING UP GOOSE

An old signed print by G. Vernon Stokes in the author's private Pontchippi Collection.

SELECTED ASPECTS OF THE
LIFE-TABLE METHOD

The conventional life table is a particular method of presenting death rates experienced by a group or population during a specified period of time. Hence, in order to accomplish the practical task of constructing a life table, the probability of dying must be estimated; however, in order to provide a brief orientation to the life table, we shall assume some probabilities of dying and examine selected mortality functions more or less superficially. Selected excerpts from a hypothetical mortality table are shown in Table 8-1-1; note that the entries are shown in symbolic form in Table 8-1-2.

Table 8-1-1. --Numerical entries of a hypothetical (current) mortality table

Age x	p_x = probability that (x) will live to age x + 1	$q_x = 1 - p_x =$ probability that (x) will die between ages x and x + 1	ℓ_x = number of persons who attain precise age x	d_x = the number, out of the ℓ_x persons attaining precise age x, who die before attaining age x + 1
(1)	(2)	(3)	(4)	(5)
96	0.75	0.25	1,600	400
97	0.50	0.50	1,200	600
98	0.25	0.75	600	450
99	0.00	1.00	150	150
100				

Example.--If ℓ_x denotes the number of persons who according to the mortality table attain precise age x in any year of time, and if q_x is the probability that (x) will die between ages x and x + 1, it follows that $d_x = (\ell_x) \times (q_x)$ where d_x is the number of deaths. In particular, in the mortality

Table 8-1-2.--Entries, in symbolic form, of a hypothetical mortality table

Age x	p_x	q_x	ℓ_x	d_x
96	p_{96}	q_{96}	ℓ_{96}	d_{96}
97	p_{97}	q_{97}	ℓ_{97}	d_{97}
98	p_{98}	q_{98}	ℓ_{98}	d_{98}
99	p_{99}	q_{99}	ℓ_{99}	d_{99}
100				

tables above, how many persons reach age 97 but do not reach age 98?

$$
\begin{aligned}
d_{97} &= (\ell_{97}) \times (q_{97}) \\
&= (1,200) \times (0.50) \\
d_{97} &= 600 .
\end{aligned}
$$

Radix of the table.--The number 1,600 is an arbitrary number with which the table is started. It is called the radix of the table; in shorthand, in this table, it is denoted ℓ_{96}. It should be clear that the table can start with birth, the number born alive (ℓ_0), or with any convenient age.

Limiting age.--The limiting age of the table is denoted by ω (lower case Greek letter omega); beyond the limiting or final age, it is assumed that the entries in the ℓ_x column are zero. The limiting age of the hypothetical table (Table 8-1-1) is 99, $\omega = 99$. That is, the highest age for which $\ell_x > 0$ is denoted ω.

Meaning.--Any single entry in the ℓ_x column or the d_x column does not have meaning by itself.

Notation: The symbol $_np_x$ denotes the probability that (x), a life aged x, will survive n years. If n = 1 the left subscript is omitted; consequently, up to this point only the symbol p_x has been used. Let ℓ_x represent the number of persons who according to the mortality table reach precise age x in any year of time. Let ℓ_{x+n} represent the number of original persons who are alive at age x + n.

Example.--In Table 8-1-1, $\ell_{96} = 1,600$ and it is called the radix of the table. If x = 96 and n = 1, $\ell_{x+n} = \ell_{96+1} = \ell_{97} = 1,200$. Let d_x denote the number, out of the ℓ_x lives attaining age x, who die before attaining age $x + 1$. Hence, $d_x = (\ell_x) \times (q_x)$. The number who attain age 96 but die before attaining age 97 can be computed thusly:

$$
\begin{aligned}
d_{96} &= (\ell_{96}) \times (q_{96}) \\
&= (1,600) \times (0.25) \\
d_{96} &= 400 .
\end{aligned}
$$

The number who attain age $x + 1$ is given by

$$
\begin{aligned}
\ell_{x+1} &= \ell_x - d_x \\
\ell_{97} &= \ell_{96} - d_{96} \\
&= 1,600 - 400 \\
\ell_{97} &= 1,200 .
\end{aligned}
$$

If $x = 96$ and $n = 3$, $\ell_{x+n} = \ell_{96+3} = \ell_{99} = 150$.

The probability that a person aged 96 will attain age 97 is given by $_np_x = \ell_{x+n}/\ell_x$; however, since $n = 1$, the left subscript is not written out explicitly; hence, $p_x = \ell_{x+1}/\ell_x$, or

$$
p_{96} = \frac{\ell_{96+1}}{\ell_{96}} = \frac{\ell_{97}}{\ell_{96}} .
$$

Numerically,

$$
p_{96} = \frac{1,200}{1,600} = 0.75 .
$$

What is the probability that an individual aged 96 will die before age 97? The probability that (x) will die between ages x and $x + 1$ is denoted q_x. Obviously, if $p_x + q_x = 1$, then $q_x = 1 - p_x$. To answer the question,

$$
\begin{aligned}
q_{96} &= 1 - p_{96} \\
&= 1 - 0.75 \\
q_{96} &= 0.25 .
\end{aligned}
$$

From Tables 8-1-1 and 8-1-2 it can be verified that

$$
\ell_x = d_x + d_{x+1} + \ldots + d_{(1)} . \tag{1}
$$

Recall the definition of w; for this illustration, $w = 99$. To illustrate Eq. (1),

$$\ell_{96} = \sum_{i=x}^{w} d_i = \sum_{i=96}^{99} d_i ,$$

observe that

$$\ell_{96} = d_{96} + d_{97} + d_{98} + d_{99}$$
$$= 400 + 600 + 450 + 150$$
$$\ell_{96} = 1,600 .$$

Expectation of life. -- The average number of years to be lived in the future by persons now aged x is called the expectation of life. The expectation of life is computed under two different assumptions.

Curtate expectation of life. -- When it is assumed that all the deaths that occur in any year of life occur at the very instant at which that year of life begins, it leads to the so-called curtate expectation of life. Such a computation neglects the fractional parts of years lived by those who die in any year of life.

It should be clear that the expectation of life is merely an arithmetic mean where the denominator is ℓ_x and the numerator is the sum of

  (those who survive to the end of the first year)
+ (those who survive to the end of the second year)
+ ...
+ (those who survive to year w).

If e_x (read "e sub-x") denotes the curtate expectation of life, it follows from the above that

$$e_x = \frac{\ell_{x+1} + \ell_{x+2} + \cdots + \ell_{w}}{\ell_x} .$$

Example. -- The curtate expectation of life of a person aged 96, utilizing the data of Table 8-1-1, is computed as follows:

$$e_{96} = \frac{\ell_{97} + \ell_{98} + \ell_{99}}{\ell_{96}}$$

$$e_{96} = \frac{1,200 + 600 + 150}{1,600}$$

$$= \frac{1,950}{1,600}$$

$$e_{96} \approx 1.22 \text{ years.}$$

The curtate expectation of life of a person aged 97, utilizing the data of Table 8-1-1, is computed as follows:

$$e_{97} = \frac{\ell_{98} + \ell_{99}}{\ell_{97}}$$

$$= \frac{600 + 150}{1,200}$$

$$e_{97} \approx 0.62 \text{ years.}$$

Complete expectation of life.--Obviously, the persons who die in a year of life do not all die at the very instant at which that year of life begins. With some notable exceptions (one in particular is the very early years of life), it is reasonable to assume that the deaths during any given year of age are distributed throughout the year in a uniform manner. This assumption implies that the time lived by persons in the year of their deaths will average out to be one-half year. Consequently, the complete expectation of life, denoted by $\mathring{e}_x$, can be computed by adding one-half to the curtate expectation of life. Thus, $\mathring{e}_x = e_x + 1/2$. For the data of Table 8-1-1,

$$\mathring{e}_{96} = e_{96} + \frac{1}{2}$$

$$\mathring{e}_{96} \approx 1.22 + 0.5$$

$$\mathring{e}_{96} \approx 1.72 .$$

Next Steps

As indicated earlier, in order to accomplish the practical task of constructing a life table, the probability of dying must be estimated. An estimate of the probability of dying may be obtained by means of a follow-up study when the status of each individual is ascertained periodically for a specified number of years after the event of "interest" or until death occurs. If the assumption is made that the mortality rate remains constant over the follow-up period, data can be combined into life-table form.

In this chapter, the event of interest is the first membership roster on which an individual's name appears (or in the case of the retriever, when he first became an open retriever). Follow-up is performed by examining membership rosters (or reports of awards in licensed open stakes). In contrast to being concerned with death rates, we are concerned with attrition or separation rates.

$$R^3 \equiv \textit{(Retired Retriever Rocking)}$$

MEMBERSHIP LIFE EXPECTANCY

Membership rosters for the Hennepin County Amateur Retriever Club, Incorporated, were located for 8 of the 9 years 1959-1967; explicitly, the roster for 1963 was not located. This necessitated making estimates of the number of old and new members as well as the total membership for 1963. In addition, even though the total membership for 1964 was available, estimates had to be made (for 1964) in terms of old and new members. Furthermore, the total membership for 1959 had to be broken out in terms of estimated old and new members. Over and above the foregoing, new "names" had to be generated and actual members had to be assigned as to date of initial membership and/or appearance on a roster. This technical note describes the procedures for making the foregoing estimates, assignments, and estimated membership status of individuals.

Estimated total membership for 1963.--The total membership (M) for 1963 was estimated by linear interpolation as follows:

> membership in 1962, M_{62} = 318;
> membership in 1964, M_{64} = 246;
> estimated membership in 1963,

$$
\begin{aligned}
M'_{63} &= M_{64} + \frac{M_{62} - M_{64}}{2} \\
&= 246 + \frac{318 - 246}{2} \\
&= 246 + 36 \\
M'_{63} &= 282 .
\end{aligned}
\tag{1}
$$

Old and New Membership

Those members who appear in a roster for the first time during the period 1960-1967 (exclusive of the 1964 roster) are considered as "new members"; all other members are considered "old members."

Old membership.-- Known total membership and known new membership are shown in the unnumbered, untitled table which follows for selected years.

Year	Number of members	
	Total	New
1959	283	(not available)
1960	341	117
1961	307	83
1962	318	70
1963	(not available)	(not available)
1964	246	(not available)
1965	255	67
1966	240	44
1967	216	37

For the 6 years shown above (1959, 1963, 1964 excluded), $^{total}M = 1,677$ and $^{new}M = 418$. Hence, the proportion of a total (t) membership which is composed of completely new (n) entrants is estimated to be

$$\frac{^{n}M}{^{t}M} = \frac{418}{1,677} = 0.2493. \tag{2}$$

Clearly, the estimated proportion of a total membership which is "old" is

$$1.0000 - 0.2493 = 0.7507. \tag{3}$$

Number of old members in 1963.--Given $^{t}M'_{63}$, an estimate of the number of old (o) members is given by

$$^{o}M'_{63} = {}^{t}M'_{63} \times \left\lceil \begin{array}{l} \text{estimated proportion of a} \\ \text{membership which is old} \end{array} \right\rceil$$
$$= (282)(0.7507)$$
$$^{o}M'_{63} = 212. \tag{4}$$

Let $x = {}^{n}M'_{63}$, then

$$^{t}M'_{63} = {}^{o}M'_{63} + x.$$

Substituting,

$$282 = 212 + x$$

$$x = 70 \text{ new members in } 1963.$$ (5)

Survival rate of new members for 1 year or more.--The proportion of new members which survive to the next roster (1 year) can be computed from the data shown in the unnumbered, untitled table below. From the foregoing, the proportion surviving for 1 year is equal to

$$\frac{\text{sum of number ''surviving 1 year or more''}}{\text{sum of number ''entering (new members)''}} = \frac{196}{311} \approx 0.6302.$$ (6)

Year	Number of members	
	Entering (new members)	Surviving 1 year or more
1959	(not available)	(not available)
1960	117	71
1961	83	54
1962	70	(not available)
1963	(not available)	(not available)
1964	(not available)	(not available)
1965	67	41
1966	44	30
1967	37	(not available)

New and old membership for 1964.--Recalling that the 1963 roster was not available, the data indicated that there were 83 members who appeared for the first time in the 1964 roster. How many of these are really new members; that is, how many of these did not appear in 1963?

To obtain an estimate, let $y = {}^{n}M'_{64}$ = number of new members in 1964. We have an estimate of the survival rate of new members for 1 year; clearly then,

$$\begin{bmatrix} \text{number who appeared} \\ \text{for first time in 1964,} \\ \text{where 1963 roster not} \\ \text{available} \end{bmatrix} = \begin{bmatrix} \text{proportion} \\ \text{surviving} \\ \text{for 1 year} \end{bmatrix} \begin{bmatrix} \text{number of} \\ \text{new members} \\ \text{in 1963} \end{bmatrix} + y$$

$$\begin{bmatrix} \text{number who appeared} \\ \text{for first time in 1964,} \\ \text{where 1963 roster not} \\ \text{available} \end{bmatrix} = (0.6302)x + y. \tag{7}$$

There were 83 apparently new entrants in 1964; substituting 83 and $x = 70$, we have

$$83 = (0.6302)(70) + y$$
$$y = 39. \tag{8}$$

Therefore, we estimate that there were 39 new members for 1964.

Old and new membership of 1959.-- Assuming that 0.7507 [Eq. (3)] of a membership is old, it is estimated that there were 212 old members and 71 new members in 1959.

Total Membership, Old and New

Making use of known data and the foregoing estimates, the unnumbered, untitled table below indicates old and new membership, 1959-1967.

Year	Number of members		
	Total	Old	New
1959	283	212 (est)	71 (est)
1960	341	224	117
1961	307	224	83
1962	318	248	70
1963	282 (est)	212 (est)	70 (est)
1964	246	207 (est)	39 (est)
1965	255	188	67
1966	240	196	44
1967	216	179	37

PROBLEMS OF DETERMINING MEMBERSHIP
STATUS OF INDIVIDUALS

Up to this point, we have been concerned only with numbers of members; however, in order to measure "membership life expectancy," data are required on individuals. In short, we need to estimate the 1959 and 1963 old and new membership by name. In order to accomplish this task, it is convenient to make use of the concept of sets.

General Comments on Sets

A collection of objects or things of any type will be called a set. For example, all female members of the HCARC for 1960 would constitute a set and each member of this group would be called either a member or an element of the set. For further discussion, see pages 56 through 59 of Chapter Four.

Application of Sets to the HCARC Membership Using Estimated Numbers for 1963

Let the universal set U consist of persons who were members for at least 1 year during the period 1959-1967.

$$n(U) = 810.$$

Example 1: Let A be the subset of U containing all persons who were members in 1959.

$$n(A) = 283.$$

Then,

$$n(A') = n(U) - n(A)$$
$$= 810 - 283$$
$$n(A') = 527 = \text{number of members who entered during 1960-1967}.$$

Let B be the subset of U containing all persons who were members in 1960.

$$n(B) = 341.$$

Now let

$$n(A \cap B) = 224 = \text{number of persons who were members in both 1959 and 1960; that is,}$$

$$n(A \cap B) = \text{number of "old" members in 1960}.$$

Also,

$$n(A \cup B) = n(A) + n(B) - n(A \cap B)$$
$$= 283 + 341 - 224$$

$$n(A \cup B) \ = \ 400 \ = \ \text{number who were members in either 1959 or 1960 or in both years 1959 and 1960.}$$

Also,

$$n(B \cap A') \ = \ n(B) - n(B \cap A)$$
$$= \ n(B) - n(A \cap B)$$
$$= \ 341 - 224$$
$$= \ 117 \ = \ \text{number of persons who were members in 1960 but were not in 1959; that is,}$$

$$n(B \cap A') \ = \ \text{number of "new" members in 1960;}$$

and

$$n(A \cap B') \ = \ n(A) - n(A \cap B)$$
$$= \ 283 - 224$$
$$= \ 59 \ = \ \text{number of persons who were members in 1959 but were not members in 1960; i.e.,}$$

$$n(A \cap B') \ = \ \text{number of 1959 members who "dropped" at end of that year.}$$

Example 2: Let C be the subset of U containing all persons who held continuous membership for the period 1959-1963 .

$$n(C) \ = \ 81 \ .$$

Let D be the subset of U containing all persons who held continuous membership for the period 1963-1967 .

$$n(D) \ = \ 87 \ ,$$

and

$$n(D') \ = \ n(U) - n(D)$$
$$= \ 810 - 87$$
$$n(D') \ = \ 723 \ = \ \text{number of persons who did not hold continuous membership in the years 1963-1967 .}$$

Also,

$$n(C \cap D') \ = \ 34 \ = \ \text{number of persons in set C who were not also in set D;}$$

$$n(C \cap D') \ = \ \text{number of persons who held continuous membership 1959-1963 but did not hold continuous membership 1963-1967 .}$$

Further,

$$n(C \cap D) \ = \ n(C) - n(C \cap D')$$
$$= \ 81 - 34$$
$$= \ 47 \ = \ \text{number of persons who were mem-}$$
bers of both sets C and D; that is,

$$n(C \cap D) \ = \ \text{number of persons in 1963 membership who held continuous membership for the years 1959-1967; more explicitly,}$$

$$n(C \cap D) \ = \ \text{number of persons who were members for the full period 1959-1967.}$$

Rules for Determining the 1963 Membership List

"Old" Membership.

1. Include all who were listed for 5 or more years. Let A_5 denote the subset of U containing all persons who held membership in the period 1959-1967 (1963 excluded) for 5 years only. Similarly, $A_6 \equiv 6$ years membership, $A_7 \equiv 7$ years, and $A_8 \equiv 8$ years. The number of members who are to be included in the 1963 roster under this rule is $n(A_5 \cup A_6 \cup A_7 \cup A_8)$. Because these 4 subsets are all mutually exclusive, we get

$$n(A_5 \cup A_6 \cup A_7 \cup A_8) \ = \ n(A_5) + n(A_6) + n(A_7) + n(A_8)$$
$$= \ 33 + 30 + 24 + 47$$
$$n(A_5 \cup A_6 \cup A_7 \cup A_8) \ = \ 134 .$$

2. Include all who were members for 2, 3, or 4 years, provided they were members in both 1962 and 1964. Let B_2 denote the subset of U containing all persons who held membership for 2 years only in the period 1959-1967 (1963 excluded) and who were also members in both 1962 and 1964. Similarly, $B_3 \equiv 3$ years membership, $B_4 \equiv 4$ years. The number of members who are to be included in the 1963 roster under this rule is

$$n(B_2 \cup B_3 \cup B_4) \ = \ n(B_2) + n(B_3) + n(B_4)$$
$$= \ 4 + 9 + 15$$
$$n(B_2 \cup B_3 \cup B_4) \ = \ 28 .$$

3. Choose at random 6 members from the combined sets who held membership during the years

(a) 1959, 1960, 1961, 1962;

(b) 1960, 1961, 1962;

(c) 1961, 1962.

Let C_2 denote the subset of U containing all persons who held membership for the years 1961 and 1962 only. Similarly, $C_3 \equiv$ years 1960, 1961, 1962 only, and $C_4 \equiv$ years 1959, 1960, 1961, and 1962 only. The total number of members from which 6 are to be selected randomly is

$$n(C_2 \cup C_3 \cup C_4) = n(C_2) + n(C_3) + n(C_4)$$
$$= 25 + 22 + 45$$
$$n(C_2 \cup C_3 \cup C_4) = 92.$$

[*Aside:* In the remainder of the discussion of the 1963 membership, the details in terms of set notation have been omitted.]

4. Choose at random 44 (i.e., 63 per cent of the 70 new members in 1962) from the set of 70 who were listed as new members for 1962. This gives us

$$134 + 28 + 6 + 44 = 212 \text{ "old" members for 1963}.$$

"New" Membership.

1. Make a list of 26 new names for members who will be listed for 1963 only (i.e., 37 per cent of the 70 new members in 1963).

2. Choose at random 31 (44 per cent of 70--44 per cent is the 2-year survival rate) from the set of 35 who were listed as members for 1964 only.

3. Choose at random 13 (of the 45) from the combined sets who held membership during the years

(a) 1964, 1965;   (8 of these)

(b) 1964, 1965, 1966;   (11 of these)

(c) 1964, 1965, 1966, 1967   (26 of these).

That is, choose 13 of the   45.

This gives us

$$26 + 31 + 13 = 70 \text{ "new" members for 1963}.$$

Application of Sets to the HCARC Membership Using Estimated
New Members for 1959

From Eq. (6) it is clear that approximately 63 per cent of new members survive for 1 or more years. Hence, 37 per cent of new members fail to survive; that is, appear in 1 roster only.

Because we had no rosters previous to 1959, the membership of 1959 was compared with the membership of 1960. The set which appeared in 1959 only was composed of 59 members (some of which were old and some of which were new). There was a total of 71 (estimated) new members in 1959; thus, there were (71) × (0.37) = 26 new members among the 59 who appeared in 1959 only. Hence, 26 names were selected strictly at random from the 59; these 26 members were estimated as having appeared in only 1 roster (1959) and were assigned to 1959 accordingly.

Clearly then, 71 − 26 = 45 members must be labelled "new" among those who appeared in 1959 and later years. These 45 were selected strictly at random from those who appeared in at least the 2 rosters 1959 and 1960; then these 45 names were assigned as being new members in 1959. The remaining 33 members who appeared in 1959 only were assumed to have been members during 1958 or some earlier year, but were not members during 1960.

Acknowledgment: Indebtedness is expressed (to E. S. and L. S. for nominating me for membership in the HCARC many years ago) to the membership of HCARC for use of the rosters for purposes of illustration, to selected individuals (particularly F. M. and F. M.) for assistance in trying to locate the 1963 roster and for insight into the history of the club. Obviously, none of these is responsible for the errors and shortcomings of the materials presented in Chapter Eight; those are monuments to me.

COHORT TABLE OF OPEN WORKING LIFE

A cohort table of working life for open retrievers follows the experience of an initial cohort of open retrievers, say, 1,000, through successive ages. The table shows the attrition in the form of observed rates; in addition, it indicates the average expectation of open working life at any specified age.

CURTATE EXPECTATION OF WORKING LIFE
FOR THE FINITE CASE

Consider an experiment that consists of following this large closed group of open retrievers, this cohort of 1,000, from the instant that each became an open retriever on January 1 of calendar year z to the instant that each was separated from the open group. The observation of interest is whether or not the individual retriever survives open status for a specified number of years, to a specified "age" x; that is, whether his name appears on rosters of open retrievers on January 1 of years $z + 1$, $z + 2$, $\ldots$, $z + k$. (It should be clear that age is elapsed time in years of open status; it is not chronological age.)

Separations from the working group of open retrievers.--A retriever was considered a separation if the retriever's name failed to appear on any subsequent roster during the period of follow-up. This implies that a retriever which appeared on a roster for year z but failed to appear on year $z + 1$, then appeared on the roster again at year $z + k$ would be considered as an open retriever during year $z + 1$ and all other intervening years up to and including year $z + k - 1$. Furthermore, observe that a retriever which appeared on a roster for year z but failed to appear on any later roster would have a survival time in the status of open retriever equal to zero. To elaborate, a survival time of zero implies that a retriever became a separation in the same instant that it became an accession.

Curtate expectation of open working life.--When all dropouts that occur in any year occur at the very instant at which that year begins (or when it is assumed that this condition holds), it leads to the so-called curtate expectation of open working life. Such a computation neglects the fractional parts of years survived in open status by those retrievers who drop out in any year.

Working Life-Table Functions

Let

x	$=$	the precise age in years (elapsed time since the retriever attained the status of open retriever) of the individuals in the group. The symbol (x) is used to represent an open retriever aged x.
ℓw_x	$=$	number in the open group at beginning of year of age x.
$_t pw_x$	$=$	probability that (x) will remain in the open group for t years, to age $x + t$.
$_t qw_x$	$=$	$1 - {_t pw_x}$ = probability of being separated from the group of open retrievers before the attainment of precise age $x + t$. When $t = 1$, it is not written explicitly; hence,
qw_x	$=$	probability of being separated from the group of open retrievers before the attainment of precise age $x + 1$.
ω	$=$	greatest age for which $\ell w_x > 0$.
μw_x	$=$	force of attrition at precise age x, 0 otherwise. Since separations can occur only at precise age x, it follows that $qw_x = \mu w_x$.

Note that the probability of separation is "piled up at points" as is shown in the figure below.

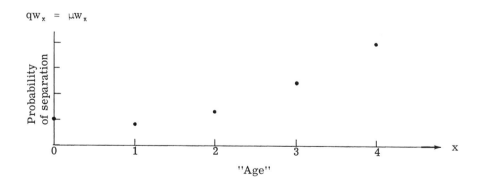

$qw_x = \mu w_x$

Probability of separation

"Age"

Interval of 1 year. -- If ℓw_x denotes the number of retrievers who according to the table of working life attain precise age x in any year, and if qw_x is the probability that (x) will be separated from the group between ages x and $x + 1$, it follows that

$$dw_x = (\ell w_x) \times (qw_x),$$

where dw_x is the number of separations. Furthermore, the number remaining in the group at age $x + 1$ is

$$\ell w_{x+1} = \ell w_x - dw_x.$$

If qw_x denotes the probability that (x) will be separated from the open
group before the attainment of exact age $x + 1$, it follows that $qw_x + pw_x = 1$ for all ages. This is the special case when $t = 1$; thus the symbol $_1pw_x \equiv$
(is identical to) pw_x. This is the probability that (x) will remain in the
group to reach age $x + 1$. Out of the ℓw_x retrievers in the cohort at age x
there are ℓw_{x+1} survivors at age $x + 1$; hence,

$$pw_x = \frac{\ell w_{x+1}}{\ell w_x}.$$

Curtate expectation of working life.--The average number of years to remain in the open group in the future by retrievers now aged x is called the
expectation of working life. Assuming that all attrition of any year takes
place at the very beginning of that year, out of an original group of ℓw_x retrievers at age x there will be ℓw_{x+1} retrievers who survive open status to
the end of the first year. A total of ℓw_{x+1} years of working life will be contributed during the first year following age x. Furthermore, the group will
contribute a total of ℓw_{x+2} additional working years during the second year
following age x; during the third year following age x, ℓw_{x+3} additional
years of working life will be contributed, and so on. By summing these whole
years and then dividing by the number of retrievers ℓw_x in the original group,
the average number of years to be contributed in the future by retrievers now
aged x can be obtained,

$$ew_x = \frac{\ell w_{x+1} + \ell w_{x+2} + \ell w_{x+3} + \ldots + \ell w_{(w)}}{\ell w_x}.$$

This is called the curtate expectation of working life because the fractional
parts of years contributed by those who separate in any year are neglected.

Example.--From the following abbreviated table of working life, it can be verified that the probability of remaining in the open group for 1 year if a retriever has been in the group 2 years is 2/3 since

$$pw_x = \frac{\ell w_{x+1}}{\ell w_x}.$$

That is, substituting x = 2,

$$pw_2 = \frac{\ell w_3}{\ell w_2}.$$

From the table, $\ell w_2 = 600$ and $\ell w_3 = 400$; hence,

$$pw_2 = \frac{400}{600} = \frac{2}{3}.$$

x to x + 1	qw_x	ℓw_x	dw_x	ew_x
0	1/4	1,000	250	1.90
1	1/5	750	150	1.53
2	1/3	600	200	0.92
3	5/8	400	250	0.38
4	1.00	150	150	0.00

The entry of 1.90 for the curtate expectation of working life at age 0 was computed as follows:

$$ew_0 = \frac{\ell w_1 + \ell w_2 + \ell w_3 + \ell w_4}{\ell w_0};$$

substituting from the table,

$$ew_0 = \frac{750 + 600 + 400 + 150}{1,000}$$

$$ew_0 \;=\; \frac{1,900}{1,000} \;=\; 1.90 \,.$$

Interval of t years.--The probability that (x) will remain in the open working group for t years, to age x + t, is denoted by $_t pw_x$, where

$$_t pw_x \;=\; \frac{\ell w_{x+t}}{\ell w_x} \,.$$

Hence,

$$_t qw_x \;=\; 1 \,-\, {}_t pw_x$$

$$ \;=\; 1 \,-\, \frac{\ell w_{x+t}}{\ell w_x}$$

$$_t qw_x \;=\; \frac{\ell w_x \,-\, \ell w_{x+t}}{\ell w_x} \quad \text{for } t = 1, \; 2, \; 3, \; \ldots \,.$$

For t = 1 and x = 0,

$$qw_0 \;=\; \frac{\ell w_0 \,-\, \ell w_1}{\ell w_0}$$

$$ \;=\; 1 \,-\, pw_0$$

$$qw_0 \;=\; \frac{dw_0}{\ell w_0} \,.$$

Definition: The curtate expectation of working life can be defined in terms of $_t pw_x$, where

$$ew_x \;=\; \sum_{t=1}^{\infty} {}_t pw_x \,. \tag{1}$$

If this definition is written out in detail for x = 0,

$$ew_0 \;=\; {}_1 pw_0 \,+\, {}_2 pw_0 \,+\, \ldots \,+\, {}_{\omega-1} pw_0 \,+\, {}_{\omega} pw_0 \,+\, \ldots \,+\, {}_{\infty} pw_0 \,.$$

Recall that $_t pw_x = \dfrac{\ell w_{x+t}}{\ell w_x}$, and substituting up to $t = \omega = 4$,

$$ew_0 \;=\; \frac{\ell w_1}{\ell w_0} \,+\, \frac{\ell w_2}{\ell w_0} \,+\, \frac{\ell w_3}{\ell w_0} \,+\, \frac{\ell w_4}{\ell w_0} \,.$$

Example.-- To verify the value $ew_0 = 1.90$ from the preceding life table,

$$ew_0 = \frac{750}{1,000} + \frac{600}{1,000} + \frac{400}{1,000} + \frac{150}{1,000}$$

$$= 0.750 + 0.600 + 0.400 + 0.150$$

$$ew_0 = 1.90, \text{ as before.}$$

Age at Separation as a Random Variable

Let

A = a random variable, observed age at time of attrition or separation from the open working group, equivalent to age at death,

and

Y = $A - x$, where x is a selected precise age (not a random value).

Then Y is a random variable which can take on only the values 0, 1, 2, 3, ... Since the curtate expectation of working life is the average age at separation, and since Y is the age at separation of each retriever, the mean of Y is the expected value of Y, where

$$E(Y) = \sum_{t=0}^{\infty} t \cdot P(Y = t). \tag{2}$$

The expression $P(Y = t)$ implies that a retriever must survive in the open group for t years and then separate in the next instant; hence,

$$E(Y) = \sum_{t=0}^{\infty} t \cdot {}_t pw_0 \cdot \mu w_t. \tag{3}$$

Equivalence of Equations (1) and (3) for $x = 0$.--It can be demonstrated that the sum of the numbers remaining at all ages greater than zero, divided by the number "alive" at age zero, is equivalent to the expected value of Y, age at attrition, for all retrievers remaining at age zero. That is, it can be shown that

$$\text{Equation (1)} = \text{Equation (3)}, \text{ for } x = 0$$

$$ew_0 = E(Y);$$

$$\sum_{t=1}^{\infty} {}_t pw_0 = \sum_{t=0}^{\infty} t \cdot {}_t pw_0 \cdot \mu w_t. \tag{4}$$

The right side of Eq. (4) is 0 when $t = 0$; thus, it follows that

$$\sum_{t=1}^{\infty} {}_tpw_0 \;=\; \sum_{t=1}^{\infty} t \cdot {}_tpw_0 \cdot \mu w_t$$

and

$$E(Y) \;=\; \sum_{t=1}^{\infty} t \cdot {}_tpw_0 \cdot \mu w_t .$$

Since $qw_t = \mu w_t$,

$$E(Y) \;=\; \sum_{t=1}^{\infty} t \cdot {}_tpw_0 \cdot qw_t$$

$$E(Y) \;=\; \sum_{t=1}^{\infty} t \cdot \frac{\ell w_t}{\ell w_0} \cdot \frac{\ell w_t - \ell w_{t+1}}{\ell w_t} .$$

Further Discussion of Age as a Random Variable

Consider an experiment that consists of following a cohort, a large closed group, of open retrievers, say, 1,000, from the instant that each became an open retriever to the instant that each was separated from the open group. Let the observation of interest be the age at attrition; the random variable is X, where X = the age at separation. The probability that the random variable X takes on a particular value is the probability that an open retriever will survive from age zero to age x, ${}_xpw_0$, then separate within the next instant, $\mu w_x dt$. If all 1,000 values of x are summed and then the sum divided by 1,000, this would equal the work life expectancy at age zero, denoted $\mathring{e}$, where also

$$E(X) \;=\; \mathring{e}w_0 \;=\; \int_0^{\infty} {}_tpw_0 dt .$$

Also,

$$\mathring{e}w_0 \;=\; \int_0^{\infty} t \cdot {}_tpw_0 \cdot \mu w_t dt .$$

Observe that $\mathring{e}w_0$ in a cohort table of working life is analogous to $\bar{x}$. One could make comparisons of $\mathring{e}w_0$ among groups utilizing the same assumptions for the distribution of $\mathring{e}w_0$ as for $\bar{x}$, say, $\bar{x} \overset{d}{=} N(\mu, \sigma_{\bar{x}}^2)$.

In this particular case of a cohort table of working life, but not in general for real populations, $\mathring{e}w_0$ is also equal to the average age at separation from the hypothetical open group.

Furthermore, $\mathring{e}w_0$ is equal to the expected value of X, E(X). If one considers (x) as receiving a reward of "1" for each complete year survived in the open group, the mathematical expectation for the whole of working life would be (the probability of surviving 1 year) $\times$ (reward of 1)

+ (the probability of surviving 2 years) $\times$ (reward of 1)

+ ...

+ (the probability of surviving $\omega - x$ years) $\times$ (reward of 1) + 1/2.

In symbols,

$$\mathring{e}w_x = pw_x \cdot 1 + {}_2pw_x \cdot 1 + {}_3pw_x \cdot 1 + \ldots$$
$$+ {}_{\omega-x}pw_x \cdot 1 + \frac{1}{2}$$
$$\mathring{e}w_x = \sum_{t=1}^{\omega-x} {}_tpw_x + \frac{1}{2}.$$

Other Random Variables and the Force of Attrition

Given a roster of 1,000 open retrievers on January 1 of calendar year z. Consider an experiment that consists of observing the survival of each of these open retrievers. The observation of interest is whether or not the individual retriever survives open status for a specified number of years, to a specified age x; that is, whether or not his name appears on rosters of open retrievers on January 1 of years z + 1, z + 2, ..., z + k.

The random variable ℓw_x.--Let the observation of interest be the number of retrievers surviving open status at age x; the random variable is ℓw_x, where

ℓw_x = number surviving in the open group at the exact instant that age x is attained for each member of the cohort.

Here ℓw_x is a random variable which takes on a value at a specified instant of time t. Age x is the simplest type of linear function of t, since x and t differ only by a constant when measured on the same scale. Furthermore, $0 \le \ell w_x < \ell w_0$ and the associated probabilities can be estimated from tables of working life. Note that the random variable ℓw_x cannot take on the value ℓw_0, because ℓw_0 in the work life table is the radix of the table, an arbitrary constant.

In this experiment, the radix $\ell w_0 = 1,000$, which is the number of newly classified open retrievers at time zero. The number of retrievers surviving in the open group at time t depends on the "age" of a retriever (where age refers to the length of time he has been classified as an open retriever). Now each retriever may drop out of the open group in the next instant after time t. If Δt is the size of that instant, then the number alive at $t + \Delta t$ depends upon the size of the instant and the age of the retriever as diagrammed below.

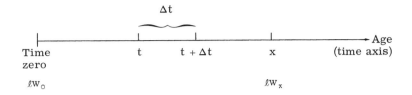

Consider the probability that a newly classified open retriever, aged zero, will survive to attain age x. Let us regard this probability as a function of x, and refer to it as the survival function $s(x)$. To be specific, over the interval $1 \le x \le 5$, let

$$s(x) \ = \ -0.125x \ + \ 0.790,$$

and

$$\ell w_x \ = \ s(x)k,$$

where $k = 1,000$.

$$\ell w_x \ = \ [-0.125x \ + \ 0.790] \times \ 1,000$$
$$\ell w_x \ = \ -125x \ + \ 790.$$

Differentiating ℓw_x with respect to x,

$$\frac{d \ell w_x}{dx} \ = \ -125,$$

which measures the rate of decrease of ℓw_x with respect to x. Let $x = 1$, then

$$\left(\frac{d \ell w_x}{dx}\right)_{x=1} \ = \ -125.$$

This means that at 1 year after attaining open status, at age 1, based on a radix of 1,000, ℓw_x is decreasing at the rate of 125 retrievers per year.

This figure depends upon the number of retrievers subject to the risk of attrition at age 1, namely,

$$\ell w_1 \ = \ -125(1) \ + \ 790$$
$$\ell w_1 \ = \ 665.$$

By dividing 125 by 665, an annual attrition rate at age $1 = 0.1880$ is obtained, a result independent of the radix of the table.

This attrition index is known as the *force of attrition* and is denoted by μw_x. It is defined as follows:

$$\mu w_x = -\frac{\frac{d\ell w_x}{dx}}{\ell w_x}.$$

Note that the definition includes a negative sign so that the force of attrition may be discussed as a positive force.

Other random variables. -- The variable ℓw_x, with the single exception of ℓw_0, and the following variables can be considered as random variables: $q w_x$, $p w_x$, $d w_x$, $L w_x$, $T w_x$, and $\mathring{e} w_x$.

OVER-DOGGED?

CHAPTER NINE

CHANGING A TEST

"Too Difficult"

Sometimes in a particular series (or combination of series), all or several of the first few entries fail the test(s). Soon many RE's, including the judges, are concerned as to whether or not the test should be changed. Referring to a single series for convenience, I use the following rule: I prefer to allow at least 3 official entries to try the test. If the first 3 entries fail, I may suggest that the test be changed; ... ; if the first 5 entries fail, I always try to have the test changed; and I may use other rules developed in this chapter. These rules are based on a strictly randomized running order (assumed). That is, not only should the published running order be random, but also I believe that, as far as is feasible, the entries should come to the line according to the listed (randomized) running order.

As a beginning, it is worthwhile to examine a real example.

Example. -- Suppose that in an open stake, the judges call back 18 retrievers for a "late" series, a tough triple mark of shackled duck on water. The judges estimate (hypothesize) that there should be about 10 "completions"; that is, they believe that about 8, or a proportion of about 0.44, will fail the test, and they assume that 10 of the retrievers are capable of completing the series. [In "acceptance sampling" language, this proportion "defective"--can't or won't complete-- on this test might be designated q, where q = 0.44.]

The test dog, an 8-year-old field champion fails the test. Then the first 5 retrievers which come to the line also fail the test. *Question:* Should the judges change the test?

Disregarding the test dog, what is the probability of a random sample of 5 entries failing the test if the true number capable of completing the test is 10 in 18?

We shall use the hypergeometric distribution (presented in Chapter Seven) to provide an answer. Let

N = 18 callbacks for this series;

r = 8, the number expected to fail this series (later we shall use k in place of r and define k = integer nearest to qN);

n = 5, the random sample of 5 entries which "happened" to be selected by a strictly random method to run early;

x = 5, the number of entries which failed the test, in the sample of 5 which ran early.

Hence, from Chapter Seven,

$$P(X = x) = \frac{\binom{r}{x}\binom{N-r}{n-x}}{\binom{N}{n}}$$

$$P(X = 5) = \frac{\binom{8}{5}\binom{10}{0}}{\binom{18}{5}}$$

$$= \frac{\frac{8!}{5!\,3!} \times \frac{10!}{0!\,10!}}{\frac{18!}{5!\,13!}}$$

$$= \frac{\frac{8 \cdot 7 \cdot 6 \cdot 5!}{5! \times 3 \cdot 2 \cdot 1} \times 1}{\frac{18 \cdot 17 \cdot 16 \cdot 15 \cdot 14 \cdot 13!}{5 \cdot 4 \cdot 3 \cdot 2 \cdot 1 \times 13!}}$$

$$= \frac{56}{8,568}$$

$$P(X = 5) \approx 0.0065$$

$$P(X = 5) < 0.01 .$$

This is less than 1 in 100, a rare occurrence; hence, by my definition (when we would expect only 8 of 18 to fail), the judges should change the test, although they can expect to change the test needlessly in about 6 in 1,000 series (in less than 1 series in 100).

[*Aside:* This example is based on an actual licensed qualifying stake; the type of test has been changed to protect the guilty.]

Comment: If the running order is not random and the (sample of) 5 entries to run "first" are "weak entries," then the judges would be taking action on a biased sample. Obviously, the randomized running order protects (over the long run) not only the contestants, but also the judges.

To be unmistakably clear, let's again examine the statement:

$$P(X = 5) < 0.01.$$

The judges must plan as follows before the test is run: For this particular example, if the true proportion capable of completing this test is approximately 0.56, then in less than 1 series in 100 series would we expect the first 5 dogs to fail the test. Hence, if we observe that the first 5 dogs do fail (x = 5), we shall take action as if a greater proportion than 0.44 would fail the test (if we ran it to its ultimate end). Consequently, we shall change the test; however, we recognize that we may be making a mistake (changing the test without cause), but we expect to be right in more than 99 series in 100. [For the reader who is not familiar with these ideas, see McMahan.[1]]

Since there is a vast bibliography on acceptance sampling, the remainder of this particular discussion is presented in "acceptance sampling terminology."

Acceptance Sampling

Let

N = lot size,

q = fraction defective,

n = sample size,

k = integer nearest to qN = number defective in lot of size N, x = number defective in a sample of size n.

P(x, n) ≡ P(N, n, k, x) = probability that exactly x defectives are found in the sample.

P(x, n) is the hypergeometric probability function, and

$$P(x, n) = \frac{\binom{k}{x}\binom{N-k}{n-x}}{\binom{N}{n}}.$$

As a special case when x = n,

$$P(n, n) = \frac{\binom{k}{n}}{\binom{N}{n}} = \frac{k(k-1) \ldots (k-n+1)}{N(N-1) \ldots (N-n+1)}.$$

Note that N is the number of entries that begins a series. If this is the first series in a stake, N is the number of actual starters; if this series is other than the first series, N is the number of callbacks to a specified series.

If k = true number of retrievers expected to fail a given series, note also that we are assuming that N − k retrievers are expected to be capable of completing the series.

Also, n is the number of retrievers we look at early in a series (our sample size) on which we make a decision concerning changing a test. My personal rule for changing a test which appears to be too difficult is to make a decision to change with 5 or fewer entries coming to the line; hence, I state the condition that n ≤ 5 for this situation.

Moreover, I shall endeavor to change a test anytime n ≥ 3 and

$$P(x, n) \leq 0.05.$$

Example. -- Suppose that we have 10 callbacks and expect 30 per cent to 34 per cent of the entries to fail the test; explicitly, let

$$N = 10, \quad q = 0.30, \quad k = qN = 3.$$

The probability that x entries fail of the first n entries which come to the line would be written P(x, n); continuing,

$$P(x, n) = \binom{3}{x}\binom{7}{n-x} / \binom{10}{n}.$$

The probability that the first entry will fail is the probability that of a sample of size one (n = 1), one will fail (x = 1); hence,

$$P(1, 1) = \binom{3}{1}\binom{7}{1-1} / \binom{10}{1}$$

$$= \frac{3!}{1!\,2!} \cdot \frac{7!}{0!\,7!} / \frac{10!}{1!\,9!}$$

$$P(1, 1) = 3/10 = 0.3.$$

We continue the test, because P(1, 1) > 0.05.

The probability that the first 2 entries will fail, that is,

$$P(2, 2) = \binom{3}{2}\binom{7}{2-2} / \binom{10}{2}$$

$$= \frac{3!}{2!\,1!} \cdot \frac{7!}{0!\,7!} / \frac{10!}{2!\,8!}$$

$$= (3 \cdot 1)/45$$

$$P(2, 2) = \frac{3}{45} = 0.07.$$

This probability is "borderline," but we stick with our rule and continue the test because P(2, 2) = 0.07, which is greater than 0.05; moreover, only 2 retrievers have come to the line.

The probability that the first 3 entries fail is

$$P(3, 3) = \binom{3}{3}\binom{7}{3-3}/\binom{10}{3} = \frac{1}{120} = 0.008.$$

We follow our rule and change the test because $P(3, 3) \leq 0.05$; P is actually less than 0.01.

Now suppose only 2 of the first 3 retrievers which come to the line fail the test. Clearly,

$$P(2, 3) = \binom{3}{2}\binom{7}{1}/\binom{10}{3} = \frac{21}{120} = 0.18.$$

$P(2, 3) = 0.18$ which is > 0.05; thus, we shall continue the test.

Now suppose that we get 3 failures in the first 4 retrievers that come to the line. We can calculate

$$P(3, 4) = \binom{3}{3}\binom{7}{1} / \binom{10}{4} = \frac{7}{210} = 0.03.$$

Since $P(3, 4) < 0.05$, we should change the test.

Suppose we get 3 failures in the first 5 entries that run:

$$P(3, 5) = \binom{3}{3}\binom{7}{2}/\binom{10}{5} = \frac{21}{252} = 0.08.$$

Run it! We may get into trouble, but we've looked at 5 entries; moreover, $P(3, 5) = 0.08$ which is greater than 0.05.

[Now continuing with this example, let's look at a situation where $x > k$; that is, we assumed k failures over the series in our model. What happens to our computations when we assign more failures to our sample than we assumed for our model? To illustrate, let $x = 4$, $k = 3$, and $n = 4$; clearly, $x > k$. Continuing,

$$P(4, 4) = \binom{3}{4}\binom{7}{4-4}/\binom{10}{4}.$$

Clearly, $P(4, 4) = 0$, because we can't take 3 things 4 at a time. Likewise, $P(4, 5) = 0.$]

Summary.--For this example with $N = 10$, if you have 3 failures in the first 3 entries coming to the line, or 3 failures in 4, change the test; otherwise, run it!

Next Steps

In the next several examples, we shall arbitrarily take selected larger values of N, and also vary values of q slightly (according to whim).

Example.-- In this situation, suppose we have 14 callbacks and we expect about 9 entries to complete a given series. Given $N = 14$, $q = 0.35$, $qN = 4.9$, so $k = 5$.

$P(x, n) = \binom{5}{x}\binom{9}{n-x}/\binom{14}{n}$		Action
$P(1, 1) = \binom{5}{1}\binom{9}{0}/\binom{14}{1} =$	$\frac{5}{14} = 0.36$	Carry on
$P(2, 2) = \binom{5}{2}\binom{9}{0}/\binom{14}{2} =$	$\frac{10}{91} = 0.11$	Carry on
$P(2, 3) = \binom{5}{2}\binom{9}{1}/\binom{14}{3} =$	$\frac{90}{364} = 0.247$	Carry on
$P(3, 3) = \binom{5}{3}\binom{9}{0}/\binom{14}{3} =$	$\frac{10}{364} = 0.027$	Change the test
$P(3, 4) = \binom{5}{3}\binom{9}{1}/\binom{14}{4} =$	$\frac{90}{1,001} = 0.09$	Carry on
$P(4, 4) = \binom{5}{4}\binom{9}{0}/\binom{14}{4} =$	$\frac{5}{1,001} = 0.005$	Obviously ...
$P(3, 5) = \binom{5}{3}\binom{9}{2}/\binom{14}{5} =$	$\frac{180}{1,001} = 0.18$	Carry on
$P(4, 5) = \binom{5}{4}\binom{9}{1}/\binom{14}{5} =$	$\frac{45}{2,002} = 0.022$	Change the test
$P(5, 5) = \binom{5}{5}\binom{9}{0}/\binom{14}{5} =$	$\frac{1}{2,002} = 0.0005$	Obviously ...

Summary.--When N = 14,   q = 0.35,   and   5 "defectives" are expected, test should be changed in the following cases:

P(3 , 3)   =   0.027 ;

P(4 , 5)   =   0.022 .

Reference the word "obviously" in the column headed "action." In order to have 4 failures in the first 4 entries that run, there must be 3 failures in the first 3 ; hence, we would have changed the test before we let 4 entries run. In short, the action is obvious.

The same reasoning follows for 5 failures in 5 . That is, in order to have 5 failures in the first 5 entries that run, there must be 4 failures in the first 4 ;   hence, we would have changed the test before we let 5 dogs run. In short, the action is obvious. In fact, these probabilities are given only to make the presentation complete.

ACTION ITEM

Explicitly write out the "*if* ... *then* ..." statements involved : Why not change the test after the first two dogs that came to the line failed ?

LKH

Example. -- Given 20 callbacks where you expect 14 entries to complete a series: $N = 20$, $q = 0.30$, $k = 6$.

$P(x, n) = \binom{6}{x}\binom{14}{n-x} / \binom{20}{n}$		Action
$P(1, 1) = \binom{6}{1} / \binom{20}{1}$	$= 0.30$	Carry on
$P(2, 2) = \binom{6}{2} / \binom{20}{2}$	$= 0.079$	Carry on
$P(2, 3) = \binom{6}{2}\binom{14}{1} / \binom{20}{3} = 0.18$		Carry on
$P(3, 3) = \binom{6}{3} / \binom{20}{3}$	$= 0.018$	Change the test
$P(2, 4) = \binom{6}{2}\binom{14}{2} / \binom{20}{4} = 0.28$		Carry on
$P(3, 4) = \binom{6}{3}\binom{14}{1} / \binom{20}{4} = 0.058$		Carry on
$P(4, 4) = \binom{6}{4} / \binom{20}{4}$	$= 0.003$	Obviously ...
$P(3, 5) = \binom{6}{3}\binom{14}{2} / \binom{20}{5} = 0.12$		Carry on
$P(4, 5) = \binom{6}{4}\binom{14}{1} / \binom{20}{5} = 0.014$		Change the test
$P(5, 5) = \binom{6}{5} / \binom{20}{5}$	$= 0.000+$	Obviously ...

Summary. --When $N = 20$, $q = 0.30$ (6 defectives), change the test when the following observations are made:

$P(3, 3) = 0.018$;

$P(4, 5) = 0.014$; otherwise continue the test.

Example.-- Suppose we have 25 starters (or callbacks) for a series; let q = 0.27, or 0.28, or 0.29 so that qN ≈ 7; even let q = 0.30 (give the entry the benefit of the doubt, round unconventionally), and use k = 7.

$P(x, n) = \binom{7}{x}\binom{18}{n-x} / \binom{25}{n}$		Action
$P(1, 1) = 7/25$	= 0.28	Carry on
$P(2, 2) = \binom{7}{2} / \binom{25}{2}$	= 0.07	Carry on
$P(2, 3) = \binom{7}{2}\binom{18}{1} / \binom{25}{3}$	= 0.16	Carry on
$P(3, 3) = \binom{7}{3} / \binom{25}{3}$	= 0.015	Change the test
$P(2, 4) = \binom{7}{2}\binom{18}{2} / \binom{25}{4}$	= 0.254	Carry on
$P(3, 4) = \binom{7}{3}\binom{18}{1} / \binom{25}{4}$	= 0.0498	Change the test
$P(4, 4) = \binom{7}{4} / \binom{25}{4}$	= 0.0028	Obviously ...
$P(3, 5) = \binom{7}{3}\binom{18}{2} / \binom{25}{5}$	= 0.10	Carry on
$P(4, 5) = \binom{7}{4}\binom{18}{1} / \binom{25}{5}$	= 0.012	Obviously ...
$P(5, 5) = \binom{7}{5} / \binom{25}{5}$	= 0.0004	Obviously ...

Summary.--When N = 25, k = 7, change the test as follows:

P(3, 3) = 0.015;

P(3, 4) = 0.0498; otherwise continue the test.

Example.-- Let N = 30 and k = 9 . What is q ?

$P(x, n) = \binom{9}{x}\binom{21}{n-x}/\binom{30}{n}$		Action
$P(1, 1) = 9/30$	$= 0.30$	Carry on
$P(2, 2) = \binom{9}{2}/\binom{30}{2}$	$= 0.08$	Carry on
$P(2, 3) = \binom{9}{2}\binom{21}{1}/\binom{30}{3}$	$= 0.19$	Carry on
$P(3, 3) = \binom{9}{3}/\binom{30}{3}$	$= 0.02$	Change the test
$P(2, 4) = \binom{9}{2}\binom{21}{2}/\binom{30}{4}$	$= 0.276$	Carry on
$P(3, 4) = \binom{9}{3}\binom{21}{1}/\binom{30}{4}$	$= 0.06$	Carry on
$P(4, 4) = \binom{9}{4}/\binom{30}{4}$	$= 0.005$	Obviously ...
$P(3, 5) = \binom{9}{3}\binom{21}{2}/\binom{30}{5}$	$= 0.12$	Carry on
$P(4, 5) = \binom{9}{4}\binom{21}{1}/\binom{30}{5}$	$= 0.019$	Change the test
$P(5, 5) = \binom{9}{5}/\binom{30}{5}$	$= 0.0009$	Obviously ...

Summary.--When N = 30 and k = 9 , change the test as follows:

$$P(3, 3) = 0.02 ;$$
$$P(4, 5) = 0.019 .$$

Example.--Now suppose we are given $N = 35$, $q = 0.20$, $qN = 7 = k$.

$P(x, n) = \binom{7}{x}\binom{28}{n-x}/\binom{35}{n}$		Action
$P(1, 1) = 7/35$	$= 0.20$	Carry on
$P(2, 2) = \binom{7}{2}/\binom{35}{2}$	$= 0.035$	Carry on*
$P(2, 3) = \binom{7}{2}\binom{28}{1}/\binom{35}{3}$	$= 0.09$	Carry on
$P(3, 3) = \binom{7}{3}/\binom{35}{3}$	$= 0.0053$	Obviously ...
$P(2, 4) = \binom{7}{2}\binom{28}{2}/\binom{35}{4}$	$= 0.15$	Carry on
$P(3, 4) = \binom{7}{3}\binom{28}{1}/\binom{35}{4}$	$= 0.019$	Change the test
$P(4, 4) = \binom{7}{4}/\binom{35}{4}$	$= 0.0007$	Obviously ...
$P(3, 5) = \binom{7}{3}\binom{28}{2}/\binom{35}{5}$	$= 0.024$	Change the test
$P(4, 5) = \binom{7}{4}\binom{28}{1}/\binom{35}{5}$	$= 0.003$	Obviously ...
$P(5, 5) = \binom{7}{5}/\binom{35}{5}$	$= 0.00006$	Obviously ...

* Carry on because 3 entries have not been tested.

Summary.--Consider changing the test if the first 2 entries fail; change the test if any 3 in the first 5 fail, because

$P(2, 2) = 0.035$ (consider);
$P(3, 4) = 0.019$;
$P(3, 5) = 0.024$.

Example.--Given $N = 40$, $q = 0.20$, and $k = 8$.

$P(x, n) = \binom{8}{x}\binom{32}{n-x} / \binom{40}{n}$		Action
$P(1, 1) = 8/40$	$= 0.20$	Carry on
$P(1, 2) = \binom{8}{1}\binom{32}{1} / \binom{40}{2}$	$= 0.33$	Carry on
$P(2, 2) = \binom{8}{2} / \binom{40}{2}$	$= 0.036$	Carry on*
$P(2, 3) = \binom{8}{2}\binom{32}{1} / \binom{40}{3}$	$= 0.09$	Carry on
$P(3, 3) = \binom{8}{3} / \binom{40}{3}$	$= 0.006$	Obviously ...
$P(2, 4) = \binom{8}{2}\binom{32}{2} / \binom{40}{4}$	$= 0.07$	Carry on
$P(3, 4) = \binom{8}{3}\binom{32}{1} / \binom{40}{4}$	$= 0.02$	Change the test
$P(4, 4) = \binom{8}{4} / \binom{40}{4}$	$= 0.0008$	Obviously ...
$P(3, 5) = \binom{8}{3}\binom{32}{2} / \binom{40}{5}$	$= 0.042$	Change the test
$P(4, 5) = \binom{8}{4}\binom{32}{1} / \binom{40}{5}$	$= 0.003$	Obviously ...
$P(5, 5) = \binom{8}{5} / \binom{40}{5}$	$= 0.00008$	Obviously ...

* Carry on because 3 entries have not been tested.

Summary.-- When $N = 40$ and $k = 8$, consider changing the test when

$P(2, 2) = 0.036$; and change the test when
$P(3, 4) = 0.02$;
$P(3, 5) = 0.04$.

Example.-- Given $N = 50$, $q = 0.20$; hence, $k = 10$.

$P(x,\ n) = \binom{10}{x}\binom{40}{n-x}/\binom{50}{n}$		Action
$P(1,\ 1) = 10/50$	$= 0.20$	Carry on
$P(1,\ 2) = \binom{10}{1}\binom{40}{1}/\binom{50}{2}$	$= 0.33$	Carry on
$P(2,\ 2) = \binom{10}{2}/\binom{50}{2}$	$= 0.037$	Carry on*
$P(2,\ 3) = \binom{10}{2}\binom{40}{1}/\binom{50}{3}$	$= 0.12$	Carry on
$P(3,\ 3) = \binom{10}{3}/\binom{50}{3}$	$= 0.006$	Obviously ...
$P(2,\ 4) = \binom{10}{2}\binom{40}{2}/\binom{50}{4}$	$= 0.15$	Carry on
$P(3,\ 4) = \binom{10}{3}\binom{40}{1}/\binom{50}{4}$	$= 0.02$	Change the test
$P(4,\ 4) = \binom{10}{4}/\binom{50}{4}$	$= 0.0009$	Obviously ...
$P(3,\ 5) = \binom{10}{3}\binom{40}{2}/\binom{50}{5}$	$= 0.044$	Change the test
$P(4,\ 5) = \binom{10}{4}\binom{40}{1}/\binom{50}{5}$	$= 0.004$	Obviously ...
$P(5,\ 5) = \binom{10}{5}/\binom{50}{5}$	$= 0.0001$	Obviously ...

* Carry on because 3 entries have not been tested.

Summary.-- When $N = 50$ and $k = 10$, consider changing the test when

$$P(2,\ 2) = 0.037;\ \text{and change the test when}$$
$$P(3,\ 4) = 0.02;$$
$$P(3,\ 5) = 0.044.$$

Example.-- Given $N = 60$, $q = 0.20$; hence, $k = 12$.

$P(x, n) = \binom{12}{x}\binom{48}{n-x}/\binom{60}{n}$		Action
$P(1, 1) = \binom{12}{1}/\binom{60}{1}$	$= 0.20$	Carry on
= probability that first entry sampled is defective, given that there are 12 defective in the lot		
$P(1, 2) = \binom{12}{1}\binom{48}{1}/\binom{60}{2}$	$= 0.33$	Carry on
= probability that 1 of the first 2 sampled is defective		
$P(2, 2) = \binom{12}{2}/\binom{60}{2}$	$= 0.037$	Carry on*
= probability that first 2 sampled are defective		
$P(2, 3) = \binom{12}{2}\binom{48}{1}/\binom{60}{3}$	$= 0.09$	Carry on
$P(3, 3) = \binom{12}{3}/\binom{60}{3}$	$= 0.006$	Obviously ...
$P(2, 4) = \binom{12}{2}\binom{48}{2}/\binom{60}{4}$	$= 0.16$	Carry on
$P(3, 4) = \binom{12}{3}\binom{48}{1}/\binom{60}{4}$	$= 0.02$	Change the test
$P(4, 4) = \binom{12}{4}/\binom{60}{4}$	$= 0.001$	Obviously ...
$P(3, 5) = \binom{12}{3}\binom{48}{2}/\binom{60}{5}$	$= 0.046$	Change the test
$P(4, 5) = \binom{12}{4}\binom{48}{1}/\binom{60}{5}$	$= 0.004$	Obviously ...
$P(5, 5) = \binom{12}{5}/\binom{60}{5}$	$= 0.0001$	Obviously ...

* Carry on because 3 entries have not been tested.

Summary.--When $N = 60$, $q = 0.20$, $n \le 5$, consider changing the test when

$P(2, 2) = 0.037$; and change the test when

$P(3, 4) = 0.02$;

$P(3, 5) = 0.046$.

Note that you consider changing the test if the first 2 dogs fail. Is this surprising to you? Why?

For Consideration

In order to provide convenient guidance for changing a test, Table 9-1 was prepared. Using this table, a judge would expect to unjustifiably change his test 1 time in 20 (0.05 level).

$N.B.$ -- In the model being used, the number of failures x cannot exceed k, $x \le k$. To illustrate, in the first "panel" of Table 9-1, N = 10, k = 2, and q = 0.20; hence, $x \le 2$. Clearly then in an actual test, if the first 3 entries failed the test, the judge would conclude that the test was too difficult (more than 1/5 of the entries would be expected to fail the test).

Two Series Combined, Another Example

Given a stake where there is a combination of two series, say, a double mark on land (series three) and a double blind (series four). Given N = 30 for series three, with q = 0.20 for series three and q = 0.30 for series four. What are the rules for changing the tests? What are the assumptions if we use the hypergeometric model? Must we change our assumptions?

Solution: For series three we have N = 30 and k = 6. See worksheet on page 384.

Frequently, in a combined series, such as series three and series four, retrievers are permitted to continue on to series four only by "invitation" of the judges. Clearly, a retriever would be invited to series four if, and only if, he had "satisfactorily passed" the test in series three. Now, as before, the test for series three should be considered for change if the first 2 retrievers fail the test, and should be changed if 3 retrievers in the first 5 tested fail the test. As-

Table 9-1.--Guidance at the 0.05 level for continuing or changing a test, selected values of N, k, and q

N = 10 k = 2 q = 0.20			Action
P(0, 1)	=	0.80000	Carry on
P(1, 1)	=	0.20000	Carry on
P(0, 2)	=	0.62222	Carry on
P(1, 2)	=	0.35555	Carry on
P(2, 2)	=	0.02222	Consider changing the test
P(0, 3)	=	0.46666	Carry on
P(1, 3)	=	0.46666	Carry on
P(2, 3)	=	0.06666	Carry on
P(0, 4)	=	0.33333	Carry on
P(1, 4)	=	0.53333	Carry on
P(2, 4)	=	0.13333	Carry on
P(0, 5)	=	0.22222	Carry on
P(1, 5)	=	0.55555	Carry on
P(2, 5)	=	0.22222	Carry on

N = 12 k = 2 q = 0.20			Action
P(0, 1)	=	0.83333	Carry on
P(1, 1)	=	0.16666	Carry on
P(0, 2)	=	0.68181	Carry on
P(1, 2)	=	0.30303	Carry on
P(2, 2)	=	0.01515	Consider changing the test
P(0, 3)	=	0.54545	Carry on
P(1, 3)	=	0.40909	Carry on

(Continued)

Note: P(x, n) indicates the probability that exactly x failures are found in the first n entries which run, given the following:
N = number of callbacks or starters,
q = the proportion of failures in N, and
k = integer nearest qN.
Additionally, note that probabilities where the action is "obviously change the test" are omitted.

Table 9-1. --(Continued) Guidance at the 0.05 level for continuing or changing a test, selected values of N, k, and q

P(2, 3)	=	0.04545	Consider changing the test
P(0, 4)	=	0.42424	Carry on
P(1, 4)	=	0.48484	Carry on
P(2, 4)	=	0.09090	Carry on
P(0, 5)	=	0.31818	Carry on
P(1, 5)	=	0.53030	Carry on
P(2, 5)	=	0.15151	Carry on

N = 14	k = 3	q = 0.20	Action
P(0, 1)	=	0.78571	Carry on
P(1, 1)	=	0.21428	Carry on
P(0, 2)	=	0.60439	Carry on
P(1, 2)	=	0.36263	Carry on
P(2, 2)	=	0.03296	Consider changing the test
P(0, 3)	=	0.45329	Carry on
P(1, 3)	=	0.45329	Carry on
P(2, 3)	=	0.09065	Carry on
P(3, 3)	=	0.00274	Change the test
P(0, 4)	=	0.32967	Carry on
P(1, 4)	=	0.49450	Carry on
P(2, 4)	=	0.16483	Carry on
P(3, 4)	=	0.01098	Change the test
P(0, 5)	=	0.23076	Carry on
P(1, 5)	=	0.49450	Carry on
P(2, 5)	=	0.24725	Carry on
P(3, 5)	=	0.02747	Change the test

N = 17	k = 3	q = 0.20	Action
P(0, 1)	=	0.82352	Carry on
P(1, 1)	=	0.17647	Carry on
P(0, 2)	=	0.66911	Carry on

(Continued)

Table 9-1.--(Continued) Guidance at the 0.05 level for continuing or
changing a test, selected values of N, k, and q

P(1, 2)	=	0.30882	Carry on
P(2, 2)	=	0.02205	Consider changing the test
P(0, 3)	=	0.53529	Carry on
P(1, 3)	=	0.40147	Carry on
P(2, 3)	=	0.06176	Carry on
P(3, 3)	=	0.00147	Change the test
P(0, 4)	=	0.42058	Carry on
P(1, 4)	=	0.45882	Carry on
P(2, 4)	=	0.11470	Carry on
P(3, 4)	=	0.00588	Change the test
P(0, 5)	=	0.32352	Carry on
P(1, 5)	=	0.48529	Carry on
P(2, 5)	=	0.17647	Carry on
P(3, 5)	=	0.01470	Change the test

N = 20 k = 4 q = 0.20			Action
P(0, 1)	=	0.79999	Carry on
P(1, 1)	=	0.20000	Carry on
P(0, 2)	=	0.63157	Carry on
P(1, 2)	=	0.33684	Carry on
P(2, 2)	=	0.03157	Consider changing the test
P(0, 3)	=	0.49122	Carry on
P(1, 3)	=	0.42105	Carry on
P(2, 3)	=	0.08421	Carry on
P(3, 3)	=	0.00350	Change the test
P(0, 4)	=	0.37564	Carry on
P(1, 4)	=	0.46233	Carry on
P(2, 4)	=	0.14860	Carry on
P(3, 4)	=	0.01320	Change the test
P(0, 5)	=	0.28173	Carry on

(Continued)

Table 9-1.--(Continued) Guidance at the 0.05 level for continuing or changing a test, selected values of N, k, and q

P(1, 5) = 0.46955	Carry on
P(2, 5) = 0.21671	Carry on
P(3, 5) = 0.03095	Change the test

N = 25 k = 5 q = 0.20	Action
P(0, 1) = 0.80000	Carry on
P(1, 1) = 0.20000	Carry on
P(0, 2) = 0.63333	Carry on
P(1, 2) = 0.33333	Carry on
P(2, 2) = 0.03333	Consider changing the test
P(0, 3) = 0.49565	Carry on
P(1, 3) = 0.41304	Carry on
P(2, 3) = 0.08695	Carry on
P(3, 3) = 0.00434	Change the test
P(0, 4) = 0.38300	Carry on
P(1, 4) = 0.45059	Carry on
P(2, 4) = 0.15019	Carry on
P(3, 4) = 0.01581	Change the test
P(0, 5) = 0.29181	Carry on
P(1, 5) = 0.45595	Carry on
P(2, 5) = 0.21456	Carry on
P(3, 5) = 0.03576	Change the test

N = 30 k = 6 q = 0.20	Action
P(0, 1) = 0.79999	Carry on
P(1, 1) = 0.20000	Carry on
P(0, 2) = 0.63448	Carry on
P(1, 2) = 0.33103	Carry on
P(2, 2) = 0.03448	Consider changing the test
P(0, 3) = 0.49852	Carry on

(Continued)

Table 9-1.--(Continued) Guidance at the 0.05 level for continuing or changing a test, selected values of N, k, and q

P(1, 3) = 0.40788	Carry on
P(2, 3) = 0.08866	Carry on
P(3, 3) = 0.00492	Change the test
P(0, 4) = 0.38773	Carry on
P(1, 4) = 0.44313	Carry on
P(2, 4) = 0.15106	Carry on
P(3, 4) = 0.01751	Change the test
P(0, 5) = 0.29826	Carry on
P(1, 5) = 0.44739	Carry on
P(2, 5) = 0.21304	Carry on
P(3, 5) = 0.03873	Change the test

N = 35 k = 7 q = 0.20	Action
P(0, 1) = 0.79999	Carry on
P(1, 1) = 0.19999	Carry on
P(0, 2) = 0.63529	Carry on
P(1, 2) = 0.32941	Carry on
P(2, 2) = 0.03529	Consider changing the test
P(0, 3) = 0.50053	Carry on
P(1, 3) = 0.40427	Carry on
P(2, 3) = 0.08983	Carry on
P(3, 3) = 0.00534	Change the test
P(0, 4) = 0.39104	Carry on
P(1, 4) = 0.43796	Carry on
P(2, 4) = 0.15160	Carry on
P(3, 4) = 0.01871	Change the test
P(0, 5) = 0.30274	Carry on
P(1, 5) = 0.44149	Carry on
P(2, 5) = 0.21191	Carry on
P(3, 5) = 0.04075	Change the test

(Continued)

Table 9-1.--(Continued) Guidance at the 0.05 level for continuing or changing a test, selected values of N, k, and q

N = 40 k = 8 q = 0.20			Action
P(0, 1)	=	0.80000	Carry on
P(1, 1)	=	0.20000	Carry on
P(0, 2)	=	0.63589	Carry on
P(1, 2)	=	0.32820	Carry on
P(2, 2)	=	0.03589	Consider changing the test
P(0, 3)	=	0.50202	Carry on
P(1, 3)	=	0.40161	Carry on
P(2, 3)	=	0.09068	Carry on
P(3, 3)	=	0.00566	Change the test
P(0, 4)	=	0.39347	Carry on
P(1, 4)	=	0.43418	Carry on
P(2, 4)	=	0.15196	Carry on
P(3, 4)	=	0.01960	Change the test
P(0, 5)	=	0.30603	Carry on
P(1, 5)	=	0.43719	Carry on
P(2, 5)	=	0.21106	Carry on
P(3, 5)	=	0.04221	Change the test
N = 45 k = 9 q = 0.20			Action
P(0, 1)	=	0.80000	Carry on
P(1, 1)	=	0.20000	Carry on
P(0, 2)	=	0.63636	Carry on
P(1, 2)	=	0.32727	Carry on
P(2, 2)	=	0.03636	Consider changing the test
P(0, 3)	=	0.50317	Carry on
P(1, 3)	=	0.39957	Carry on
P(2, 3)	=	0.09133	Carry on
P(3, 3)	=	0.00591	Change the test

(Continued)

Table 9-1.--(Continued) Guidance at the 0.05 level for continuing or changing a test, selected values of N, k, and q

P(0, 4)	=	0.39534	Carry on
P(1, 4)	=	0.43128	Carry on
P(2, 4)	=	0.15221	Carry on
P(3, 4)	=	0.02029	Change the test
P(0, 5)	=	0.30856	Carry on
P(1, 5)	=	0.43391	Carry on
P(2, 5)	=	0.21038	Carry on
P(3, 5)	=	0.04331	Change the test

N = 50 k = 10 q = 0.20			Action
P(0, 1)	=	0.80000	Carry on
P(1, 1)	=	0.20000	Carry on
P(0, 2)	=	0.63673	Carry on
P(1, 2)	=	0.32653	Carry on
P(2, 2)	=	0.03673	Consider changing the test
P(0, 3)	=	0.50408	Carry on
P(1, 3)	=	0.39795	Carry on
P(2, 3)	=	0.09183	Carry on
P(3, 3)	=	0.00612	Change the test
P(0, 4)	=	0.39683	Carry on
P(1, 4)	=	0.42900	Carry on
P(2, 4)	=	0.15240	Carry on
P(3, 4)	=	0.02084	Change the test
P(0, 5)	=	0.31056	Carry on
P(1, 5)	=	0.43133	Carry on
P(2, 5)	=	0.20983	Carry on
P(3, 5)	=	0.04417	Change the test

N = 55 k = 11 q = 0.20			Action
P(0, 1)	=	0.79999	Carry on

(Continued)

Table 9-1.--(Continued) Guidance at the 0.05 level for continuing or changing a test, selected values of N, k, and q

$P(1, 1)$	=	0.19999	Carry on
$P(0, 2)$	=	0.63703	Carry on
$P(1, 2)$	=	0.32592	Carry on
$P(2, 2)$	=	0.03703	Consider changing the test
$P(0, 3)$	=	0.50482	Carry on
$P(1, 3)$	=	0.39664	Carry on
$P(2, 3)$	=	0.09224	Carry on
$P(3, 3)$	=	0.00628	Change the test
$P(0, 4)$	=	0.39803	Carry on
$P(1, 4)$	=	0.42715	Carry on
$P(2, 4)$	=	0.15255	Carry on
$P(3, 4)$	=	0.02128	Change the test
$P(0, 5)$	=	0.31218	Carry on
$P(1, 5)$	=	0.42925	Carry on
$P(2, 5)$	=	0.20939	Carry on
$P(3, 5)$	=	0.04486	Change the test

N = 60 k = 12 q = 0.20			Action
$P(0, 1)$	=	0.80000	Carry on
$P(1, 1)$	=	0.20000	Carry on
$P(0, 2)$	=	0.63728	Carry on
$P(1, 2)$	=	0.32542	Carry on
$P(2, 2)$	=	0.03728	Consider changing the test
$P(0, 3)$	=	0.50543	Carry on
$P(1, 3)$	=	0.39555	Carry on
$P(2, 3)$	=	0.09257	Carry on
$P(3, 3)$	=	0.00642	Change the test
$P(0, 4)$	=	0.39902	Carry on
$P(1, 4)$	=	0.42562	Carry on
$P(2, 4)$	=	0.15267	Carry on

(Continued)

Table 9-1. --(Continued) Guidance at the 0.05 level for continuing or
changing a test, selected values of N, k, and q

P(3, 4)	=	0.02165	Change the test
P(0, 5)	=	0.31352	Carry on
P(1, 5)	=	0.42753	Carry on
P(2, 5)	=	0.20901	Carry on
P(3, 5)	=	0.04543	Change the test

N = 10	k = 3	q = 0.30	Action
P(0, 1)	=	0.70000	Carry on
P(1, 1)	=	0.30000	Carry on
P(0, 2)	=	0.46666	Carry on
P(1, 2)	=	0.46666	Carry on
P(2, 2)	=	0.06666	Carry on
P(0, 3)	=	0.29166	Carry on
P(1, 3)	=	0.52500	Carry on
P(2, 3)	=	0.17500	Carry on
P(3, 3)	=	0.00833	Change the test
P(0, 4)	=	0.16666	Carry on
P(1, 4)	=	0.50000	Carry on
P(2, 4)	=	0.30000	Carry on
P(3, 4)	=	0.03333	Change the test
P(0, 5)	=	0.08333	Carry on
P(1, 5)	=	0.41666	Carry on
P(2, 5)	=	0.41666	Carry on
P(3, 5)	=	0.08333	Carry on

N = 12	k = 4	q = 0.30	Action
P(0, 1)	=	0.66666	Carry on
P(1, 1)	=	0.33333	Carry on
P(0, 2)	=	0.42424	Carry on
P(1, 2)	=	0.48484	Carry on

(Continued)

Table 9-1. --(Continued) Guidance at the 0.05 level for continuing or
changing a test, selected values of N, k, and q

P(2, 2)	=	0.09090	Carry on
P(0, 3)	=	0.25454	Carry on
P(1, 3)	=	0.50909	Carry on
P(2, 3)	=	0.21818	Carry on
P(3, 3)	=	0.01818	Change the test
P(0, 4)	=	0.14141	Carry on
P(1, 4)	=	0.45252	Carry on
P(2, 4)	=	0.33939	Carry on
P(3, 4)	=	0.06464	Carry on
P(0, 5)	=	0.07070	Carry on
P(1, 5)	=	0.35353	Carry on
P(2, 5)	=	0.42424	Carry on
P(3, 5)	=	0.14141	Carry on
P(4, 5)	=	0.01010	Change the test

N = 14 k = 4 q = 0.30			Action
P(0, 1)	=	0.71428	Carry on
P(1, 1)	=	0.28571	Carry on
P(0, 2)	=	0.49450	Carry on
P(1, 2)	=	0.43956	Carry on
P(2, 2)	=	0.06593	Carry on
P(0, 3)	=	0.32967	Carry on
P(1, 3)	=	0.49450	Carry on
P(2, 3)	=	0.16483	Carry on
P(3, 3)	=	0.01098	Change the test
P(0, 4)	=	0.20979	Carry on
P(1, 4)	=	0.47952	Carry on
P(2, 4)	=	0.26973	Carry on
P(3, 4)	=	0.03996	Change the test
P(0, 5)	=	0.12587	Carry on

(Continued)

Table 9-1.--(Continued) Guidance at the 0.05 level for continuing or changing a test, selected values of N, k, and q

P(1, 5)	=	0.41958		Carry on
P(2, 5)	=	0.35964		Carry on
P(3, 5)	=	0.08991		Carry on
P(4, 5)	=	0.00499		Change the test

N = 17 k = 5 q = 0.30				Action
P(0, 1)	=	0.70588		Carry on
P(1, 1)	=	0.29411		Carry on
P(0, 2)	=	0.48529		Carry on
P(1, 2)	=	0.44117		Carry on
P(2, 2)	=	0.07352		Carry on
P(0, 3)	=	0.32352		Carry on
P(1, 3)	=	0.48529		Carry on
P(2, 3)	=	0.17647		Carry on
P(3, 3)	=	0.01470		Change the test
P(0, 4)	=	0.20798		Carry on
P(1, 4)	=	0.46218		Carry on
P(2, 4)	=	0.27731		Carry on
P(3, 4)	=	0.05042		Carry on
P(0, 5)	=	0.12798		Carry on
P(1, 5)	=	0.39996		Carry on
P(2, 5)	=	0.35552		Carry on
P(3, 5)	=	0.10665		Carry on
P(4, 5)	=	0.00969		Change the test

N = 20 k = 6 q = 0.30				Action
P(0, 1)	=	0.69999		Carry on
P(1, 1)	=	0.30000		Carry on
P(0, 2)	=	0.47894		Carry on
P(1, 2)	=	0.44210		Carry on

(Continued)

Table 9-1.--(Continued) Guidance at the 0.05 level for continuing or changing a test, selected values of N, k, and q

P(2, 2) = 0.07894	Carry on
P(0, 3) = 0.31929	Carry on
P(1, 3) = 0.47894	Carry on
P(2, 3) = 0.18421	Carry on
P(3, 3) = 0.01754	Change the test
P(0, 4) = 0.20660	Carry on
P(1, 4) = 0.45077	Carry on
P(2, 4) = 0.28173	Carry on
P(3, 4) = 0.05779	Carry on
P(0, 5) = 0.12912	Carry on
P(1, 5) = 0.38738	Carry on
P(2, 5) = 0.35216	Carry on
P(3, 5) = 0.11738	Carry on
P(4, 5) = 0.01354	Change the test

N = 25 k = 8 q = 0.30	Action
P(0, 1) = 0.68000	Carry on
P(1, 1) = 0.32000	Carry on
P(0, 2) = 0.45333	Carry on
P(1, 2) = 0.45333	Carry on
P(2, 2) = 0.09333	Carry on
P(0, 3) = 0.29565	Carry on
P(1, 3) = 0.47304	Carry on
P(2, 3) = 0.20695	Carry on
P(3, 3) = 0.02434	Change the test
P(0, 4) = 0.18814	Carry on
P(1, 4) = 0.43003	Carry on
P(2, 4) = 0.30102	Carry on
P(3, 4) = 0.07525	Carry on
P(0, 5) = 0.11646	Carry on

(Continued)

Table 9-1.--(Continued) Guidance at the 0.05 level for continuing or
changing a test, selected values of N, k, and q

P(1, 5) = 0.35836	Carry on
P(2, 5) = 0.35836	Carry on
P(3, 5) = 0.14334	Carry on
P(4, 5) = 0.02239	Change the test

N = 30 k = 9 q = 0.30	Action
P(0, 1) = 0.70000	Carry on
P(1, 1) = 0.30000	Carry on
P(0, 2) = 0.48275	Carry on
P(1, 2) = 0.43448	Carry on
P(2, 2) = 0.08275	Carry on
P(0, 3) = 0.32758	Carry on
P(1, 3) = 0.46551	Carry on
P(2, 3) = 0.18620	Carry on
P(3, 3) = 0.02068	Change the test
P(0, 4) = 0.21839	Carry on
P(1, 4) = 0.43678	Carry on
P(2, 4) = 0.27586	Carry on
P(3, 4) = 0.06436	Carry on
P(0, 5) = 0.14279	Carry on
P(1, 5) = 0.37798	Carry on
P(2, 5) = 0.33598	Carry on
P(3, 5) = 0.12378	Carry on
P(4, 5) = 0.01856	Change the test

N = 35 k = 11 q = 0.30	Action
P(0, 1) = 0.68571	Carry on
P(1, 1) = 0.31428	Carry on
P(0, 2) = 0.46386	Carry on
P(1, 2) = 0.44369	Carry on

(Continued)

Table 9-1.--(Continued) Guidance at the 0.05 level for continuing or changing a test, selected values of N, k, and q

P(2, 2)	=	0.09243	Carry on
P(0, 3)	=	0.30924	Carry on
P(1, 3)	=	0.46386	Carry on
P(2, 3)	=	0.20168	Carry on
P(3, 3)	=	0.02521	Change the test
P(0, 4)	=	0.20294	Carry on
P(1, 4)	=	0.42521	Carry on
P(2, 4)	=	0.28991	Carry on
P(3, 4)	=	0.07563	Carry on
P(0, 5)	=	0.13092	Carry on
P(1, 5)	=	0.36005	Carry on
P(2, 5)	=	0.34291	Carry on
P(3, 5)	=	0.14028	Carry on
P(4, 5)	=	0.02439	Change the test

N = 40 k = 12 q = 0.30			Action
P(0, 1)	=	0.69999	Carry on
P(1, 1)	=	0.30000	Carry on
P(0, 2)	=	0.48461	Carry on
P(1, 2)	=	0.43076	Carry on
P(2, 2)	=	0.08461	Carry on
P(0, 3)	=	0.33157	Carry on
P(1, 3)	=	0.45910	Carry on
P(2, 3)	=	0.18704	Carry on
P(3, 3)	=	0.02226	Change the test
P(0, 4)	=	0.22403	Carry on
P(1, 4)	=	0.43015	Carry on
P(2, 4)	=	0.27298	Carry on
P(3, 4)	=	0.06740	Carry on
P(0, 5)	=	0.14935	Carry on

(Continued)

Table 9-1.--(Continued) Guidance at the 0.05 level for continuing or changing a test, selected values of N, k, and q

P(1, 5) = 0.37339	Carry on
P(2, 5) = 0.32859	Carry on
P(3, 5) = 0.12638	Carry on
P(4, 5) = 0.02106	Change the test

N = 45 k = 14 q = 0.30	Action
P(0, 1) = 0.68888	Carry on
P(1, 1) = 0.31111	Carry on
P(0, 2) = 0.46969	Carry on
P(1, 2) = 0.43838	Carry on
P(2, 2) = 0.09191	Carry on
P(0, 3) = 0.31677	Carry on
P(1, 3) = 0.45877	Carry on
P(2, 3) = 0.19880	Carry on
P(3, 3) = 0.02565	Change the test
P(0, 4) = 0.21118	Carry on
P(1, 4) = 0.42236	Carry on
P(2, 4) = 0.28400	Carry on
P(3, 4) = 0.07573	Carry on
P(0, 5) = 0.13907	Carry on
P(1, 5) = 0.36055	Carry on
P(2, 5) = 0.33480	Carry on
P(3, 5) = 0.13853	Carry on
P(4, 5) = 0.02539	Change the test

N = 50 k = 15 q = 0.30	Action
P(0, 1) = 0.70000	Carry on
P(1, 1) = 0.30000	Carry on
P(0, 2) = 0.48571	Carry on
P(1, 2) = 0.42857	Carry on

(Continued)

Table 9-1. --(Continued) Guidance at the 0.05 level for continuing or changing a test, selected values of N, k, and q

P(2, 2)	=	0.08571	Carry on
P(0, 3)	=	0.33392	Carry on
P(1, 3)	=	0.45535	Carry on
P(2, 3)	=	0.18749	Carry on
P(3, 3)	=	0.02321	Change the test
P(0, 4)	=	0.22735	Carry on
P(1, 4)	=	0.42629	Carry on
P(2, 4)	=	0.27127	Carry on
P(3, 4)	=	0.06914	Carry on
P(0, 5)	=	0.15321	Carry on
P(1, 5)	=	0.37068	Carry on
P(2, 5)	=	0.32435	Carry on
P(3, 5)	=	0.12777	Carry on
P(4, 5)	=	0.02254	Change the test

N = 55 k = 17 q = 0.30			Action
P(0, 1)	=	0.69090	Carry on
P(1, 1)	=	0.30909	Carry on
P(0, 2)	=	0.47340	Carry on
P(1, 2)	=	0.43501	Carry on
P(2, 2)	=	0.09158	Carry on
P(0, 3)	=	0.32155	Carry on
P(1, 3)	=	0.45553	Carry on
P(2, 3)	=	0.19698	Carry on
P(3, 3)	=	0.02591	Change the test
P(0, 4)	=	0.21643	Carry on
P(1, 4)	=	0.42049	Carry on
P(2, 4)	=	0.28033	Carry on
P(3, 4)	=	0.07576	Carry on
P(0, 5)	=	0.14428	Carry on

(Continued)

Table 9-1.--(Concluded) Guidance at the 0.05 level for continuing or
changing a test, selected values of N, k, and q

P(1, 5) = 0.36071	Carry on
P(2, 5) = 0.32980	Carry on
P(3, 5) = 0.13741	Carry on
P(4, 5) = 0.02599	Change the test

N = 60 k = 18 q = 0.30	Action
P(0, 1) = 0.70000	Carry on
P(1, 1) = 0.29999	Carry on
P(0, 2) = 0.48644	Carry on
P(1, 2) = 0.42711	Carry on
P(2, 2) = 0.08644	Carry on
P(0, 3) = 0.33547	Carry on
P(1, 3) = 0.45289	Carry on
P(2, 3) = 0.18778	Carry on
P(3, 3) = 0.02384	Change the test
P(0, 4) = 0.22953	Carry on
P(1, 4) = 0.42375	Carry on
P(2, 4) = 0.27014	Carry on
P(3, 4) = 0.07028	Carry on
P(0, 5) = 0.15575	Carry on
P(1, 5) = 0.36889	Carry on
P(2, 5) = 0.32160	Carry on
P(3, 5) = 0.12864	Carry on
P(4, 5) = 0.02353	Change the test

$P(x,\ n)\ =\ \binom{6}{x}\binom{24}{n-x}/\binom{30}{n}$		Action
$P(1,\ 1)\ =\ \binom{6}{1}/\binom{30}{1}$	$=\ 0.20$	Carry on
$P(2,\ 2)\ =\ \binom{6}{2}/\binom{30}{2}$	$=\ 0.03$	Consider changing the test
$P(2,\ 3)\ =\ \binom{6}{2}\binom{24}{1}/\binom{30}{3}$	$=\ 0.09$	Carry on
$P(3,\ 3)\ =\ \binom{6}{3}/\binom{30}{3}$	$=\ 0.005$	Change the test
$P(3,\ 4)\ =\ \binom{6}{3}\binom{24}{1}/\binom{30}{4}$	$=\ 0.02$	Change the test
$P(3,\ 5)\ =\ \binom{6}{3}\binom{24}{2}/\binom{30}{5}$	$=\ 0.04$	Change the test

suming that the test for series three does not require changing, then 20 per cent of the entries in series three are expected to fail the test and, consequently, 80 per cent (24 entries) are expected to pass.

Suppose A represents the event that y retrievers in a sample of n who enter series three pass the test. Also, let B denote the event that z of these same y retrievers fail the test for series four. The probability of the compound event A and B is given by

$$P(A \cap B)\ =\ P(A)\ \cdot\ P(B|A),$$

where P(B|A) is the conditional probability of B, given A. The conditional probability is required since we are considering the case where retrievers will be invited to series four only if they "pass" the test for series three. As shown previously,

$$P(A)\ =\ P(y,\ n)\ =\ \frac{\binom{24}{y}\binom{6}{n-y}}{\binom{30}{n}}.$$

Note that the hypergeometric probability function is appropriate for series three since series four does not influence series three. However, for the conditional probability of B, given A, the hypergeometric probability function is not appropriate. Observe that

$$P(B|A) \text{ does not equal } \frac{\binom{k}{z}\binom{y-k}{m-z}}{\binom{y}{m}},$$

where m is the sample size and k is the largest integer in 0.3y (0.3 being the "fraction defective" for the test of series four). Since m must equal y,

$$\binom{y}{m} = \binom{y}{y} = 1,$$

while the factors in the numerator are non-negative integers and, hence, the product could be an integer exceeding 1. This is contrary to our definition of probability and, therefore, the hypergeometric function is unacceptable.

If we are willing to assume that for the retrievers who pass the test of series three, probabilities for passing the test of series four are approximately equal, then the binomial probability function is appropriate for the conditional probability $P(B|A)$. Consequently,

$$P(B|A) = \binom{y}{z}(0.3)^z (0.7)^{y-z},$$

and Table 7-19 (pages 269 through 271) may be used. Our criterion for changing the test for series four is the probability of $B|A$. If $P(B|A) < 0.05$, then change the test.

y	z	P(B|A)	Action for series four
1	1	0.30	Carry on
2	2	0.09	Carry on
3	3	0.03	Change the test
4	3	0.08	Carry on
5	4	0.03	Change the test
6	4	0.06	Carry on
7	5	0.03	Change the test

ACTION ITEMS

Item 1. -- Compare the use of the assumption underlying the application of the binomial probability distribution as follows: (1) In series one and two versus series four and five; (2) in an ordinary licensed stake versus a national championship; (3) in an open stake versus a qualifying stake.

Question: Does this mean that judges must be careful of the use of the "invitation tool"?

Comment: I have never desired to use (nor desired to be a party to the use of) the invitation tool; moreover, I don't expect to ever use it if I can avoid it.

Item 2.--Fiasco at Norco: In an amateur stake in a licensed trial on a Sunday in February, there were 34 entries listed in the program with the usual scratch or two. The first two tests (attempted) consisted of a double marked fall, one dead pheasant thrown in water (a pothole) and a flying shot hen--all in heavy cover and relatively rough terrain; then, after the marks were picked up, a double blind was run immediately without leaving the line (call this a combination of series

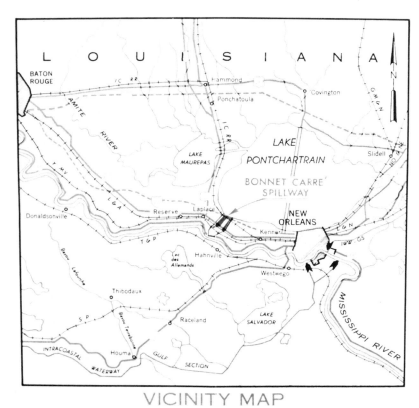

VICINITY MAP

VICINITY MAP OF THE BONNET CARRÉ SPILLWAY

(From Mississippi River Commission, U.S. Army Engineer District, New Orleans, Corps of Engineers, 1969.)

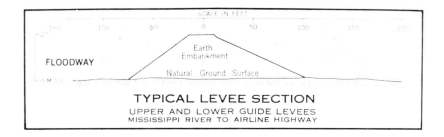

TYPICAL LEVEE SECTION

UPPER AND LOWER GUIDE LEVEES
MISSISSIPPI RIVER TO AIRLINE HIGHWAY

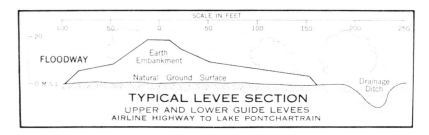

TYPICAL LEVEE SECTION

UPPER AND LOWER GUIDE LEVEES
AIRLINE HIGHWAY TO LAKE PONTCHARTRAIN

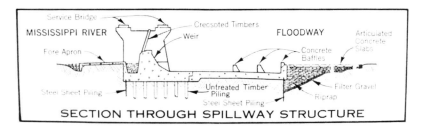

SECTION THROUGH SPILLWAY STRUCTURE

SELECTED DETAILS CONCERNING THE BONNET CARRÉ SPILLWAY

(From Mississippi River Commission, U.S. Army Engineer District, New Orleans, Corps of Engineers, 1969.)

one and series two). After approximately one and one-half hours of running, and after poor dog work by the test-dog and, say, 5 of the entries themselves (the first 5 entries), the test was called off.

Given N = 34, choose a value of q for series one and a value of q for series two. Compute the probabilities required and state when you would change the test if you should encounter such a situation.

After reconnoitering a nearby area, the judges decided to relocate the test(s) and changed them to a double mark with a single blind. Hence, the first dog ran at approximately 10:00 a.m. To conserve time, the blind became optional (by "invitation" of the judges), and at least half the listed entries failed to reach the "third series"; in fact, several entries of a relatively small field were eliminated after being judged on two falls. The test which we shall call the third series consisted of a triple mark using shackled duck thrown into pot-holes (wading water) and the "fourth series" was a blind at the same site (as that of the "water" triple).

To summarize, after "false-starting" at shortly after 8:00 a.m., the trial was terminated after six hours at 4:00 p.m. on a sunny afternoon in the deep South; running time remained. Four places and three JAM's were awarded.

Question: We know that when we shoot upland game birds, occasionally one falls in water. In a field trial, do we increase the variability in a test when pheasant are thrown or shot (deliberately) to fall in water? In short, should a pheasant, as a mark, be thrown or shot to fall in water?

Question: Obviously, this was a stake where championship points were awarded. Discuss setting up water tests, with some of the greatest water resources for retriever trials in the world at hand, and utilizing no swimming water.

Question: Amateurs "pay the freight," although those entries who completed this trial were given one, and only one, shot pheasant. Do you think this is a sound procedure in general?

Item 3. -- A reader who prefers other percentages of callbacks can follow these worked examples to prepare his own guidelines and rules for changing a test.

"Too Easy"

The art of judging involves treading a fine line. If the test is too difficult, the dogs can't complete it or they do such poor work that the joy is taken from it. On the other hand, in order to separate performances, the tests must not be too easy; in fact, it is assumed that if a test is difficult enough to yield a satisfactory degree of separation, then some retrievers would be expected to fail the test. Moreover, if every retriever in a large stake passed every test, the judges would have rough going (within the usual limitations of time and resources) in selecting the performances deserving awards in that stake. Thus, it seems worth examining a criterion for changing a test in the event that it appears too easy. Again, we shall make use of the hypergeometric distribution and an example.

Take $N = 30$ and $k = 9$. The probability of having the first 8 retrievers pass the test, when $N = 30$ and $k = 9$, is 0.035. This is a rare occurrence (i.e., less than 1 in 20), so I would suggest to my co-judge that the test be changed and made more difficult (unless there were extenuating circumstances such as excellent separation among the performances). See the worksheet on the following page.

Rule of Thumb

For practical purposes, the first 5 entries provide "sufficient" information for changing or not changing a test (due to its being "too difficult"). There is no excuse whatsoever for not changing a test if the first 5 entries fail that test.

$$P(x, n) = \binom{9}{x}\binom{21}{n-x}/\binom{30}{n}$$ Action

[As before, x is the number who fail the test and $n - x$ pass in a "sample" of size n. If $n - x$ is large compared to n (i.e., if x is small compared to n) the test would appear to be too easy.] Now observe the following probabilities:

$$P(0, 1) = \binom{9}{0}\binom{21}{1}/\binom{30}{1} = 0.700 \qquad \text{Carry on}$$

$$P(0, 2) = \binom{9}{0}\binom{21}{2}/\binom{30}{2} = 0.483 \qquad \text{Carry on}$$

$$P(0, 3) = \binom{9}{0}\binom{21}{3}/\binom{30}{3} = 0.328 \qquad \text{Carry on}$$

$$P(0, 4) = \binom{9}{0}\binom{21}{4}/\binom{30}{4} = 0.218 \qquad \text{Carry on}$$

$$P(0, 5) = \binom{9}{0}\binom{21}{5}/\binom{30}{5} = 0.143 \qquad \text{Carry on}$$

$$P(0, 6) = \binom{9}{0}\binom{21}{6}/\binom{30}{6} = 0.091 \qquad \text{Carry on}$$

$$P(0, 7) = \binom{9}{0}\binom{21}{7}/\binom{30}{7} = 0.057 \qquad \text{Carry on}$$

$$P(0, 8) = \binom{9}{0}\binom{21}{8}/\binom{30}{8} = 0.035 \qquad \text{Change the test}$$

REFERENCE

1. McMahan, C. A. *Rudiments of Biometry*, Ann Arbor, Michigan: Edwards Brothers, Inc., 1967.

A pittance of practice may be worth a tome of theory.

NOTES TO CHAPTER NINE

Reference example on page 360 which is repeated here for convenience. Example: Suppose we have 25 starters (or callbacks) for a series; let q = 0.27, or 0.28, or 0.29 so that qN ≈ 7; even let q = 0.30 (give the entry the benefit of the doubt, round unconventionally), and use k = 7.

The solution as presented on page 360 is addressed to the problem before any of the callbacks or starters run. In contrast, suppose 3 entries have run the test; the judges know how many, if any, of these entries failed the test. Clearly, the judges have additional information; the question is different. The next paragraph is addressed to a different question than the one posed and answered on page 360.

A different question: What is the probability (P) that the test will be changed after 4 retrievers have run due to the fact that 3 of these 4 have failed the test? We must realize that a conditional probability is required. That is, exactly 2 of the first 3 must fail the test and then the fourth retriever must fail. Consequently,

$$P = P(2, 3) \times P(\text{next retriever fails})$$

$$= \frac{\binom{7}{2}\binom{18}{1}}{\binom{25}{3}} \times \frac{5}{22}$$

$$P = 0.037 .$$

In terms of events, if E is the event of 2 retrievers failing out of the first 3 and F is the event of 3 failing out of the first 4, then we desire the probability of both events E and F occurring. That is,

$$P(E \text{ and } F) = P(E) \times P(F|E)$$
$$= P(2, 3) \times P(F|E)$$
$$P(E \text{ and } F) = P(2, 3) \times \frac{5}{22} .$$

CHAPTER TEN

MEASURING RETRIEVER PERFORMANCE

It is believed that performance of a retriever enthusiast (RE) as a judge, even what he measures, is not only closely related to but depends on his philosophy of judging.

PHILOSOPHY OF JUDGING: NEGATIVE VERSUS POSITIVE

Assuming, of course, that each judge recognizes that there is grave responsibility associated with judging another man's dog, if a qualified judge is selected at random and if he could verbalize his philosophy of judging, no doubt there would be aspects of that philosophy which could be labelled negative and aspects which could be labelled positive. The purpose of this section is to explicitly outline some philosophical aspects of judging, tentatively classify them as either negative or positive or applicable to both, and to initiate rudimentary discussion; no answers are provided.

Philosophy for Callbacks in Licensed Open Stakes

In this section, we are concerned with *attitude* in judging. For purposes of discussion, I shall focus on two extremes called "negative judging" ("destructive judging") and "positive judging." (Note clearly that we shall make no attempt to classify judges into two distinct groups, "positive judges" and "negative judges." As indicated above, it is assumed that the philosophy of any one judge is a mixture of both positive aspects and negative aspects of philosophy.)

Negative judging philosophy (NJP).-- The judge with negative philosophy behaves as though he considers the stake (which he is judging) to be a contest between the judges *versus* retrievers and their handlers,

rather than a contest among the various retriever-handler teams. At this end of the scale, a judge seeks some reason or reasons (weaknesses or faults) which he thinks will justify his eliminating a dog from the stake.

This philosophy is reflected by the judge who says: "I like to allow a dog two mistakes. Now, he may make both mistakes on the same marked fall; that is, (1) he may not mark it, and (2) then he may not handle." Other remarks such as the following characterize negative philosophy: "I've seen enough of that retriever for this stake." "We don't want to see any more of him, do we?"

A judge with negative philosophy desires to call back only those dogs whose performances meet some arbitrary mental image or standard which he believes he has established and can maintain, not only over a series, but over an entire stake, as well as among trials. Ideally, the negatively oriented judge would like to eliminate all entries which do not have perfect or near perfect work. He designs his tests to eliminate dogs. Such a judge either explicitly or implicitly assumes that he can collect data, under trial conditions, which meet high standards of accuracy and reliability.

He assumes great ability to detect and count number of whistles, number of casts, number of "refusals" (line, whistle, and cast), but he probably has never demonstrated that ability to an impartial jury. He assumes that his co-judge has similar ability.

[*Aside:* Roughly speaking, "cast" refers to explicit signals by a handler (to direct a retriever) through head and/or body movement, as well as arm and hand signals. Some handlers "side-step" without explicit arm and hand movements; by definition (even though some handlers try to fool the judges), this is a "cast."]

To justify the elimination of dogs, the judge with "negative philosophy" counts faults; he may record these faults systematically, e.g., as in the following dummy table.

Entry number _____

Fault associated with		Series					
		1	2	3	4	5	6
Creeping	(c)						
Honoring	(h)						
Pick-up	(pu)						
Popping	(p)						
Delivery	(d)						
Water entry	(we)						
Hissing	(hs)						
"Leg-lifting"	(ll)						
Whining	(w)						

He may also count refusals in some systematic manner, say, as follows.

Refusals	
Whistle	Cast

Such a judge further assumes that he can make unerring decisions based on such data. Clearly, the dog does not get the benefit of the doubt under "negative judging."

Comment: If field-trialers will tolerate this philosophy, a judge following these principles might expect to get little criticism on his callbacks. He probably would expect to seldom call back a dog which should be dropped for making mistakes, but should expect to call back entries with faultless performances but who lack class ("pigs"); however, he may often drop energetic dogs which have given classy, workmanlike performances, but who have committed some faults. In the case of "ties," one might expect him to make errors against the classy dog. [*Analogy:* In baseball, the "tie is decided in favor of the runner"--not so under "negative judging."]

On the surface, such a policy would seem to favor the professionally trained dog; the true amateur may have somewhat smaller probability of staying in the contest.

Positive judging philosophy (PJP).--Winning retrievers must possess that hard-to-define attribute called class. The judge with a positive philosophy seeks some feature(s) or attribute(s) which he believes distinguishes a particular retriever and/or the retriever's performance from "the pack" on that day. [*Aside:* To be explicit, some positive qualities to be watched for are as follows: eagerness, enthusiasm, keenness, concentration on marking, directness in going to a well-scrutinized fall (accurate marking), self-confidence and perserverence in the search, hustle and pace regardless of difficulty of the cover, use of wind, willingness to take directions from his handler, (on order) retrieving quickly and briskly with a good carry, delivering tenderly to hand, and obviously other such qualities as steadiness, nose, and the like.] The judge whose philosophy centers at this end of the scale designs his tests so that qualities of excellence will be brought out; his goal is to select the best dog or dogs in the stake by seeking out and recording the good points of a retriever's performance. Such a judge "likes to see them run"; he is constantly aware that the major goal is to select the top retriever, not to eliminate the "less than perfect" retriever. He views the trial as a qualification contest; he would like to "qualify" all worthy contenders in that stake; he seeks a "healthy" list of qualifiers. To elaborate on qualification: He seeks one dog that qualifies, without any reservation whatsoever, to be labelled winner; he seeks a subgroup of retrievers who qualify to be considered in every possible pair for a specified share of the nine and one-half points available in the stake; ... ; he seeks a subgroup of retrievers who qualify to take a step in the direction of being labelled ... champion; he seeks a subgroup of retrievers who possibly can qualify for the opportunity of competing in the ... championship stake; he seeks a subgroup of retrievers who, after, say, i = 5 series (and a clear winner), qualify to be called back if another series were to be conducted; he ... .

The judge who possesses a positive philosophy toward judging may set himself a more difficult task than does the judge who is negatively oriented. A judge who "counts refusals," who eliminates entries on the basis of "faults," has merely to call back those retrievers who do not demonstrate such faults. On the other hand, the positively oriented judge must exercise judgment throughout the entire performance; he must constantly (and consistently) compare, evaluate, and judge; he must "weed out" the faultless plugs from the cream of the crop. The data collected by the positive judge may not be solely "number of faults, refusals, ... ," but the data must be sufficient to allow "unerring decisions," and the judge assumes that he possesses the ability to make such decisions based upon his data, and possesses the ability to detect differences between performances and desirable attributes in the performances.

The judge with positive philosophy considers the stake to be a contest among teams composed of retrievers and their handlers. Under this philosophy, a workmanlike, classy job deserves to be called back (time and conditions permitting), even though it takes perfect or near perfect work to win a trophy. Such a philosophy "forces" the judge to set practical, straightforward, tough, demanding tests without tricks or gimmicks to confuse the entries.

Comment: The "positive attitude" requires a judge to decide exactly what he is looking for in a retriever; he is definitely "opinionated." Under a positive judging policy, the judge expects to call back most of the entries which would be called back under a negative judging system; however, he may drop retrievers that do not have

... , class and drive (necessary for the status quo and/or breed improvement) even though these retrievers have made no "mistakes." The foregoing notwithstanding, time and conditions permitting, he may expect to call back some dogs who might have been eliminated under the negative policy. The positive judge makes his callbacks on the basis of comparison; his task is especially difficult when time and conditions are limited, because his decisions are based upon judgment rather than upon faults. When time and conditions dictate that a large proportion of entries be eliminated, the reasons for eliminating those entries in the "gray area" may not be obvious to handlers, owners, and gallery judges, and the positive judge may find that defending his decisions (to a handler, ...) is not as easy for him as it might be for the negative judge.

In short, a judge with a positive attitude keeps clearly in mind that the major task is to render judgment and that the necessary authority accompanies the sweeping responsibility.

ACTION ITEMS

Even though I have never been enrolled in nor exposed to a formal course in philosophy, I reckon a well-trained, genuine philosopher would flinch at talk about "the philosophy of judging" or "the philosophy of business competition" or "the philosophy of news reporting." Nevertheless, such popular usage does demonstrate that the regard is for primary (basic or first) principles. To a like degree, the remark "philosophy of life" seems to refer to a set of basic convictions according to which a man governs or regulates his personal behavior. In fact, years ago G. K. Chesterton asserted "... the most important single thing to know about a person is his philosophy of life." Paraphrased for use in the context of this book: Given a gentleman (or lady), the most important single thing to know about a judge of retriever field trials is his set of primary beliefs which guide his conduct (particularly concerning retrievers and the field trial game).

Item 1.--Question for discussion: How is a judge's philosophy (primary beliefs or basic assumptions) for judging American retriever field trials related to the decisions he makes?

Even for one such as me who does not really know what is meant by philosophy, it has been a revealing experience for me to attempt to catalog many of my basic beliefs concerning retrievers, trials, and judging, and to place alongside these beliefs their logical implications in a format essentially as that in the worksheet which follows. Because many of my underlying beliefs (the elements of my philosophy) are explicitly expressed in various places in this book, I shall not repeat them here [although I did systematically present a subset of them

Belief of the judge	Logical implications
1.	1_a 1_b . . . 1_k
2.	2_a 2_b . . . 2_k
. . .	. . .
n.	n_a n_b . . . n_k

at least once in public (at a meeting of the New Orleans Retriever Club, September, 1969)].

Item 2.--Attempt to itemize the elements of your philosophy of judging and explicitly state the logical implications of each guiding principle.

Item 3.--Does the bird dog make a cast?

Counting Refusals

It is assumed here that the judge understands clearly, and can distinguish, the difference between recast and resending due to confusion.   Moreover, that he recognizes the problem of distinguishing between " *a* cast refusal" and "refusing to cast--take casts."

Example of refusals, whistle and cast.--When does a retriever fail to honor a whistle?

Handler 1: Beeeep! The dog sits. There is no doubt; he honored the whistle.

Handler 2: Beeeep! Beep! The dog sits. (This handler habitually blows a long and a short whistle.) Will both judges invariably agree that this dog honored "the whistle"? Or will one judge contend that this dog "slipped" one whistle?

Handler 3: Beeeep! Tweet! Tweet! The dog sits. What now?

.

.

.

Handler k: Beeeep! Beep! The dog fails to heed. Clearly, there is a refusal, but has the dog refused more than one whistle?

When does a dog fail to honor a cast (arm and hand and/or explicit body movement)?

ACTION ITEMS

In 1935, while a student at Clemson, I made use of moving pictures in an attempt to improve my performance in the high jump. In 1946, I studied with Ralph Barnes at the University of Iowa, where we made use of "movies" in certain aspects of industrial engineering, particularly, "time and motion studies." Now for over 20 years, I have found such films invaluable in evaluating gundog performance in the field and in measuring and improving ability to judge. It seems to me that films could be routinely used in the training of judges and in improving the retriever field trial game. As a suggestion, a possible experiment is outlined in this context.

Item 1.--Measurement experiment: Secure five nationally recognized competent handlers. Have each handler select a young all-age retriever who is not yet "finished"; be sure that he is competent, but not .... Now we have five ordered pairs (teams), namely;

A = (handler one, retriever one)
B = (handler two, retriever two)
C = (handler three, retriever three)
D = (handler four, retriever four)
E = (handler five, retriever five).

Obviously, we would assign the letter identification to the teams by a strictly random process.

Next, have two eight-point judges, say, Judge X and Judge Z, set up five blinds, say two on land, two on water, and one clearly involving both land and water. Identify the blinds as B_1, B_2, B_3, B_4, B_5.

Request each team to run B_1, where the order of running is determined randomly; say, the order is as follows:

$$B, \quad E, \quad A, \quad C, \quad D.$$

Record each performance on each blind on film, complete with sound; carefully identify each blind and each performance.

Next, request each retriever to run B_2, where again the order of running is determined randomly; say the order for B_2 is as follows:

D, A, E, B, C.

Again record each performance on film, complete with sound, and properly identified.

Continuing, for B_3 suppose the randomized order is as follows:

E, B, C, D, A.

For B_4, the randomized order could be as follows:

A, C, D, E, B.

And for blind five, B_5, the randomized order for retrieving the blind might be as follows:

Team C, Team D, Team B, Team A, Team E.

In tabular form, it is clear that the effect of order in which the blinds are run has been randomized "away" (hopefully).

Blind	Order of running				
	(1)	(2)	(3)	(4)	(5)
1	B	E	A	C	D
2	D	A	E	B	C
3	E	B	C	D	A
4	A	C	D	E	B
5	C	D	B	A	E

[*Aside:* Note that we have used a 5 × 5 Latin square as a point of departure.]

Summing up to this point. -- Now we have 25 performances on film (5 retrievers tested on 5 blinds), where performances on the film are ordered as follows:

Blind 1: B's performance; E's performance; A's performance; C's performance; and D's performance.

Blind 2: D's performance; A's performance; E's performance; B's performance; and C's performance.

.
.
.

Blind 5: C's performance; D's performance; B's performance; A's performance; and E's performance.

Item 2.-- Suppose we would like the judges to look at the blinds in some other sequence, say, one performance on the first blind, then another team's performance on the second blind, ... , then the last team's performance on the last blind. We can simply reorder the performances on the film. We assigned five positions (columns) of running order in our earlier tabulation, so we can order the performances in

$$5! = 5 \cdot 4 \cdot 3 \cdot 2 \cdot 1 = 120 \text{ ways.}$$

One (obvious) way in which the film could be spliced would be from the tabulation:

Performance of B on B_1
Performance of D on B_2
Performance of E on B_3 from column (1)
Performance of A on B_4
Performance of C on B_5

Performance of E on B_1
Performance of A on B_2
Performance of B on B_3 from column (2)
Performance of C on B_4
Performance of D on B_5

. . .

Performance of D on B_1 ⎫
Performance of C on B_2 ⎪
Performance of A on B_3 ⎬   from column (5).
Performance of B on B_4 ⎪
Performance of E on B_5 ⎭

Note that for the first film sequence, we ordered the performances according to the *rows* of our tabulation; for this film sequence, we have ordered the performances according to the *columns*.

Item 3.--Now suppose we ask each judge we test to independently record the number of whistle and cast refusals. This particular experiment does not involve an evaluation of overall performance, nor does it involve comparisons among entries; the experiment is artificial. A dummy table for recording these data might be as follows.

Film on performance of		Number of refusals	
Retriever	On blind	Whistle	Cast
B	B_1		
D	B_2		
E	B_3		
A	B_4		
C	B_5		
E	B_1		
.	.		
.	.		
.	.		
D	B_5		
.	.		
.	.		
.	.		
.	.		
.	.		
.	.		
E	B_5		

Item 4.--Comparison of results: The completed film can be submitted to a series of judges, and their results can be compared for both number of whistle refusals and number of cast refusals. In short, variability among judges can be obtained with regard to source, namely, blind, handler-retriever team, and judge.

*Item 5.--*After a "long" period of elapsed time, these same judges could be tested again on their ability to count refusals. Under certain assumptions, this replication could provide evidence concerning measurement error (see definition later in this chapter).

Suggestive Outline of Retriever Qualities Sought and Judges' Tools

J believes that a judge should be testing purposefully for particular characteristics when he sets up a test; moreover, *J* believes that a judge should know explicitly what he is testing for and state it clearly. *J* satisfies the assumptions concerning the judge (stated elsewhere in this book); one of these assumptions is that the judge is thoroughly familiar with *Standing Recommendations of the Retriever Advisory Committee* and the current color-book. In addition, *J* thinks that a judge might profit if he thinks of his repertoire as being a kit of tools; that is, *J* thinks that a judge should know, in an organized fashion, what tools are available to him to combine and utilize in a test. Because oftentimes one tends to overlook the obvious, *J* has found it convenient to keep ready-reference checklists (not all-inclusive) to refresh his memory.

Conceivably, the judges could (theoretically) set up tests to test explicitly for one or more selected characteristics of open retrievers, such as those in the following (incomplete) list.

> Nose
>
> Brains
>
> Marking and memory ability
>
> :

Drive

Softness of mouth

Line manners

.

.

.

Ability to use the wind

Ability to take a line

.

.

.

Attention

.

.

.

Willingness to handle

Courage

.

.

.

.

SELECTED FACTORS THAT JUDGES MIGHT
CONSIDER AS TOOLS

There are many so-called variables, V_{ij}, that a judge can choose, manipulate, or accept at the level with which they occur. It is worthwhile to list some of these that obviously come to mind; in fact, it is believed that each judge should keep his own list of such factors (both the obvious ones and the not-so-obvious ones). Obviously, any particular test involves a combination of these so-called variables.

Time and Number of Entries

The importance of time as a factor or variable and its maximum exploitation is stressed by guidelines and by experienced judges. Each

Behold, the master of the judging process can't master the cold, lightening, ... , rain, and thunder. *The author playing the role of judge, in the rain, with his judging book protected by clear plastic, licensed open stake, Middle Tennessee Amateur Retriever Club, March 9, 1968 (excised from a picture by Bob Steber: Courtesy Bob Steber and The Nashville Tennessean).*

First annual competition for the Governor's Trophy at the Bonnet Carré Spillway: The author collecting data for making judgments in the open stake, 1968.

judge needs rules to work by. To illustrate, criticize this hypothesis: The first series and/or the first combination of tests should not take more than a mean time of 5 minutes per dog in any open stake of 35 or more entries. By combining tests, say, the first and second series, judges may often save time. Running series back-to-back may also conserve time; cars, cover, canvas ready-boxes and blinds, and the like, can be used to separate back-to-back tests.

Weather

Judges have to take the weather pretty much as it comes, but whether or not you like the weather or not, judges can obtain information concerning the forecasts as well as estimated probabilities of changes; moreover, they can estimate at what time of day to expect the lowest and highest temperatures. Hence, they can exploit cold, frost, dew, heat, rain, sleet, snow, wind, sunshine, clouds, and the like, to assist in testing fairly for selected characteristics.

Wind.--Wind is so obviously important and useful to judges that no comment probably is required. Undeniably, both direction and velocity of the wind can be either highly variable, or static, or somewhere in between in any given test. Judges can and often do exploit the wind to good advantage, say, falls or blinds crosswind, downwind, directly into the wind, or other varying angles; but the newly initiated members of the fraternity might well keep in mind the lyrics of a song popular in the 1940's which lead up to the conclusion "that's why we call the wind Maria!"

ACTION ITEMS

Often judges set tests where glare on water as well as the sun interferes. Assume a clear day and bright sunshine.

Item 1.--Assume constant wind of 10 m.p.h. from a given essentially westerly direction. Set up a water triple starting at noon and *intentionally* plan for glare to be a problem late in the afternoon. Demonstrate that you can intentionally "make a mistake." Check late in the afternoon to see if you made the mistake.

Item 2.--Assume wind from due west at 10 m.p.h., the sun sets at due west, and the first dog runs at 1:00 p.m. You estimate that the sun will be "low" between 4:30 and 5:30 p.m., but you must use that daylight to finish the test. Set up a land test consisting of 4 retrieves: a double mark (a dead pheasant and a flying hen) followed by a double blind (a short blind of 40 yards and a long blind of 170 yards).

In order to have downwind marks and falls, your line must face essentially east; your back is to the sun. Your terrain forbids running behind the line. How do you set the test to avoid the retriever's having to look directly into the sun when he responds to the whistle (on the blinds) between 4:30 and 5:30 in the afternoon?

Terrain

The judges can choose to exploit either land or water or a combination of the two, always taking background and skyline into consideration.

Land.--Among the choices (levels of this variable) the judges have are knolls, fences, brush, clumps, trees, logs, hills, ditches, terraces, row crops, other crops, roads, dry rice paddies, plough, sand, mud, points, woods, rushes, sagebrush, tules, cattails, briars, and/ or other.

Water.-- The judges may have many choices of this variable; they may have all wading water, all swimming water, moving versus still water, swimming water followed by wading water and vice versa, open water versus other, bayous, sloughs, channels and water-filled ditches, variable distances of the water from the line, location of decoys, boats or no boats, intermittent land, islands, and other.

Combined land and water.--Many combinations of water and land or land and water are obviously available.

Cover. -- Cover may be available in many choices, from plough to stubble to standing crops; or say, scanty, moderate, ... , or heavy marsh; sand or mud; other (see "land").

Up or down. --Oftentimes judges have the choice of placing the line where tests can be run down from embankments, fills, levees, or downhill across a valley and then up a hill, or uphill ... , and the like.

Game

Supply and condition of game may vary from trial to trial. Game can be either live or dead, duck (drake versus duck) or pheasant (cock versus hen).

Falls and Game

Falls can be either controlled or uncontrolled; that is, thrown dead pheasant versus shot flier, shot live duck versus thrown shackled or dead duck. Number of falls can vary from zero, a flyaway, to three or more.

Guns (Gunners)

Length of ride-out on fliers can be agreed upon in consultation with the gunners and in accordance with their recommendations. Number of shots by Guns can be specified; that is, more than one shot can be required of one or more Guns.

Guns can be asked to fire one or more dry shots. Guns can be retired versus retained in place and kept clearly visible. Handlers can be required to handle a gun and shoot or not shoot.

Firing Order

Obviously, there are many choices of the order of showing the falls to the dog. For an illustration, see Chapter Six for all possible combinations of the triple (marked) fall.

Trailing and Paths

The problem of paths and trailing is always in the back of the mind of the thoughtful judge; it tends to vary with cover, wind, time, number of dogs, and other factors in a stake. Sometimes, retrieves may be received away from the line to reduce the probability of trailing.

Blinds

Judges have the choice of cold blinds (removed from the area of falls) versus combining blinds with marked falls. Blinds can be run before marks which will follow in the area (cold) or can follow marked falls.

Location of blinds in relation to marked falls can be varied between falls, outside of falls, on the nearside of Guns, beyond Guns, and other. Guns can be positioned in the field when blinds are being run or Guns can be hidden, not placed in the field or withdrawn completely. Moreover, blinds can be set up with or without diversions.

In combined seen and unseen falls, retrieves of marked falls can be received behind "hides" (cars, cover, canvas, and the like), if necessary, to allow blinds to be planted.

ACTION ITEM

This preliminary (sketchy) outline of qualities sought in retrievers and judges' tools which has been set forth for consideration is conspicuously incomplete. This inexhaustive outline was purposefully prepared with deficiencies and left incomplete (items were actually deleted), because it is believed that each judge should go through a thought-provoking exercise for himself. Hence, it is suggested that he who judges review pertinent literature on the retriever and retriever field trials; then, using his own experience and know-how, prepare his own checklists for ready-reference (and review his checklists before each judging assignment).

Illustration of Why Tests are Set

Earlier, it was pointed out that "... $\mathcal{J}$ believes that a judge should know explicitly what he is testing for and state it clearly." The tests described in Figure 10-1 (short blind, double marked fall, long blind) were designed for several purposes:

   1.   To see if the entry would take a "good line" and handle sharply on a short blind.

   2.   To see if the entry could mark a long fall--flying pheasant, essentially downwind.

   3.   To see if the entry could remember a fall (dead pheasant) past an old blind, after having picked up a flying pheasant; moreover, to see if he would drive (past the old blind with not more than a mere honor of his nose) through cold water directly to such a fall.

   4.   To see if, after picking up a flying pheasant, the entry would take a line past an old blind, back into cold water, through an old fall, on up a hill to another unseen fall. If he drifted with the wind, would he still handle into the wind?

   5.   To test for steadiness while another dog worked.

In short, the tests were explicitly designed for lining ability, control, marking, memory, courage, nose, and steadiness.

Increasingly more difficult.--Ideally, $\mathcal{J}$ would like to design tests where each successive test is somewhat more difficult than the previous test.

Probability of separating a specified pair of open retrievers selected strictly at random.--Let

P_M = probability of separation based on a "tough" mark,

P_{MM} = probability of separation based on a "tough" (marked) memory retrieve,

P_{LB} = probability of separation based on a "tough" land blind,

P_{WB} = probability of separation based on a "tough" water blind.

Using Pontchippi (McMahan) type tests and Pontchippi (McMahan) ability

Figure 10-1. -- Blind, double mark (mark and memory), blind, honoring. Pick up B₁ ; mark and pick up mark and memory, M₁ and M₂ or M₂ and M₁ ; pick up B₂ after the marked falls.

to evaluate performances under trial conditions, the relative magnitude of the probability of separating any pair of open retrievers selected strictly at random is as follows (from Chapter Fourteen):

$$P_M \quad < \quad P_{MM} \quad < \quad P_{LB} \quad < \quad P_{WB} .$$

From the foregoing, if "difficulty" is operationally defined in terms of probability of separation, it follows logically why McMahan prefers to begin a stake with mark and memory retrieves, more explicitly, why he prefers not to begin with a blind.

ACTION ITEM

Assertion: The "tough, honest water blind" is the most difficult portion of the open curriculum to teach the retriever. If the water blind were legislated out of open stakes, there would be 10 to 100 times more field champions. Discuss. Is the water blind the most difficult "subject" to teach? With the number of trials conducted today, would you expect 10 to 100 times more field champions than we have?

In practice, the ideal of making each test more difficult than the previous test is not only difficult, but is also elusive. In addition, the other judge may have strong feelings about starting an open stake with a land blind; even when a pair of judges is able to design tests along what they think is a continuum of difficulty, circumstances developing during a trial may dictate changes.

Example. -- In a licensed amateur stake which I judged in the spring of 1968, we had planned (for the fifth series) a difficult marked triple on pheasant (two fliers, one dead); the dead bird, first down, was to be thrown on a hillside beyond (across) a sizeable lake (and the water was cold--February). When we came to the fifth series, we decided to change the test and make it somewhat easier; this decision was based on the quality of dog work observed up to that point, and on the fact that only two entries had really topnotch work.

Proportion called back. -- I like to call back four out of five dogs after each series. For convenience, designate the double marked fall as the first series, and designate the two blinds as the second series (see Figure 10-1 again). Hence, for the third series, we would like to call back

$$\frac{4}{5} \times \frac{4}{5} \quad \text{or} \quad \frac{16}{25} \quad \text{of the starters.}$$

There were 33 starters (35 listed in the program); we would like to have

$$(33) \times \left(\frac{16}{25}\right) = 21.12 \quad \text{entries}$$

back for the third series. Actually, 22 were called back, so by these standards the tests could not be labelled "too difficult."

Whose test(s). -- Oftentimes after tests are set and run, a critic or critics will comment that those tests reflect Judge A; they are too tough; Judge B would not set tests that difficult. These are unjustified assertions, in that both judges must contribute to the design of tests.

"Can't wait fast enough." -- On numerous occasions in my life, it seemed to me that time just would not pass. For the reader who feels that we have not gotten to the heart of measurement "fast enough," we are at last ready to face up squarely to the problems.

MEASUREMENT

It is assumed that the experienced RE at least has a vague notion of what can be measured and how. Moreover, since this is a book on methods and theory, the (measurement) process itself would seem to be an appropriate topic to discuss. There is yet another valid reason for discussing the measurement process. It is well-known that after completing a given series, the novice handler almost invariably is concerned with the numerical score assigned to his retriever. Likewise, the neophyte judge usually begins his judging career utilizing some sort of numerical scoring system. In view of such widespread concern with numerical scoring, it seems practically mandatory to include an oversimplified examination of the whole process of measurement.

Thesis.--The thesis of this chapter is that the judge in the field has to make two decisions as far as the measurement process goes: (1) He must decide to call a retriever back or not to call him back, and (2) in the process of making the awards, he must compare every retriever with every other retriever, in pairs; that is, for each pair, the judge must exercise judgment and make a decision that one performance is better than the other. This is "all" he has to do.

Since the judgmental process is complex, the mechanical process of measuring must be as simple as practicable. Hence, McMahan asserts that there is no need to use any such (interval) scoring system as 10 points per bird, 10 points per series, or the like--not even as quick reference for making callbacks.

"Standing Recommendations"

The "standing recommendations" quoted below appear to be valid, and should be followed in the field:

> ... Before arriving at their final placings in any stake, the *Judges should make direct comparisons, series for series, between all ... their dogs under consideration* for those places. Such comparisons permit each Judge to be certain that the dog placed first has given a relatively better performance throughout the stake than the second-place dog. ... The fourth-place dog should be compared directly with all that are unplaced ... .

> ... In the final ... analysis of the various perfor-
> mances, a direct and detailed comparison of the work by one
> dog versus the work of another .... Careful comparisons
> are heartily recommended ....
>
> ... When the stake is completed, the several Judges will
> arrive at their final decision about placings on the basis of
> which dog, relatively, did better work than another in each
> of the several series ....

In quoting the foregoing material, I carefully "edited out" any reference to scores, because I think scores are not only useless, but are also dangerous. It seems to me that when a judge writes down a score, he appears "to be stuck with it." In fact, I assert that entries should be called back on a comparative basis only--never on the basis of a cut-off score.

Note that "comparative basis only" implies (1) no pre-set absolute standards of passability; and (2) only tentative classification of "callback" or "not callback" (except for complete failure to "bring back the meat") on a per dog basis--no final decision until all entries have been observed.

To be even more explicit, in a 50 dog stake, I'd want to run under a judge who is aware that over the trial $\binom{50}{2}$ or 1,225 comparisons can be made, that his decision (based on gross judgment and gross comparison) regarding the callbacks is most important, and that, in order to make the final placings, at most he merely has to choose between two retrievers at any one time.

Measurement, Scales, and Errors

Quantitative description is called measurement. Hence, measurement amounts to an assignment of symbols or numerals to events or objects in accordance with an explicit set of rules. With gross oversimplification, "measuring instruments" can be classified into nominal scales, ranking scales, and other scales to include interval and ratio scales. As a point of departure, I state dogmatically that as American trials are conducted and judged (as of 1970), interval and ratio scales should not be used by judges in the field (the basis for this statement appears later in this chapter).

Examples of a nominal scale.--On each marked fall in an open stake, a retriever is classified as either "breaking" (not steady, say, $\bar{S}$) or "not breaking" (steady, S), even though the judges usually explicitly classify only those retrievers who "break" and must be eliminated from the stake. On a test involving a triple mark, the retriever is classified by whether he was "handled" (H) or was "not handled" ($\bar{H}$). Moreover, after each retrieve, the judges classify the entry either as "hardmouthed" (rarely) or "not hardmouthed" (the usual implicit classification). On a handling test in an open stake, a retriever is classified as either "completing under control" or "completing the retrieve out of control." These are examples of measurement, where the process amounts to mere classification, the naming process, plus the assignment of a symbol. This scale is involved in many fundamental aspects of each and every American licensed retriever field trial. To elaborate with one more explicit example: At the end of each series (except the last), the judges furnish a list of retrievers to be tested further (in the next series); hence, each retriever has been classified as either a "callback" (C) or "not a callback" ($\bar{C}$)-- dropped. To the experienced retriever enthusiast (RE), the obvious importance (to the entry) of this classification needs no further comment.

Examples of a ranking scale.--If two performances can be told apart, classified, and if in addition one of the performances has more of a specified quality than the other, an ordinal or ranking scale can be used. Style may be difficult to measure, because we don't usually think in "units of style"; however, we can state an opinion that one retriever is more stylish than another. Likewise, it is difficult to state how much better the line manners of one retriever are than the line manners of another retriever; nevertheless, we can clearly prefer the line manners of one over those of another.

On a single marked fall, one retriever, A, goes "directly" to the fall, and another retriever, B, hunts a "wide area"; we can say that A's performance was better than B's (even though we don't dare say how much better); in short, A ranks higher than B on this retrieve. Derby C hits the water with speed and splash, but derby D "tip-toes through the tules" slowly into the water; most judges probably would rank C's water-entry over D's water-entry, even though no attempt would be made to measure how much better C's water-entry is than D's.

The judging of any retriever trial requires comparison after comparison after comparison--extensive use of the ranking scale. "How much better," in an absolute sense, is not involved, only that one retriever is relatively better than another; in fact, most American judges would be better off if they never concerned themselves in the practical judging situation with "how much" in terms of "blank number of units" better. At the risk of being obnoxiously repetitious, this last statement implies that (as of 1970) scales of greater complexity than ranking scales, namely, interval and ratio scales, should not be used in the field by most judges of American retriever trials.

To continue with another example, when two judges announce that a trial is over, I assume that they have a clear and obvious winner, W. That is, I assume that they have examined (compared) their data on the leading performances in that stake and have concluded that W's performance outranks all other performances; note particularly that the judges are not required to specify how much W's performance surpasses the performance of the second placed retriever. In short, an ordinal (ranking) scale can be used (in all the foregoing cases) because the symbols greater than (>) and less than (<) are appropriate. When two performances cannot be ranked one over the other, judges would classify them essentially indistinguishable ("equal").

As was indicated earlier, it is well-known that over a licensed trial, the judges are required to make many comparisons. If a set of judges has terminated an open stake after obtaining a clear and obvious winner after several series, I assume that a first task will be to make the comparisons necessary for preparing a list of callbacks for the "next series"--if one were to be conducted. Obviously, then comparisons must be made to determine the places; this is sometimes expedited by ranking into two groups, say, clearly JAM's versus not clearly JAM's (to be considered for places). Then after several additional comparisons, it must turn out that the performance of the winner (first place), say, P_1, must outrank the second place performance, say, P_2; symbolically, $P_1 > P_2$. The second place performance must outrank the third place performance, P_3; in shorthand, $P_2 > P_3$. The third place performance must outrank the fourth place performance, that is, $P_3 > P_4$. Finally, the fourth place performance must outrank the performance of the best performance among those awarded JAM's.

[*Aside: Random assigning of places.*--There must have been a clear winner; otherwise, additional series would have been conducted to find the retriever to whom first place would be awarded. Ideally, other places should be clearly differentiated also, but occasionally this ideal cannot be attained within the limited time available. If two judges cannot distinguish a noticeable difference (that makes a difference) between, say, third and fourth place, then I suggest the judges consider determining third place with a randomizing device. I make this suggestion in spite of the fact that each time this opinion is voiced, it evokes not only vigorous but almost unanimous protest.]

Up to this point in the placings, the results of the comparisons are known only to the judges themselves. The announcement will indicate

$$P_1 > P_2 > P_3 > P_4 > P_{any\ JAM},$$

but the judges are not required to assert that it is or is not equidistant between P_1, P_2, P_3, and P_4. Neither are they required to specify the distance in terms of certain units between any two performances, say, between P_2 and P_3. In short, "how much" in terms of specified units is not even involved; the task is to rank the performances--

to establish *relative* position.

Thus it is clear that, at most, measurement of retriever performance is "measurement by paired comparisons." If 5 retrievers complete a trial, we have to make $\binom{5}{2}$ or 10 comparisons to determine the places. As a result, we then have the 5 retrievers ranked.

Example.-- In a 25 dog stake, suppose the following numbered entries complete the trial (and we have an obvious winner):

$$19, \quad 13, \quad 24, \quad 2, \quad 5.$$

Suppose that by gross inspection we observe that entry number 5 is the winner; we start with entry 5 and compare this retriever with every other retriever:

$$
\begin{array}{llll}
5 & vs & 2 & \text{and we see} & 5 > 2, \\
5 & vs & 13 & \ldots & 5 > 13, \\
5 & vs & 19 & \ldots & 5 > 19, \\
5 & vs & 24 & \ldots & 5 > 24,
\end{array}
$$

where we read the symbol > as "is better than." Now by gross inspection, we observe that number 24 appears to be second, so we compare 24 with the other 3 (the winner, 5, has been excluded):

$$
\begin{array}{llll}
24 & vs & 2 & \text{and} & 24 > 2, \\
24 & vs & 13 & \ldots & 24 > 13, \\
24 & vs & 19 & \ldots & 24 > 19;
\end{array}
$$

thus, number 24 is awarded second place. For third place, let's try number 2 versus the other 2 retrievers (5 and 24 have been placed):

$$2 \quad vs \quad 13 \quad \text{and} \quad 2 > 13,$$
$$2 \quad vs \quad 19 \quad \ldots \quad 2 > 19;$$

hence, number 2 is awarded third place. For fourth place, we compare entries 13 and 19:

$$13 \quad vs \quad 19 \quad \text{and} \quad 19 > 13;$$

so number 19 is awarded fourth place. Obviously, entry 13 is awarded the JAM.

Now we have the 5 retrievers ranked as follows:

First position: 5, who ranked above 4 retrievers.
Second position: 24, who ranked above 3 retrievers.
Third position: 2, who ranked above 2 retrievers.
Fourth position: 19, who ranked above 1 retriever.
Fifth position: 13, who ranked above 0 retriever.

In shorthand,

$$5 \quad > \quad 24 \quad > \quad 2 \quad > \quad 19 \quad > \quad 13.$$

We have ranked the five retrievers by making all possible paired comparisons. Note that we have used no scores whatsoever; the effort was made in deciding whether or not one retriever was better than another retriever in this stake. We merely look at our sketches and notes (data) on the performances of two retrievers and choose one; ... ; and repeat until we have made all possible paired comparisons.

Examples of interval and ratio scales.--If in addition to being able to classify and rank two objects it is also possible to state that one object is a specified number of units more than another, one may use an interval scale, say, degrees on a clinical thermometer. In addition, if the scale has a true zero point, it is called a ratio scale, such as pounds.

Again, I believe the evidence indicates that judges should not attempt to use an interval scale (much less a ratio scale) in judging performances of retrievers in American field trials. Nevertheless, interval scoring scales are discussed in the next section because so many RE's seem to use them. Moreover, such scales may be of value in discussing theoretical aspects of judging (in Chapters Twelve and Thirteen).

Danger!--There is danger in attempting to use too complex a scale. One should not attempt to use a ranking scale when only a nominal scale is appropriate; neither should one attempt to use an interval scale when only a ranking scale is appropriate.

[*Aside:* "*Gozintarin.*"-- Perhaps grade school youths learn long division earlier today, but I recall being introduced to the subject in the fourth grade. Moreover, when I was a youngster, a much higher proportion of the adult population of the South couldn't read, write, and do arithmetic.

A proud parent who couldn't do long division might, in order to "show-off" his child, have made a statement somewhat like this: "Why don't you do some 'gozintarin' for Aunt Ell?" What he meant is the following:

$$
\begin{array}{r}
554 \\
554 \overline{)306916} \\
2770 \\
\hline
2991 \\
2770 \\
\hline
2216 \\
2216 \, .
\end{array}
$$

That is, 554 *goes into* (gozinta) 3,069 five times, with 299 left over; 554 also *gozinta* 2,991 five times with 221 left over; and 554 *gozinta* 2,216 exactly four times.

It seems that many judging procedures, particularly scoring systems, have been passed from one person to another without critical examination, and that much of what's "left over" in judging remains at the "gozintarin" level.]

MEASUREMENT STUDY, ERROR

In Chapter Six, The Triple Mark, we considered the problem of degree of difficulty in setting up a triple. Triads were utilized and the analysis was made in terms of paired comparisons. From Table 6-4, an index of consistency could be calculated; this would provide a measure of a judge's ability to rank ways of setting up a triple with respect to difficulty. Note that no "right answer" is provided since a judge could be consistent and yet be "wrong."

ACTION ITEM

Review pages 151 through 169 of Chapter Six.

Definition of Measurement Error
The failure of a single judge to assign the same classification or score to (essentially) the same performance under essentially the same conditions (or to data on that performance) is called measurement error.

(The contribution of each judge who participated in the experiments described herein is gratefully acknowledged.)

Experiment Number One, Measurement Error
Several years ago, I prepared diagrams of 9 retriever performances on a marked land triple; then I had a mirror image prepared for each performance. These 18 diagrams were well coded and ordered strictly at random. Each of several judges was provided a set of these 18 diagrams, each set being in a different random order, and each judge was furnished the following instructions.

Judging American Retriever Trials
Experiment Number One

Identification number: ___0000000___

Experience of judge: Check most experienced category.

( ) "Five-point open and five-point amateur judge."

( ) "Five-point open judge."

( ) "Five-point amateur judge."

( ) Judged at least one open stake in a licensed trial.

( ) Judged at least one amateur stake in a licensed trial.

( ) Handled at least one entry which placed or received a JAM in an open stake in a licensed trial.

( ) Handled at least one entry which placed or received a JAM in an amateur stake in a licensed trial.

( ) Handled at least one entry which placed in a qualifying stake in a licensed trial.

( ) Other (specify): _____

_____

_____ .

INSTRUCTIONS

1.   Refer to the diagrams which follow and make these assumptions: This is the first series in an open all-age stake in a licensed trial. There is no wind (dead calm). It is a land triple: the first bird is a dead hen pheasant, the second bird is a shot flying hen pheasant, and the last bird down is a shot flying cock pheasant. In all situations, assume that the retriever picks up the birds in the following order: cock pheasant first (last bird down picked up first), flying hen second, and the dead hen last (this was the first bird thrown). In some of the diagrams, the cock pheasant is on the left as in Figure 1; in other diagrams, the cock pheasant is on the right as in Figure 2 . [Figures not reproduced here.]

Action Item: Inspect Figures 1 and 2 on the preceding two pages. [Again, figures not included here.]

[You are going to be requested to evaluate retriever performance on this test; however, the score (grade or classification) you assign will be used only for providing a quick method for callbacks.]

2. Further assume that you have 18 identical Labrador retrievers with respect to appearance (but not performance) as follows: black, male, exactly 5 years of age, medium-fast, stylish, merry tail, good nose, and the like.

3. On each of the next 18 pages, you have a diagram which shows the path of a retriever to each fall. [*Note:* The diagrams are not included in this book.] Use any classification (grading or scoring) system whatsoever; please assign a classification (grade or score) to each performance.

4. Assume that each retriever returns directly to the handler (no leg-lifting, no drops, no re-gripping, and the like).

5. Check or describe the scoring system which you plan to use:
    - ( )   10 points per series (a possible score of 10).
    - ( )   10 points per bird (a possible score of 30); that is, sum of the score on the first retrieve, plus the score on the second retrieve, plus the score on the third retrieve.
    - ( )   Letter grades: A, best; B; C; D; and so on.
    - ( )   Other (describe): _____

    _____

    _____.

6. In this experiment you do not have to rank or place the entries at the conclusion of the trial; you are merely asked to assign classifications (grades or scores).

7. Do not look back! Assign a classification (grade or score); turn
the page; do not look back!

As stated explicitly in instruction "1," this experiment was conducted to generate data for callbacks; however, my experience leads
me to infer that "most" judges who assign numerical scores use those
scores to assist in assigning places (ranks). Suppose then, for purposes of illustration, that we examine the data from five purposefully
selected (a nonrandom sample of) judges under the assumption that
these data are later used to assign ranks (places).

Ten points per bird.--A high proportion of the judges who participated in this experiment used a system of 10 points per bird, 30
points for the series. Even though no evidence was obtained from this
experiment concerning how this system is carried out over a stake,
does this imply that a stake composed of, say, a land triple (3 birds),
a land blind (1 bird), a water triple (3 birds), and a water blind (1
bird) would have a total of 80 points (more explicitly, 60 points for
marks and 20 points for blinds)? If so, a short "diversion" mark
has the same weight as the tough water blind, and marks are weighted
three times greater than are blinds (see pages 434 through 444). Is
this what the judge really desires?

Philosophy.--Even gross inspection of the results of this experiment indicates that these judges apparently reflect different philoso-
phies. For example, some judges seemed to desire that the dog pick
up the first bird that he went after, the shot flying cock, quickly; if he
didn't, he was penalized severely. Other judges seemed to desire that
the retriever do only workmanlike jobs on the first two retrieves, but
that the job on the long memory bird (thrown dead pheasant) was the
really important retrieve.

Results from experiment number one are presented in Tables
10-1, 10-2, 10-3, 10-4, and 10-5.

Arithmetic errors.--In the field on licensed judging assignments,

Table 10-1.--Scores assigned by Judge Number One using 10 points per bird, by type of bird, original sketch (O) and mirror image (MI), and rank in terms of score for the series, experiment number one, 1965-1966

Sketch of performance of retriever	Shot cock		Shot hen		Dead hen		Score for series		Rank by scores	
	O	MI	O	MI	O	MI	O	MI	O	MI
A	10	10	10	10	5	5	25	25	1	1
B	5	5	4	5	10	10	19	20	5	4
C	5	5	5	5	6	6	16*	16	7.5	8
D	6	7	5	5	5	5	16	17	7.5	7
E	9	9	7	7	5	4	21	20	3	4
F	8	**	10	**	3	**	21	[21]**	3	2**
G	10	10	7	7	4	3	21	20	3	4
H	10	10	5	6	3	3	18	19	6	6
J	5	5	4	4	4	3	13	12	9	9

* Judge calculated score to be 21.

** Either did not complete and return, or was not provided due to the author's error.

Table 10-2.--Scores assigned by Judge Number Two using 10 points per bird, by type of bird, original sketch (O) and mirror image (MI), and rank in terms of score for the series, experiment number one, 1965-1966

Sketch of performance of retriever	Shot cock		Shot hen		Dead hen		Score for series		Rank by scores	
	O	MI	O	MI	O	MI	O	MI	O	MI
A	10	10	10	10	6	6	26	26	1	1
B	6	7	6	7	10	10	22	24	2.5	2
C	5	7	5	7	7	8	17	22	8	4
D	7	7	6	5	5	6	18	18	7	8
E	10	10	9	8	3	3	22	21	2.5	6
F	9 –	9	10	10	3	3	22 –	22	4.5	4
G	10	10	9 –	9	3	3	22 –	22	4.5	4
H	10	10	6 +	7	3	3	19	20	6	7
J	4	5	5	5	3	3	12	13	9	9

Note: Data are presented as they were reported.

Table 10-3. --Grades assigned by Judge Number Three using a letter grade per series, original sketch (O) and mirror image (MI), and rank in terms of grade for the series, experiment number one, 1965-1966

Sketch of performance of retriever	Grade for series		Rank in terms of grade	
	O	MI	O	MI
A	C	C	2	2
B	B	B	1	1
C	D	D	4.5	4
D	D	F	4.5	7.5
E	D	D	4.5	4
F	F	D	8	4
G	D	F	4.5	7.5
H	F	F	8	7.5
J	F	F	8	7.5

Table 10-4.--Scores assigned by Judge Number Four using 10 points per bird, by type of bird, original sketch (O) and mirror image (MI), and rank in terms of score for the series, experiment number one, 1965-1966

Sketch of performance of retriever	Shot cock		Shot hen		Dead hen		Score for series		Rank by scores	
	O	MI	O	MI	O	MI	O	MI	O	MI
A	10	10	10+	10	7+	7	28[sic]	27	1	1
B	7	9	6+	7+	10	10	23+	26+	2	2
C	8	5	7	4	8	6	23*	15	3	8
D	8+	8+	7	7	5+	5	21[sic]	20+**	6.5	6
E	10	9	9+	9	2	3	21+	21	5	4
F	9	9	10	10	2	2	21	21	6.5	4
G	10	10	9	9	3	2	22	21	4	4
H	10	10	8	7+	2	2	20	19+	8	7
J	4	3	4	4	2+	3	10+	10	9	9

Note: Data are presented as they were reported, except as noted below.

* Judge calculated score to be 25 .

** Judge calculated score to be 22 +.

Table 10-5.--Scores assigned by Judge Number Five using 10 points per bird, by type of bird, original sketch (O) and mirror image (MI), and rank in terms of score for the series, experiment number one, 1965-1966

Sketch of performance of retriever	Shot cock		Shot hen		Dead hen		Score for series		Rank by scores	
	O	MI	O	MI	O	MI	O	MI	O	MI
A	10	10	10	10	$8\frac{1}{2}$	8	$28\frac{1}{2}$	28	1	1
B	9	9	8	8	10	10	27	27	2	2
C	9	9	8	8	$8\frac{3}{4}$	$8\frac{1}{2}$	$25\frac{3}{4}$	$25\frac{1}{2}$	3	3.5
D	9	9	8	8	8	8	25	25	4	5
E	$9\frac{1}{2}$	$9\frac{1}{2}$	$9\frac{1}{2}$	9	5	6	24	$24\frac{1}{2}$	6	6
F	$9\frac{1}{2}$	$9\frac{1}{2}$	$9\frac{3}{4}$	$9\frac{1}{2}$	4	5	$23\frac{1}{4}$	24	7	7
G	10	10	$9\frac{1}{2}$	$9\frac{1}{2}$	5	6	$24\frac{1}{2}$	$25\frac{1}{2}$	5	3.5
H	10	10	$8\frac{1}{2}$	8	4	$4\frac{1}{2}$	$22\frac{1}{2}$	$22\frac{1}{2}$	8	8
J	$7\frac{1}{2}$	7	7	7	5	5	$19\frac{1}{2}$	19	9	9

Note: Data are presented as they were reported.

I have been impressed by the arithmetic errors made by my co-judges. In this experiment, many judges made numerical errors in the totals for the series; in fact, two out of these (selected) judges made important errors in addition. (*Note:* The overall grade for the series was not made explicitly different from the sum of the three retrieves since the judge indicated that the grade for the series was the sum of the scores on each individual retrieve.) For example, in Table 10-1, a score of 21 was reported erroneously for a score of 16; had this error not been detected, it would have changed the rank of retriever C from 7.5 to 3.5. [Judge Four, Table 10-4, made two serious errors in the operation of adding scores. Consequences: (1) retriever C would have been awarded second place rather than third place; (2) retriever D would have been awarded third place rather than ranked sixth.]

In view of the many errors in the operation of adding reported in this experiment, in combination with observed errors under trial conditions, I have a hunch that on this basis alone, judges should seriously consider avoiding the use of scoring systems where arithmetic operations are required. In short, my hypothesis is that errors in arithmetic occur frequently in American retriever trials and influence the assignment of places.

The complexity of the scale used in this experiment by Judge Number Three did not exceed a ranking scale; Judge Number Three did not use as complex a scale as an interval scoring system (Table 10-3). Note that he could not perform arithmetic operations on his data; hence, he could not make arithmetic errors. Moreover, his grading system forces him to compare; he is not wedded to some number which has great unreliability. Even when his grading system is unreliable, namely,

> D on the original,   F on the mirror image (sketch D),
>
> F on the original,   D on the mirror image (sketch F),
>
> D on the original,   F on the mirror image (sketch G),

he cannot stop; he must compare to determine whether or not he really intends a grade, say, F.

Judge Number Five used an interval system of scoring, namely, 10 points per bird (Table 10-5). The range of his scores was 6, from 4 to 10. Note that he did not stop with the seven digits 4, 5, 6, 7, 8, 9, 10, but he made use of "quarter points." If this system is followed to its logical conclusion, there would be $7 \times 4 = 28$ "scores" that he could use if he made use of the scale only from 4 to 10. *Question:* Does this judge intend to use such a "refined system" just for callbacks? Or does he intend to place his dogs based on such a system?

Let's examine his scores (from Table 10-5) for the series in detail, to include totals, and note the direction of the differences, d, where

$$d = (\text{score for original}) - (\text{score for mirror image});$$

refer to worksheet below. This judge assigned essentially the same

Sketch	Score for series		Positive or negative d
	O	MI	
A	$28\frac{1}{2}$	28	+
B	27	27	0
C	$25\frac{3}{4}$	$25\frac{1}{2}$	+
D	25	25	0
E	24	$24\frac{1}{2}$	−
F	$23\frac{1}{4}$	24	−
G	$24\frac{1}{2}$	$25\frac{1}{2}$	−
H	$22\frac{1}{2}$	$22\frac{1}{2}$	0
J	$19\frac{1}{2}$	19	+
Total	220.00	221.00	$(+) = 3$ $(-) = 3$

total score to the originals as to the mirror images. In addition, the direction of the differences averaged out, three were positive, three were zero, and three were negative. This leads me to hypothesize that this judge merely complicated matters for himself by using quarter points; in short, his use of quarter points merely added a component of random error which gave him no useful information whatsoever.

Comparison of ranks in terms of scores on original sketches versus mirror image sketches.--These data give an estimate of measurement error. Overall, it appears that judges perform fairly well; however, there are disturbing elements which deserve further consideration. Why, for example in Table 10-4, was retriever C ranked third on the original sketch and eighth on the mirror image?

ACTION ITEM

There are many aspects of Tables 10-1 through 10-5 that have not been explicitly discussed here. Examine the data and discuss.

Variability Among Judges Using Ranking Procedures, Experiment Number Two

This experiment was designed to measure variability among judges when ranking procedures were used. This experiment was identified as "experiment number two" and was conducted immediately following "experiment number one."

Instructions.-- Each judge was provided instructions as follows: Given nine performances from experiment number one, please assign a rank to each performance. That is, give rank number one to the best performance, ... , and rank number nine to the poorest performance. If you cannot distinguish between two or more performances, clip the pages together and place them in the appropriate position.

Comment: Note that (in this second experiment) a judge could look at all nine originals at one time, shift positions of the sketches, make paired comparisons; in short, he actually had the opportunity to perform "primary ranking." He could "look back," where in experiment number one he could not look back.

Results on experiment number two, for the same five judges as are reported in Tables 10-1 through 10-5 (experiment number one), are reported in Table 10-6.

Table 10-6.--Rank of sketches of the performances of nine "identical retrievers" on the same land triple mark, ranked independently by five different "open" judges, 1965-1966

Sketch of performance of retriever	Rank assigned by Judge Number				
	One	Two	Three	Four	Five
A	1	1	2	1	1
B	5.5	2	1	2	2
C	8	3	5	7	3
D	5.5	4	7	6	4.5
E	2.5	6	6	4	4.5
F	2.5	5	4	3	8
G	4	7	3	5	6
H	7	8	8	8	7
J	9	9	9	9	9

Conclusion: Undoubtedly, there is great variability among judges in the criteria used in comparing one performance with another. At least, these five judges had considerable disagreement.

ACTION ITEM

Conduct a similar experiment at a conference for judges; discuss results and criteria utilized.

Results from experiment number one and experiment number two have been combined and are reported in Table 10-7.

Concluding Comment

Like most experiments, this experiment was clearly artificial. In addition, the purpose of this particular triple was not explicitly stated, and this is important to the good judge. Nevertheless, these judges were presented with essentially identical data. With a single exception, they agreed that the performance of A was the best and the performance of J was the worst. Since there was considerable disagreement otherwise, it is not surprising that judgments vary under trial conditions when not only each "official judge," but each "gallery judge" as well, collects his own data.

From this experiment, it does seem clear that judges can recognize perfect or near perfect work as well as recognize failure or near failure. On the other hand, there is little evidence that judges have a clear conception of how to evaluate performances which are somewhat less than perfect.

The foregoing notwithstanding, it is believed that variability among judges can be reduced by participating in well-organized club discussions or workshops on evaluation of retriever performance.

Discussion of Selected Aspects of an Interval Scale--Theory

This portion of this chapter concerns scoring with an interval scale; it should not be used in the practical judging situation; it is for theoretical purposes only. The judge in this section is imaginary; we shall call him Ji; we shall pretend that he can use an interval scale and assign scores to retriever performances (reliably and accurately).

Sums

Ten points per bird retrieved. -- Some hypothetical (imaginary) judges could attempt to judge a field trial by assigning a score to each bird retrieved, say, 10 points for a perfect job, then they could add

Table 10-7.--Rank by five judges of original sketches of performances of nine identical retrievers, in terms of scores or grades assigned and by actual ranking (comparison), combined data from experiments one and two, 1965-1966

| Sketch of performance of retriever | Judge One | | Judge Two | | Judge Three | | Judge Four | | Judge Five | |
	Score	Ranked by Rank	Score	Ranked by Rank	Grade	Ranked by Rank	Score	Ranked by Rank	Score	Ranked by Rank
A	1	1	1	1	2	2	1	1	1	1
B	5	5.5	2.5	2	1	1	2	2	2	2
C	7.5	8	8	3	4.5	5	3	7	3	3
D	7.5	5.5	7	4	4.5	7	6.5	6	4	4.5
E	3	2.5	2.5	6	4.5	6	5	4	6	4.5
F	3	2.5	4.5	5	8	4	6.5	3	7	8
G	3	4	4.5	7	4.5	3	4	5	5	6
H	6	7	6	8	8	8	8	8	8	7
J	9	9	9	9	8	9	9	9	9	9

Source: Tables 10-1 through 10-6.

the scores to obtain a total score. Suppose that an open stake consists of 4 series, namely, a land triple, a land blind, a water triple, and a water blind; in other words, 6 "marks" and 2 blinds.

    Let

$$x = \text{score for a marked fall, and}$$
$$y = \text{score for a blind retrieve.}$$

The possible sum for marked falls would be:

$$\text{Possible sum for marks} = \sum_{i=1}^{6} x_i$$
$$= x_1 + x_2 + x_3 + x_4 + x_5 + x_6$$
$$\text{Possible sum for marks} = 60,$$

if each $x_i = 10$.

$$\text{Possible sum for blind retrieves} = \sum_{j=1}^{2} y_j$$
$$\text{Possible sum for blind retrieves} = 20,$$

if each $y_j = 10$.

Hence, the ratio of possible sums (weights) for marks to blinds is 60 to 20 or 3 to 1, even though 2 series have been on marked falls and 2 series on blind retrieves. If the hypothetical judge desires this type of ratio, it would be his privilege; the point is that the Ji should realize the ratio being used.

    Ten points per series.--If it is possible for an entry to score a possible 10 points per series, then in this example, since 2 series were composed of marks and 2 series were composed of blinds,

$$\text{possible sum for marks} = \sum_{i=1}^{2} x_i$$
$$\text{possible sum for marks} = 20;$$
$$\text{possible sum for blinds} = \sum_{j=1}^{2} y_j$$
$$\text{possible sum for blinds} = 20.$$

Hence, the ratio of weights for marks to blinds is equal, 20 to 20.

Furthermore, 2 series were held on land, a possible 20 points, and 2 series were held on water, a possible 20 points.

Averages

Mean (arithmetic).-- Ordinarily, when we refer to "*the* average" we intend the arithmetic mean, where each observation (score) has equal weight. Make believe that a judge, Ji, uses a 10-point scoring system, but that he calculates a mean score for each series. Given the following scores for a land triple: 10, 8, and 6.

Let

x_1 = score on first bird retrieved,

x_2 = score on second bird retrieved,

x_3 = score on third (last) bird retrieved.

By definition, the arithmetic mean is the value computed by adding the individual scores (x_i) and dividing by the number (n) of scores. Symbolically, let $\overline{x}$ (read "x-bar") refer to the observed arithmetic mean of a group (a sample) of scores. In shorthand, the mean (arithmetic) is defined as follows for this example:

$$\overline{x} = \frac{x_1 + x_2 + x_3}{3}.$$

Substituting the values of x_1, x_2, and x_3, numerically,

$$\overline{x} = \frac{10 + 8 + 6}{3}$$

$$\overline{x} = 8.$$

The definition of the mean in this example could be written as

$$\overline{x} = \frac{\sum_{i=1}^{3} x_i}{3}$$

(read $\sum_{i=1}^{3} x_i$ as "the sum of x-sub-i, from i = 1 to i = 3") and in general,

$$\overline{x} = \frac{\sum_{i=1}^{n} x_i}{n},$$

where the Greek capital letter sigma (Σ) indicates "sum of" and n is the number of observations.

Weighted mean. -- In Cane Creek Swamp, three duck blinds A, B, and C, had been constructed. Flight patterns, in combination with sound safety precautions, resulted in shot duck falling at essentially three locations and there was only one retriever located on a platform in front of blind C. The retriever made the following retrieves of duck to include "bonus duck":

> 4 shot from blind A at 120 yards,
> 7 shot from blind B at 60 yards,
> 5 shot from blind C at 20 yards.

What was the average length of retrieve per duck killed?

To solve this simple problem, multiply 120 yards by 4 (because there are 4 cases of 120-yard retrieves), 60 yards by 7, and 20 yards by 5, add, and then divide by the total number of duck, or 16. The result is as follows:

$$\frac{4 \times 120 + 7 \times 60 + 5 \times 20}{16} = \frac{1,000}{16} = 62.5 \text{ yards.}$$

It is useful to regard such a procedure as one of finding the "weighted mean" of the lengths of the retrieves. The weight of each kind of retrieve is the measure of its importance in the problem, and, obviously, it is equal to the number of duck involved in each case. To calculate the weighted mean, we multiply each retrieve by its weight, add the products, and divide by the sum of the weights as shown on the following page.

Retrieve, x_i (length of re- trieve in yards) (1)	Weight, w_i (number of duck retrieved) (2)	Retrieve times weight, $w_i x_i$ (3)
120	4	480
60	7	420
20	5	100
	16	1,000

Hence, the weighted mean $= 1,000/16 = 62.5$.

The products in column (3) can be given a special name. Retrieving 1 duck 20 yards is considered the same "amount of retrieving" as carrying 20 duck 1 yard. Thus the last product, 100, could be regarded as 100 duck retrieved 1 yard; likewise, the sum of products, 1,000, could be regarded as retrieving 1,000 duck 1 yard. The weighted mean retrieve is the equivalent number of duck carried 1 yard (or, "duck yards") divided by the actual number of duck.

Notation: It is convenient to utilize shorthand for the weighted mean (WM), where if x_i is a value and w_i its weight,

$$WM = \frac{w_1 x_1 + w_2 x_2 + \ldots + w_n x_n}{w_1 + w_2 + \ldots + w_n},$$

and utilizing the sign of summation,

$$WM = \frac{\sum_{i=1}^{i=n} w_i x_i}{\sum_{i=1}^{i=n} w_i}, \tag{1}$$

and, where the context is perfectly clear,

$$WM = \frac{\sum wx}{\sum w}.$$

Numerical example.--In the previous numerical example,

$$w_1 = 4, \quad w_2 = 7, \quad \text{and} \quad w_3 = 5,$$

while

$$x_1 = 120, \quad x_2 = 60, \quad \text{and} \quad x_3 = 20.$$

The average length of retrieve per duck killed can be obtained in terms of the weighted mean; hence,

$$WM = \frac{\sum\limits_{i=1}^{3} w_i x_i}{\sum\limits_{i=1}^{3} w_i},$$

and writing in expanded form,

$$
\begin{aligned}
WM &= \frac{w_1 x_1 + w_2 x_2 + w_3 x_3}{w_1 + w_2 + w_3} \\
&= \frac{(4)(120) + (7)(60) + (5)(20)}{4 + 7 + 5} \\
&= \frac{480 + 420 + 100}{16} \\
&= \frac{1,000}{16} \\
WM &= 62.5.
\end{aligned}
$$

The idea of the weighted mean is applicable to multiple retrieves in a test in a field trial; that is, tests in which the importance or difficulty of the retrieves is not equal; hence, scores (if one such as Ji could use an interval scale) to be combined are not simply the sum of separate scores or the simple average of separate scores.

Weights derived from consideration and judgment as to relative importance.--Suppose that a field trial was held in Cane Creek Swamp. Further suppose that the line was at blind C for a test involving a triple mark, where the first marked duck was thrown at blind A, approximately 120 yards; the second duck down was at blind B, or 60 yards away; and the last mark was in front of blind C, about 20 yards out.

Theoretically, let our imaginary judge Ji use a 10-point scoring system per series in combination with 10 points per bird, where each bird in a multiple-bird test is weighted according to the estimated difficulty of the retrieve. (Carefully note that we are now concerned with a weighted mean.) To be concrete and objective for purposes of illustration, suppose further that this (hypothetical) judge Ji assigns weights according to the relative length of the retrieve; that is,

6 points for the long bird,
3 points for the second bird down, and
1 point for the short bird,

because the long bird is 6 times as far away as the short bird, and the middle bird is 3 times as far away as the short bird.

Obviously, a judge considers more than mere distance to a fall (or blind) in assessing difficulties and hazards associated with marking a fall and/or making a retrieve; in the present context, for purposes of illustration, these estimates of difficulties are quantified (in terms of relative distance) in the form of weights to be assigned. Furthermore, the judge always keeps in mind that according to the rules, every bird must be picked up and the performance on each retrieve evaluated; in short, each bird "counts" and the retriever must complete the test to be eligible to be called back or to receive an award.

In practice, the weights would have been determined by the judge's careful consideration and judgment (here, for simplicity, the weights are relative lengths of the retrieves). Note that no longer are the weights the number of duck as in a previous example; the observation x_t is in terms of the score assigned by the judge based on his judgment of the observed performance of the retrieve.

In this example, we desire a weighted mean, where as before, the numerator is a weighted sum (WS) based on a possible score of 10 for each series. Hence,

$$WM_{10} \; = \; \frac{WS}{10} \; = \; \frac{\sum_{i=1}^{n} w_i x_i}{10} \, ,$$

where the subscript 10 denotes the sum of the weights and for a triple or 3 retrieves

$$WM_{10} \; = \; \frac{\sum_{i=1}^{3} w_i x_i}{10}$$

$$WM_{10} \; = \; \frac{w_1 x_1 \; + \; w_2 x_2 \; + \; w_3 x_3}{10} \, .$$

In this example, the first bird down was the long one at blind A, so $w_1 = 6$; the second bird down was out 60 yards with an assigned weight of $w_2 = 3$; and the last bird down, although picked up first, had an assigned weight of $w_3 = 1$. Hence, in this example, the weighted sum for the performance of a retriever in this series would be

$$WM_{10} \; = \; \frac{(6)(x_1) \; + \; (3)(x_2) \; + \; (1)(x_3)}{10} \, . \tag{2}$$

Note that all this planning has taken place before the first retriever runs. As any experienced field-trialer knows, the hypothetical judge might change his weights after seeing several retrievers perform; then he would have to return to his notebook and recalculate all scores.

A specified performance of a retriever.--Suppose that a retriever receives the following scores per bird, what score will he receive for the test?

9 for the short bird;

7 for the second bird down; and

5 for the long retrieve which, by dog's choice, was picked up last.

Noting that $x_1 = 5$, $x_2 = 7$, and $x_3 = 9$, and substituting in Eq. (2),

$$WM_{10} = \frac{(6)(5) + (3)(7) + (1)(9)}{10}$$

$$= \frac{30 + 21 + 9}{10}$$

$$= 60/10$$

$$WM_{10} = 6.$$

Unsound method number one.--Note the result when a hypothetical judge using 10 points per bird simply adds his 3 scores and divides by 3 to obtain a simple arithmetic mean (AM), the common average;

$$AM = \frac{x_1 + x_2 + x_3}{3}$$

$$= \frac{5 + 7 + 9}{3}$$

$$= 21/3$$

$$AM = 7.$$

Note that in general WM $\neq$ AM, and in this case WM $\neq$ AM because $6 \neq 7$.

In the judging situation.--A hypothetical judge in a hypothetical licensed trial obviously cannot be bothered with computing explicit weighted averages. If he uses a 10 points per series scoring system,

undoubtedly he assigns weights based on experience and intuition, and
these weights are reflected in the single (hypothetical) score he assigns to the performance.

Conclusion: In a test involving multiple retrieves, the competent hypothetical judge does not assign a possible k points per bird
and then proceed to record the simple average or simple sum of the
points.

Variability

Ranking according to total score (sums) or according to means
does not take into account the consistency (or lack of consistency) of
a retriever in a trial.

Range.--The range of scores gives an idea of the spread, the dis-
persion, or the unlikeness of individual scores. The distance (recall
that we are discussing an interval scale) between the highest and lowest values observed is called the range. In an earlier example, we
had 3 scores on a triple, 10, 8, and 6. The highest value is 10,
the lowest value is 6; hence, the range is 10 − 6 or 4.

Example.--Suppose that our imaginary judge uses a 10-point interval scale and assigns a single score for each series. Given 2 retrievers with identical total scores to be compared over 4 series as
follows:

$$\text{Retriever One } (R_1): \quad 10, \quad 10, \quad 10, \quad 2;$$
$$\text{Retriever Two } (R_2): \quad 8, \quad 8, \quad 8, \quad 8.$$

The range for R_1 is 10 − 2 = 8; the range for R_2 is 8 − 8 = 0.
Hence, R_2 might be preferred over R_1 because his work was good
and was less variable.

Sum of squares (ss) about the mean.--If the sample mean is subtracted from each observation in the sample, obviously, this gives a
deviation of each observation from the mean; then if each of these de-

viatons is squared, and if all such squared deviations are added together, the result is the sum of the squared deviations, which is called
the "sum of squares" (ss) about the mean. That is, in longhand,

"add up" (each observation − mean)^2,

and in shorthand,

$$ss \; = \; \sum_{i=1}^{n} (x_i - \overline{x})^2 \, .$$

It should be clear intuitively that (in a retriever trial where each retriever must make the same number of retrieves as every other retriever) the ss measures how different the individual scores are
from each other.

In our example, where $x_1 = 10$, $x_2 = 8$, $x_3 = 6$,

$$\overline{x} \; = \; \frac{10 + 8 + 6}{3} \; = \; 8 \, ,$$

the sum of squares, ss $= \; (x_1 - \overline{x})^2 \; + \; (x_2 - \overline{x})^2 \; + \; (x_3 - \overline{x})^2$,   and
substituting,

$$
\begin{aligned}
ss \; &= \; (10 - 8)^2 \; + \; (8 - 8)^2 \; + \; (6 - 8)^2 \\
&= \; (2)^2 \; + \; (0)^2 \; + \; (-2)^2 \\
&= \; 4 + 0 + 4 \\
ss \; &= \; 8 \, .
\end{aligned}
$$

Example. -- Suppose that our imaginary judge uses a 10-point scale
and assigns a single score for each series. Given 2 retrievers over
4 series as follows:

Retriever One (R_1)		Retriever Two (R_2)	
First series	10	First series	8
Second series	10	Second series	8
Third series	10	Third series	8
Fourth series	2	Fourth series	8
Sum	32	Sum	32
Mean	8	Mean	8

$$ss = (10 - 8)^2 + (10 - 8)^2$$
$$+ (10 - 8)^2 + (2 - 8)^2$$
$$= (2)^2 + (2)^2 + (2)^2 + (-6)^2$$
$$ss = 48.$$

$$ss = (8 - 8)^2 + (8 - 8)^2 + (8 - 8)^2$$
$$+ (8 - 8)^2$$
$$= (0)^2 + (0)^2 + (0)^2 + (0)^2$$
$$ss = 0.$$

Both retrievers have the same score (total or average), but Retriever Two is more consistent; hence, Ji might decide that

$$R_2 > R_1,$$

and declare Retriever Two to be the better in this trial.

Exploring Possibilities of Using Composite Scores

For purposes of discussion, assume that our imaginary judge Ji can use an interval scale "reliably and accurately." Also assume that Ji is seeking winning and placing retrievers who score high consistently (who give "good" performances with small variability). Further assume that Ji wants to be highly objective and let the combination of total score and range determine those who get the awards. Given a 4 series stake where Ji uses the "10 points per series scoring system," what combination of 4 scores, total, and range will beat another given combination?

Groups.--For convenience, we shall use the roster method of specifying "combinations of scores," call them "groups" composed of six elements as follows:

Score on the first series, S_1,

score on the second series, S_2,

score on the third series, S_3,

score on the fourth series, S_4,

total score over four series, T, and

range between the lowest and highest score, R.

Hence, each group will be composed of

$$\{S_1, \quad S_2, \quad S_3, \quad S_4, \quad T, \quad R\}.$$

To illustrate from an earlier example, a retriever had scores of

$$S_1 = 10, \quad S_2 = 10, \quad S_3 = 10, \quad S_4 = 2,$$

so over 4 series the total T = 32, and the range R = 8. This can be indicated in "group notation" as

$$\{10, \quad 10, \quad 10, \quad 2, \quad 32, \quad 8\}.$$

Possible number of groups. -- Excluding 0, thus using scores of 1 to 10, there are 10^4 or 10,000 possible combinations of scores (10,000 groups) with totals from 4 to 40 and ranges from 0 to 9. [See Notes to Chapter Ten.]

The question is, which group C_i (combination) beats another group C_j?

Comment: Clearly, the following group cannot be beaten:

$$C_1 = \{10, \quad 10, \quad 10, \quad 10, \quad 40, \quad 0\}.$$

If equal weight is assigned to each series, the following 4 groups, all equal, would beat the other 9,995 groups:

$$C_2 = \{10, \quad 10, \quad 10, \quad 9, \quad 39, \quad 1\},$$
$$C_3 = \{10, \quad 10, \quad 9, \quad 10, \quad 39, \quad 1\},$$

$$C_4 = \{10, \quad 9, \quad 10, \quad 10, \quad 39, \quad 1\},$$
$$C_5 = \{\ 9, \quad 10, \quad 10, \quad 10, \quad 39, \quad 1\}.$$

ACTION ITEMS

Item 1.--Suppose we ask Ji to rank the following four groups. How do you think he would rank them? (Assume equal weight for each series.)

$$C_6 = \{7, \quad 7, \quad 7, \quad 7, \quad 28, \quad 0\},$$
$$C_7 = \{6, \quad 8, \quad 6, \quad 8, \quad 28, \quad 2\},$$
$$C_8 = \{5, \quad 7, \quad 7, \quad 9, \quad 28, \quad 4\},$$
$$C_9 = \{6, \quad 6, \quad 6, \quad 10, \quad 28, \quad 4\}.$$

How would you rank them? Make all six paired comparisons,

$$C_6 \quad vs \quad C_7,$$
$$C_6 \quad vs \quad C_8,$$
$$C_6 \quad vs \quad C_9,$$
$$C_7 \quad vs \quad C_8,$$
$$C_7 \quad vs \quad C_9, \quad \text{and}$$
$$C_8 \quad vs \quad C_9,$$

making use of totals, ranges, and scores, series by series. Explicitly state your rationale.

Assign unequal weights to each series, and re-rank these four groups. Compare this ranking with your ranking of the four groups assuming equal weight.

Item 2.--Suppose we ask Ji to rank the following four groups:

$$C_{10} = \{\ 8, \quad 10, \quad 7, \quad 9, \quad 34, \quad 3\},$$
$$C_{11} = \{\ 8, \quad 9, \quad 9, \quad 8, \quad 34, \quad 1\},$$

$$C_{12} = \{\ 8,\quad 8,\quad 8,\quad 10,\quad 34,\quad 2\},$$
$$C_{13} = \{10,\quad 8,\quad 6,\quad 10,\quad 34,\quad 4\}.$$

Rank the preceding four groups and justify your ranking. (Assume equal weight for each series.)

Now assign unequal weights to the series; e.g., consider S_4 the water blind and weight the scores for S_4. Again rank the four groups and justify your ranking.

NUMBERS OF SUBCLASSES FOR A RANKING SYSTEM

Eleven-Point Scale ("Ten-Point System")

Suppose that a judge uses 11 classifications as follows:

0 (failure), 1, 2, 3, 4, 5, 6, 7, 8, 9, 10 ("pluperfect").

Suppose that dogs come to the line for a double mark and a double blind, 4 retrieves; further suppose there are 33 starters and that each dog is allowed to try every retrieve. Clearly, there are

$$33 \times 4 = 132 \text{ retrieves.}$$

Random assignment of classification.--If the performance on each retrieve is classified by a strictly random process, one would expect $132 \div 11$ or 12 retrieves in each classification such as is shown in the tabulation below.

Classification	0	1	2	3	4	5	6	7	8	9	10
Expected frequency	12	12	12	12	12	12	12	12	12	12	12

Obviously, in a field trial scores are not assigned at random. Moreover, the frequencies reflect the quality of the retrievers, and the type and difficulty of the test, and other factors. If the tests are "easy, " no doubt there will be few observed scores of 5 or less.

ACTION ITEM

Make a frequency distribution of classifications you actually assigned to (a) each retrieve and/or (b) each test in a stake which you judged recently. Note that you can complete this action item even if you do not use an interval scoring system.

Report as of November, 1959.--I kept records on several picnic trials (where I tried out a 10 points per series system) and found that my assignments concentrated on certain classes while others were seldom used.

Conclusion: An 11-point scale is too detailed for my use in the preliminary crude classification process. *Action:* Try a scheme with fewer classes.

Eight-Point Scale ("Seven-Point System")

Next I tried 8 classifications as follows:

X (failure), G, F, E, D, C, B, A ("pluperfect").

Again suppose that a dog comes to the line for a double mark, then a single mark and a long blind, 4 retrieves; suppose that there are 38 starters and that each dog tries every retrieve. There are 152 retrieves and with random assignment we would expect 19 (152 ÷ 8) retrieves in each classification as indicated in the following tabulation.

Classification	X	G	F	E	D	C	B	A
Expected frequency	19	19	19	19	19	19	19	19

Using a table of random numbers, I came up with results such as tabulated below.

Classification	X	G	F	E	D	C	B	A
Expected frequency	19	19	19	19	19	19	19	19
Observed frequency	15	18	17	20	15	22	23	22

I tried the eight classes; one result follows for (each retrieve in) a licensed open stake (test as described above). Clearly, the tests

Classification	X	G	F	E	D	C	B	A	Total
Observed frequency	1	0	0	2	9	24	29	87	152
Proportion of total retrieves	0.00+	0.00	0.00	0.01	0.06	0.16	0.19	0.57	1.00

are too easy and/or the classification scheme is too detailed; 99 per cent of the retrieves were classified into 5 categories.

Inasmuch as I assign performance on each series to a single category, it is of interest to examine the classification process by series. If we consider the 4 retrieves as consisting of 2 series, we shall have 38 × 2 or 76 category designations; we shall expect (on a random basis) 9.5 retrieves. Results for the 2 series are presented in the tabulation below. Clearly, there were 2 unused classifications

Classification	X	G	F	E	D	C	B	A	Total
Expected frequency	9.5	9.5	9.5	9.5	9.5	9.5	9.5	9.5	76
Observed frequency	1	0	0	1	8	24	19	23	76
Proportion	0.01	0.00	0.00	0.01	0.11	0.32	0.25	0.30	1.00

and 98 per cent of the performances were classified into 4 categories.

Conclusion as of June, 1962.-- Based on extensive evidence, I conclude that I do not need as many as 8 subgroups. *Action:* I shall try a system using 6 classes.

Six Classifications

My experience indicates that not more than six classifications are needed for crude working purposes (see Addenda to this chapter). I have used the following symbolism:

First rate (top notch)	Δ
Star performance (earned stars)	*
Middling (meritorious)	M
Only fair (square)	□
Poor (inadequate)	π
Failure	Ohh!

More elaborate definitions follow:

Δ   *First rate:* Descriptive of lining or "near lining" the blind; pinpointing or near pinpointing marks. Outstanding in every way.

*   *Star performance:* Descriptive of consistent "star-class" performance; could win an open stake.

M   *Middling:* Descriptive of good solid, workmanlike job; deserving of merit.

□   *Only fair:* Descriptive of a job that is just borderline field trial calibre. Ideally, trophy winners should have not more than one □.

π   *Poor:* Descriptive of completing the test, but performance below field trial standards. One π should eliminate an open retriever from receiving a JAM.

Ohh!   *Failure:* Did not get the meat and/or was disqualified.

The six classifications, as given, may be considered ordinal because they are ranked. However, the retrievers which are assigned to each classification are not ranked and so the measurement scale would be considered nominal.

[*Aside:* This absurd symbolism was selected to discourage its being copied and used uncritically by another judge; this is to encourage each judge to think about the problem and to create his own shorthand--symbols which cannot be arithmetically manipulated.]

Non-additive classification procedure.--The use of nominal or ranking (ordinal) scales forces the judge to compare. Good judges will "run" until a winner is obvious; however, many times the other places are not obvious. Nevertheless, gross comparisons can be made quickly and the group of top dogs will clearly stand out. Secondarily, if a judge avoids the use of a numerical system of evaluating retriever performance, then he avoids not only attempting an extremely complex measurement procedure (hence, a hazardous one), but he also avoids simple errors in addition--especially in cumulative totals.

Warning!--The experienced judge who has been using an interval scale and who changes over to a nominal or ranking scale should practice before he judges a licensed stake. I suggest that he either gallery judge or judge a club trial. It is predicted that, at first, he will not like the change. However, he will soon realize that use of the nominal or ranking scale forces comparison after comparison after comparison. After all, the game merely requires that relative performances be determined.

ACTION ITEMS

Item 1.--Discuss the following basic principle which is alleged to be followed by some judges of open stakes: "Keep the marks short and the blinds long, and you won't get into serious trouble." What type of dog will such a policy tend to select as the trophy winner?

Item 2.--At the conclusion of the amateur stake at Florida, spring, 1968, among those called back for the i + 1 series (which was not run, of course), were the only two dogs who had not handled on a particular marked fall. One of these was a clear and obvious winner not only in my book, but to the other judge, and to the "gallery judges" also. This dog was awarded first place. The dog we placed second had excellent work, not even a near "should handle," but he popped at the edge of the water on the water blind; that pop did not please me; in fact, in most trials if my dog did that I would yell "heel!" Would such a pop "ruin" an ordinary day's hunt? Make any assumptions you desire for purposes of discussion; then discuss placing a dog who handles sharply on a marked fall versus placing a dog which pops at the edge of cold water (on a water blind where many handlers had trouble getting their dogs into water), takes his back clearly, another whistle 10 yards into the water, and a cast 45 degrees back, and another whistle 20 yards from the edge of the water and another good cast 45 degrees back (the 2 signals were sharp "direct backs," but the dog took the backs at 45 degrees).

Item 3.--Double mark followed by double blind: In a licensed open stake at Nashville which I judged in the spring of 1968, the second series was run along with the third series on one trip to the line. The second series consisted of a double land mark; the third series was a double land blind (see sketch on the following page).

Instructions were given by means of a test dog; explicitly, pick up the marks, then pick up B₁ (the short blind) before B₂.

Alternate possibility (not conducted), a test of control.-- Discuss the test if it had been run as a "test of control" under the following instructions:

    1.   Retrieve the shot flier first.

    2.   Retrieve the short blind second.

    3.   Retrieve the dead memory bird third.

    4.   Lastly, retrieve the long (170 yards) blind.

Question: Could performance in retrieving the shot flier be evaluated

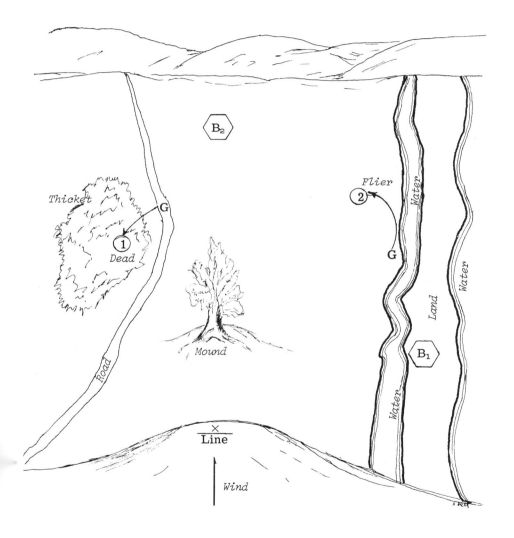

in terms of marking ability? Discuss the many aspects of this test from the point of view of the dog, the handler, and the judge. What type of retriever would you expect to do the best job on this test? Do you consider this a trick test?

[*Aside:* For the record, I did not even discuss this test with my co-judge; neither did I consider running it in this particular field trial.]

A second alternative. -- Suppose that instruction "1" was replaced by the following instruction, call it "1a":

1a. Retrieve one of the marked falls first; performance on this retrieve will be evaluated in terms of a marked fall.

Remainder of the test is a test of control; that is, proceed to and follow instruction "2."

Instruction "3" could be replaced by some such statement as the following:

3a. Retrieve the memory bird (the other marked fall which has not been retrieved).

After completion of instruction 3a, proceed to foregoing instruction "4."

How do these modifications affect your evaluation procedures, opinions, and considerations as a judge?

Item 4.--Given a land blind directly across a 15 m.p.h. wind (which started in the middle of the series) essentially as shown in the sketch on the following page. [*Aside:* I did not set this test.]

Three entries, A, B, and C, "ran across" the 15 m.p.h. wind, as depicted in the sketch.

A was falsely lined upwind; undoubtedly, he did not drift with the wind as the handler probably expected; he picked up the blind on two sharp whistles.

B was falsely lined upwind exactly as A; he faded with the wind and terrain; he picked up the blind without a whistle.

C was lined directly toward the blind, faded with the wind, and picked up the blind with one sharp whistle.

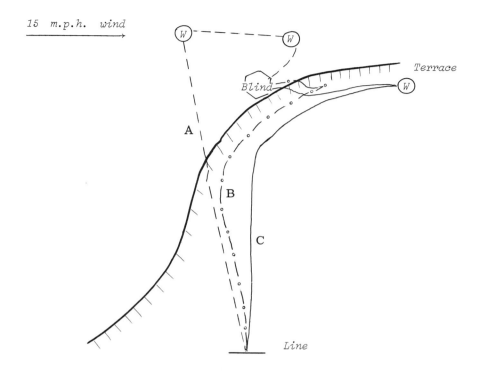

15 m.p.h. wind

Terrace

Blind

Line

Make the following decisions:

A > B   ( ) Yes   ( ) No.
A > C   ( ) Yes   ( ) No.
B > C   ( ) Yes   ( ) No.

Rank the three performances from best to poorest. Discuss and justify your ranking.

PONTCHIPPI JUDGING FORM

Each experienced judge has usually developed his own form for taking notes during a trial. The Pontchippi Judging Form has been

modified many times, and I shall not describe it in detail here; however, there are a few aspects which deserve mention. Here are a few
instructions by McMahan, to McMahan.

(3)
Manners-Style:

(ms) (mS) (Ms) (MS)

Judging Form

(2)
Stake:

(D) (Q) (A) (O)

(1)

NUMBER

(1)   *Number (only).*--Enter number of entry here.   Do not
identify entry otherwise; do not identify entry by name of handler,
name of retriever, by type of retriever, or by any distinguishing characteristics whatsoever.   Recall that I want to judge this entry by performance which I witness and that which I witness only, not by the
retriever's reputation nor his handler nor owner.   Enter the entry
number on the back of the form also.

(2)   *Stake.*--Check as follows: (D)́ if derby,   (Q)́ if qualifying,   (A) if amateur, and   (O) if open.   Omit on all sheets except
the top one which remains.

(3)   *Manners-Style.*--Check as follows each time entry comes
to the line: (ms) if poor manners and poor style, (mS) if poor manners and good style,   (Ms) if good manners and poor style, and (MS)
if both good manners and good style.   After four series, a well-
mannered entry with good style would have four checks as follows:

(ms)   (mS)   (Ms)   (MS) .

(4)   *Tentative decision for callback of an entry.*--While the
performance of an entry is fresh in my memory, make a tentative decision as to whether or not this retriever is to be tested further in this
stake.   This tentative decision can be recorded as follows:

(D)   (?)   (B);

indicate decision as follows: Check (Ď) if I definitely want the entry dropped; check (?̌) if I am doubtful or undecided; and check (B̌) if I definitely want him back for further testing.

Independent Callbacks

Obviously, procedures utilized by a specified pair of judges in-volve a cooperative endeavor. The other judge willing, I prefer to have the callbacks determined so that one judge does not influence the decisions of the other judge; I prefer to follow procedures outlined in this section.

First, I give a card such as (1) to the other judge, call him "Judge Number One" (J_1); then I take a similar card (2), call McMahan "Judge Number Two" (J_2); the other card (3), labelled "Official Callbacks" is given to the marshal assisting with the running of the stake. Such cards can be used with up to 48 entries for 6 series (and can be adapted easily to larger stakes).

<table>
<tr><td align="center">(1)</td><td align="center">(3)</td><td align="center">(2)</td></tr>
</table>

Judge Number One							Official Callbacks							Judge Number Two					
Series: 2 3 4 5 6							Series: 2 3 4 5 6							Series: 2 3 4 5 6					
1	2	3	4	5	6		1	2	3	4	5	6		1	2	3	4	5	6
7	8	9	10	11	12		7	8	9	10	11	12		7	8	9	10	11	12
13	14	15	16	17	18		13	14	15	16	17	18		13	14	15	16	17	18
19	20	21	22	23	24		19	20	21	22	23	24		19	20	21	22	23	24
25	26	27	28	29	30		25	26	27	28	29	30		25	26	27	28	29	30
31	32	33	34	35	36		31	32	33	34	35	36		31	32	33	34	35	36
37	38	39	40	41	42		37	38	39	40	41	42		37	38	39	40	41	42
43	44	45	46	47	48		43	44	45	46	47	48		43	44	45	46	47	48

Pontchippi, 1965　　　　Pontchippi, 1965　　　　Pontchippi, 1965

End of first series. -- J_1 circles "2" on his card as shown and then circles the number of each entry he desires to drop. J_2 circles "2" on his card as shown and then circles the number of each entry he desires to drop.

Judge Number One
Series: ② 3   4   5   6

Judge Number Two
Series: ② 3   4   5   6

Both cards are handed to the assisting marshal who circles his card for those entries both judges desire to drop. If there is disagreement, one of the following actions can be followed: (1) Any entry that one judge desires to see further is called back, provided of course, that the entry has not been guilty of a disqualifying fault and/or provided there are not other overwhelming reasons for dropping the entry or entries in question. Or (2) the judges can discuss the entries in question and jointly come to a decision.

All cards are modified accordingly, numbers of entries dropped lined through, cards returned to the appropriate judge, and the assisting marshal announces the callbacks.

End of other series. -- Essentially similar appropriate procedures are followed at the end of each series, including the end of the last series run in the stake. [*Exception:* Callbacks (as such) are not announced at the end of the last series.]

Continuous Register

For convenience, a continuous register of entries is kept throughout the stake; an illustration is shown on the next page.

Termination of the Stake

Considering our agreed upon plans, available time, and number of entries remaining, if I have a clear and obvious winner after, say,

PONTCHIPPI CONTINUOUS REGISTER OF ENTRIES

Number	SERIES						Number	SERIES					
	1	2	3	4	5	6		1	2	3	4	5	6
1							31						
2							32						
3							33						
4							34						
5							35						
6							36						
7							37						
8							38						
9							39						
10							40						
11							41						
12							42						
13							43						
14							44						
15							45						
16							46						
17							47						
18							48						
19							49						
20							50						
21							51						
22							52						
23							53						
24							54						
25							55						
26							56						
27							57						
28							58						
29							59						
30							60						

four or more series, I may recommend that we terminate the stake.

Task number one.--From those entries who completed the last series conducted, I first select the entries which would be called back *if* we were to decide to conduct another series. No entry will be awarded a judges' award of merit in an open or amateur stake unless I would be willing to call him back for further testing.

Task number two.--Since we have an obvious winner, I next decide which entries obviously will receive judges' awards of merit only, those who clearly will not be in contention for places.

Task number three.--The entries remaining must now be ranked to determine the places. Tentative classifications assigned for quick reference for callbacks must not be considered further. We must perform a tentative ranking and then explicitly compare second with third, second with fourth, and second with fifth; then third with fourth, third with fifth; then fourth with fifth and fourth with any of the others retained for awards of merit. This comparison must be made series by series and/or bird by bird, taking into consideration all the data which have been generated throughout the stake.

To assure that such comparisons are explicitly made in the attempt to rank, two boxes are printed on the back of each judging form.

(11) *Comparison, series by series.*--When the trial is over, I compare all place entries with others obviously in contention, series by series. I use the following notation: $(0, 0)$ if I cannot distinguish a noticeable difference in performance; $(+, 0)$ or $(0, +)$ if one "beats" the other slightly; and $(+, -)$ or $(-, +)$ if one defeats the other by a material margin.

For example, in the comparison on the next page, entry 5 and entry 54 were about the same in the first series; 5 definitely beat 54 in the second series; 5 was slightly superior to 54 in the third series; again, there was no noticeable difference in the fourth series; and 5 was slightly superior to 54 in the fifth series. Clearly, 5 must be ranked ahead of 54 .

[*Warning to young judges.*-- At the end of a trial (after the two

PONTCHIPPI

(11)

Series	Entry number	
	5	54
1	0	0
2	+	−
3	+	0
4	0	0
5	+	0
6		

Series	Entry number	
1		
2		
3		
4		
5		
6		

judges have a clear and obvious winner), some judges pressure the young judge by handing him a list of his placings with some such statement as, "see if you agree with these," or "try these for size." Stop! Do not read that list until you have made your own placings independently! These "widely travelled" judges have found (either consciously or unconsciously) that this is a convenient gimmick to get "quick agreement" from the other judge. *Analogy:* Many administrators make decisions, and look for "good reasons" later; in short, they do not make decisions based on the facts. Be sure you make your placings based on your facts; don't use your data to help justify the other judge's placings.

Comment: If you will carefully observe some of these "widely travelled" judges and evaluate their performances over several trials according to explicit criteria, would you be surprised to find that they may actually know very little about "dogs"? Could the following assertion be true? *Assertion:* They may have found a few "things" (field tricks) that retrievers can't do well and they repeatedly set those "tricks," although they may fool themselves and think they disguise them.]

VARIABILITY IN PERFORMANCE

Analogy (danger!).--The examination for certification "open retriever" (award of ribbons and silver in a licensed open stake) on a
given weekend consists of four basic subjects: marking on land, marking on water, blinds on land, and water blinds; moreover, demonstrated proficiency can be required in combinations of these subjects.
In addition, the examination includes line manners, heeling, honoring,
and other subjects.   Failure to pass any of the basic subjects in a licensed open stake should dictate that no high place be awarded to this
retriever.   Consistently workmanlike performance or better is required; borderline performance is clearly not preferred. In short, to
be promoted in school requires passing grades in *all* the major subjects.

Ideally, we seek a winner who consistently does perfect work over
a stake; who was awarded over five series, say, a group of tentative
classifications

$$\{\Delta_1, \quad \Delta_2, \quad \Delta_3, \quad \Delta_4, \quad \Delta_5\},$$

where

Δ_1 = tentative classification for performance on first
series,

Δ_2 = tentative classification for performance on second series,

.
.
.

Δ_5 = tentative classification for performance on fifth
series,

and, dropping the subscripts for convenience, written

$$\{\Delta, \quad \Delta, \quad \Delta, \quad \Delta, \quad \Delta\}.$$

In practice, such high-level consistent performance is seldom the case.

If, for theoretical discussion, we assume that over five series in a particular stake

      a.   the tests are all equal in difficulty,

      b.   the weight, the importance, of each series is the same,

      c.   each test is explicitly designed to test for different qualities (even though there is some obvious overlap) required in an ideal retriever who is to be certified as possessed of qualities fit to compete in a championship stake, and

      d.   no information is available other than these highly tentative classifications,

then one might argue that a group of tentative classifications

$$C_1 \; = \; \{*, \; *, \; *, \; *, \; *\}$$

should beat a group of tentative classifications

$$C_2 \; = \; \{\triangle, \; \triangle, \; \triangle, \; \triangle, \; \square\}.$$

In short, even though the performances in C_2 surpass the performances in C_1 in four out of five series, C_1 demonstrates consistent star performance (competency) in all qualities tested, but C_2 demonstrates only borderline fitness in the qualities tested for in the fifth series. The sequence C_2 shows great variability in performance. *Question:* Is spectacular work in four of five series, under the assumptions specified, a sufficient condition (for ...), the element of luck always being important in retriever field trials?

When the foregoing methods are followed to their logical conclusion, one could easily run across two groups such as

$$C_2 \; = \; \{\triangle, \; \triangle, \; \triangle, \; \triangle, \; \square\}$$

versus

$$C_3 \; = \; \{M, \; M, \; M, \; M, \; M\}.$$

Which retriever would you rather take home? Which retriever would you rather send to the ... national "to represent your club"? To which retriever would you rather breed your good bitch, if you were required to keep and campaign the puppies? William F. Brown faced up to these problems in *Retriever Gun Dogs*.[1]

In a particular trial where the assumptions outlined earlier hold, if you lost all your notes and diagrams and had to choose between two retrievers based on tentative classifications only, would you be willing to give the decision to the

$$C_3 = \{M, \ M, \ M, \ M, \ M\}$$

rather than

$$C_2 = \{\Delta, \ \Delta, \ \Delta, \ \Delta, \ \square\} \ ?$$

ACTION ITEMS

Item 1. -- In the immediately foregoing discussion, assume that the tests become increasingly more difficult as the stake progresses, and that the weight of each series is related one to one with the difficulty of the test. What is your decision, and why?

Continuing under these assumptions, suppose that the two groups were as follows:

$$C_1{}' = \{*, \ *, \ *, \ *, \ *\}$$

and

$$C_2{}' = \{\square, \ \Delta, \ \Delta, \ \Delta, \ \Delta\}.$$

Which group do you prefer, and why? Formulate a rule for decision-making in such situations.

Item 2. -- Reference the continuum of the probability of separation, page 411. Such a continuum is closely related to the condition of limited time in which to conduct a stake. Discuss.

McMahan, caught in the act of judging a licensed open stake, Mobile, Friday, February 26, 1965. (Photo by CRY)

The "field trial way": The author with Kube in 1961 to illustrate the "two-hand take." In an actual shooting situation, would you routinely lay your gun on the ground to accept game from your retriever? (Photo by RLS)

Close-up of the author in action as he looked through his judging book again, open stake, Calcasieu Retriever Club, July 14, 1968 (photo by Bob Dennie, Louisiana Wild Life and Fisheries Commission).

Item 3.--An older retriever has become "trial-wise." In the first series, a land triple, he "goes" when the judge calls his number (no break). The handler yells "heel!" He commands the retriever to sit by his side; then he sends the dog. Discuss. In the second and third series combined, a double mark and double blind, again the retriever goes on his number (no break). Again, heel! The handler commands the retriever to sit by his side; then he sends the dog. Discuss.

Item 4.--What is meant by "sheep-doggin" in retriever trials? Can the amount of sheep-doggin be measured? Have you ever read a book on training a sheep dog? Have you ever seen a sheep dog trial? Request an RE to investigate the subject in depth and make a report at a club meeting. Discuss.

Item 5.--What we used to do: Select a panel of RE's, each RE with 25 or more years of experience in the retriever field trial game. Ask each one to describe one or more procedures (for conducting a trial) which have been dropped over the years. Should one or more of these procedures be reinstituted? Discuss.

REFERENCE

1. Brown, William F. *Retriever Gun Dogs,* New York: A. S. Barnes and Co., Inc., 1945, pp. 93-94.

A pittance of practice may be worth a tome of theory.

NOTES TO CHAPTER TEN

1. Comments on Sets and Sequences

Suppose someone asks the question: How many possible subsets are there in a set, including the null set (the empty set)? If a set S consists of n elements, then there are 2^n possible subsets including the null set.

Proof: We are asking for the number of combinations we can make of n things (elements) taking r elements at a time, where $r = 0, 1, \ldots, n$:

$$\sum_{r=0}^{n} \binom{n}{r} x^r = (1 + x)^n.$$

Take $x = 1$ and we get

$$\sum_{r=0}^{n} \binom{n}{r} = (1 + 1)^n = 2^n.$$

A second question might be: How many possible sequences are there per single entry in a stake composed of 4 series, where a judge uses a 10-point scoring system, 0 excluded, and S_i ($i = 1$ to 4) refers to the score in series 1 to 4 respectively, explicitly, S_1, S_2, S_3, S_4?

Consider the set of elements $\{1, 2, \ldots, 9, 10\}$.

    a. How many distinct subsets of 4 elements can be obtained?

Answer: The number of combinations of 10 things taken 4 at a time. That is,

$$\binom{10}{4} = \frac{10!}{6! \, 4!}$$

$$\binom{10}{4} = \frac{10 \cdot 9 \cdot 8 \cdot 7}{4!} = 210.$$

Note: This question does not apply to the scores in a stake, since it does not permit a judge to award the same score in two different series.

    b. If the 4 elements chosen are to represent scores on 4 different series, how many subsets can be obtained?

Answer: The number of permutations of 10 things taken 4 at a time. That is,

$$\frac{10!}{(10-4)!} = \frac{10!}{6!} = 10 \cdot 9 \cdot 8 \cdot 7 = 5,040.$$

In problems a and b above, we are sampling from the 10 elements without replacement (see comment below in item c).

c. Consider a new problem. Suppose the 4 elements chosen are to represent the scores of a retriever who competes in 4 series with scores S_1, S_2, S_3, S_4. We are looking for the number of different sequences of scores.

Answer:

$$\binom{10}{1} \cdot \binom{10}{1} \cdot \binom{10}{1} \cdot \binom{10}{1} = 10 \cdot 10 \cdot 10 \cdot 10$$
$$= 10^4 = 10,000.$$

In this case we are sampling from the 10 elements (scores) with replacement.

Note that the sequence of scores S_1, S_2, S_3, S_4 cannot be considered a subset of the set $\{1, 2, \ldots, 9, 10\}$ because we can have, say, $S_1 = S_2$, whereas the original set contains only one element corresponding to each assignable score.

d. Suppose we do not require the retriever to complete all four series. That is, he may be eliminated (or withdrawn) at the end of either series one, two, or three.

Question: How many sequences of scores are possible using either one series, two series, three series, or four series?

Answer:

One series	10 sequences
Two series	$10 \cdot 10 = 10^2$ sequences
Three series	$10 \cdot 10 \cdot 10 = 10^3$ sequences
Four series	$10 \cdot 10 \cdot 10 \cdot 10 = 10^4$ sequences
Total	$10 + 10^2 + 10^3 + 10^4 = 11,110.$

2.   "Should Handle"

It is well-known that many decisions (on the part of the handler) may be required in handling a single retriever through an open stake. Likewise, many decisions are required on the judge's part in evaluating (measuring) the quality of the performance of a handler and his retriever. I leave it to the interested RE to examine the voluminous literature on decision-making; he has a job on his hands even if he limits his inquiry to only two alternate courses of action. [Nevertheless, the dedicated RE will undoubtedly find it rewarding to consult a soundly written elementary book on hypothesis testing or decision-making (if he is not already familiar with these ideas).] I shall set forth one set of circumstances for discussion.

Over many open stakes, suppose that an experienced, well-qualified handler, H, has kept records which indicate the relative frequency (r.f.) of his retriever's being "dropped" under two conditions. Assume that H thinks his retriever should be "handled" on a marked fall: the r.f. with which his retriever is not called back is greater if H handles than if H does not handle.

Accordingly, H decides to never handle on a marked fall unless a judge explicitly tells him to "handle your retriever." In short, H decides to never make the decision for the judge as to whether he (the handler) should handle (SH) [or should not handle $(\overline{SH})$]. That is, H decides to force the judge to make his own decisions.

If the handler H follows the foregoing rule, *then* a judge must judge in some such framework as that of the following on each and every marked fall (H_0 indicates the hypothesis under test, the null hypothesis, while H_1 denotes the alternative hypothesis):

H_0:   The handler should handle.

versus

H_1:   The handler should not handle.

Possible errors are set forth in tabular form on the following page.

ACTION ITEM

Discuss the section entitled "Should Handle." Is the foregoing hypothesis set from the point of view of the handler or the judge? Does it make any difference?

Observed action taken by handler	Description of "true situation"*	
	Should handle (SH)	Should not handle (S̄H̄)
Handled	OK--correct decision	Error--handler pays price unnecessarily
Did not handle	Error--judge must charge H accordingly	OK--correct decision

* To repeat, the judge must make the decision of what is true, SH or S̄H̄, for each marked fall.

3. Further Illustrations of Variability

Data illustrating variability in the conduct of tests involving only marks (and memory) were presented in the Notes to Chapter Six. In this note, data illustrating variability in conducting tests which are composed solely of a blind or blinds as well as blind-mark combinations are presented in Tables 10-N-1, 10-N-2, 10-N-3, and 10-N-4.

ACTION ITEMS

Item 1.--Reference Table 10-N-4 regarding open water blind, 1969. Also reference rules of logic examined in Chapter Three. Formulate valid arguments to examine the following two questions: Operationally, what are some implications of a pair of judges setting such a test? Does the setting of such a test logically imply that these judges approve the training methods required to force an open retriever to satisfactorily perform such a trick?

Item 2.--Compare the data of Table 10-N-5 with data presented in Notes to Chapter Six and in these notes.

Item 3.-- How long does it take a retriever to run 100 yards? "How big" is the variability? Is there an "age effect"? How fast can a retriever swim 100 yards? How much variability is there, both among retrievers and "within" retrievers? Does speed depend on the mark, say, dummies versus game? Do you know of anyone who has extended the work of Dick Hecker? (Note that I have not!) (See Richard H. Hecker, Vol. 17, Number 6, *Field Trial News*, August, 1960, page 7.) What does "how fast ... ?" (speed) have to do with retriever performance in the field? Does "age effect" affect marking and/or

Table 10-N-1. --Elapsed time in minutes and seconds between arrival on the line (event A) and delivery of bird to hand (event B) of second marked fall, and selected statistical measures, 33 performances on land tests, first and second series (combined) of a licensed open stake, 1969

Observations (arrayed from low to high)		Frequency of occurrence	Cumulative frequency	Percentile (approximate)
Collected in minutes and seconds	Transformation to seconds for calculations			
2 : 45	165	1	1	3
2 : 53	173	1	2	6
2 : 57	177	1	3	9
3 : 07	187	1	4	12
3 : 09	189	1	5	15
3 : 13	193	1	6	18
3 : 14	194	1	7	21
3 : 18	198	1	8	24
3 : 20	200	1	9	27
3 : 33	213	1	10	30
3 : 39	219	1	11	33
3 : 44	224	1	12	36
3 : 48	228	2	14	42
4 : 00	240	1	15	45
4 : 04	244	1	16	48
4 : 12	252	1	17	52
4 : 14	254	1	18	55
4 : 15	255	1	19	58
4 : 16	256	1	20	61
4 : 32	272	1	21	64
4 : 34	274	1	22	67
4 : 36	276	1	23	70
4 : 47	287	2	25	76
5 : 12	312	1	26	79
5 : 14	314	1	27	82
5 : 37	337	1	28	85
5 : 41	341	1	29	88
5 : 49	349	1	30	91
6 : 00	360	1	31	94
6 : 05	365	1	32	97
6 : 25	385	1	33	100

Note.--First series was land blind; second series was marked double (from same line) with one flying pheasant; the foregoing accomplished on a single trip to one line. Event A: retriever passes well-defined point (line) in front of judges; event B: retriever delivers second marked retrieve to hand.

(Continued)

Table 10-N-1.--(Concluded) Elapsed time in minutes and seconds between arrival on the line (event A) and delivery of bird to hand (event B) of second marked fall, and selected statistical measures, 33 performances on land tests, first and second series (combined) of a licensed open stake, 1969

Selected Statistical Measures

Mean	=	256	seconds
Median	=	252	seconds
Range	=	220	seconds
Low	=	165	seconds
High	=	385	seconds
Variance	=	3, 824	square seconds
Standard deviation	=	61. 8	seconds
Coefficient of variation	=	24. 2	per cent

Reported number of starters: 34;
    missed observations (observer error or failure to complete the test): 1.

Starting time (event A for first entry): 8 : 22 a. m.

Time series ended (event B for last entry): 11 : 50 a. m.

Elapsed time for the first series: 3 hours 28 minutes.

Description of cover: Mixed--Pontchippi middling and Pontchippi stubble.

Table 10-N-2.--Elapsed time in minutes and seconds between arrival on the line (event A) and retriever delivers bird to hand (event B), and selected statistical measures, 26 performances on a long land blind, third series of a licensed open stake, 1969

Observations (arrayed from low to high)		Frequency of occurrence	Cumulative frequency	Percentile (approximate)
Collected in minutes and seconds	Transformation to seconds for calculations			
1:28	88	1	1	4
1:35	95	1	2	8
1:56	116	1	3	12
1:57	117	1	4	15
1:58	118	1	5	19
2:00	120	1	6	23
2:01	121	1	7	27
2:02	122	1	8	31
2:03	123	2	10	38
2:04	124	1	11	42
2:05	125	1	12	46
2:12	132	1	13	50
2:13	133	1	14	54
2:20	140	2	16	62
2:23	143	1	17	65
2:26	146	1	18	69
2:29	149	2	20	77
2:34	154	1	21	81
2:35	155	1	22	85
2:55	175	1	23	88
3:17	197	1	24	92
3:25	205	1	25	96
3:31	211	1	26	100

Note.--Event A: Handler arrives with retriever at well-defined point on the line. Event B: Retriever delivers (releases) bird to handler.

(Continued)

Table 10-N-2.--(Concluded) Elapsed time in minutes and seconds between arrival on the line (event A) and retriever delivers bird to hand (event B), and selected statistical measures, 26 performances on a long land blind, third series of a licensed open stake, 1969

Selected Statistical Measures

Mean	=	139	seconds
Median (interpolated value)	=	132.5	seconds
Range	=	123	seconds
Low	=	88	seconds
High	=	211	seconds
Variance	=	917.16	square seconds
Standard deviation	=	30.3	seconds
Coefficient of variation	=	21.7	per cent

Reported number of callbacks: 28; missed observations (observer error or failure to complete the test): 2.

Starting time (event A for first entry): 12 : 40 p.m.

Time series ended (event B for last entry): 2 : 10 p.m.

Elapsed time for the third series: 1 hour 30 minutes.

Description of cover: Mixed--Pontchippi heavy and Pontchippi stubble.

Table 10-N-3.--Elapsed time in minutes and seconds between event F, handler sends retriever for first blind, and event G, release of dead bird by retriever on retrieve to hand of second blind, and selected statistical measures, 33 performances on double land blind, second series of a licensed open stake, 1969

Observations (arrayed from low to high)		Frequency of occurrence	Cumulative frequency	Percentile (approximate)
Collected in minutes and seconds	Transformation to seconds for calculations			
2:26	146	1	1	3
2:29	149	1	2	6
2:35	155	2	4	12
2:38	158	1	5	15
2:42	162	2	7	21
2:44	164	1	8	24
2:45	165	2	10	30
2:58	178	1	11	33
3:07	187	1	12	36
3:14	194	1	13	39
3:16	196	1	14	42
3:23	203	1	15	45
3:24	204	1	16	48
3:25	205	1	17	52
3:28	208	1	18	55
3:34	214	1	19	58
3:40	220	1	20	61
3:43	223	2	22	67
3:48	228	2	24	73
3:53	233	1	25	76
4:00	240	1	26	79
4:04	244	1	27	82
4:06	246	1	28	85
4:07	247	1	29	88
4:15	255	1	30	91
4:18	258	1	31	94
4:32	272	1	32	97
4:47	287	1	33	100

(Continued)

Table 10-N-3.--(Concluded) Elapsed time in minutes and seconds between event F, handler sends retriever for first blind, and event G, release of dead bird by retriever on retrieve to hand of second blind, and selected statistical measures, 33 performances on double land blind, second series of a licensed open stake, 1969

Selected Statistical Measures

Mean	=	3 minutes 25 seconds
Median	=	3 minutes 25 seconds
Range	=	2 minutes 21 seconds
Low	=	2 minutes 26 seconds
High	=	4 minutes 47 seconds
Variance	=	1,537 square seconds
Standard deviation	=	39 seconds
Coefficient of variation	=	19.1 per cent

Number called back for the second series: 35;
    missed observations (observer error): 1 (and 1 entry failed the test).

Starting time (event F for first entry): 1:00 p.m.

Time series ended (event G for last entry): 4:10 p.m.

Elapsed time for the second series: 3 hours 10 minutes.

Geographical description: The test was conducted from a line in front of an elevated road; i.e., the road was 5 feet ± 0.5 feet above the level of the area where the blind was planted. The first blind was approximately 89 yards to the right-front, through a pothole. The second blind was approximately 108 yards to the left-front with an angle of 56°45′ between straight lines to the blinds, where the vertex was "where the retriever sat." The foregoing measurements were made after the trial by means of steel tape and transit (see footnote to Table 6-N-2).

Table 10-N-4.--Elapsed time in minutes and seconds between event E, handler sends retriever, and event F, retriever releases retrieved bird to handler, and selected statistical measures, 16 performances on single water blind, third series of a licensed open stake, 1969

Observations (arrayed from low to high)		Frequency of occurrence	Cumulative frequency	Percentile (approximate)
Collected in minutes and seconds	Transformation to seconds for calculations			
1:59	119	1	1	6
2:00	120	1	2	12
2:40	160	1	3	19
2:41	161	1	4	25
2:52	172	1	5	31
2:56	176	1	6	38
3:02	182	1	7	44
3:10	190	1	8	50
3:22	202	1	9	56
3:23	203	1	10	62
3:26	206	1	11	69
3:29	209	1	12	75
3:31	211	1	13	81
3:48	228	1	14	88
3:49	229	1	15	94
4:06	246	1	16	100

Selected Statistical Measures

Mean	= 3 minutes 8 seconds
Median (interpolated value)	= 3 minutes 16 seconds
Range	= 2 minutes 7 seconds
Low	= 1 minute 59 seconds
High	= 4 minutes 6 seconds
Variance	= 1,313 square seconds
Standard deviation	= 36 seconds
Coefficient of variation	= 19.2 per cent

(Continued)

Table 10-N-4. --(Concluded) Elapsed time in minutes and seconds between event E, handler sends retriever, and event F, retriever releases retrieved bird to handler, and selected statistical measures, 16 performances on single water blind, third series of a licensed open stake, 1969

Number called back for the third series: 24;
    missing observations (entry failed test): 8.

Starting time (event E for first entry): 8:25 a.m.

Time series ended (event F for last entry): 10:19 a.m.

Elapsed time for the third series: 1 hour 54 minutes.

Geographical description: None (see note on ... circus dog).

[*Note: On selecting a circus dog.* --In measuring the "angle into the water" (given that the vertex is at the edge of the water, the angle between the "shoreline" and a direct line to the blind), the person doing the measuring has considerable leeway even when the shoreline is only slightly irregular. In short, "the angle into the water" is somewhat arbitrary (within limits).

As this test was set, if the line had been at the edge of the water, then the angle into the water could have reasonably been measured to be 13 degrees 30 minutes using a surveyor's instrument (theodolite with the telescope mounted--transit). Even when the tripod was set (out) on a point, the angle into the water measured less than 20 degrees.

The actual line was about 20 paces (McM) back from the water. By trignometric methods, it was estimated that the distance from the line to the blind was approximately 109 yards.]

Table 10-N-5. --Mean time in minutes per retriever and number of retrievers for basis of estimate (shown in parentheses), by type of test, National Amateur Championship Stake, 1965

Type of data	Double mark, mixed bag	Double blind, water	Single mark and land blind	Triple mark, water	Triple mark, land; honor
Minutes	7-8	6	5	8	7
(Number of retrievers)	(55)	(39)	(33)	(28)	(25)
Type of data	Single mark, water; and water blind	Double mark, land; double blind, land	Triple mark, water	Cold blind, water	Triple mark, land
Minutes	9	7	13	10	8
(Number of retrievers)	(19)	(17)	(11)	(9)	(7)

Source of data: Retriever Field Trial News 1(5): 4-6 (June, 1965).

marking and remembering ability? List and discuss purposes served by considering such topics as these (aside from satisfying our intellectual curiosity which *per se* is obviously important).

Item 4.--Outline the conditions under which the following data on planning factors might be applicable: moving from one location to another location for the next series: 45 minutes; on marks on land, allow 1 and one-half minutes per marked fall (per bird); where honoring is involved, allow 15 to 30 seconds additional per entry. [*Source:* Essentially these data were presented at a judging conference.] For marked duck, predominantly swimming water, wnat is a good estimate of time required in terms of seconds per yard (where total distance to the falls and return is estimated in yards)?

4. Judging, Training Techniques, Breed Improvement

Technics.--Selected thingumagigs have contributed to training retrievers for a long time, namely, the choke (and/or spike) collar, rope, whistle, whip, slingshot, ... , the "air rifle" ("BB gun") and "shotgun" to name a few. Since World War II, the CO_2 (BB or pellet) pistol, the electric prod, the "dummy launcher, " ... , and the so-called electronic remote control device have come into widespread use.

From time to time, an imaginative trainer, standing on the shoulders of the past, has added a new wrinkle or two in combination with engineering developments (and likewise being blessed with getting his hands on a top retriever), has gained national recognition.

Judging confounded with training methods (and breed improvement).--During my 30 years of contact with the retriever field trial game in America, there has been tremendous interaction between tests (judging) and training. As judges have devised tests that were failed in a trial, trainers have gone home and devised methods for training to "solve" those tests. As a consequence, not only has "average" field trial performance "improved, " but the top jobs are "outstanding." It is well-known, for example, that to obtain a first place in an open stake, long straight lines are (almost) mandatory. Today, some trainers "line" their retrievers for a quarter of a mile or more in practice sessions. Now, to elaborate on angling into the water.

Sharp, acute angle into the water.--How many "top" (professional or amateur) trainers do you know really know how to train a retriever to "line into the water at a sharp angle" (where the line is a considerable distance back from the water)? Careful observations made on selected top trainers, over many retrievers per trainer, lead me to believe that even within this group, real "know-how" for teaching this trick is not widespread (always keeping in mind the possible limitations of the retriever) as of the late 1960's.

Why set up a test involving a sharp angle into the water?--Possible assumptions: A retriever must be well-trained to perform well on this test; some judges think it is a "good" measure of the level of training. Moreover, judges who want to "get rid of dogs fast" may use this test to good advantage.

Suppose an RE made three statements as follows:

p: The angle into the water is sharp (on this test).

q: The retriever performs well (on this test).

r: The retriever is well-trained.

Then suppose he presented the following argument:

$$(p \wedge q) \rightarrow r$$
$$\frac{q}{r}\ .$$

Has he presented a valid argument? Is this form of argument explicitly presented in Chapter Three?

What is the history of using the sharp angle into the water as a test in open stakes? What trainer first demonstrated genuine proficiency in training retrievers to "take a sharp" angle into the water?

The 1970's.--Undoubtedly, present training methods will become more widespread. No doubt someone will develop a sound, completely interference proof "remote trainer" that will work with high reliability up to and including 220 yards in water (not just water resistent but water ...). [*Aside:* As far as I know (although I have not personally tested all of them), no "electronic remote control device" on the commercial market as of 1969 meets these criteria.] But what young trainer is on the horizon who will be the "genius of the 70's"? In view of the developments over the last two decades, I hypothesize that there will be a leveling-off in improvement of training methods as well as in top performance in retriever field trials. What do you think will be the next "break-through"?

ADDENDA

Empirical Distributions, Six Classifications

As back-up, materials from a 1968 judging assignment are provided in Tables 10-A-1, 10-A-2, and 10-A-3.

Frequency of tentative gross classification. -- The "test" involved four retrieves as follows: a short blind, a marked dead pheasant (first down) and a marked shot flying hen (last fall), and a long blind. For purposes of tabulation, any failure to get the meat (uncompleted portion of the test) is considered a failure (even though the handler gave up before attempting); that is, if a retriever failed on the short blind, he will be tabulated as having four failures.

Given 33 starters, there were (33 × 4) or 132 possible retrieves.

Table 10-A-1. --Number and percentage of retrieves of all starters, by gross tentative classification and by type of retrieve, "first test" (four birds), licensed trial, Amateur Stake, North Florida Amateur Retriever Club, Spring, 1968

Type of retrieve	Gross tentative classification					
	Δ	*	M	□	π	Ohh!
Short blind	9 (3)	33 (11)	33 (11)	21 (7)	0 (0)	3 (1)
Flying pheasant (last fall)	36 (12)	24 (8)	18 (6)	12 (4)	6 (2)	3 (1)
Dead pheasant (first fall)	27 (9)	21 (7)	3 (1)	27 (9)	6 (2)	15 (5)
Long blind	6 (2)	18 (6)	30 (10)	15 (5)	6 (2)	24 (8)
Total	20 (26)	24 (32)	21 (28)	19 (25)	5 (6)	11 (15)

Note: Percentage of retrieves is the observation of interest; hence, number of retrieves is shown in parentheses.

Table 10-A-2.--Number and percentage of retrieves of 10 starters awarded ribbons, by gross tentative classification and by type of retrieve, "first test" (four birds), licensed trial, Amateur Stake, North Florida Amateur Retriever Club, Spring, 1968

Type of retrieve	Gross tentative classification					
	Δ	*	M	□	π	Ohh!
Short blind	10 (1)	50 (5)	40 (4)	0 (0)	0 (0)	0 (0)
Flying pheasant (last fall)	70 (7)	10 (1)	20 (2)	0 (0)	0 (0)	0 (0)
Dead pheasant (first fall)	40 (4)	30 (3)	0 (0)	30 (3)	0 (0)	0 (0)
Long blind	10 (1)	30 (3)	40 (4)	20 (2)	0 (0)	0 (0)
Total	32 (13)	30 (12)	25 (10)	12 (5)	0 (0)	0 (0)

Note: Percentage of retrieves is the observation of interest; hence, number of retrieves is shown in parentheses.

Table 10-A-3. --Number and percentage of retrieves of 23 starters not awarded ribbons, by gross tentative classification and by type of retrieve, "first test" (four birds), licensed trial, Amateur Stake, North Florida Amateur Retriever Club, Spring, 1968

Type of retrieve	Gross tentative classification					
	Δ	*	M	□	π	Ohh!
Short blind	9 (2)	26 (6)	30 (7)	30 (7)	0 (0)	4 (1)
Flying pheasant (last fall)	22 (5)	30 (7)	17 (4)	17 (4)	9 (2)	4 (1)
Dead pheasant (first fall)	22 (5)	17 (4)	4 (1)	26 (6)	9 (2)	22 (5)
Long blind	4 (1)	13 (3)	26 (6)	13 (3)	9 (2)	35 (8)
Total	14 (13)	22 (20)	20 (18)	22 (20)	7 (6)	16 (15)

Note: Percentage of retrieves is the observation of interest; hence, number of retrieves is shown in parentheses.

SPRINGERS

"Never send a dog for a runner till it is out of sight."

An old signed print by G. Vernon Stokes in the author's private Pontchippi Collection.

A signed color print by Maud Earl (dated 1906). From the author's private Pontchippi Collection.

CHAPTER ELEVEN

PONTCHIPPI MATHEMATICS

In the previous chapter on measuring retriever performance (Chapter Ten), I presented considerable evidence for not using arithmetic operations and for not using an interval or a ratio scale. If a dedicated retriever enthusiast (RE) arrives at the same conclusion as I have, he could justifiably ask: "Just what do you propose?" I propose a simplified system of mathematics which arose from practical procedures in judging American retriever field trials. For the experienced judge, such a mathematical system should make for clearer thinking on the judging process, as well as provide him with a sound basis for analyzing his results. For the novice at judging, it is believed that this chapter provides a method for developing sound judging techniques.

Background

It seems to me that most discussions of our retriever field trial game are not only biased, but are also emotional. Even when we try to be objective, when we discuss the retriever field trial game in ordinary language, our statements and ideas often seem garbled and complicated; they are easily misunderstood. Even our "rules and guidelines" for the game are subject to varied interpretation, to include misinterpretation. In contrast, mathematics enables RE's to communicate with each other in a language that is unambiguously clear. Moreover, whatever two or more RE's (anywhere in the world) are talking about in a mathematical argument, they must stick to the subject; they cannot wander into irrelevancies, they cannot slip in new assumptions, nor change meanings even slightly from those with which they started.

487

A mathematics (for the retriever field trial game) provides us tools of great power because of the generality of its symbolic formulation, and because the individual propositions are studied in their logical relationships to other propositions. Even though by definition mathematics is an abstract discipline, it is not stagnant; it is growing. (In passing, carefully note that abstractness does not mean having one's head in a cloud, and that generality does not imply vagueness.)

In 1901, Bertrand Russell[1] asserted that "mathematics may be defined as the subject in which we never know what we are talking about, nor whether [or not] what we are saying is true." This statement (accurately) characterizes the retriever mathematics presented in this chapter in that (1) our definitions rest on some undefined terms, and (2) our proofs rest upon some unproved assumptions involving those undefined terms.

This should suffice as a warm-up.

Overview

First and foremost, I must assume that a judge (among other things) knows retrievers, ... , can make judgments, and will make judgments. I prefer and propose a system of retriever mathematics that requires no arithmetic operations such as addition, subtraction, multiplication, and division, and no relationships other than equal to ($=$) or greater than ($>$); where only two scales are used, namely, ranking and nominal scales; and where only three decisions are made (but they are made repeatedly: (1) performance of retriever A is equal to performance of retriever B ($A = B$); (2) performance of retriever A is better than (or worse than) performance of retriever B ($A > B$ or $B > A$); and (3) at the end of each series, retriever A is either a callback (C) or a drop ($\overline{C}$), retriever B is either (C) or ($\overline{C}$), ...

At the end of each series, I propose to tentatively classify the group (set) of retrievers who started that series into four mutually exclusive subgroups (subsets) as follows:

S_E : the subgroup (subset) of entries who must be eliminated, such as those who broke, who failed to return with the meat, ... , or who retrieved a decoy.

S_{π}: the subgroup (subset) of entries whose performances were tentatively classified as poor, π (with high probability of being eliminated).

S_B : the subgroup (subset) of entries whose performances clearly left something to be desired, borderline; where further detailed comparisons must be made to decide for each entry whether to call him back or to drop him (label him as C or $\overline{C}$).

S_W : the subgroup (subset) of entries whose performances were tentatively classified as workmanlike or better.

These are just routine procedures with most "good judges" with whom I have had first-hand experience.

In terms of Venn diagrams, let the rectangle below represent S, all entries in the open stake of a trial which appear on the roster of the printed program. S_1 indicates the subset of entries who start the trial, who run series one.

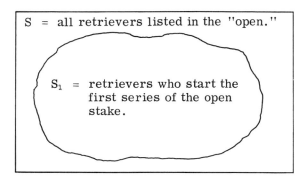

S = all retrievers listed in the "open."

S_1 = retrievers who start the first series of the open stake.

[*Aside:* N(S) = the number of retrievers listed in the open stake, say, 55, N(S) = 55; $N(S_1)$ = the number of starters, say, $N(S_1)$ = 53 .]

At the end of the first series, S_1 has been tentatively partitioned as follows.

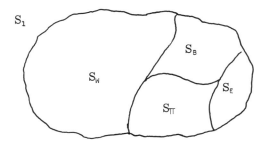

Comparisons are made to assure that there were no gross misclassifications.

Obviously, the entries of subset S_E must be dropped; it is highly probable that the entries of subset S_{π} will likewise be dropped. On the other hand, the entries of subset S_W will more than likely be called back. Clearly, then, the next task is to prepare the list of callbacks; that is, divide S_1 into C and $\overline{C}$. Then comparisons are required within the subset S_B to determine which entries are to be called back (C); furthermore, comparisons must be made of the poorest performances of entries called back with the best performances of entries dropped. In short, S_1 now becomes

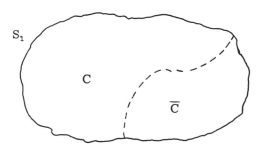

The members of subset C are the starters for the next series, and will be designated as the subset S_2.

The plan is to follow essentially these procedures at the end of each successive series, including the last.

WELL OVER

An old signed print by G. Vernon Stokes in the author's private Pontchippi
Collection.

POINTER

An old print from a painting by A. Cooper, R.A. (1787-1868) (drawn on stone by Thomas Fairland), in the author's private Pontchippi Collection.

A MATHEMATICAL SYSTEM FOR JUDGING

A mathematical system is a collection of statements beginning with some unproved (but acceptable) assumptions involving some undefined terms (basic terms) in which all further statements follow logically from the assumptions and all new terms are defined in terms of the basic terms ("a closed deductive system").

I will now show that retriever judging can be accomplished within the framework of a simple mathematical system which involves only two relationships (> and =) and a measurement scale no more complex than ranking performances. I would like to emphasize that no interval measurements are necessary.

Definitions

1. A set was defined in the second technical note to Chapter Eight as a collection of objects or things of any type. The N retrievers listed on the program in an open stake (an open stake roster) would constitute a set which I might denote by $S = \{R_1, R_2, \ldots, R_N\}$, where S denotes the universal set, R denotes the retriever, and the subscript indicates the running order (the entry number assigned by a strictly random process at the drawing), or more simply, $S = \{1, 2, \ldots, N\}$. The set of retrievers who enter the ith series is a subset of S which I shall call S_i. For example, $S_4 = \{R_3, R_7, R_8, R_{10}, R_{13}, R_{20}\}$ or $S_4 = \{3, 7, 8, 10, 13, 20\}$. Also, the retrievers who are awarded JAM's would constitute a subset of S as well as a subset of S_1, S_2, $\ldots$. Further, S_{i+1} is a subset of S_i.

2. The true "performances" of any two retrievers, say, R_j and R_k, are always different. That is, at some stage in the performances a "just noticeable difference" (jnd) occurs. If this difference is favorable to R_j, denote it by δ (lower case Greek letter delta) and write $R_j = R_k + \delta$. An equivalent statement is $R_j > R_k$ which is interpreted as "R_j's performance surpasses that of R_k." If the jnd cannot be detected by a particular judge, write $R_j = R_k$. Note that no

numerical value is being assigned to δ .

Assumptions

1. In comparing the performances of two retrievers R_j and R_k, it is always possible to state that either $R_j = R_k$ or that $R_j > R_k$. (It is assumed that we can arbitrarily place the label j on the superior retriever.)

2. At the end of the ith series, set S_i can be separated (partitioned) into the following mutually exclusive subsets: $S_i = S_E \cup S_{TT} \cup S_B \cup S_W$, where

> S_E is the subset of retrievers whose elimination from the contest is mandatory,
>
> S_{TT} is the subset of retrievers having poor performances with small probability of being able to place in the stake even though all subsequent performances are perfect,
>
> S_B is the subset of retrievers which (for the present) will be called borderline,
>
> S_W is the subset of retrievers with performances that are clearly workmanlike or better.

Theorems

Theorem 1: If $R_1 > R_2$ and $R_2 > R_3$, then $R_1 > R_3$.

Hypothesis: R_1 is better than R_2 and R_2 is better than R_3.

Conclusion: R_1 is better than R_3.

Proof: By definition 2,

$$R_1 = R_2 + \delta_1 \text{ and}$$
$$R_2 = R_3 + \delta_2 . \text{ Hence,}$$
$$R_1 = R_2 + \delta_1$$
$$= (R_3 + \delta_2) + \delta_1$$
$$= R_3 + (\delta_1 + \delta_2)$$
$$R_1 = R_3 + \delta , \text{ where}$$
$$\delta = \delta_1 + \delta_2 ; \text{ therefore,}$$
$$R_1 > R_3 .$$

Theorem 2: If $R_1 = R_2$ and $R_2 > R_3$, then $R_1 > R_3$.

Proof:

$$R_2 = R_3 + \delta$$
$$R_1 = R_2$$
$$= R_3 + \delta; \quad \text{therefore,}$$
$$R_1 > R_3.$$

Theorem 3: If $R_1 > R_2$ and $R_2 = R_3$, then $R_1 > R_3$.

Proof:

$$R_1 = R_2 + \delta$$
$$= R_3 + \delta; \quad \text{therefore,}$$
$$R_1 > R_3.$$

Comments on the Theorems

Theorems 1 and 2 are helpful in that they show that whenever $R_1 > R_2$ or $R_1 = R_2$ it is not necessary to compare R_1 with any re- trievers that are outranked by R_2. Theorem 3 can be applied simi- larly. The reader will observe that with N entries there can never be fewer than N − 1 comparisons nor more than $\frac{1}{2}N(N-1)$. For example, with N = 12, the minimum number of comparisons is 11 and the maximum number is 66.

Recommended Action in Judging

Since it is assumed that judges desire a clear and obvious winner at the end of the stake, it may be advisable to terminate the stake at the end of any series after the entries have been thoroughly tested on both land and water and this objective has been achieved. We shall also require that four or more entries remain after the last series (i.e., after the stake is terminated).

1. At the end of the ith series prior to termination of the stake, classify each retriever as callback (C) or not callback ($\overline{C}$) as follows:

a. Classify as C all members of subset S_W, and as $\overline{C}$ all members of subsets S_E and S_{π}.

b. For all members of subset S_B make comparisons with the members in group C and perhaps also group $\overline{C}$ in order to determine their appropriate classifications.

[Note that theorems 1, 2, and 3 can well be applied here.]

2. At the termination of the stake, there exists a clear and obvious winner. This leaves the task of placing second, third, and fourth, and making the judges' awards of merit. A sound procedure is to classify all entries as C or $\overline{C}$ just as though another series were to be run. The entries receiving first, second, third, and fourth place should come from the subset S_W (and from S_B if more entries are needed), and the rankings should be made by paired comparisons. JAM's can then be awarded to the remaining members of S_W and, in addition, the members of S_B should be compared directly with those awarded JAM's from the S_W set in order to decide whether or not some of this set (the S_B set) should receive JAM's.

A Field Trial Example

In a licensed trial, spring, 1968, there were 55 entries listed on the program. Hence, N = 55. Two entries, numbers 27 and 46, were scratched, leaving N_1 = 53 starters. That is,

$$S_1 = \{1, 2, \ldots, 26, 28, \ldots, 45, 47, \ldots, 54, 55\}.$$

At the end of the first series, S_1 was partitioned as follows:

$$S_E = \{7, 29\},$$

[*Aside:* Number 7 "broke" and number 29 demonstrated unacceptable line manners.]

$$S_{TT} = \{2, 5, 14, 20, 28, 40, 44, 49, 54\},$$
$$S_B = \{3, 12, 33, 55\},$$
$$S_W = \{\text{remaining 38 entries}\}.$$

After making direct comparisons of the members of S_B with the clearly poorest (performances of the) members of S_W and also with the best members of S_{TT}, entries 3, 12, 33, and 55 were dropped. [*Aside:* In this particular instance, all the entries in the borderline set, S_B, were dropped. Obviously, this is not always the case.] Thus, at the end of series one (S_1),

$$\overline{C} = S_E \cup S_{TT} \cup S_B$$
$$= \{2, 3, 5, 7, 12, 14, 20, 28, 29, 33,$$
$$40, 44, 49, 54, 55\}$$

and

$$C = S_W .$$

Note that S_1 has been partitioned into two subsets, $\overline{C}$ and C.

For the second series, $N_2 = 38$. At the end of the second series, S_2 was partitioned into

$$S_E = \{23, 53\},$$
$$S_{TT} = \{4, 13, 19, 22, 30, 35, 45\},$$
$$S_B = \{26, 47\},$$
$$S_W = \{\text{remaining 27 entries}\}.$$

Again, as in series one, after making comparisons the members of S_B were classified in $\overline{C}$. [*Aside:* Again, it so happened that all entries in the set S_B were dropped; clearly, this is not always the situation.] Now,

$$S_2 = \overline{C} \cup C, \quad \text{where for series two,}$$
$$\overline{C} = S_E \cup S_{TT} \cup S_B$$
$$= \{4, 13, 19, 22, 23, 26, 30, 35, 45, 47, 53\},$$

and

$$C = \{\text{remaining 27 entries}\}.$$

For the third series, $N_3 = 27$. At the end of the series, S_3 was partitioned into

$$S_E = \{1, \quad 10, \quad 25\},$$
$$S_{TT} = \{15, \quad 16, \quad 18, \quad 32, \quad 36, \quad 42, \quad 52\},$$
$$S_B = \varphi \text{ (an empty set, i.e., no borderline cases),}$$

and

$$S_W = \{\text{remaining } 17 \text{ entries}\}.$$

So,

$$\overline{C} = S_E \cup S_{TT} \text{ and}$$
$$C = S_W.$$

For the fourth series, $N_4 = 17$. At the end of the series, entry number 31 was an obvious winner;

$$S_E = \{39, \quad 41\} \quad \text{and}$$
$$S_{TT} = \{17, \quad 21, \quad 24, \quad 34\}.$$

The set of callbacks, if an additional series were to be run, would be

$$C = \{6, \quad 8, \quad 9, \quad 11, \quad 31, \quad 37, \quad 38, \quad 43, \quad 48, \quad 50, \quad 51\}.$$

By gross comparison it was clear that entries 9, 37, 38, 48, and 50 should receive JAM's, leaving only entries 6, 8, 11, 43, and 51 in contention for places 2, 3, and 4. By direct comparison it was evident that $R_{51} > R_{43}$ (i.e., entry or retriever number 51 surpassed retriever number 43 in performance), $R_{51} > R_{11}$, $R_{51} > R_6$, $R_{51} > R_8$. Therefore, entry number 51 was awarded second place. Similarly, $R_{43} > R_{11}$, $R_{43} > R_6$, $R_{43} > R_8$, so entry number 43 was awarded third place. Further, $R_{11} > R_8$ and $R_8 > R_6$ and, consequently, $R_{11} > R_6$. Thus, entry number 11 received fourth place, and entries 8 and 6 were awarded JAM's (in addition to entries 9, 37, 38, 48, and 50).

Comment: Undoubtedly, some retriever enthusiasts have encountered difficulty in following the explanations of this chapter; in contrast, the proofs might have appeared absurdly simple. Keep in mind that it requires no unusual ability to follow mathematical ideas; recall the proverb: "What one fool can do, another can." In short, I believe that if we are going to improve the judging process, mathematics must play a role in it; hence, the dedicated RE must learn to read and appreciate the language.

REFERENCE

1. Russell, Bertrand (1901). "Recent Work on the Principles of Mathematics," *International Monthly* 4:84.

And I s'pose he really wants us to ... .

A pittance of practice may be worth a tome of theory.

NOTES TO CHAPTER ELEVEN

In Great Britain a different scoring system is used when judging gundogs at game fairs from that used when judging field trials. The system employed for game fair tests could be equated to the system all too frequently utilized in the field in America. What are the basic differences between British and American field trials? What are the basic differences between British game fair tests and British field trials? What are the basic differences between British game fair tests and American field trials? Are these basic differences reflected in scoring systems?

CHAPTER TWELVE

CALLBACKS AND ONE JUDGE

If a retriever is to be considered when the final awards are made, being called back after each series (for generality, say, series i) for further testing is obviously of vital importance to the retriever-handler team. Consequently, one of the most important tasks of a judge is to prepare his list of entries to be tested in the next series (for convenience, referred to as "callbacks"). Since the complement of being called back is elimination, it would appear that understanding the implications of procedures used for eliminating entries from further consideration in a stake would be basic for a judge to perform well.

Even though judges perform in pairs, it does seem worthwhile to focus our discussion on the problems of one judge initially; after all, each of us sees the stake through the eyes of a single judge. Later, in Chapter Thirteen we shall examine callbacks somewhat more realistically, namely, from the point of view of two judges.

NOMINAL AND RANKING SCALES ONLY

I shall assume (after Chapters Ten and Eleven) that the open-minded retriever enthusiast is convinced that we not only do not require interval and ratio scales in our judging process, but that we also avoid many pitfalls and complications when we do without them.

Pontchippi Classification

For convenience, and convenience only, in our discussions in this section, I shall again utilize the six categories outlined in Chapter

Ten which are repeated for easy reference below:

First rate   Δ
   (top notch)

Star performance   *
   (earned stars)

Middling   M
   (meritorious)

Only fair   □
   (square)

Poor   π
   (inadequate)

Failure   O
   (Ohh!)

Distribution of Classifications

By distribution, I shall mean the relative frequency with which I expect each classification to be assigned over the long run. Depending upon the difficulty of the tests, judging ability, and dog work, the distribution of classifications will probably vary from trial to trial.

A hypothetical example.-- One judge, after keeping careful records over several trials, might use a distribution such as the following as his model (such a model is not a "good" model of my judging):

Classification	Percentage of performances
Δ	9
*	18
M	23
□	23
π	18
O	9 .

In fact, each judge could have a unique distribution.

Pontchippi distribution suggested by empirical data.--Suppose that one assumes that there will be 10 per cent outright failure (either "no meat" or mandatory elimination), and further assumes that the distribution of the other classifications "follows a straight line," then a possible model (i.e., distribution) might be as follows:

Classification	Percentage of performances
Δ	24
*	21
M	18
□	15
π	12
O	10 .

Displayed by means of a graph in terms of probabilities (rather than percentages), the distribution consists of points as shown below:

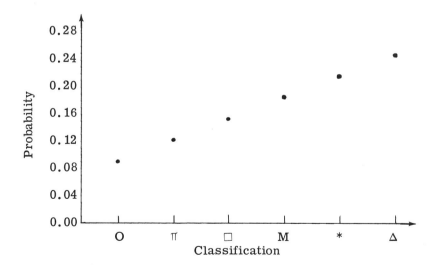

With a single judge this system of classification can easily be included in the mathematical system for judging treated earlier (Chapter Eleven) and the recommended action given there will apply. For example, entries receiving classifications of Δ, *, and M should go into the S_W subset, and those earning $\square$ should be placed in the S_B subset, those earning π should be placed in the S_π subset, and those assigned O (mandatory elimination) should be placed in the S_E subset. With this procedure for classifying entries and within the restrictions suggested in Chapter Eleven, at the end of any series, the judge is able to say that all entries assigned Δ, *, or M are to be classified as callbacks (C) and all assigned π or O are to be classified as not callbacks $(\overline{C})$. This leaves the group of entries assigned to classification $\square$ to be evaluated by direct comparisons to determine which ones should be called back.

MONTE CARLO SIMULATION

Repeatedly we hear that there is much luck concerned with retriever field trials, that chance plays a big role. If we are to simulate a complicated stake or trial and study it in terms of several of the interacting aspects or factors, the simulation must contain random variations. By means of Monte Carlo methods, a stake or trial can be simulated according to some hypothetical model. Random numbers are sequentially chosen from selected distributions to determine not only the initial conditions, say, the running order, but also other random processes in a stake.

Since some senior retriever enthusiasts may not be familiar with the concept of simulation using a high-speed electronic digital computer, it seems worthwhile to explore at least one factor as background material.

Analysis of Time (Ratio Scale), An Example

It is well-known that time is a precious commodity to a field trial judge, that time available influences the number that can be called back, and yet, when one tries to analyze the effects of selected factors, he is overwhelmed with the complex interrelationships and uncontrolled random variations.

The foregoing notwithstanding, suppose that we wished to examine the time that it takes to conduct an open stake. Clearly, it depends upon such factors as the following: number of entries, types of tests, whether or not other stakes are in progress concurrently, number of handlers with multiple entries, ... , distance to other stakes and traffic control, mechanics for re-supplying birds to gun locations, ... , number of no-birds (whether first, second, or third in a triple), ... , honoring versus not honoring, quality of dog work, terrain (land or water), ... , weather, and other factors.

In order to obtain some information for planning purposes on a per dog basis, as well as on a per retrieve basis (and otherwise), a colleague and I collected data on licensed open stakes in 1961 and 1962. We each used two stop watches independently (four stop watches) to measure elapsed time for various factors (listed earlier) over a trial.

To be even more specific, say that we observed a combination test, explicitly, a double land mark and a double land blind. With one stop watch, each of us recorded the elapsed time for each entry from the time he left the ready box, ran, and returned (crossed a line corresponding to the ready box) behind the line of judges. With the second stop watch, each of us measured the time for each retrieve. Suppose that we observed 30 retrievers in this series. We had observations in minutes and seconds on the time it took each retriever to make each retrieve, and in addition, we had 30 observations (in minutes and seconds) on time for each entry to run, from which we could hypothesize true average values and true measures of variation for simulation purposes.

[*Aside:* It is little wonder that (when we are setting up tests for a stake) those who judge with me are impressed with my great concern for the time element.]

Back in 1962, I realized that a retriever field trial involves so many variables (factors) and chance plays so great a part that no "complete" mathematical analysis was possible. Consequently, after normal working hours during the summer (of 1962), an associate and I explored the possibility of simulating a retriever field trial on a high-speed electronic digital computer.

Not only did we analyze the "time element" by simulating 1,000 trials with 35 entries each, but we also examined other topics. To illustrate a simple case, given a stake of 35 open retrievers, it is well-known that they are not of equal competence and ability. If we assign an estimate of quality based on past performance records, then assign differential probabilities of placing (say we have 3 to 5 strata), what are the results if we allow a certain amount of luck (chance) to influence the outcome? How often do the better dogs get dropped on a mere chance basis? What is the probability that a dog that is kept that should be dropped will be there to haunt the judge at the final summing-up?

Among the factors we examined was running order. Assume that scenting and other conditions change over a series such that the average probability of classification changes materially after the first 12 dogs run. How does running order influence the probability of a retriever being in the group to receive ribbons?

Also, we examined the influence on classification assigned after, say, three, superior performances followed by a fair performance versus three poor performances followed by a fair performance.

[Explicitly, program such that a fair performance following three Δ's is assigned a π; and three π's followed by a □ is assigned a *.]

[*Aside:* In order to demonstrate ("show-off") simulation involving one judge to an RE, I had the computer print such phrases as follows:

Number of entries: _____.
Series number: _____.
Number of entry on the line: _____.
Number of entry in the ready box: _____.

Judge says signal when ready.

Handler signals ready.

Judge calls number _____.

Entry number _____ runs.

Classification assigned by judge: _____.

.
.
.

All entries have run.

Number of entry and classification (list).

Inspect list of classifications to drop manually.

List of callbacks.

End this series.

.
.
.
.]

It should be clear that such simulations produce "tons of data." Moreover, we attempted to combine the various analyses into an integrated system to evaluate how unknown factors influence a trial.

Obviously, all such findings are beyond the scope of this book. Here I shall illustrate a simple case involving percentage of callbacks without other complicating factors simply to demonstrate that simulation using various classification distributions might provide insight into (1) just how difficult tests in the different series should be, (2) how the results should be classified in order to make appropriate callbacks, and (3) other aspects which may provide food for thought.

SIMULATION OF A TRIAL WITH ONE JUDGE

To simulate a trial with one judge we first need to choose a distribution of classification. Suppose we choose the one previously shown and make our classifications using a table of two-digit random numbers. For a review of the random number procedure see Chapter Five, pages

74 to 84 and Table 5-4. The classifications can be made as follows:

Random numbers obtained	Classification made	Per cent of total
00 through 23	Δ	24
24 through 44	*	21
45 through 62	M	18
63 through 77	□	15
78 through 89	π	12
90 through 99	O	10

With this procedure of classification we would expect to get about 63 per cent of the entries in any series falling into the subset S_w (24 + 21 + 18 = 63) and these entries are always callbacks. If we desire, say, 70 per cent callbacks, then we need only (in our simulation process) to take 7/15 of the 15 per cent expected in the □ classification. This 7 per cent out of 15 per cent corresponds to the fraction of the □ classification group which is called back after direct comparisons are made. In the trial simulation, since we cannot make the comparisons (and, further, do not wish to do so in a simulation), we will obtain 7/15 of the □ group by using a table of random numbers. If any of the numbers 01 through 07 occur, we classify the entry as a callback, whereas, if any of the numbers 08 through 15 occur we classify the entry as not callback. We would expect this procedure to give us (over the long run) 70 per cent of entries as callbacks in any series. [Aside: Seventy per cent is not *the* right percentage; it is not a magic number; it was arbitrarily chosen for this illustration.] For example, with 35 original entries, after series 1 we would expect to call back 70 per cent of 35 or 24 entries. After series 2, we could expect 70 per cent of 24 or 17 entries; after series 3, 70 per cent of 17 or 12 entries. After series 4, there would be expected about 8 entries. The above simulation procedure (over the long run) would place about 22 per cent in the 2 subsets S_E and $S_π$ following each series.

Results of simulating 1, 000 retriever field trials on a high-speed electronic computer (using one judge and 45 starters) are presented in Tables 12-1 and 12-2 .

Table 12-1. --Theoretical and observed proportion p_i of retrievers entering series i, called back for series i + 1, and proportion $\prod_{k=1}^{i} p_k$ of the original starters (45) called back for series i + 1, Pontchippi nominal scale, 1, 000 simulated field trials with a single judge, 1968

Series i	p_i		$\prod_{k=1}^{i} p_k$	
	Theoretically expected	Observed in 1, 000 trials	Theoretically expected	Observed in 1, 000 trials
1	0. 70	0. 696	0. 700	0. 696
2	0. 70	0. 700	0. 490	0. 487
3	0. 70	0. 698	0. 343	0. 340
4	0. 70	0. 697	0. 240	0. 238

It can be seen in Table 12-2 that the standard deviation (s.d.) of the percentage dropped after series i is exactly equal to s.d. of the percentage called back for series i + 1 for each series i. This is true because these two percentages always add up to a constant 100 per cent for every series. However, note that the s.d. for the number of entries dropped after series i is not equal to the s.d. for the number of entries called back for series i + 1 for every value of i. Although it is true that these numbers add up for each series to the number of entries which enter that series, the number entering series i will be expected to vary from trial to trial in 1, 000 simulated trials. Hence, the s.d.'s will be expected to vary.

These tables provide considerable additional information which shall not be explicitly pointed out here. For example, based on the

Table 12-2.--Mean and standard deviation (s.d.) of the numbers and percentages of entries dropped after series i, and called back for series i + 1, and the percentage of original starters remaining after series i, Pontchippi nominal scale, 1,000 simulated field trials with a single judge, 1968

Series i	Number*				Percentage* of those entering series i				Percentage* of original starters called back for series i + 1	
	Dropped after series i		Called back for series i + 1		Dropped after series i		Called back for series i + 1			
	Mean	s.d.	Mean	s.d.	Mean	s.d.	Mean	s.d.	Mean	s.d.
1	13.7	3.1	31.3	3.1	30.4	6.8	69.6	6.8	69.6	6.8
2	9.4	2.6	21.9	3.3	30.0	8.0	70.0	8.0	48.7	7.4
3	6.6	2.3	15.3	3.3	30.2	10.0	69.8	10.0	34.0	7.2
4	4.6	2.0	10.7	3.0	30.3	12.2	69.7	12.2	23.8	6.6

*Forty-five original entries with probability of being called back after series i equal to 0.70. Numbers and percentages may vary slightly due to rounding procedures.

data of Table 12-2, if a test is set to call back 70 per cent of those entering series 4, a judge would expect to call back 90 per cent in about 1 in 20 series. Clearly then, given 90 per cent callbacks after series 4, critics must be careful not to make remarks such as the following: "that test was a failure; it was not difficult enough"; or "they wasted a test, they didn't prove a thing"; neither does it follow that "the judge got no separation." These statements may be true, but obviously such inferences are not justified solely on 90 per cent callbacks.

Plainly, there are 45,000 starters in 1,000 field trials of 45 starters each. The theoretical probability of "completing" a trial, under the assumptions laid on for the simulations reported (Table 12-3) in this chapter, is

$$0.70 \times 0.70 \times 0.70 \times 0.70 = 0.2401 \approx 0.24 ;$$

whereas, the empirical probability is (where relative frequency is treated as probability)

$$\text{Pr(completing)} = \frac{10,697}{45,000} \approx 0.24 .$$

The probability of perfect or near perfect work over four series, four Δ's is (theoretical):

$$\text{Pr(all } \Delta\text{'s)} = 0.24 \times 0.24 \times 0.24 \times 0.24$$
$$= 0.00331776 \approx 0.003 ,$$

and (empirical):

$$\text{Pr(all } \Delta\text{'s)} = \frac{150}{45,000} = \frac{1}{300} \approx 0.003 .$$

The probability of at least one borderline performance or worse

Table 12-3. --Observed frequency and relative frequency distributions, probability, and rank according to probability of occurrence of classifications assigned to "retrievers" finishing a trial (Pont-chippi nominal scale), 1,000 simulated field trials, 45 starters each trial, with a single judge, 1968

Classification (1)	Number of "categories" (2)	Frequency (f) (3)	Relative frequency (4)	Probability of classification (5)	Rank according to probability of occurrence (6)
4 △	1	150	0.0033	0.0033	21
3 △, 1 *	4	511	0.0114	0.0116	6
3 △, 1M	4	437	0.0097	0.0100	9
3 △, 1 □	4	155	0.0034	0.0039	20
2 △, 2 *	6	678	0.0151	0.0152	4.5
2 △, 1 *, 1M	12	1,195	0.0266	0.0261	1
2 △, 1 *, 1 □	12	459	0.0102	0.0102	8
2 △, 2 M	6	477	0.0106	0.0112	7
2 △, 1M, 1 □	12	413	0.0092	0.0087	12
2 △, 2 □	6	78	0.0017	0.0017	27

(Continued)

Table 12-3.--(Continued) Observed frequency and relative frequency distributions, probability, and rank according to probability of occurrence of classifications assigned to "retrievers" finishing a trial (Pontchippi nominal scale), 1,000 simulated field trials, 45 starters each trial, with a single judge, 1968

Classification (1)	Number of "categories" (2)	Frequency (f) (3)	Relative frequency (4)	Probability of classification (5)	Rank according to probability of occurrence (6)
1Δ, 3*	4	404	0.0090	0.0089	10.5
1Δ, 2*, 1M	12	1,008	0.0224	0.0229	2
1Δ, 2*, 1□	12	401	0.0089	0.0089	10.5
1Δ, 1*, 2M	12	860	0.0191	0.0196	3
1Δ, 1*, 1M, 1□	24	672	0.0149	0.0152	4.5
1Δ, 1*, 2□	12	149	0.0033	0.0030	22
1Δ, 3M	4	289	0.0064	0.0056	18
1Δ, 2M, 1□	12	296	0.0066	0.0065	16
1Δ, 1M, 2□	12	128	0.0028	0.0025	24
1Δ, 3□	4	16	0.0004	0.0003	32

(Continued)

Table 12-3.--(Continued) Observed frequency and relative frequency distributions, probability, and rank according to probability of occurrence of classifications assigned to "retrievers" finishing a trial (Pontchippi nominal scale), 1,000 simulated field trials, 45 starters each trial, with a single judge, 1968

Classification (1)	Number of "categories" (2)	Frequency (f) (3)	Relative frequency (4)	Probability of classification (5)	Rank according to probability of occurrence (6)
4 *	1	80	0.0018	0.0019	26
3 *, 1 M	4	289	0.0064	0.0067	14.5
3 *, 1 □	4	129	0.0029	0.0026	23
2 *, 2 M	6	351	0.0078	0.0086	13
2 *, 1 M, 1 □	12	280	0.0062	0.0067	14.5
2 *, 2 □	6	52	0.0012	0.0013	29
1 *, 3 M	4	222	0.0049	0.0049	19
1 *, 2 M, 1 □	12	237	0.0053	0.0057	17
1 *, 1 M, 2 □	12	96	0.0021	0.0022	25
1 *, 3 □	4	13	0.0003	0.0003	33

(Continued)

Table 12-3.--(Concluded) Observed frequency and relative frequency distributions, probability, and rank according to probability of occurrence of classifications assigned to "retrievers" finishing a trial (Pontchippi nominal scale), 1,000 simulated field trials, 45 starters each trial, with a single judge, 1968

Classification (1)	Number of "categories" (2)	Frequency (f) (3)	Relative frequency (4)	Probability of classification (5)	Rank according to probability of occurrence (6)
4 M	1	40	0.0009	0.0010	30
3 M, 1 □	4	83	0.0018	0.0016	28
2 M, 2 □	6	40	0.0009	0.0010	31
1 M, 3 □	4	9	0.0002	0.0002	34
4 □	1	0	0.0000	0.0000†	35
Total	256	10,697‡	0.2377§	...	...

Total number of starters in 1,000 trials: 45,000.

† Probability (4 □) = 0.000024 ≈ 0.0.

‡ (10,697)/(45,000) ≈ 0.2377 ≈ 24 per cent.

§ Proportion completing all trials ≈ 0.2377 ≈ 24 per cent.

over four series can be computed as follows:

number that did not finish $= 45,000 - 10,697 = 34,303$,

of those who finished, those assigned at least one $\square$ $= 3,706$;

$$\Pr(\text{one } \square \text{ or worse}) = \frac{34,303 + 3,706}{45,000} = 0.845.$$

The complement of the above, the probability of workmanlike per-formance or better in each and every series, is

$$\Pr(M \text{ or better}) = 1.000 - 0.845 = 0.155.$$

Recall that this entire simulation is based on the *false* assumption that all 45 starters are of equal ability; each classification is assigned independently within each series, thus, cumulative information is not considered for elimination.

It seems worthwhile to make some further comments about Table 12-3. Since four series are being run, the results for an entry who finishes the trial can be any one of the following five basic types:

(1) 4 series with the same classification;

(2) 3 series with 1 type classification and 1 series with a different type;

(3) 2 series with 1 type classification and 2 series with another type;

(4) 2 series with 1 type classification and a different type in each of the remaining 2 series;

(5) a different classification for each series.

The total number of separate classifications can be obtained by com-bining the number of possibilities for the five preceding cases. Namely,

$$\binom{4}{1} + \binom{4}{2} \cdot \binom{2}{1} + \binom{4}{2} + \binom{4}{3} \cdot \binom{3}{1} + \binom{4}{4}$$

$$= 4 + 12 + 6 + 12 + 1 = 35.$$

Note that $\binom{4}{3}\binom{3}{1} = 12$ is obtained for case (4) as follows: In the four series, two series will receive the same classification and the remaining two series will be given classifications which are different from the previous two and also different from each other. First choose from the four possible classifications the three which will be used. This can be done in $\binom{4}{3}$ different ways. After the three are selected, then choose the one type which will be assigned to two series. This can be done in $\binom{3}{1}$ ways. Altogether, we have $\binom{4}{3} \times \binom{3}{1} = 12$ ways.

Using the distribution of classification of page 506 to simulate a trial with 1 judge and calling back only 7 per cent of the 15 per cent in the □ classification, we can determine the possible categories of classification and their probabilities for those entries who complete a trial. For example, if 4 series are run there are $4 \times 4 \times 4 \times 4 = 256$ groups of categories which fall into 35 separate classifications as displayed in column (1) of Table 12-3.

The 256 groups may be counted as follows using the 5 basic types:

Type 1: 4 series with same classification gives $\frac{4!}{4!} = 1$.

Type 2: 3 series with 1 type classification and 1 series with a different type gives $\frac{4!}{3!\,1!} = 4$.

Type 3: 2 series with 1 type classification and 2 series with another type gives $\frac{4!}{2!\,2!} = 6$.

Type 4: 2 series with 1 type classification and a different type in each of the remaining 2 series gives $\frac{4!}{2!\,1!\,1!} = 12$.

Type 5: a different classification for each series gives $\frac{4!}{1!\,1!\,1!\,1!} = 24$.

Now applying the possibilities for the 35 separate classifications, we get

$$4(1) \; + \; 12(4) \; + \; 6(6) \; + \; 12(12) \; + \; 1(24) \;\; = \;\; 256 \, .$$

The probability that an entry receives a specified group of classifications follows the multinomial distribution where p_Δ, p_*, p_M, $p_\square$, p_{TT}, and p_0 are the respective probabilities of classification for a single series and n_Δ, n_*, n_M, $n_\square$, n_{TT}, n_0 are the corresponding number of times that classification is received. Note that $p_\Delta + p_* + p_M + p_\square + p_{TT} + p_0 = 1$ and $n_\Delta + n_* + n_M + n_\square + n_{TT} + n_0 = n$ = number of series run.

For Table 12-3 we need a slight modification in the multinomial, since we are concerned only with those entries that have survived the four series. The desired change is to let, say, $p_\square' = 0.07$, whereas, $p_\square = 0.15$. The probability that an entry will receive the classification 2Δ, $1*$, $1\square$ is equal to the term involving $p_\Delta^2 p_* p_\square'$ in the expansion of the multinomial $(p_\Delta + p_* + p_M + p_\square' + p_{TT} + p_0)^4$:

$$\mathrm{Pr}(2\Delta, \; 1*, \; 1\square) \;\; = \;\; \frac{n!}{n_\Delta! \, n_*! \, n_\square!} \; p_\Delta^{\,n_\Delta} p_*^{\,n_*} (p_\square')^{\,n}$$

$$= \;\; \frac{4!}{2! \, 1! \, 1!} \; (0.24)^2 \, (0.21)^1 \, (0.07)^1$$

$$\mathrm{Pr}(2\Delta, \; 1*, \; 1\square) \;\; = \;\; 0.0102 \, .$$

CONDITIONAL PROBABILITIES

The simulation of this chapter (see page 506) is based on the assumption that each classification is assigned independently within each series. That is, results of prior series do not affect future series so long as the entry is called back. An alternate model for simulation might be as follows: Assume that the classification in series $i + 1$ will not differ from the classification in series i by more than two categories, and let us assign the following conditional probabilities arbitrarily:

$$\Pr(\Delta_{t+1}|\Delta_t) = 0.50, \quad \Pr(*_{t+1}|\Delta_t) = 0.30, \quad \Pr(M_{t+1}|\Delta_t) = 0.20;$$
$$\Pr(\Delta_{t+1}|*_t) = 0.25, \quad \Pr(*_{t+1}|*_t) = 0.40, \quad \Pr(M_{t+1}|*_t) = 0.25,$$
$$\Pr(\square_{t+1}|*_t) = 0.10;$$
$$\Pr(\Delta_{t+1}|M_t) = 0.10, \quad \Pr(*_{t+1}|M_t) = 0.20, \quad \Pr(M_{t+1}|M_t) = 0.40,$$
$$\Pr(\square_{t+1}|M_t) = 0.20, \quad \Pr(\pi_{t+1}|M_t) = 0.10;$$
$$\Pr(*_{t+1}|\square_t) = 0.10, \quad \Pr(M_{t+1}|\square_t) = 0.20, \quad \Pr(\square_{t+1}|\square_t) = 0.40,$$
$$\Pr(\pi_{t+1}|\square_t) = 0.20, \quad \Pr(O_{t+1}|\square_t) = 0.10.$$

Further, let us agree to eliminate an entry if he is classified as π or O (Ohh!) in any series.

Now let us determine the probability (see page 519 to follow) that an entry will complete a trial of 4 series and be called back for series 5, given that he has received a particular classification in series 1.

We list below the categories of classification (and their respective probabilities) which will result in the entry being eliminated.

Case one.--The entry receives a Δ in series 1.

Possible categories for elimination	Probability		
Δ M π	$0.50 \times 0.20 \times 0.10$	=	0.0100
* M π	$0.30 \times 0.25 \times 0.10$	=	0.0075
* $\square$ π	$0.30 \times 0.10 \times 0.20$	=	0.0060
* $\square$ O	$0.30 \times 0.10 \times 0.10$	=	0.0030
M M π	$0.20 \times 0.40 \times 0.10$	=	0.0080
M $\square$ π	$0.20 \times 0.20 \times 0.20$	=	0.0080
M $\square$ O	$0.20 \times 0.20 \times 0.10$	=	0.0040
M π	0.20×0.10	=	0.0200
			0.0665

Probability of elimination $|\Delta$ in series 1 is 0.0665;

Pr(completing trial $|\Delta$ in series 1) $= 1 - 0.0665 = 0.9335.$

Case two.--The entry receives a * in series 1.

Possible categories for elimination	Probability		
Δ M π	$0.25 \times 0.20 \times 0.10$	=	0.005
* M π	$0.40 \times 0.25 \times 0.10$	=	0.010
* □ π	$0.40 \times 0.10 \times 0.20$	=	0.008
* □ O	$0.40 \times 0.10 \times 0.10$	=	0.004
M M π	$0.25 \times 0.40 \times 0.10$	=	0.010
M □ π	$0.25 \times 0.20 \times 0.20$	=	0.010
M □ O	$0.25 \times 0.20 \times 0.10$	=	0.005
M π	0.25×0.10	=	0.025
□ M π	$0.10 \times 0.20 \times 0.10$	=	0.002
□ □ π	$0.10 \times 0.40 \times 0.20$	=	0.008
□ □ O	$0.10 \times 0.40 \times 0.10$	=	0.004
□ π	0.10×0.20	=	0.020
□ O	0.10×0.10	=	0.010
			0.121

Pr(completing trial | * in series 1) $= 1 - 0.121 = 0.879$.

Case three.--The entry receives an M in series 1.

Possible categories for elimination	Probability		
Δ M π	$0.10 \times 0.20 \times 0.10$	=	0.002
* M π	$0.20 \times 0.25 \times 0.10$	=	0.005
* □ π	$0.20 \times 0.10 \times 0.20$	=	0.004
* □ O	$0.20 \times 0.10 \times 0.10$	=	0.002
M M π	$0.40 \times 0.40 \times 0.10$	=	0.016
M □ π	$0.40 \times 0.20 \times 0.20$	=	0.016
M □ O	$0.40 \times 0.20 \times 0.10$	=	0.008
M π	0.40×0.10	=	0.040
□ M π	$0.20 \times 0.20 \times 0.10$	=	0.004
□ □ π	$0.20 \times 0.40 \times 0.20$	=	0.016

☐ ☐ O	$0.20 \times 0.40 \times 0.10$	$= 0.008$
☐ π	0.20×0.20	$= 0.040$
☐ O	0.20×0.10	$= 0.020$
π	0.10	$= \underline{0.100}$
		0.281

Pr(completing trial|M in series 1) $= 1 - 0.281 = 0.719$.

Case four.--The entry receives a ☐ in series 1.

Possible categories for elimination	Probability	
* M π	$0.10 \times 0.25 \times 0.10$	$= 0.0025$
* ☐ π	$0.10 \times 0.10 \times 0.20$	$= 0.0020$
* ☐ O	$0.10 \times 0.10 \times 0.10$	$= 0.0010$
M M π	$0.20 \times 0.40 \times 0.10$	$= 0.0080$
M ☐ π	$0.20 \times 0.20 \times 0.20$	$= 0.0080$
M ☐ O	$0.20 \times 0.20 \times 0.10$	$= 0.0040$
M π	0.20×0.10	$= 0.0200$
☐ M π	$0.40 \times 0.20 \times 0.10$	$= 0.0080$
☐ ☐ π	$0.40 \times 0.40 \times 0.20$	$= 0.0320$
☐ ☐ O	$0.40 \times 0.40 \times 0.10$	$= 0.0160$
☐ π	0.40×0.20	$= 0.0800$
☐ O	0.40×0.10	$= 0.0400$
π	0.20	$= 0.2000$
O	0.10	$= \underline{0.1000}$
		0.5215

Pr(completing trial|☐ in series 1) $= 1 - 0.5215 = 0.4785$.

The probability that an entry will complete a trial is equal to 1 minus the probability that he will be eliminated. Let B denote the event of a particular classification being given in the first series. Suppose that for the event B there are n possible categories for elimination. Then, if A is the event of elimination, we have A =

$A_1 \cup A_2 \cup \ldots \cup A_k \cup \ldots \cup A_n$ where A_k denotes the event of elimination by the kth category. Consequently,

$$Pr(A|B) = \frac{Pr(A \cap B)}{Pr(B)}$$

$$= \frac{Pr[(A_1 \cup A_2 \cup \ldots \cup A_k \cup \ldots \cup A_n) \cap B]}{Pr(B)}$$

$$= \frac{Pr(A_1 \cap B) + Pr(A_2 \cap B) + \ldots + Pr(A_k \cap B) + \ldots + Pr(A_n \cap B)}{Pr(B)}$$

since the A_k are mutually exclusive events.

Now $Pr(A_k \cap B) = Pr(B) \cdot Pr(A_k|B)$, so

$$Pr(A|B) = Pr(A_1|B) + Pr(A_2|B) + \ldots$$
$$+ Pr(A_k|B) + \ldots + Pr(A_n|B).$$

To demonstrate the calculations involved in cases 1, 2, 3, and 4, take case 2 with A_k being the category of classification $*M\square O$. Here the entry received the classifications $*$, M, $\square$, O, respectively, in the first 4 series. We wish to find the probability that he will receive classifications M in series 2, $\square$ in series 3, and O in series 4, given that he received $*$ in series 1. If we insert a subscript to indicate the series in which the classification is given we can write (since classification in a series depends only upon the classification in the immediately preceding series)

$$Pr(M_2 \square_3 O_4|*_1) = Pr(M_2|*_1) \cdot Pr(\square_3|M_2) \cdot Pr(O_4|\square_3)$$
$$= 0.25 \times 0.20 \times 0.10 = 0.005.$$

All other terms are calculated in similar manner.

Further work.--In order to examine the probability of the best retriever finishing (and winning) the trial, the 45 starters were divided into 9 groups of 5 each. Within each group, probabilities were adjusted differentially; e.g., group 1 had the largest probability of receiving high classifications and the smallest probability of receiving low classifications; ... ; group 5 retained the same probabilities as those used for the simulations in Tables 12-1 through 12-3; ... ; the probabilities for group 9 were adjusted to expect somewhat lower classifications. Clearly, this is beyond the scope of this chapter; hence, I leave it to the interested reader to simulate trials wherein he can examine such problems as he desires.

INTERVAL SCALE

It seems worthwhile to include some theoretical work for judging based on an interval scale. To be specific, (a) interval scales may be appropriately used in some other fields of judging; (b) moreover, it may be fruitful to demonstrate difficulties which are encountered when such a scale is used; and finally (c) those retriever judges who insist on using an interval scale need guidance. Consequently, in Technical Note 12-1, "Partitions Subject to Restrictions on the Sum of the Components," recurrence formulas are developed for finding the number of i-part partitions of integers subject to certain restrictions on the elements or components of the partitions. An extensive set of *Tables of Partitions* by Gupta, Gwyther, and Miller, was published for the Royal Society by the Cambridge University Press in 1958. These tables and the accompanying bibliography do not appear to indicate, from the titles and the materials which I have examined, that work has been done for the case in which the integer n is partitioned into m integral components subject to m restrictions on the sum of the components. This technical note does place m restrictions on the sum of the components. Furthermore, the partitions used in this note present a little theory behind the very practical case for judging a series of contests or subcontests as well as for simulating such problems.

To illustrate practical application, those formulas developed in the technical note are utilized to generate theoretical values in a framework for judging. Then these theoretical values are checked empirically by simulating 1,000 retriever field trials with a computer.

Since I believe that a judge of an American retriever field trial should not use interval and ratio scales in his judging, this technical note (12-1) has been written deliberately so that it can stand on its own outside the context of this book. Moreover, the simulation has assumed random assignment of scores using a uniform distribution (equal probability type distribution) which obviously not only involves an unrealistic assumption, but also is the simplest case; however, results of simulation procedures involving more realistic assumptions have been prepared for publication elsewhere by Fields and McMahan.

[*Aside:* I cannot resist stating that any judge who uses an interval or ratio scale after reading Chapters Ten and Eleven will be expected to not only be able to read but to also understand Technical Note 12-1 thoroughly--with all its implications.]

N.B.--A major part of Technical Note 12-1 was worked out in detail and written by Dr. Raymond I. Fields. Mind you, the author alone could not have brought the ideas to fruition without his contributions. In fact, a manuscript containing much of this same material was prepared several years ago under joint authorship (with him).

Product notation.--An analogous notation to the capital Greek letter sigma, Σ, is obtained by substituting the capital Greek letter pi, Π, for Σ. Accordingly, the terms resulting from substituting the integers for the index are multiplied instead of added.

A pittance of practice may be worth a tome of theory.

SPANIEL AND WILD DUCK

An old print engraved by R. G. Eunson from a painting by Richard Ansdell, in the author's private Pontchippi Collection.

WINDING

An old signed print by G. Vernon Stokes in the author's private Pontchippi Collection.

PARTITIONS SUBJECT TO RESTRICTIONS
ON THE SUM OF THE COMPONENTS

Introduction

It is well-known that judges are utilized in many types of contests. It would appear that understanding the implications of procedures used for eliminating entries from further consideration at certain stages of such contests would be basic for a judge to perform well. Furthermore, the complement of elimination, that is, being called back for further testing, is obviously of vital interest to the contestant since in most cases if a contestant is not called back, he is not considered when the final awards are made.

Judging in a Particular Frame of Reference

The case in which the integer n is partitioned into m integral components subject to m restrictions on the sum of the components is approached in terms of computing cutoff scores for judging "regular official" American retriever trials. Usually at such a trial, each stake consists of four or more sub-contests called series where each series is composed of at least one test. The entire trial is conducted under well-defined procedures where two, and only two, judges are required in each stake with rare exceptions. At the conclusion of a stake, judges are required to divide the entries who completed all series into two groups, those to be awarded and those not to be awarded ribbons. Among the subset to be awarded ribbons, four places, first, second, third, and fourth, must be assigned with no splitting of places. Furthermore, any retriever who is awarded a place in a stake must have competed in all tests held for any dog in that stake. In arriving at the final placings, if one considers measurement in terms of nominal, ranking, interval, and ratio scales, a judge is required to make use of no more complex a scale than a ranking scale but in general, his task is not an easy one.

After each series has been completed, judges may call back for further testing those retrievers who completed the tests of the current series and all previous series, and whom the judges desire to test further. Those entries who are called back for further testing are known as callbacks. Most judges use some kind of measurement (classification A, B, C, ... , or more involved) to allow them to announce the callbacks quickly. This paper is limited to the discussion of an interval scale for determining callbacks; the assigning of the four places, which at most is a ranking procedure, is beyond the scope of this paper.

It is presumed that judges would like to be generous in their callbacks. Since it is mandatory that judges drop retrievers who score zero on any tests, judges are careful in setting up tests as well as in establishing cutoff points. For a stake starting with 40 entries, many judges would like in the neighborhood of 9 or 10 entries, on the average, to complete the first 4 series with performances meriting being called back for a fifth series if such a series were required to determine a winner; such judges might expect to drop only about 5 retrievers at the end of the first series. For illustration, this could amount to dropping about 1/8 of the starters at the end of the first series, about 1/3 of the survivors of the first series at the end of the second series, about 2/5 of those surviving the second series at the end of the third series, and about 1/3 at the end of the fourth series. The proportion of the original group remaining after 4 series under these arbitrary assumptions would be about 23 per cent.

The Problem

In view of the frame of reference outlined above, this paper can be thought of as being concerned with the explicit problem of computing cutoff scores on an interval scale that would be expected to provide specified percentages of callbacks. Even though this study is made from the point of view of a single judge, the investigation can be extended to two judges by more complex procedures as suggested later.

Scores, Cumulative Scores, and Partitions

Let X_i denote the score for a specified retriever on the ith series where

$$X_i = 0, 1, 2, \ldots, t.$$

For most of the discussion in this paper, zero scores are excluded although zero scores are utilized in determining cumulative scores for callbacks.

Let L_i = lowest cumulative score called back to be tested further in series $i + 1$.

The cumulative score of a specified retriever having no zero scores after i series can be obtained as follows:

$$S(i, \quad L_{i-1} + K_i) = \sum_{j=1}^{i} X_j \tag{1}$$

where K_i (the excess in score above the cutoff score) is a positive integer whose range is from 1 to $ti - L_{i-1}$ and where t is the maximum value on the interval scale used by the judge. At first glance, simpler notation like S_i might appear preferable; however, in using Eq. (2) later, it was more convenient to symbolize the cutoff score separately.

At the end of the first series, the cumulative score consisting of only one score can be obtained from

$$\sum_{j=1}^{i} X_j = L_{i-1} + K_i$$

by substituting $i = 1$; hence,

$$\sum_{j=1}^{1} X_j = L_{1-1} + K_1$$
$$= L_0 + K_1$$

where $L_0 = 0$

since a retriever has a score of zero at the beginning of the trial, so

$$\sum_{j=1}^{1} X_j = K_1.$$

At the end of the second series the cumulative score of a specified retriever is

$$\sum_{j=1}^{2} X_j = X_1 + X_2$$

with the restriction that no cumulative score can be lower than L_1. By use of Eq. (1), cumulative scores can be found at the completion of each subsequent series.

Let $f(i, L_{i-1} + K_i)$ denote the "frequency" for cumulative score $S(i, L_{i-1} + K_i)$ for a specified retriever which does not score zero in the ith series. This frequency f is really the number of ordered i-part partitions of $S(i, L_{i-1} + K_i)$ of the type $(X_1, X_2, \ldots, X_i)$ where X_j is an integer in the interval $1, 2, \ldots, t$ and this partition is subject to the restrictions

$$L_{i-1} < \sum_{j=1}^{i} X_j < ti + 1 .$$

Explicitly, $f(i, L_{i-1} + K_i)$ is the number of distinct integral, positive solutions to the system of inequalities

$$L_{i-1} < \sum_{j=1}^{i} X_j < ti + 1 \text{ for } i = 1, 2, 3, \ldots .$$

Disregarding scores of zero, the possible cumulative scores

$$S(i + 1, L_i + K_{i+1})$$

in series $i + 1$ are $L_i + K_{i+1}$ where K_{i+1} is an integer whose range is from

$$1 \text{ to } t(i + 1) - L_i .$$

To illustrate, suppose that a judge uses a scale for determining callbacks from $0, 1, \ldots, 7$, that is, let $t = 7$. All possible scores in the first series and all possible scores in the second series can be shown as 64 ordered pairs; however, 15 of these ordered pairs would contain a zero. Since a zero score indicates failure to complete a series, that retriever must be eliminated from the stake; hence, ordered pairs containing zero are not considered.

As stated above, $t = 7$ and for the first series, $i = 1$. Let $L_1 = 1$ be the cutoff score, that is, the score required to be called back to be tested in the second series. Then, the number of possible cumulative scores excluding all zero scores in series $i + 1$, the second series, is

$$7(i + 1) - L_i = 13 .$$

The 13 different possible cumulative scores can be computed from $L_t +$ K_{t+1} as shown earlier and can be verified from a tabulation of the 49 ordered pairs by computing the sum of each ordered pair. Furthermore, the frequency with which each possible cumulative score can occur can be obtained by inspecting such a tabulation. As the number of the series increases, it becomes increasingly difficult to enumerate all the possible i-part partitions which yield a given cumulative score; hence, the methods developed next are useful for obtaining the number of ways in which specified cumulative scores can arise.

When $f(i,\ L_{t-1} + K_t)$ denotes the frequency for cumulative score $S(i,$ $L_{t-1} + K_t)$ in the ith series, it follows that

$$f(i + 1,\ L_t + K_{t+1}) = \sum_{h=1}^{K_{t+1}} C_1(h) \cdot f(i,\ L_t + h - 1)$$

$$- \sum_{h=1}^{K_{t+1}} C_2(h) \cdot f(i,\ L_t + h - t - 1) \qquad (2)$$

where

$$C_1(h) = \begin{cases} 1 & \text{for } 1 \le h \le ti + 1 - L_t \\ 0 & \text{otherwise} \end{cases}$$

and
$$C_2(h) = \begin{cases} 0 & \text{for } 1 \le h \le t \\ 1 & \text{for } t + 1 \le h \le K_{t+1}. \end{cases}$$

$C_1(h)$ and $C_2(h)$ are readily suggested by inspection of a listing of scores and frequencies in the preparation of Table 1. Since $C_1(h)$ and $C_2(h)$ depend upon the scoring scale utilized, the method can be easily modified.

Suppose for example that a judge desires to know the number of ways, called frequencies in this paper, that a specified cumulative score can be obtained at the end of the fourth series. In particular, say he desires to find the number of ordered 4-part partitions of the cumulative score (sum) of 24 using integers 1 through 7 subject to a cutoff of 12 to be called back for the fourth series. Let $t = 7$, $i = 3$, $L_3 = 12$, $K_4 = 12$.

$$S(i + 1,\ L_t + K_{t+1}) = S(4,\ 24) = 24.$$

$$C_1(h) = \begin{cases} 1 & \text{for } 1 \le h \le 10 \\ 0 & \text{otherwise} \end{cases}$$

Table 1.--Theoretical "frequency" f or number of ordered i-part partitions for each possible nonzero cumulative score at the completion of series i, where i = 1, 2, ..., 5, subject to arbitrary restrictions on cutoff scores L_{i-1} with number of zero scores, number called back and number dropped for four series with t = 7

Series one Score	f	Series two Score	f	Series three Score	f	Series four Score	f	Series five Score	f
$L_1 = 1$	1	2	1	7	5	13	33	18	151
2	1	3	2	8	11	14	69	19	317
3	1	4	3	9	18	15	102	20	493
4	1	5	4	10	24	16	130	21	642
5	1	$L_2 = 6$	5	11	29	$L_4 = 17$	151	22	758
6	1	7	6	$L_3 = 12$	33	18	166	23	842
7	1	8	7	13	36	19	176	24	898
		9	6	14	33	20	149	25	782
		10	5	15	28	21	116	26	636
		11	4	16	21	22	84	27	470
		12	3	17	15	23	56	28	325
		13	2	18	10	24	35	29	210
		14	1	19	6	25	20	30	126
				20	3	26	10	31	70
				21	1	27	4	32	35
						28	1	33	15
								34	5
								35	1
Total number of nonzero partitions	7		49		273		1302		6776
Number of zeroes	1		7		39		186		968
Total number of possible partitions including zeroes	8		56		312		1488		7744
Number of partitions called back for series i + 1	7		39		186		968		
Number of partitions dropped at completion of series	1		17		126		520		

$$C_2(h) = \begin{cases} 0 & \text{for } 1 \le h \le 7 \\ 1 & \text{for } 8 \le h \le 12 \end{cases}.$$

$$f(i + 1, \; L_i + K_{i+1}) = f(4, 24) = \sum_{h=1}^{10} f(3, 11 + h)$$

$$- \sum_{h=8}^{12} f(3, 4 + h)$$

$$= \sum_{h=6}^{10} f(3, 11 + h)$$

$$= 15 + 10 + 6 + 3 + 1 = 35,$$

the frequencies being obtained from Table 1.

In series $i + 1$ the total number of possible not all different cumulative scores including zeroes is $(t + 1) \, F(i)$ where $F(i)$ is the total number of cumulative scores $\ge L_i$ in series i. Thus, $F(i)$ is the number of cases where the scores qualify as callbacks. Furthermore, it is convenient to think of $(t + 1) \, F(i)$ as being composed of two quantities A and B as follows:

$$(t + 1) \, F(i) = A + B$$

where

$$A = F(i) = \begin{array}{l} \text{number of scores with zero for} \\ \text{series } i + 1 \text{ and} \end{array}$$

$$B = \sum_{K_{i+1} = 1}^{t(i+1) - L_i} f(i + 1, \; L_i + K_{i+1}).$$

Observe in passing that $B = t \, F(i)$. Substituting the right side of Eq. (2)

$$B = \sum_{K_{i+1} = 1}^{t(i+1) - L_i} \left[\sum_{h=1}^{K_{i+1}} C_1(h) \cdot f(i, \; L_i + h - 1) \right.$$

$$\left. - \sum_{h=1}^{K_{i+1}} C_2(h) \cdot f(i, \; L_i + h - t - 1) \right].$$

Selected Cases

To gain further insight into the formula given by Eq. (2) as well as to simplify selected computations, some special cases are examined where $t = 7$.

Case One

When $K_{i+1} < 8$, $C_1(h) = 1$ and $C_2(h) = 0$. Hence, the second summation of Eq. (2) drops out and

$$f(i + 1, \ L_i + K_{i+1}) = \overset{K_{i+1}}{\underset{h=1}{\Sigma}} (1) \cdot f(i, \ L_i + h - 1).$$

For example, the total number f of ordered 5-part partitions of 22 (cumulated score at the end of 5 series) satisfying the L_i restrictions is 758 since $i = 4$, $K_5 = 5$, $L_4 = 17$ and

$$\begin{aligned} f(5, \ 22) &= \overset{5}{\underset{h=1}{\Sigma}} f(4, \ 16 + h) \\ &= 151 + 166 + 176 + 149 + 116 \\ &= 758. \end{aligned}$$

Case Two

When $K_{i+1} > 7i + 1 - L_i \geq 7$,

$$C_1(h) = \begin{cases} 1 \ \text{for} \ 1 \leq h \leq 7i + 1 - L_i \\ 0 \ \text{otherwise} \end{cases}$$

$$C_2(h) = 0 \ \text{for} \ 1 \leq h \leq 7.$$

Again substituting in Eq.(2)

$$f(i + 1, \ L_i + K_{i+1}) = \sum_{h=1}^{7i+1-L_i} f(i, \ L_i + h - 1)$$

$$- \overset{K_{i+1}}{\underset{h=8}{\Sigma}} f(i, \ L_i + h - 8).$$

Observe that $7i + 1 - L_i$ replaces K_{i+1} as the limit of the first summation since $C_1(h) = 0$ for any K_{i+1} which is greater than $7i + 1 - L_i$. Also observe that the index of the second summation begins with 8 since $C_2(h)$ is zero for $h < 8$.

Now consider the second expression

$$\overset{K_{i+1}}{\underset{h=8}{\Sigma}} f(i, \ L_i + h - 8). \tag{3}$$

Let $u = h - 7$ or $h = u + 7$ so that when $h = 8$, $u = 1$ and when $h = K_{i+1}$, $u = K_{i+1} - 7$. Then

$$L_i + h - 8 = L_i + (u + 7) - 8$$
$$= L_i + u - 1 .$$

Hence, expression (3) becomes

$$\sum_{u=1}^{K_{i+1}-7} f(i, \ L_i + u - 1)$$

and writing in terms of original notation, is identical with

$$\sum_{h=1}^{K_{i+1}-7} f(i, \ L_i + h - 1) .$$

Rewriting

$$f(i + 1, \ L_i + K_{i+1}) = \sum_{h=1}^{7i+1-L_i} f(i, \ L_i + h - 1)$$

$$- \sum_{h=1}^{K_{i+1}-7} f(i, \ L_i + h - 1) .$$

Since the first terms of the summation are the same, they cancel and

$$f(i + 1, \ L_i + K_{i+1}) = \sum_{h=K_{i+1}-6}^{7i+1-L_i} f(i, \ L_i + h - 1) .$$

As a check when $i = 3$, $L_3 = 12$, and $K_4 = 12$, it follows that

$$f(4, 24) = \sum_{h=6}^{10} f(3, \ 11 + h)$$
$$= 15 + 10 + 6 + 3 + 1 = 35$$

which was obtained by Eq.(2) earlier.

Simulation of a Trial with One Judge

The methods illustrated in this paper were used to construct Table 1. By first selecting a particular column f, then by utilizing the entries in the second line from the bottom of the table as the numerator and the entry on the third line above the bottom of the table as the denominator of a fraction, the proportion of entries expected to be called back if scores were assigned to retrievers strictly at random can be computed. This procedure is illustrated in the discussion which follows.

Theoretical Proportions with t = 7

Recall that the possible scores which can be assigned by one judge to the performance of a specified retriever in a single series are as follows: 0, 1, 2, 3, 4, 5, 6, or 7. Call back any retriever for further testing if he scored 1 (L_1 = 1) or greater on the first series; obviously, each retriever who scored 0 on the first series is eliminated. A judge using such a rule will expect to eliminate 1/8 of the entries. If the total number of entries in a stake is 35, about 30 or 31 retrievers or 87.5 per cent will be called back for the second series on the average.

All possible scores at the end of the second series can be listed in the form of ordered pairs where the scores of each retriever would be contained in 1 of 56 ordered pairs [see the number 56 in column (4) of Table 1]. By adding the two elements of an ordered pair, the accumulated total score after two series is obtained. Consequently, cutoff scores for callbacks can be obtained from the frequency of ordered pairs (Table 1).

At the end of the second series, call back any retriever for further testing if his total accumulated score is greater than or equal to 6 (L_2 = 6) and if he has no score of 0. This rule will eliminate 17 ordered pairs [last line of column (4)] and call back 39 ordered pairs; 17/56 or about 30 per cent of those retrievers entering the second series are eliminated by the application of this rule. In terms of the original entries in the stake, 39/64 or about 61 per cent remain in the trial for the third series.

All possible scores at the end of the third series can be listed in the form of ordered triplets. There were 39 ordered pairs called back for the third series; hence, after each retriever had completed the third series with 8 possible scores in the third series, there would be 312 possible ordered triplets [third line from bottom of column (6)]. These 312 ordered triplets can be used to select cutoff scores for callbacks for the fourth series.

At the end of the third series, call back any retriever for further testing if his accumulated score is greater than or equal to 12 $(L_3 = 12)$ and provided he has no 0 score. This will eliminate 126 ordered triplets and call back 186 ordered triplets; 126/312 or about 40 per cent of retrievers entering the third series are eliminated by the application of this rule.

In terms of the number of original entries in the stake 93/256 or about 36 per cent remain in the trial for the fourth series. If 35 retrievers entered the original stake about 13 will be expected to enter the fourth series.

In a similar manner data in Table 1 can be used to compute the proportion of entries expected to enter the fifth series. If the judges have a clear winner, it is this subset of retrievers who will be awarded ribbons and from which the places will be chosen.

Clearly, different cutoff scores could be chosen to eliminate other proportions in each series.

Theoretical Ratios and Percentages for Selected Values of t

Selected theoretical measures of callbacks are presented in Table 2. Note that the denominator of each fraction is written as $(t + 1)^1$ where $t + 1$ is the number of points on the scale utilized by the judge.

Empirical Results

One thousand trials utilizing one judge were simulated on a computer by assigning the score to each retriever on each series by a system of random numbers. Theoretical proportions expected to be called back along with empirical results are shown in Table 3. Other results in both numbers and percentages with estimates of variability are given in Table 4.

Extension of the Problem to Two Judges

If two judges are to be used, it is realistic to assume that their scores are randomly assigned except for the restriction that their scores X_t will not differ by more than some constant k. With this restriction, the probabilities will not all be equal for obtaining the various possible scores in a series. In such a case, Eq. (2) must be modified to include a weighting factor which is a function of the total number of points scored by any entry in a single series.

Table 2.--Approximate percentages p_i of those entering series i expected to be called back for series $i + 1$ and approximate percentages $\prod\limits_{i=1}^{k} p_i$, and fractions of the original starters expected to survive series k ($k = 1$, 2, 3, 4) for three selected values of t, four arbitrary values of L_i, and four series

Series	t								
	5			7			9		
	L_i	p_i	$\prod\limits_{i=1}^{k} p_i$	L_i	p_i	$\prod\limits_{i=1}^{k} p_i$	L_i	p_i	$\prod\limits_{i=1}^{k} p_i$
1	1	83	$\dfrac{5}{6} \approx 83$	1	88	$\dfrac{7}{8} \approx 88$	1	90	$\dfrac{9}{10} = 90$
2	4	73	$\dfrac{22}{6^2} \approx 61$	6	70	$\dfrac{39}{8^2} \approx 61$	7	73	$\dfrac{66}{10^2} = 66$
3	8	67	$\dfrac{88}{6^3} \approx 41$	12	60	$\dfrac{186}{8^3} \approx 36$	15	59	$\dfrac{390}{10^3} = 39$
4	12	64	$\dfrac{336}{6^4} \approx 26$	17	65	$\dfrac{968}{8^4} \approx 24$	22	61	$\dfrac{2364}{10^4} \approx 24$

Table 3.--Theoretical and observed proportion p_i of retrievers entering series i called back for series i + 1 and proportion $\prod_{k=1}^{i} p_k$ of the original starters called back for series i + 1, t = 7, L_1 = 1, L_2 = 6, L_3 = 12, L_4 = 17, 1,000 simulated field trials, 1965

Series	p_i		$\prod_{k=1}^{i} p_k$	
	Theoretically expected	Observed in 1,000 trials	Theoretically expected	Observed in 1,000 trials
1	.875	.874	.875	.874
2	.696	.702	.609	.614
3	.596	.598	.363	.366
4	.649	.650	.236	.238

Table 4.--Mean and standard deviation (s.d.) of the numbers and percentages of entries dropped after series i and called back for series i + 1 and the percentage of original starters remaining after series i, $t = 7$, $L_1 = 1$, $L_2 = 6$, $L_3 = 12$, $L_4 = 17$, 1,000 simulated field trials, 1965

Series i	Number*				Percentage* of those entering series i				Percentage* of original starters called back for series i + 1	
	Dropped after series i		Called back for series i + 1		Dropped after series i		Called back for series i + 1			
	Mean	s.d.	Mean	s.d.	Mean	s.d.	Mean	s.d.	Mean	s.d.
1	4.4	2.0	30.6	2.0	12.6	5.8	87.4	5.8	87.4	5.8
2	9.1	2.6	21.5	2.9	29.8	8.3	70.2	8.3	61.4	8.1
3	8.7	2.6	12.8	2.7	40.2	10.5	59.8	10.5	36.6	7.8
4	4.5	1.9	8.3	2.4	35.0	13.4	65.0	13.4	23.8	7.0

*Thirty-five original entries; numbers and percentages may vary slightly due to rounding procedures.

Conclusions

Inspection of results of 1, 000 simulated trials indicates that the recurrence formulas closely predict the empirical outcomes. To call attention to particular cases, the percentage of original starters called back for series i + 1 is a random variable having the binomial distribution with 35 independent trials, each with probability of success equal to $\prod_{k=1}^{i} p_k$ as given in Table 3. Relatively large variability and close relationship of observed means and standard deviations to theoretical values are demonstrated in Table 4. It is left to the reader to reference the general case of which the present development is a special case.

ACKNOWLEDGMENTS

Indebtedness is expressed to Professor Raymond I. Fields of the University of Louisville, to Professor Robert H. Deupree, and to Lynne K. Hammett for the collaboration and assistance which made this article possible. Obviously the author is solely responsible for any and all shortcomings.

BIBLIOGRAPHY

Gupta, H., Gwyther, C. E., and Miller, J. C. P., *Tables of Partitions*. Cambridge: Cambridge University Press, 1962.

Riordan, J., *An Introduction to Combinatorial Analysis*. New York: John Wiley and Sons, Inc., 1958.

Ryser, H. J., *Combinatorial Mathematics*. New York: John Wiley and Sons, Inc., 1963.

TECHNICAL NOTE 12-2

Example of needed research. -- Elsewhere in this book, it has been pointed out that we have only scratched the surface in the attempt to understand the retriever game and the judging process. To illustrate specifically, several years ago my own careful observations led me to hypothesize (under certain explicit assumptions) that performance on marked falls, say, a triple on land, is not only related to, say, direction and angle of the throw, but may also be a function of the ratio

$$\frac{\text{(distance between two specified falls, } d_{ij})}{\text{(length [distance] of a fall from the line, } \ell_i)} ,$$

where i refers to the number of the fall of interest and j to the number of an adjacent fall.

I analyzed this problem and wrote a 30-or-so page manuscript; I even tested some of my hypotheses in the field with first-rate retrievers, but much further work needs to be done. To elaborate on a "simple" case, given a triple mark on land essentially as follows:

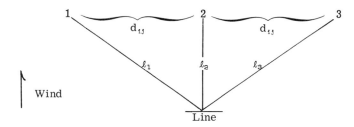

Among the ratios of possible interest are as follows:

$$\frac{d_{12}}{\ell_1}, \quad \frac{d_{21}}{\ell_2}, \quad \frac{d_{23}}{\ell_2}, \quad \frac{d_{32}}{\ell_3} .$$

Question: At what value of the ratio does the probability become high that an open retriever selected at random will "fail the test"? Extend this analysis to varying lengths of falls and distances between falls (include falls that appear to be "over and under" but clearly are not).

An approach to a simplified version of the problem.--Let us make four assumptions on the "simple case of the triple mark on land." (1) The three falls lie in a straight line and are fired or thrown from left to right (with respect to the handler, H, at the line) in the order dead bird, dead bird, live bird. Let F_1, F_2, and F_3 denote the locations of the three falls, respectively. (2) Locations F_1 and F_3 are fixed and are equidistant from H. Thus, the line $F_1 F_3$ is a fixed distance and $\ell_1 = \ell_3$. (3) Under each set of test conditions retrievers with equal ability are used. (4) Each retriever uses the same order of pickup.

We are now in position to seek answers (through experimentation) to a simpler question: At what location of F_2 along the line $F_1 F_3$, and for what value of ℓ_1 (recall $\ell_1 = \ell_3$), does the probability become high that an open retriever selected at random will "fail the test"?

Procedure.-- Use rectangular coordinates and choose as the origin the midpoint of the line $F_1 F_3$; call this point O. Denote the distance of F_2 from O (OF_2) by x_1, where x_1 is considered negative in the direction of (the dead bird at) F_1 and positive in the direction of (the shot live bird at) F_3. The handler (H) is located on a line through point O which is perpendicular to the line $F_1 F_3$. Denote the distance OH by x_2 and, for convenience, let x_2 take on only positive values. In our experiment (theoretically) we can vary the values of x_1 from $-(F_1 F_3/2)$ to $+(F_1 F_3/2)$ and (likewise, theoretically) we can vary the values of x_2 from just barely greater than 0 to $\sqrt{\ell_1^2 - (F_1 F_3/2)^2}$ (see sketch below).

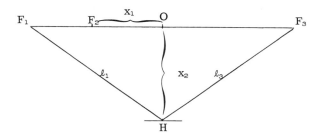

Now let Y be some numerical measure of performance on a test conducted with selected values for x_1 and x_2. Obviously, Y is a function of the variables x_1 and x_2. If we choose n pairs of values of x_1 and x_2 for our experiment then we shall choose randomly from our "equal ability" group of retrievers to conduct our test.

We may write

$$Y_u = \varphi(x_{1u}, x_{2u}) + \varepsilon_u,$$

where $u = 1, 2, \ldots, n$ represents the n observations in the experiment and x_{1u} and x_{2u} represent the levels of the variables (i.e., factors) on the uth observation. In statistical terminology, the function φ is called the response surface and ε_u measures the random error in the uth observation. If φ is known, we can predict the test response (performance on the test) for a retriever (chosen at random from our equal ability group) for given distances x_1 and x_2. If φ is not known, we can often find a satisfactory approximation for φ with a quadratic expression in the variables x_1 and x_2. Also, from this approximation, values of x_1 and x_2 can be found to minimize (or maximize) our quadratic estimate of Y.

For an actual experiment, if the distance from F_1 to F_3 is 100, we might select values of $x_1 = -20, -15, -10, -5, 0, 5, 10, 15, 20$ and values of $x_2 = 50, 75, 100, 125$, where the unit of measurement is yards. In this experiment (using the foregoing data), we have 9 levels for factor x_1 and 4 levels for factor x_2. We can say that we have a 9×4 factorial experiment. With only a single replication of the experiment, n would take the value of $9 \times 4 = 36$. That is, 36 observations would be made as to the "score" on the test (clearly, we would use 36 retrievers of "equal ability" on the test). (It is well-known that the response surface could be approximated with a 3^2 factorial.)

Clearly, if a judge can measure retriever performance "well" on at least an interval scale, he might conduct such an experiment as proposed here. Nevertheless, this does lead to some interesting questions. (1) What type of "score" is permissible? Can it be yes or no (i.e., 1 or 0)? Or, must it be of "ranked order" or some higher degree of measurement? (2) With $d_{12} = F_1 F_2 = (F_1 F_3/2) - |x_1|$ and $\ell_1 = \sqrt{[(1/2) F_1 F_3]^2 + x_2^2}$, can we use the obtained values of x_1 and x_2 for minimizing the estimate of Y to obtain an approximation of d_{12}/ℓ_1 which also minimizes Y?

CHAPTER THIRTEEN

CALLBACKS AND TWO JUDGES

In the previous chapter (Chapter Twelve) we examined the process of arriving at a list of callbacks (after each series) from the point of view of a single judge, J. (I shall assume that the reader is completely familiar with the previous chapter, including notation and definitions.) In this chapter, we examine the process from the point of view of two judges, Judge One, J_1, and Judge Two, J_2.

NOMINAL AND RANKING SCALES ONLY

Background

Suppose that two judges independently used a nominal scale such as the six classifications which we have been using, namely,

$$\Delta, \quad *, \quad M, \quad \Box, \quad \pi, \quad O.$$

There are 36 possible ordered pairs of tentative classifications of the form (classification assigned by first judge, J_1, classification assigned by second judge, J_2). Explicitly, the 36 ordered pairs are as follows:

$(\Delta, \Delta),\quad (\Delta, *),\quad (\Delta, M),\quad (\Delta, \Box),\quad (\Delta, \pi),\quad (\Delta, O)$

$(*, \Delta),\quad (*, *),\quad (*, M),\quad (*, \Box),\quad (*, \pi),\quad (*, O)$

$(M, \Delta),\quad (M, *),\quad (M, M),\quad (M, \Box),\quad (M, \pi),\quad (M, O)$

$(\Box, \Delta),\quad (\Box, *),\quad (\Box, M),\quad (\Box, \Box),\quad (\Box, \pi),\quad (\Box, O)$

$(\pi, \Delta),\quad (\pi, *),\quad (\pi, M),\quad (\pi, \Box),\quad (\pi, \pi),\quad (\pi, O)$

$(O, \Delta),\quad (O, *),\quad (O, M),\quad (O, \Box),\quad (O, \pi),\quad (O, O).$

Clearly, it is absurd to assume that one judge would assign an O and
the other judge would assign a Δ to the same performance. Even
though judges may not agree closely with each other (as was illustrated
with limited data in Chapter Ten and is also well-known), we shall assume that two judges can agree fairly closely. For example, on a
given performance, if J_1 assigns M, we shall assume that J_2 assigns *, or M, or $\square$; hence, the ordered pairs (all possible pairs
when J_1 assigns M) under this assumption are

$$(M, *),   (M, M),   \text{or}   (M, \square) .$$

Note that if we are given that Judge One assigned an M and if the
classification of the second judge is to be assigned strictly at random,
the probability is 1/3 that a * will be assigned by Judge Two, 1/3
that M will be assigned, and 1/3 that $\square$ will be assigned. In
shorthand,

$$Pr(* \text{ by } J_2 | J_1 \text{ assigns } M) = 1/3 ,$$
$$Pr(M \text{ by } J_2 | J_1 \text{ assigns } M) = 1/3 ,$$
$$Pr(\square \text{ by } J_2 | J_1 \text{ assigns } M) = 1/3 .$$

In addition to the above assumption, we shall make other explicit
assumptions throughout this chapter. In particular, we shall not always make the probabilities for the assignment by J_2 equally likely.

Assumptions

1. Each judge, on each performance, independently uses the
same nominal scale of measurement, namely, the six classifications
Δ, *, M, $\square$, π, O.

2. When the classifications are ranked in order of preference,
the measures recorded by the two judges for any single performance
will not differ by more than one classification rank except for the case
of classification O which should always be the same for both judges.

Procedures for Making Callbacks

The objective is to separate all the entries in a given series into the mutually exclusive subsets S_E, S_{π}, S_B, and S_W and then determine the callbacks. The S_E subset is uniquely determined (i.e., clearly defined). However, with two judges the individual classifications (with the exception of O) may differ, and so, the composition of the remaining subsets must be considered. It appears logical to place in subset S_W (automatic callback) any entry whose classification by either judge is not lower than M. Likewise, we should place in subset S_{π} (automatic not callback) an entry (not mandatorily eliminated) whose classification by either judge is no higher than π. This leaves for the borderline subset S_B the group of all entries with a classification of □ by one or both judges. The two judges might jointly make the paired comparisons for each entry of the S_B subset against the entries with poorest performances in the S_W subset as well as against the best performances in the S_{π} subset in order to fairly determine which entries of S_B should be callbacks. It might be expected that the entries in S_B who received a classification of M from one judge would be called back while those entries in S_B who received a classification of π from one judge would not be called back. Those entries in S_B receiving a classification of □ from both judges would require additional consideration. [Aside: An alternative method is for each judge to independently partition the entries in each series into the mutually exclusive subsets S_W, S_B, S_{π}, and S_E, and select the desired callbacks from the S_B subset after making his own comparisons. The two judges could then call back all entries which either judge wished to call back.]

SIMULATION OF A TRIAL WITH TWO JUDGES

Recall that the model (i.e., distribution) and random numbers were as follows for simulation with only one judge:

Random numbers obtained	Classification made	Per cent of total
00 through 23	Δ	24
24 through 44	*	21
45 through 62	M	18
63 through 77	□	15
78 through 89	π	12
90 through 99	O	10

Using the foregoing and a table of two-digit random numbers, for each entry first choose a classification to be made by Judge One (obviously, this is the procedure outlined in "Simulation of a Trial with One Judge"). Next, for this entry select a classification to be made by Judge Two in the following manner (six different categories must be considered):

1. If Judge One assigns classification O, then Judge Two assigns classification O.

For the remaining categories, a table of one-digit random numbers can be used (see Table 5-3). (*Note:* For convenience, i.e., simplicity, we are assuming in categories 2, 3, 4, and 5 that the permissible classifications assigned by Judge Two are equally likely to occur.)

2. If Judge One assigns the classification π, assign for Judge Two the classification π if the number 1 is obtained from the table of random numbers, or the classification □ if the number 2 is obtained.

3. If Judge One assigns the classification □, assign for Judge Two the classification π if the number 0 is obtained from the table of random numbers, the classification □ if the number 1 is obtained, the classification M if the number 2 is obtained.

4. If Judge One assigns the classification M, assign for Judge Two the classification □ if the number 0 is obtained from the table of random numbers, the classification M if the number 1 is obtained, the classification * if the number 2 is obtained.

5. If Judge One assigns the classification *, assign for Judge Two the classification M if the number 0 is obtained from the table of random numbers, the classification * if the number 1 is obtained, the classification Δ if the number 2 is obtained.

6. If Judge One assigns the classification Δ, assign for Judge Two the classification * if the number 0 is obtained from the table of random numbers, the classification Δ if the number 1, the number 2, or the number 3 is obtained.

It will be observed that with the exception of categories 1 and 6 the random digit 1 assigns the same classification for Judge Two as for Judge One, while 0 indicates a lower classification and 2 a higher classification.

After classifications have been assigned by both judges, the entry is placed in the subset S_W if both judges have classified the entry no lower than M. In the simulation procedure it is not necessary to distinguish between the subsets S_E and S_{π} since all members of both subsets are not called back. We might, for convenience, call $S_E \cup S_{\pi} = S_{E\pi}$ a single subset. It follows that an entry will be placed in the $S_{E\pi}$ subset and not called back if the entry has received a classification by either judge which is no higher than π. In the borderline subset S_B we have all entries who have received a classification of □ by either judge. To determine the set of callbacks C, do the following:

1. Include all members of subset S_W.

2. From S_B include all entries that have received a classification of M from one judge.

3. Label as $S_{\square}$ the subset of S_B containing all entries who received a classification of □ from both judges. Use a randomizing technique on the members of $S_{\square}$ (if desired) and on the remaining members of S_B to obtain additional callbacks and to secure the desired percentage of callbacks.

Using the distribution of classification adopted for the "Simulation of a Trial with One Judge" and applying the procedure suggested above for the trial with two judges, we obtain the following results:

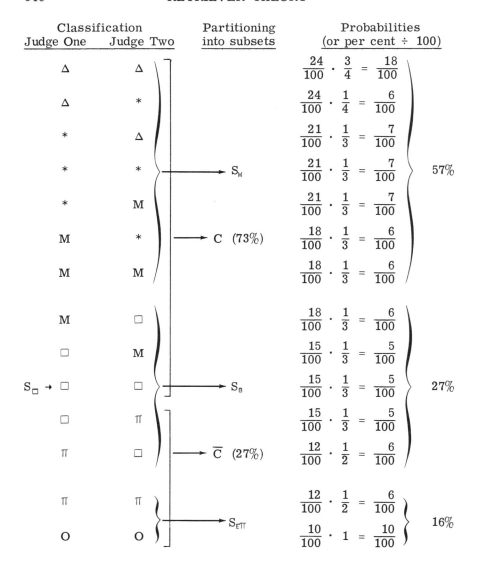

| Classification | | Partitioning | Probabilities |
| Judge One | Judge Two | into subsets | (or per cent ÷ 100) |

$$\Delta \qquad \Delta \qquad\qquad \frac{24}{100} \cdot \frac{3}{4} = \frac{18}{100}$$

$$\Delta \qquad * \qquad\qquad \frac{24}{100} \cdot \frac{1}{4} = \frac{6}{100}$$

$$* \qquad \Delta \qquad\qquad \frac{21}{100} \cdot \frac{1}{3} = \frac{7}{100}$$

$$* \qquad * \qquad \longrightarrow S_W \quad \frac{21}{100} \cdot \frac{1}{3} = \frac{7}{100} \qquad 57\%$$

$$* \qquad M \qquad\qquad \frac{21}{100} \cdot \frac{1}{3} = \frac{7}{100}$$

$$M \qquad * \qquad \longrightarrow C \ (73\%) \quad \frac{18}{100} \cdot \frac{1}{3} = \frac{6}{100}$$

$$M \qquad M \qquad\qquad \frac{18}{100} \cdot \frac{1}{3} = \frac{6}{100}$$

$$M \qquad \square \qquad\qquad \frac{18}{100} \cdot \frac{1}{3} = \frac{6}{100}$$

$$\square \qquad M \qquad\qquad \frac{15}{100} \cdot \frac{1}{3} = \frac{5}{100}$$

$$S_\square \to \square \qquad \square \qquad \longrightarrow S_B \quad \frac{15}{100} \cdot \frac{1}{3} = \frac{5}{100} \qquad 27\%$$

$$\square \qquad \pi \qquad\qquad \frac{15}{100} \cdot \frac{1}{3} = \frac{5}{100}$$

$$\pi \qquad \square \qquad \longrightarrow \overline{C} \ (27\%) \quad \frac{12}{100} \cdot \frac{1}{2} = \frac{6}{100}$$

$$\pi \qquad \pi \qquad\qquad \frac{12}{100} \cdot \frac{1}{2} = \frac{6}{100}$$

$$\qquad\qquad\qquad \longrightarrow S_{E\pi} \qquad\qquad\qquad\qquad 16\%$$

$$O \qquad O \qquad\qquad \frac{10}{100} \cdot 1 = \frac{10}{100}$$

An examination of the probabilities shown in the above worksheet suggests that we do include all of the $S_\square$ subset in the callback set C. With this distribution of classification we would expect (over the long run) to get 73 per cent callbacks in each series.

Empirical Results

Using the foregoing probabilities, 1,000 trials utilizing two judges were simulated on a computer. Results are shown in Tables 13-1 and 13-2.

Table 13-1.--Theoretical and observed proportion p_i of retrievers entering series i, called back for series i + 1, and proportion $\prod_{k=1}^{i} p_k$ of the original starters (45) called back for series i + 1, Pontchippi nominal scale, 1,000 simulated field trials with two judges, 1968

Series i	p_i		$\prod_{k=1}^{i} p_k$	
	Theoretically expected	Observed in 1,000 trials	Theoretically expected	Observed in 1,000 trials
1	0.73	0.730	0.730	0.730
2	0.73	0.725	0.533	0.529
3	0.73	0.733	0.389	0.388
4	0.73	0.731	0.284	0.284

"Ratings"

Within a single series.--Using two judges, clearly there are two classifications assigned to each performance within each series, namely, the classification assigned by the first judge and the classification assigned by the second judge. In the simulation of a trial with two judges it was advisable to identify the classification made in a series by Judge One in order to determine the permissible classifications to be made in that series by Judge Two (and their corresponding probabilities). However, in the practical situation, it is customary for the judges not to announce (to the public) individual classifications. Hence, it is more realistic to disregard which judge made a classification and to combine the equivalent sets of classifications (resulting in callbacks

Table 13-2.--Mean and standard deviation (s.d.) of the numbers and percentages of entries dropped after series i, and called back for series i + 1, and the percentage of original starters remaining after series i, Pontchippi nominal scale, 1,000 simulated field trials with two judges, 1968

| Series i | Number* | | | | Percentage* of those entering series i | | | | Percentage* of original starters called back for series i + 1 | |
| | Dropped after series i | | Called back for series i + 1 | | Dropped after series i | | Called back for series i + 1 | | | |
	Mean	s.d.	Mean	s.d.	Mean	s.d.	Mean	s.d.	Mean	s.d.
1	12.1	3.0	32.9	3.0	27.0	6.7	73.0	6.7	73.0	6.7
2	9.0	2.7	23.8	3.3	27.5	7.7	72.5	7.7	52.9	7.4
3	6.4	2.3	17.5	3.3	26.7	9.2	73.3	9.2	38.8	7.3
4	4.7	2.1	12.8	3.0	26.9	10.8	73.1	10.8	28.4	6.7

*Forty-five original entries with probability of being called back after series i equal to 0.73. Numbers and percentages may vary slightly due to rounding procedures.

for a series) into subgroups which we shall call "ratings." We shall, therefore, combine the equivalent sets of classifications (resulting in callbacks) for a series with their respective probabilities as follows:

"Ratings"		Probabilities
2 Δ → A		0.18
1 Δ, 1 * → B		0.13
2 * → C		0.07
1 *, 1 M → D		0.13
2 M → E		0.06
1 M, 1 □ → F		0.11
2 □ → G		0.05 .

We have seven mutually exclusive ratings (A through G) which merit a callback in a single series.

Ratings over four series, counts.--In a trial consisting of 4 series, there are $7 \times 7 \times 7 \times 7 = 2,401$ groups of rating categories which fall into 210 separate sets of ratings. We obtain this count in a manner similar to that of Chapter Twelve dealing with a single judge. Namely,

$$\binom{7}{1} + \binom{7}{2} \cdot \binom{2}{1} + \binom{7}{2} + \binom{7}{3} \cdot \binom{3}{1} + \binom{7}{4}$$
$$= 7 + 42 + 21 + 105 + 35 = 210 .$$

The 2,401 groups may be counted by

$$7(1) + 42(4) + 21(6) + 105(12) + 35(24)$$
$$= 7 + 168 + 126 + 1,260 + 840 = 2,401 .$$

The numbers in parentheses are the same multinomial coefficients as used in Chapter Twelve.

Listing of ratings.--A listing of the 210 sets of ratings can be visualized as follows:

4A

3A, 1B

3A, 1C

$$\vdots$$

Probabilities in terms of ratings. -- It is of interest to consider a few probabilities (involved), using the multinomial distribution.

1. $\Pr(1A, 2B, 1C) = \dfrac{4!}{1! \, 2! \, 1!} (0.18)(0.13)^2 (0.07) = 0.0026$.

2. $\Pr(3\Delta, 3*, 2\square) = \Pr(3B, 1G) + \Pr(1A, 1B, 1C, 1G)$

$= \dfrac{4!}{3! \, 1!} (0.13)^3 (0.05) + \dfrac{4!}{1! \, 1! \, 1! \, 1!} (0.18)(0.13)(0.07)(0.05)$

$\approx 0.00044 + 0.00197 \approx 0.0024$.

3. $\Pr(2\Delta, 2*, 2M, 2\square) = \Pr(1A, 1C, 1E, 1G) + \Pr(1A, 1C, 2F)$

$\quad + \Pr(1A, 2D, 1G) + \Pr(2B, 1E, 1G) + \Pr(2B, 2F)$

$= \dfrac{4!}{1! \, 1! \, 1! \, 1!} (0.18)(0.07)(0.06)(0.05)$

$+ \dfrac{4!}{1! \, 1! \, 2!} (0.18)(0.07)(0.11)^2$

$+ \dfrac{4!}{1! \, 2! \, 1!} (0.18)(0.13)^2 (0.05)$

$+ \dfrac{4!}{2! \, 1! \, 1!} (0.13)^2 (0.06)(0.05) + \dfrac{4!}{2! \, 2!} (0.13)^2 (0.11)^2$

$\approx 0.00091 + 0.00183 + 0.00183 + 0.00061 + 0.00123$

≈ 0.0064.

Detailed Listing, Two Judges, Four Series

If we desire to list according to the classifications Δ, *, M, and $\square$, then we need to consider 15 basic types. For four series and two judges we can have:

1. All 8 alike;   e.g.,   8△,   8*,   8M,   8□
2. 7 alike, 1 different;   e.g.,   7△,   1□
3. 6 alike, 2 others alike; e.g., 6△,   2*
4. 6,   1,   1;   e.g.,   6*,   1M,   1□
5. 5,   3;   e.g.,   5*,   3□
6. 5,   2,   1;   :
7. 5,   1,   1,   1;   :
8. 4,   4;   .
9. 4,   3,   1;
10. 4,   2,   2;
11. 4,   2,   1,   1;
12. 3,   3,   2;
13. 3,   3,   1,   1;
14. 3,   2,   2,   1;
15. 2,   2,   2,   2.

Counts.--These 15 basic types lead to 165 distinct categories of classification as follows:

1. $\binom{4}{1}$ = 4

2. $\binom{4}{2} \cdot \binom{2}{1}$ = 12

3. $\binom{4}{2} \cdot \binom{2}{1}$ = 12

4. $\binom{4}{3} \cdot \binom{3}{1}$ = 12

5. $\binom{4}{2} \cdot \binom{2}{1}$ = 12

6. $\binom{4}{3} \cdot \binom{3}{2} \cdot \binom{2}{1}$ = 24

7. $\binom{4}{1}$ = 4

8. $\binom{4}{2}$ = 6

9. $\binom{4}{3} \cdot \binom{3}{2} \cdot \binom{2}{1} = 24$

10. $\binom{4}{3} \cdot \binom{3}{1} = 12$

11. $\binom{4}{2} \cdot \binom{2}{1} = 12$

12. $\binom{4}{3} \cdot \binom{3}{2} = 12$

13. $\binom{4}{2} = 6$

14. $\binom{4}{3} \cdot \binom{3}{1} = 12$

15. $\binom{4}{4} = 1$

In all there are $4^8 = 65,536$ different sets of classifications considering only $\triangle$, $*$, M, and $\square$ throughout the trial of 4 series. This number may also be obtained as follows:

$$4 \cdot \frac{8!}{8!} + 12 \cdot \frac{8!}{7!} + 12 \cdot \frac{8!}{6!\,2!} + 12 \cdot \frac{8!}{6!} + 12 \cdot \frac{8!}{5!\,3!}$$

$$+ 24 \cdot \frac{8!}{5!\,2!} + 4 \cdot \frac{8!}{5!} + 6 \cdot \frac{8!}{4!\,4!} + 24 \cdot \frac{8!}{4!\,3!}$$

$$+ 12 \cdot \frac{8!}{4!\,2!\,2!} + 12 \cdot \frac{8!}{4!\,2!} + 12 \cdot \frac{8!}{3!\,3!\,2!}$$

$$+ 6 \cdot \frac{8!}{3!\,3!} + 12 \cdot \frac{8!}{3!\,2!\,2!} + 1 \cdot \frac{8!}{2!\,2!\,2!\,2!}$$

$$= 4(1) + 12(8) + 12(28) + 12(56) + 12(56) + 24(168)$$

$$+ 4(336) + 6(70) + 24(280) + 12(420) + 12(840)$$

$$+ 12(560) + 6(1120) + 12(1680) + 1(2520)$$

$$= 4 + 96 + 336 + 672 + 672 + 4,032 + 1,344 + 420$$

$$+ 6,720 + 5,040 + 10,080 + 6,720 + 6,720$$

$$+ 20,160 + 2,520 = 65,536.$$

Note that some of the sets will be empty when the trial is simulated. One such set is $5*$, $3\square$. We leave it to the reader to observe why it is empty.

Probabilities of ratings in terms of detailed classifications by both judges.--If we desire a system for calculating the probabilities for the various combinations of classification, we can use the following technique: Write

$$Pr(A) = x_\Delta^2, \qquad Pr(B) = x_\Delta x_*, \qquad Pr(C) = x_*^2,$$
$$Pr(D) = x_* x_M, \qquad Pr(E) = x_M^2, \qquad Pr(F) = x_M x_\square,$$
$$Pr(G) = x_\square^2.$$

Now expand the multinomial

$$(x_\Delta^2 + x_\Delta x_* + x_*^2 + x_* x_M + x_M^2 + x_M x_\square + x_\square^2)^4$$

and group all terms with identical symbols. Consider, say, the group containing $x_\Delta^2 x_*^2 x_M^2 x_\square^2$. It will consist of five terms obtained from the multinomial expansion and the sum of the five terms gives $Pr(2\Delta, 2*, 2M, 2\square)$. Likewise, the group containing $x_\Delta^3 x_*^3 x_\square^2$ consists of two terms and gives $Pr(3\Delta, 3*, 2\square)$. See the numerical examples given earlier. Please note one important point in both the single judge and two judge trials: The number of possible classifications is calculated using the number of classifications given an entry in a trial; i.e., 4 for 1 judge in 4 series; 8 for 2 judges in 4 series. For example, $5*$, $3M$ (see type 5, page 551) involves $\frac{8!}{5! \, 3!} = 56$; i.e., it can occur in 56 ways of the total number 65,536. In contrast, the probabilities are calculated using the number of series; e.g.,

$$
\begin{aligned}
Pr(5*, 3M) &= Pr(2C, 1D, 1E) + Pr(1C, 3D) \\
&= \frac{4!}{2! \, 1! \, 1!}(0.07)^2(0.13)(0.06) + \frac{4!}{1! \, 3!}(0.07)(0.13)^3 \\
&= 12(0.07)^2(0.13)(0.06) + 4(0.07)(0.13)^3 \\
&= 0.00045864 + 0.00061516 \\
Pr(5*, 3M) &\approx 0.0011.
\end{aligned}
$$

INTERVAL SCALE

Again, it does seem worthwhile to include some work on an interval scale. Hence, in Technical Note 13-1, entitled "Theorem for Cumulative Frequencies Applied to Judging Contests," recurrence formulas are developed for computing the relative frequency with which certain cumulative scores are expected to appear, subject to certain restrictions. These formulas apply to one, two, or more judges. To illustrate practical applications, these formulas are utilized to generate theoretical values in a framework for judging.

Simulation procedures involving two judges were based on a uniform distribution--obviously, an unrealistic assumption since I see no need for interval scales in judging retriever trials. Results of simulation procedures involving more realistic assumptions have been prepared for publication elsewhere by Fields and McMahan.

Technical Note 13-1, like Technical Note 12-1, was written to stand on its own outside the context of this book. Much of this material is contained in a manuscript (prepared in 1966) authored by Fields and McMahan, where obviously Dr. Fields provided the mathematical know-how. Verily, Dr. Fields would be listed as the senior author of this note except for the fact that he claims not to be a retriever man.

Product notation.--An analogous notation to the capital Greek letter sigma, Σ, is obtained by substituting the capital Greek letter pi, Π, for Σ. Accordingly, the terms resulting from substituting the integers for the index are multiplied instead of added.

A pittance of practice may be worth a tome of theory.

Signed print dated 1902 (No. 12) by Maud Earl. From the author's private Pontchippi Collection.

SCHOOL

An old signed print by G. Vernon Stokes in the author's private Pontchippi Collection.

THEOREM FOR CUMULATIVE FREQUENCIES
APPLIED TO JUDGING CONTESTS

Introduction

Many types of contests are conducted in terms of sub-contests, rounds, or series. Often judges of such contests drop contestants from further consideration at the end of a particular series. Obviously, being called back for further testing is of paramount importance to the contestant, since in most cases if a contestant is not called back, he is not considered when the final awards are made.

In this paper, it is assumed that each series is composed of one or more tests and after each series has been completed, judges may call back for further testing those contestants who completed the tests of the current series and all previous series, and whom the judges desire to test further. For convenience, contestants who are called back for further testing are designated as callbacks. Selection of a winner or winners or any ranking procedure involving entries which completed the entire contest are beyond the scope of this paper.

Development of a "Frequency Theorem" for One Judge

Assuming that a judge uses an integral scale and scores are assigned randomly, if t is the maximum value of the integral scale used by the judge, then in any series the possible scores for a contestant are $0, 1, 2, \ldots, t$, and these scores are equally likely to occur. Thus, in series one (the "first series"), the set of possible scores is the complete set of one-part partitions of t (with zero included) where there are $t + 1$ scores in this set. In series two, any one of $t + 1$ possible scores (again assumed to be equally likely) can be assigned and this would result in $(t + 1)^2$ possible equally likely ordered pairs for the first two series. These pairs are of the form (X_1, X_2), where X_1 is the score assigned in series one and X_2 is the score assigned in series two. The possible cumulative scores $X_1 + X_2$ constitute the set $0, 1, 2, \ldots, 2t$ ($2t + 1$ scores in all) and these cumulative scores are not equally likely. For example, a score of zero can only be obtained by (0, 0) whereas a score of three can be obtained by (0, 3), (1, 2), (2, 1), (3, 0).

If restrictions are imposed such that an entry is eliminated when he scores zero in any series or when his cumulative score after j series is less than L_j (the "cut-off score") for j = 1, 2, ... , i, then the probability that a specified entry (having no zero score in any series) will have a cumulative score of, say, n points after i series is the number of possible ordered i-part partitions of n (subject to the restrictions

$$\sum_{j=1}^{i-1} X_j \geq L_{i-1}$$

with $X_j \neq 0$, j = 1, 2, ... , i, where $i \geq 2$ and X_j is the score for the jth series) divided by $(t + 1)^i$.

Suppose we replace n by $S(i, L_{i-1} + K_i)$. That is, $S(i, L_{i-1} + K_i)$ denotes the cumulative score at the end of i series, where the actual cumulative score is $L_{i-1} + K_i$. Note that L_{i-1} is the cutoff score after i − 1 series, so K_i is the excess in score above this cutoff score.

Let $f(i, L_{i-1} + K_i)$ denote the number of ordered i-part partitions of $S(i, L_{i-1} + K_i)$ such that

$$\sum_{j=1}^{i} X_j = S(i, L_{i-1} + K_i) = L_{i-1} + K_i \geq L_{i-1} + X_i$$

and X_j is a positive integer for j = 1, 2, ... , i which does not exceed t .

The probability that a specified contestant (which does not score zero in any series) will have a cumulative score of $S(i, L_{i-1} + K_i)$ after i series is

$$\frac{f(i, L_{i-1} + K_i)}{(t + 1)^i} .$$

Since this fraction is the relative frequency with which the cumulative score $S(i, L_{i-1} + K_i)$ is expected to appear, it seems natural to call the symbol $f(i, L_{i-1} + K_i)$ a "frequency" for cumulative score $S(i, L_{i-1} + K_i)$.

Since $f(i + 1, L_i + K_{i+1})$ depends upon $f(i, L_{i-1} + K_i)$, certain recursive relationships may be established. In series $i + 1$, K_{i+1} is the excess above the cutoff score L_i and $L_i + K_{i+1}$ is the cumulative score. Since we are only concerned with those entries who survive the cutoff score of L_i, it is more convenient to replace

$$f(i, \; L_{i-1} + K_i) \quad \text{by} \quad f(i, \; L_i + h - 1)$$

with the idea of letting $L_i + K_{i+1} - (L_i + h - 1) = K_{i+1} + 1 - h$ represent the additional score to be earned in series $i + 1$. In this form, h should be an integer (the index of summation) taking on the values 1, 2, 3, $\ldots$. Since $K_{i+1} + 1 - h$ cannot exceed t, we see that if zero scores are to be excluded, then h cannot exceed K_{i+1}. Moreover, excluding zero scores in the $i + 1$ series, we can prove a useful theorem.

Theorem:

$$f(i + 1, \; L_i + K_{i+1}) = \overset{K_{i+1}}{\underset{h=1}{\Sigma}} C_1(h) \cdot f(i, \; L_i + h - 1)$$

$$- \overset{K_{i+1}}{\underset{h=1}{\Sigma}} C_2(h) \cdot f(i, \; L_i + h - t - 1)$$

where
$$C_1(h) = \begin{cases} 1 & \text{for } 1 \le h \le ti + 1 - L_i \\ 0 & \text{for } ti + 2 - L_i \le h \le t(i + 1) - L_i \end{cases}$$

and
$$C_2(h) = \begin{cases} 0 & \text{for } 1 \le h \le t \\ 1 & \text{for } t + 1 \le h \le K_{i+1}. \end{cases}$$

Proof: The minimum and maximum cumulative scores which are possible in entering series $i + 1$ are L_i and ti respectively, and the possible scores to be assigned in series $i + 1$ are 1, 2, $\ldots$, t. Thus, the possible cumulative scores after $i + 1$ series are $L_i + 1$, $L_i + 2$, $\ldots$, $ti + t$, the maximum being $ti + t = t(i + 1)$. Therefore, K_{i+1}, the excess score above L_i (the cutoff score) must be an integer from 1 to $t(i + 1) - L_i$.

Case one. --First consider the case where $K_{i+1} \le t$. A specified cumulative score $L_i + K_{i+1}$ for series $i + 1$ (under the foregoing restrictions) can be obtained in one of the following mutually exclusive ways: (1) the entry has a cumulative score of L_i in i series and then scores K_{i+1} in series $i + 1$;

(2) the entry has a cumulative score of $L_i + 1$ in i series and then scores $K_{i+1} - 1$ in series $i + 1$; ... ; (K_{i+1}) the entry has a cumulative score of $L_i + K_{i+1} - 1$ in i series and then scores 1 in series $i + 1$.

The frequency in this case for the cumulative score $L_i + K_{i+1}$ is the sum of the number of ordered i-part partitions (under the restrictions imposed) of L_i, L_{i+1}, ... , $L_i + K_{i+1} - 1$. Thus, for $K_{i+1} \leq t$,

$$f(i + 1, \ L_i + K_{i+1}) = \sum_{h=1}^{K_{i+1}} f(i, \ L_i + h - 1).$$

Case two.--If we next consider the case when $K_{i+1} > t$, we note that the cumulative score of $L_i + K_{i+1}$ in series $i + 1$ cannot be obtained by adding a score in the $i + 1$ series to L_i. However, it can be obtained in the following ways: (1) cumulative score of $L_i + K_{i+1} - t$ in i series, and score of t in series $i + 1$; (2) cumulative score of $L_i + K_{i+1} - t + 1$ in i series, and score of $t - 1$ in series $i + 1$; ... the sequence continues ... ; (t) cumulative score of $L_i + K_{i+1} - 1$ in i series, and score of 1 in series $i + 1$, provided $L_i + K_{i+1} - 1 \leq ti$ (the maximum cumulative score for i series). That is, $K_{i+1} \leq ti + 1 - L_i$.

Therefore, for $t + 1 \leq K_{i+1} \leq ti + 1 - L_i$, we have

$$f(i + 1, \ L_i + K_{i+1}) = \sum_{h=K_{i+1}-t+1}^{K_{i+1}} f(i, \ L_i + h - 1).$$

Case three.-- For the third case, $ti + 2 - L_i \leq K_{i+1} \leq t(i + 1) - L_i$, the sequence is as in case two, except that it terminates with ti cumulative score in i series and score of 1 in series $i + 1$. Hence, $L_i + h - 1 = ti$ for the final term in the summation and $h = ti + 1 - L_i$. Thus, the upper limit on the summation is $ti + 1 - L_i$.

Now it is possible to summarize the three mutually exclusive cases for K_{i+1}.

Case one: $1 \leq K_{i+1} \leq t$.

$$f(i + 1, \ L_i + K_{i+1}) = \sum_{h=1}^{K_{i+1}} f(i, \ L_i + h - 1).$$

Case two: $t + 1 \leq K_{i+1} \leq ti + 1 - L_i$.

$$f(i + 1, \; L_i + K_{i+1}) = \sum_{h = K_{i+1} - t + 1}^{K_{i+1}} f(i, \; L_i + h - 1).$$

Case three: $ti + 2 - L_i \leq K_{i+1} \leq t(i + 1) - L_i$.

$$f(i + 1, \; L_i + K_{i+1}) = \sum_{h = K_{i+1} - t + 1}^{ti + 1 - L_i} f(i, \; L_i + h - 1).$$

Note that the summation has exactly t terms in case two and t terms or less in cases one and three.

It is possible to find a single expression which will combine cases one, two, and three. In summing frequencies in series i to obtain frequencies in series i + 1, the lowest cumulative score that can be used is L_i whereas the highest cumulative score is ti. If the frequency is written in the form $f(i, \; L_i + h - 1)$, the lowest possible value of h is 1 and the highest possible value of h is $ti + 1 - L_i$. Note that $K_{i+1} - h + 1$ is the score to be earned in series i + 1 for each value of h. We need, therefore, an expression of the type

$$\sum_{h = 1}^{K_{i+1}} C_1(h) \cdot f(i, \; L_i + h - 1) \tag{1}$$

where $$C_1(h) = \begin{cases} 1 & \text{for } 1 \leq h \leq ti + 1 - L_i \\ 0 & \text{for } h \geq ti + 2 - L_i. \end{cases}$$

However, the sum can never contain more than t terms, and also, when $K_{i+1} > t$, certain terms must be subtracted from the beginning of the series, namely,

$$\sum_{r = 1}^{K_{i+1} - t} f(i, \; L_i + r - 1). \tag{2}$$

If we choose to make the upper limit in (2) the same as in (1), we must make the change of variable $r = h - t$. That is, $h = r + t$ so that when r = 1, h = t + 1, and when $r = K_{i+1} - t$, $h = K_{i+1}$. Expression (2) then becomes

$$\sum_{h=t+1}^{K_{t+1}} f(i, \ L_t + h - t - 1).$$

An equivalent form is

$$\sum_{h=1}^{K_{t+1}} C_2(h) \cdot f(i, \ L_t + h - t - 1)$$

where $\qquad\qquad C_2(h) = \begin{cases} 0 & \text{for } 1 \le h \le t \\ 1 & \text{for } t + 1 \le h \le K_{t+1}. \end{cases}$

Combining expressions (1) and (2) we obtain

$$f(i + 1, \ L_t + K_{t+1}) = \sum_{h=1}^{K_{t+1}} C_1(h) \cdot f(i, \ L_t + h - 1)$$

$$- \sum_{h=1}^{K_{t+1}} C_2(h) \cdot f(i, \ L_t + h - t - 1)$$

where $\quad C_1(h) = \begin{cases} 1 & \text{for } 1 \le h \le ti + 1 - L_t \\ 0 & \text{for } ti + 2 - L_t \le h \le t(i + 1) - L_t \end{cases}$

and $\quad C_2(h) = \begin{cases} 0 & \text{for } 1 \le h \le t \\ 1 & \text{for } t + 1 \le h \le K_{t+1}. \end{cases}$

Thus, the theorem is proved.

"Frequency" Formulas for One or More Judges

Let
- t = maximum value of the integral scale used by a judge,
- j = number of judges,
- L_t = cutoff score,
- $S(i + 1, \ L_t + j - 1 + K_{t+1})$ = cumulative score at end of $i + 1$ series, and
- $f(i + 1, \ L_t + j - 1 + K_{t+1})$ = corresponding frequency.

By using a recursion formula based on $f(i, \ L_t + h - 1)$,

$$f(i + 1, \ L_t + j - 1 + K_{t+1})$$

can be obtained.

Now $K_{i+1} + j - 1$ is the excess score above cutoff, and

$$L_i + j - 1 + K_{i+1} - (L_i + h - 1) = K_{i+1} + j - h$$

is the score to be earned in series $i + 1$ for each value of h. It will be convenient to introduce a weight $W(h, K_{i+1}, j)$ proportional to the probability that $K_{i+1} + j - h$ points will be scored in series $i + 1$ with the constant of proportionality being the smallest number which makes $W(h, K_{i+1}, j)$ an integer.

Note that for $j = 1$, the scores $0, 1, \ldots, t$ are equally likely, the constant of proportionality is $t + 1$, and all weights are taken as one.

Consider the following three mutually exclusive cases which form an exhaustive set.

Case one: $j \le K_{i+1} \le j(t - 1) + 1$.

$$f(i + 1, L_i + j - 1 + K_{i+1}) = \overset{K_{i+1}}{\underset{h=1}{\Sigma}} W(h, K_{i+1}, j)$$
$$\cdot f(i, L_i + h - 1).$$

The cumulative score $L_i + j - 1 + K_{i+1}$ can be earned in $i + 1$ series by having $h = 1$ and a cumulative score L_i after i series, then earning $K_{i+1} + j - 1$ in series $i + 1$; $h = 2$ and a cumulative score $L_i + 1$ after i series, then earning $K_{i+1} + j - 2$ in series $i + 1$; $\ldots$; and $h = K_{i+1}$ and a cumulative score $L_i + K_{i+1} - 1$ after i series, then earning j in series $i + 1$. Note that a score less than j in series $i + 1$ means that at least one judge assigned a zero score.

The maximum score earned here, $K_{i+1} + j - 1$, cannot exceed jt. Therefore, $K_{i+1} + j - 1 \le jt$ or

$$K_{i+1} \le jt - j + 1 = j(t - 1) + 1,$$

which explains the limits on the interval for case one.

When the excess score $(K_{i+1} + j - 1)$ above cutoff L_i is greater than jt (the maximum score to be awarded in series $i + 1$), we cannot obtain the cumulative score $L_i + j - 1 + K_{i+1}$ by adding a score in series $i + 1$ to L_i. This will be the case when $K_{i+1} + j - 1 > jt$. That is, when $K_{i+1} + j -$

$1 \geq jt + 1$, which means that $K_{t+1} \geq jt - j + 2$ or $K_{t+1} \geq j(t - 1) + 2$. In this case, however, the cumulative score $L_t + j - 1 + K_{t+1}$ can be obtained in the following ways: (1) cumulative score of $L_t + j - 1 + K_{t+1} - jt$ in i series and a score of jt in series $i + 1$; (2) cumulative score of $L_t + j - 1 + K_{t+1} - jt + 1$ in i series and a score of $jt - 1$ in series $i + 1$; ... ; $(jt - j + 1)$ cumulative score of $L_t + j - 1 + K_{t+1} - j$ in i series and a score of j in series $i + 1$, provided that $L_t + j - 1 + K_{t+1} - j \leq jti$ which is the maximum cumulative score possible for i series. This last restriction means that $K_{t+1} \leq jti + 1 - L_t$.

This brings us to *case two:* $j(t - 1) + 2 \leq K_{t+1} \leq jti + 1 - L_t$.

$$f(i + 1, \ L_t + j - 1 + K_{t+1}) \ = \ \sum_{h = K_{t+1} - jt + j}^{K_{t+1}} W(h, \ K_{t+1}, \ j)$$
$$\cdot \ f(i, \ L_t + h - 1).$$

Note that case two may not exist for some values of i and L_t.

There remains *case three:* $jti + 2 - L_t \leq K_{t+1} \leq jt(i + 1) - L_t - 1$.

$$f(i + 1, \ L_t + j - 1 + K_{t+1}) \ = \ \sum_{h = K_{t+1} - jt + j}^{jti + 1 - L_t} W(h, \ K_{t+1}, \ j)$$
$$\cdot \ f(i, \ L_t + h - 1).$$

In case two, the summation always has exactly $j(t - 1) + 1$ terms whereas the summation for cases one and three always has $j(t - 1) + 1$ terms or less. These three cases may be incorporated into a single expression (the single expression for two judges is given later as Eq. (5) on page 565).

General Aspects of the Explicit Problem for Two Judges

Frame of reference.--At "regular, official" American retriever trials, each stake usually consists of four or more series where each series is composed of at least one test. The entire trial is conducted under well-defined procedures where, except for national championships, only two judges are used in each stake. After each series has been completed, the two judges may call back for further testing those retrievers who completed the tests of the current series and all previous series, and whom the judges desire to test further. Explicitly, this example involves two judges who are concerned with computing cutoff scores on an interval scale that would be expected to provide specified percentages of callbacks.

Two assumptions. -- First assumption: Each judge utilizes the integral scoring scale 0, 1, 2, ... , t. Second assumption: Scores are randomly assigned by each judge except for the restriction that their scores will not differ by more than one; that is, if Y_1 is the score of one judge and Y_2 is the score of the other judge, then $Y_1 - 1 \leq Y_2 \leq Y_1 + 1$.

Development of Weights, W_x

Let V = sum of the scores of the two judges for a specified entry in any series. Then $V = Y_1 + Y_2$ and ranges from 0 to 2t. There are $2t + 1$ possible values for V such that $0 \leq V \leq 2t$, and

$$\Pr(V = x) = \sum_{m=0}^{x} \Pr(Y_1 = m) \cdot \Pr(Y_2 = x - m | Y_1 = m). \tag{3}$$

There are two distinct cases depending upon whether the judges assign the same score or different scores.

Case when judges award the same score. -- In Eq. (3), $Y_1 = Y_2$ and $m = x - m$, so $m = (x/2)$ where x is an even integer.

$$\Pr(V = x) = \Pr\left(Y_1 = \frac{x}{2}\right) \cdot \Pr\left(Y_2 = \frac{x}{2} | Y_1 = \frac{x}{2}\right).$$

Hence,

$$\Pr(V = x) = \begin{cases} \dfrac{1}{t+1} \cdot \dfrac{1}{2} = \dfrac{3}{6(t+1)} & \text{for } x = 0 \\[2mm] \dfrac{1}{t+1} \cdot \dfrac{1}{3} = \dfrac{2}{6(t+1)} & \\ \text{for } x = 2, \ 4, \ 6, \ \ldots, \ 2t - 2 & \\[2mm] \dfrac{1}{t+1} \cdot \dfrac{1}{2} = \dfrac{3}{6(t+1)} & \text{for } x = 2t. \end{cases}$$

Case when judges award different scores. -- In Eq. (3), $|Y_1 - Y_2| = 1$. That is, $|m - (x - m)| = 1$, so m can take on the values $(x - 1)/2$ and $(x + 1)/2$ where x is an odd integer.

$$Pr(V = x) = Pr\left(Y_1 = \frac{x-1}{2}\right) \cdot Pr\left(Y_2 = \frac{x+1}{2}\Big|Y_1 = \frac{x-1}{2}\right)$$

$$+ Pr\left(Y_1 = \frac{x+1}{2}\right) \cdot Pr\left(Y_2 = \frac{x-1}{2}\Big|Y_1 = \frac{x+1}{2}\right).$$

Hence,

$$Pr(V = x) = \begin{cases} \dfrac{1}{t+1} \cdot \dfrac{1}{2} + \dfrac{1}{t+1} \cdot \dfrac{1}{3} = \dfrac{5}{6(t+1)} \\ \quad \text{for } x = 1 \\[2mm] \dfrac{1}{t+1} \cdot \dfrac{1}{3} + \dfrac{1}{t+1} \cdot \dfrac{1}{3} = \dfrac{4}{6(t+1)} \\ \quad \text{for } x = 3, \ 5, \ 7, \ \dots, \ 2t-3 \\[2mm] \dfrac{1}{t+1} \cdot \dfrac{1}{3} + \dfrac{1}{t+1} \cdot \dfrac{1}{2} = \dfrac{5}{6(t+1)} \\ \quad \text{for } x = 2t-1. \end{cases}$$

In any series, it will be convenient to assign weights to any score x, say, W_x, such that W_x is proportional to the probability that $V = x$; for example,

$$\left. \begin{aligned} W_x &= 3 \text{ for } x = 0 \text{ or } x = 2t \\ &= 5 \text{ for } x = 1 \text{ or } x = 2t-1 \\ &= 2 \text{ for } x = 2, \ 4, \ 6, \ \dots, \ 2t-2 \\ W_x &= 4 \text{ for } x = 3, \ 5, \ 7, \ \dots, \ 2t-3. \end{aligned} \right\} \tag{4}$$

Single expression. -- It is now possible to combine cases one, two, and three into a single general expression for $f(i + 1, \ L_i + j - 1 + K_{i+1})$ as well as to indicate weights for one and two judges.

The weighting factor, $W_1(h, \ K_{i+1}, \ j)$ where h is an index of summation, is determined by the number of points to be scored in series $i + 1$ under the two assumptions.

The set of weights, $W_1(h, \ K_{i+1}, \ j)$, is directly related to the previously given W_x and is the set of smallest positive integers which are proportional to the probabilities that $K_{i+1} - h + j$ points will be scored in series $i + 1$. The proportionality constants are $t + 1$ and $6(t + 1)$ respectively, for one and two judges.

The following theorem is now established:

$$f(i + 1, \ L_1 + j - 1 + K_{i+1}) = \sum_{h=1}^{K_{i+1}} C_1(h) \cdot W_1(h, \ K_{i+1}, \ j)$$
$$\cdot \ f(i, \ L_1 + h - 1)$$
$$- \sum_{h=1}^{K_{i+1}} C_2(h)$$
$$\cdot \ W_2(h - jt + j - 1, \ K_{i+1}, \ j)$$
$$\cdot \ f(L_1 + h - jt + j - 2) \qquad (5)$$

where
$$C_1(h) = \begin{cases} 1 & \text{for } 1 \leq h \leq jti + 1 - L_1 \\ 0 & \text{otherwise} \end{cases}$$

$$C_2(h) = \begin{cases} 0 & \text{for } 1 \leq h \leq j(t - 1) + 1 \\ 1 & \text{for } j(t - 1) + 2 \leq h \leq K_{i+1}, \end{cases}$$

$$W_1(h, \ K_{i+1}, \ j) = 1 \ \text{for } j = 1$$

$$W_1(h, \ K_{i+1}, \ 2) = \begin{cases} 5 & \text{when } K_{i+1} - h + 2 = 2t - 1 \\ 3 & \text{when } K_{i+1} - h + 2 = 2t \\ 2 & \text{when } K_{i+1} - h + 2 \text{ is even and } \neq 2t \\ & \text{or } 2t - 1 \\ 4 & \text{when } K_{i+1} - h + 2 \text{ is odd and } \neq 2t \\ & \text{or } 2t - 1, \end{cases}$$

and

$$W_2(m, \ K_{i+1}, \ j) = W_1(m, \ K_{i+1}, \ j) \ \text{for any } m.$$

Numerical Examples

Suppose that two judges utilize a scoring scale with $t = 7$. In the first series, scores of 0 and 1 are weighted 3 and 5 respectively, as determined by Eq. (4), page 564. The remaining scores and weights are shown in Table 1. The weighted frequencies for series two are calculated from the weighted frequencies for series one by using either Eq. (5), this page, or the appropriate one of the three special cases. Similarly, the weighted frequencies for series three may be calculated from the weighted frequencies for series two.

To illustrate the use of the three special cases, let us take $i = 2$, $L_2 = 11$, $j = 2$, and $t = 7$. The special cases are defined as follows:

Table 1.—Theoretical weighted frequency for each possible nonzero cumulative score at the completion of series i where $i = 1$, 2, 3, and 4, subject to arbitrary restrictions on cutoff scores L_{i-1} with possible weighted frequency of zero scores, weighted frequency called back, and weighted frequency dropped for four series with $t = 7$ and $j = 2$

Series one			Series two			Series three			Series four		
Score	Weighted frequency	Cumulative weighted frequency	Score	Weighted frequency	Cumulative weighted frequency	Score	Weighted frequency	Cumulative weighted frequency	Score	Weighted frequency	Cumulative weighted frequency
2	2	2	4	4	4	13	128	128	25	6,368	6,368
3	4	6	5	16	20	14	424	552	26	19,472	25,840
4	2	8	6	24	44	15	624	1,176	27	27,352	53,192
5	4	12	7	32	76	16	952	2,128	28	41,624	94,816
6	2	14	8	44	120	17	1,240	3,368	29	48,888	143,704
7	4	18	9	48	168	18	1,624	4,992	30	62,916	206,620
8	2	20	10	64	232	19	2,000	6,992	31	69,000	275,620
9	4	24	11	64	(dropped)	20	2,288	9,280	32	82,084	357,704
10	2	26	12	84		21	2,648	11,928	33	85,952	(dropped)
11	4	30	13	80		22	2,848	14,776	34	96,892	
12	2	32	14	104		23	3,184	(dropped)	35	98,512	
13	5	37	15	100		24	3,368		36	110,748	
14	3	40	16	136		25	3,756		37	113,872	
			17	108		26	3,564		38	109,144	
			18	116		27	3,640		39	100,496	
			19	92		28	3,366		40	91,832	
			20	96		29	3,324		41	81,640	
			21	76		30	2,936		42	71,840	
			22	76		31	2,604		43	61,536	
			23	60		32	2,196		44	51,256	
			24	56		33	1,888		45	41,792	
			25	44		34	1,560		46	33,512	
			26	37		35	1,284		47	26,448	
			27	30		36	1,028		48	20,328	
			28	9		37	792		49	15,296	
						38	600		50	11,048	
						39	413		51	7,696	
						40	279		52	5,017	
						41	135		53	3,012	
						42	27		54	1,566	
									55	540	
									56	81	

	Series one	Series two	Series three	Series four
Total nonzero weighted frequency	40	1,600	54,720	1,597,760
(Possible weighted frequency of zeroes if zeroes allowed)	(8) (dropped)	(48 × 8 = 384)	(48 × 936 = 44,928)	(48 × 70,648 = 3,391,104)
(Possible weighted frequency of zeroes produced by nonzeroes)	(0)	(40 × 8 = 320)	(1,368 × 8 = 10,944)	(39,944 × 8 = 319,552)
Possible weighted frequency of zeroes	8	704	55,872	3,710,656
Total possible weighted frequency	48	2,304	110,592	5,308,416
Weighted frequency called back	40	1,368	39,944	1,240,056
Total nonzero weighted frequency plus possible weighted frequency of zeroes produced by nonzeroes	48	1,920	65,664	1,917,312

Case one: $j \le K_{t+1} \le j(t - 1) + 1,$ so
                $2 \le K_3 \le 13.$

Case two: $j(t - 1) + 2 \le K_{t+1} \le jti + 1 - L_t,$ so
                $14 \le K_3 \le 18.$

Case three: $jti + 2 - L_t \le K_{t+1} \le jt(i + 1) - L_t - 1,$ so
                $19 \le K_3 \le 30.$

Since the cumulative score at the end of series $i + 1$ is $L_t + j - 1 + K_{t+1}$, which for our assumed values becomes $K_3 + 12$, we see that cumulative scores will fall in the following categories:

> *Case one:*   2 to 25.
> *Case two:*   26 to 30.
> *Case three:*   31 to 42.

Example 1: Cumulative score = 17.

$$S(i + 1, L_t + j - 1 + K_{t+1}) = S(3, 17) = 17,$$
$$K_3 + 12 = 17, K_3 = 5, \text{and case one applies.}$$

Hence, $$f(3, 17) = \sum_{h=1}^{5} W(h, K_3, j) f(2, h + 10).$$

The score to be earned in the third series is $K_{t+1} + j - h = 7 - h$, which is even when h is odd and is odd when h is even. Consequently,

$$W(h, K_3, j) = \begin{cases} 2 & \text{for } h = 1, 3, 5 \\ 4 & \text{for } h = 2, 4. \end{cases}$$

Thus,

$$f(3, 17) = 2f(2, 11) + 4f(2, 12) + 2f(2, 13)$$
$$+ 4f(2, 14) + 2f(2, 15)$$
$$= 2(64) + 4(84) + 2(80) + 4(104) + 2(100)$$
$$f(3, 17) = 1,240.$$

Example 2: Cumulative score = 26.

$$S(i + 1,\ L_i + j - 1 + K_{i+1}) = S(3,\ 26) = 26,$$
$$K_3 = 14,\ \text{hence, case two applies},$$

and
$$f(3,\ 26) = \sum_{h=2}^{14} W(h,\ K_3,\ j) f(2,\ h + 10).$$

The score to be earned is $K_{i+1} + j - h = 16 - h$, which is even when h is even.

$$W(h,\ K_3,\ j) = \begin{cases} 3 & \text{for } h = 2 \\ 5 & \text{for } h = 3 \\ 2 & \text{for } h \text{ even and} \neq 2 \\ 4 & \text{for } h \text{ odd and} \neq 3. \end{cases}$$

Thus,

$$\begin{aligned} f(3,\ 26) &= 3f(2,\ 12) + 5f(2,\ 13) + 2f(2,\ 14) + 4f(2,\ 15) \\ &\quad + 2f(2,\ 16) + 4f(2,\ 17) + \ldots + 4f(2,\ 23) \\ &\quad + 2f(2,\ 24) \\ &= 3(84) + 5(80) + 2(104) + 4(100) + \ldots \\ &\quad + 4(60) + 2(56) \\ f(3,\ 26) &= 3,564. \end{aligned}$$

Example 3: Cumulative score = 35.

$$S(i + 1,\ L_i + j - 1 + K_{i+1}) = S(3,\ 35) = 35,$$
$$K_3 = 23,\ \text{so case three applies}.$$

Hence,
$$f(3,\ 35) = \sum_{h=11}^{18} W(h,\ K_3,\ j) f(2,\ h + 10).$$

The score to be earned is $K_{i+1} + j - h = 25 - h$, which is odd when h is even.

$$W(h,\ K_3,\ j) = \begin{cases} 3 & \text{for } h = 11 \\ 5 & \text{for } h = 12 \\ 2 & \text{for } h \text{ odd} \neq 11 \\ 4 & \text{for } h \text{ even} \neq 12. \end{cases}$$

Thus,

$$
\begin{aligned}
f(3\,,\;35) \;=\; & 3f(2\,,\;21) \;+\; 5f(2\,,\;22) \;+\; 2f(2\,,\;23) \;+\; 4f(2\,,\;24) \\
& +\; 2f(2\,,\;25) \;+\; 4f(2\,,\;26) \;+\; 2f(2\,,\;27) \\
& +\; 4f(2\,,\;28) \\
\;=\; & 3(76) \;+\; 5(76) \;+\; 2(60) \;+\; 4(56) \;+\; 2(44) \\
& +\; 4(37) \;+\; 2(30) \;+\; 4(9) \\
f(3\,,\;35) \;=\; & 1,284 \,.
\end{aligned}
$$

Concluding Remarks

Expected proportions of contestants to be called back for further testing can be calculated directly from Table 1. Clearly, other such tables could be easily constructed using desired integral values of i, j, L_{t-1}, and t. Moreover, this theorem enables one to simulate judging contests, say, by using randomly generated digits, although in such simulations, no actual judging takes place.

ACKNOWLEDGMENTS

Indebtedness is expressed to Professor Raymond I. Fields of the University of Louisville, to Professor Robert H. Deupree, and to Lynne K. Hammett for the collaboration and assistance which made this article possible. Obviously the author is solely responsible for any and all shortcomings.

BIBLIOGRAPHY

Gupta, H., Gwyther, C. E., and Miller, J. C. P., *Tables of Partitions*. Cambridge: Cambridge University Press, 1962.

Riordan, J., *An Introduction to Combinatorial Analysis*. New York: John Wiley and Sons, Inc., 1958.

Ryser, H. J., *Combinatorial Mathematics*. New York: John Wiley and Sons, Inc., 1963.

ADDENDA

Kube's Second Law of Judging

Kube's second law of judging states that "if a judge tries to use an interval scale, retrievers are in trouble." Stated in terms of mathematical symbols, say, for three birds in a triple,

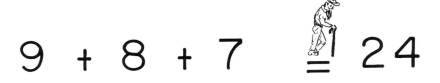

$$9 + 8 + 7 \quad \ne \quad 24$$

where is the mathematical symbol for *hardly ever*; i.e., the symbol

 denotes *hardly ever equals*.

CHAPTER FOURTEEN

A JUDGE JUDGES HIS JUDGMENT

The concept of judging, as such, has already been discussed, but I ask again: What is judging? Is judging the mere process of counting? Is judging the mere process of adding up scores, such as they are? Is judging "planning for tomorrow"? Most of us will readily admit that decisions which judges make today influence our investment in the future. Moreover, we have assumed that a judge's philosophy influences his decisions.

The major concern of this entire book is with the concepts of judging; lessons are to be learned if we are to develop concepts clearly and come to know what our philosophy of judging retriever trials really is. How might a judge learn more about his judging performance? Some RE's assert that poor judges are easy to classify; "good" judges are not so easy to classify. How good a judge are you? Some methods and techniques for self-evaluation of one's judging performance are presented in this chapter [although some material in this chapter might just as logically have been presented in Chapter Ten (Measuring Retriever Performance)].

In the main, this chapter describes how one judge goes about evaluating selected aspects of his own performance as a judge of retrievers in the field--an attempt at objective self-appraisal of his judging.

Ranking Based on Paired Comparisons

Suppose that 8 retrievers complete the fourth and final series of a stake. If we pair each retriever with every other retriever, there will be $\binom{8}{2}$ or 28 possible pairs of retrievers. Now suppose a judge refers to his judging sheets and, in addition, makes use of recalled information. If there is a noticeable (real) difference between the performances over the entire stake between the 2 retrievers in each of the 28 pairs, then it is well-known (as was shown in Chapter Six) that the 8 performances can be ranked from the poorest to the best. Obviously, one could use the same procedures for ranking performances on a given series or even on a single retrieve.

Test Toughness and Evaluation Perplexities

In the discussion which follows, it is assumed that grading or classification procedures are entangled with the process of determining whether or not one type of test is more difficult than another. Hence, it is convenient to focus first on the concept of "difficulty of the test."

Degree of Difficulty of the Test

Suppose one set out to answer a general question such as that which follows: Is the open water blind the most difficult test? In reply, most experienced field-trialers will start "if-ing" and call for more specific information. Nevertheless, the question I'm asking concerns the expected degree of difficulty; it concerns the average degree of difficulty of all tests in licensed open stakes over a long period of time, say, a year.

Now suppose that we concern ourselves with tests conducted either wholly on land (pheasant on land with no water involved, for convenience, called "pure land") or on water (duck falling in water with a clear splash easily seen by the dog, involving at least 50 per cent swimming water, with ridges, islands, cover, and the like--"pure water"). For the moment, we shall not be concerned with, that is, we shall exclude "mixed bags," such as a shot pheasant on land and two shackled duck on water. Clearly then, we have a test either on land or on water, one factor (terrain) at two levels (land or water).

Further suppose that we are concerned only with three basic types of tests: marking (M), memory (M & M), and blind (B). For sim-

plicity, let's conduct blinds separately from marks at different locations (call these blinds "cold blinds"); more explicitly, let's be concerned only with the marked "triple" and single blind. Hence, we
shall discuss (only) the following four tests:

    1.   Land triple on pheasant, one flier: We shall classify the
first bird retrieved as the mark (M); each of the other two birds retrieved shall be classified as a memory bird (M & M).

    2.   Water triple, three shackled drakes: The first drake
retrieved shall be classified as the M; the other two, as M & M.

    3.   Land blind: Move to a location at least one mile distant
from the land triple with different type of terrain; plant a dead pheasant.

    4.   Water blind: Move to "different water" at least one mile
from the water triple; plant a dead duck.

    [*Aside:*   These more or less absurd conditions are laid on
for unmistakable clarity.]

Theoretically, the degree of difficulty (DD) of a test can be con-
ceptualized in terms of many variables. Suppose, for purposes of
simplification, that we assume most of our problems away. For example, assume constant direction and velocity of the wind, an over-
cast day with constant light, identical flight of each bird, consistent
shooting, constant terrain and water; in fact, assume all factors to be
constant except those explicitly involved with the statements below:

    1.   Degree of difficulty (DD) may be associated with the
previous test run.

    2.   DD may be associated with the age of the dog.

    3.   DD may be associated with the individual dog.

    4.   DD may be associated with terrain (land or water).

    5.   DD may be associated with type of retrieve, namely,
M, M & M, B.

    6.   DD may be associated with the individual judge.

Moreover, DD may be associated with many other factors which we
shall not mention, much less consider here.

Degree of test difficulty confounded with difficulty of evaluation of performance. --Suppose we set out to assess the difficulty of a test in terms of the observed relative frequency (probability) of separating the performances of a pair of retrievers selected at random. That is, the greater the probability of not having indistinguishable performances (ties), the more difficult the test. A factor which gets confounded with degree of difficulty of the test is the task of completing our judging sheets (collecting data), comparing the two performances, and deciding which one is better than the other. Realizing that there is usually little difficulty in evaluating perfect work, a question which comes to mind immediately is the following: Which is easier to grade, an M or an M & M?

7. Short of failure, the less perfect the work of a pair of retrievers on a given test, the more difficult may be the task of ranking the two performances.

8. Performances on blinds (B) may be easier to evaluate than performances on M or M & M.

9. Water blinds may be easier to evaluate than land blinds.

Probability of Separation

In view of the foregoing, in the remainder of this discussion, we shall make no attempt to isolate the influence of the factor degree of difficulty of a test from the factor degree of difficulty of evaluating. We shall be concerned with the continuum of the probability of separation, say, by type of test.

Data on probability of separation (degree of difficulty of tests confounded with problems of evaluation). --In my opinion, any retriever enthusiast who judges should keep careful records of the tests he used and the problems he encountered. Moreover, he should conduct post-evaluation critiques of his judging performances. In other words, he must have empirical evidence which indicates to him which tests of those he conducted gave the greatest probability of separation; moreover, he should have an estimate of that probability.

ACTION ITEMS

Item 1.--Ability to mark and remember: Some experienced RE's assert that they believe there is little difference in marking and remembering ability of, say, the top 25 American open retrievers. Others assert that there are great differences among the retrievers in this group of 25. By way of example, still others refer to well-known field and national champions by name, and comment that particular dogs are or were not "good markers"--the handler (by name) lined these dogs to the falls. [*Aside:* Recall that $\mathcal{J}$ knows there are many obvious as well as "not-so-obvious" ways to "line" a dog.] Moreover, these RE's assert they "know this" because of the surprise manifested by the retriever when he suddenly "ran over" the fall. *Question:* How could a retriever enthusiast possibly *know* that this dog was surprised? In short, did the RE make an inference? What justification does he have for making such an inference?

Item 2.--Program for a club meeting: Well in advance of a club meeting, request one of your most experienced judges to design an idealized experiment to test the following two hypotheses:

(1) H_0: There is no difference in marking and memory abilities of top open retrievers.

(2) H_0: Marking ability is indistinguishable from lining ability in a group of top open retrievers.

Allow the designer of your experiment to make any assumptions he so desires (whatever assumptions he needs); for example, allow him to assume unlimited money, assume one week of time, assume access to all retrievers and handlers who completed 10 or more series of a national championship stake, ... , and other.

Discuss his proposal.

DIFFERENTIAL DISCRIMINATION BY TYPE OF TEST

"My tests."-- Throughout this book and particularly in this chapter,

the word "my" may often be used where I explicitly recognize (even though I may not mention it) that "my" obviously means "our." Every experienced judge knows that setting up tests, conducting a stake, and ranking the entries who "complete," is a joint effort of the judges. One judge may dominate the other, but even the most submissive judge cannot avoid influencing the action. The above notwithstanding, for convenience in this book, I repeat that often I shall refer to "my tests" or I shall present analyses of "my judging performance."

Assumptions

Assumption number one. -- It is assumed that marking, memory, and forgetting are merely aspects of the same process. To elaborate, first a retriever must mark; if he is to remember, it amounts to "retaining the marks" for an additional interval of time; forgetting is merely the failure to remember.

Assumption number two. -- The more the test requires a retriever to depend on directions from the handler, the more separation the test provides; that is, tests discriminate in the following rank order: M < M & M < B.

Assumption number three, a frame of reference. -- I approach all judging assignments of licensed open stakes in the following frame of reference: I assume that I am primarily concerned with one calendar year only, say, 1967; I am primarily concerned only with retrievers who have never won a licensed open stake up to the date January 1, 1967, but who will become field champions during 1967; I assume that each field champion will run in the 1967 national championship. I assume that if I focus as indicated above, all other eventualities will be adequately handled. Under these conditions, because there are $n_{\ell o}$ licensed open stakes during 1967, at most there will be n_{fc} field champions made in 1967 (among these retrievers); then clearly, $n_{fc} \leq n_{\ell o}$.

Assumption number four, certification. -- It is assumed that an open judge who awards a first place knows he is certifying that the first place dog is competent in all phases of open work and has the right and competence to participate in the national championship stake.

Assumption number five, consistency. -- It is assumed that the winner has demonstrated competence and workmanlike jobs in all phases of his performance. Obviously, I prefer brilliant consistent work (consistently brilliant work).

Assumption number six, differential discrimination. -- I assume that if a pair of open retrievers is selected at random, the type of test that I set up will determine the probability that I can discriminate (a noticeable difference) between the performances of the two retrievers.

Noticeable difference is defined to be a difference "large enough" so that if I were to draw a random sample of five eight-point judges, I would expect four out of five independent judgments to agree not only that a noticeable difference existed (although the difference might not be large enough to declare a winner), but also on the direction of the difference.

Assumption number seven. -- Other entries will be separated if the process used separates those dogs called back for the $i + 1$ series, where i series are conducted in the stake.

Assumption number eight, parameters of the probability of discrimination. -- Parameters, based upon tests which I was involved in setting up and data from judging sheets which I recorded in licensed trials plus other information, McMahan's best estimates (for McMahan as judge), of the probability of discrimination by broad category of test are given below:

M	M & M		B (Land)	B (Water)

Little discrimination				Great discrimination
$\pi = 0.25$	0.4		0.75	$\pi = 0.9$

$$\pi$$

Assumption number nine, differential penalty.--I shall assure that all those retrievers who finish and receive a JAM or higher can mark, remember, handle on land, and handle on water. In view of the differential probability of separation, I shall assess penalties for poor work accordingly.

Discussion of Tests of Marking Ability, the Easy Extreme

For this discussion, a mark is the first bird retrieved which the entry sees fall (in a series where control is not specified by the judges).

Every experienced judge knows that if he runs 40 entries on a solid triple (one downwind bird, hopefully two essentially downwind), some of the dogs will fail to retrieve the first bird and will have to be handled. This does not necessarily imply that this particular triple is a good test of a retriever's ability to mark. In short, an experienced judge knows that some dogs will goof-up "no matter what you run them on."

The probability of McMahan's not being able to separate a pair of open retrievers selected at random by using a marking test is 0.75 $(1.00 - 0.25)$. It is well-known that performance in a given trial is influenced greatly by the variability within open retrievers. That is, Retriever A may win one weekend and Retriever B may win the next weekend; ... ; and yet another retriever may win another weekend. To what extent does $\pi = 0.25$ indicate that we can really separate open retrievers with regard to marking ability? In other words, how much of our "one chance in four" merely reflects variability (within) and luck? (Many damnfools can set up marks which require handling; many damnfools can set up tests which only one or two entries can complete; only the best judges can set up tests which will allow retrievers to mark without handling, allow "most" retrievers to complete, but which will provide "good" separation.)

In view of the above, should we assume competency to mark for open retrievers? If we do assume such competency, then the tests of

ALL PUCKERED UP WITH THOUGHT

An old signed print by G. Vernon Stokes in the author's private Pontchippi Collection.

Microseconds after Kube told McMahan "go to hell" (on the water blind after going into the fifth series "top dog").

marking become merely exercises for the enjoyment of the dogs and the handlers (inasmuch as the spectator component is essentially negligible). My answer to the question is no; an open judge must not assume competency to mark. A necessary condition for a well-trained, competent retriever is that he can and will mark (on any given occasion). One reason that marks are run in trials is for the retriever to demonstrate to each set of judges independently that he has that necessary condition (on a given day). A competent judge might not expect "marks" to separate entries with high probability--marks do reflect variability not only within animals, but also many other factors.

Discussion of the Water Blind, the Other Extreme

My experience leads me to believe that the water blind has the greatest power to discriminate among open retrievers. What is it about the open water blind that makes it so crucial? Is it the application to the practical situation? It is not difficult to convince a Louisiana duck hunter (wildfowler to my British friends) of the importance and difficulty of the water blind. For example, I have hunted duck near the Mouth of The River for years. On such a hunt, Kube has brought duck to bag which would not have been bagged without the aid of a retriever. Oftentimes, I have handled in such a way as to make the retrieve by a circuitous water route in order to avoid the really difficult, if not impractical, task of retrieving through the mud and a possible encounter with nutria, snakes, and other dangers. Moreover, this has to be accomplished where such a blind retrieve may precede and/or follow numerous marked falls.

In open stakes where the water blind is reserved for a late series (and many judges "claim" to object to this practice), are the judges, in effect, saying that the open water blind is *the* test of an open retriever? No matter how well the retriever performs on other tests, this test is crucial--actually, the necessary *and* sufficient condition for certification as Open All-age Retriever. All other series are merely preliminaries (necessary, but not sufficient); they simply serve to (reduce the large entry and) limit the field to possible open all-age retrievers--they are screening devices only. Except for the fact that Kube could not (at least, I didn't teach her to) do the water blind in a licensed, all-age stake, under the right combination of circumstances she would probably be a field champion. But because she could not do the water blind (in combination with top work on the other tests), no judge awarded her first place in a trial, no matter how brilliant her work in other series. If she had been given first place, she might run in the national, take up a space, and have small probability of surviving the first open water blind.

In open stakes where the water blind is used in an early series, are the judges, in effect, also saying that the open water blind is the test of an open retriever? The retriever who cannot perform up to the standards set for this given test has no business competing with open all-age retrievers; hence, eliminate him from the field--"make way for the big boys" to demonstrate their prowess on a given day (in tests which are necessary but not sufficient).

Obviously, in my opinion, the open water blind does have the greatest discriminatory power. Does that make the open water blind by definition the "toughest" open test? Would being the toughest open test justify the most critical (most severe) scoring? Does the greater discriminatory power of the water blind reflect real differences between performances or does it reflect the judge's ability to distinguish between performances (versus judge's ability to distinguish between, say, performance on marked falls)?

Are there one or more other basic assumptions, explicit or implicit, understood by veteran field trial competitors, underlying the concept of the open water blind? Even to the novice, it is clear that competence must be demonstrated in the water blind as in each test in a given stake; however, does competence mean the same thing on the water blind as on other tests? "Competence" may suggest another point of confusion: Is lack of competence failure to complete a test?

Is competence "just bare passability"? Is competence measured in terms of quality of other performances? Is competence "good, solid, workmanlike performance"? To repeat: Is competence measured differently in different series in a particular stake, for example, second series land blind versus fifth series water blind?

ACTION ITEM

As a senior judge, I find it difficult to set tests for competent open retrievers which will test marking ability and marking ability plus memory to my satisfaction. In post-evaluation of my judging performance in an open stake, I find that my winners are determined largely by handling tests. That is, if I make the marking and memory tests difficult enough to really test for these abilities, then often they too become handling tests.

From this experience, it appears to me that there may not be large differentials in the ability to mark and remember in open retrievers that are placed in open stakes of licensed trials. If the memory birds are extremely difficult, the handlers appear to assist their dogs materially by lining them; I do not have a clear-cut point as to where excessive lining begins (when or when not to penalize for excessive lining is oftentimes beyond my ability to distinguish clearly). Moreover, the evidence indicates that I tend to "weight" slight differences in performances on blinds more heavily than slight differences on marks. It follows that I may be more inclined to equate two "marking jobs" than two "jobs on a blind."

Discuss.

ILLUSTRATION OF
POST-EVALUATION OF A JUDGING PERFORMANCE

Pontchippi Critique Form

During the week following each licensed trial which I judge, routinely I conduct a critique of my performance as a judge. I wish to examine such topics and questions as follows (as well as others): How could I have improved the tests within the restrictions of time, support personnel, land, water, weather, and so on? Did I place any dogs that should not have been placed? Did I drop some dogs that should not have been dropped? Did I award some JAM's which should not have been awarded? Should I have awarded others? ... ? Where else did I goof? Would I have taken home the winner if he had been presented to me as a gift? Would I have kept him in my kennel and campaigned him with pride? Would he be a credit to the breed? Would he be expected to improve the breed? Clearly, these questions must be answered from my judge's notes alone, without the information from my co-judge.

I use Pontchippi Critique Form A, one version of which is shown in Figure 14-1, to assist me in answering some of these questions, particularly as to what retrieves and tests proved to be "separators."

For illustration, consider an open stake. Did the tests of marking ability discriminate well? Did the tests of marking and memory discriminate adequately? Did the blinds really prove to be the separators? Was the outcome of the trial most heavily influenced by the water blind?

Note that Pontchippi Critique Form A forces me to consider not only each series, but a gross description of what ability was being tested; moreover, it forces me to make comparisons not only series by series, but bird by bird as well, weighted according to my personal bias. In addition, I have to face up to the fact that I may have (many) "no decisions"; fortunately, we don't have to rank the entries who receive JAM's. However, we do have to assure that the best JAM's rank below fourth place and that those who completed the trial who were not awarded JAM's rank below those to whom we awarded JAM's. In short, the form does not remove opinion and bias; it does force one to explicitly examine his bias and face up to some of his shortcomings as a judge.

Symbolism: M = mark; M & M = mark and memory; B_{HW} = blind, heavily weighted; B_{LW} = blind, lightly weighted; SB_{LW} = short blind (diversion), lightly weighted; LB_{HW} = long blind, heavily weighted; D_{R_1} = first duck retrieved; D_{R_2} = second duck retrieved; D_{R_3} = last duck retrieved; D = decision; and $\overline{D}$ = no decision.

Series One

Entry		
M		
M & M		
D		

Series Two

Entry		
M		
B_{HW}		
D		

Series Three

Entry		
M		
SB_{LW}		
LB_{HW}		
D		

Series Four

Entry		
$M_{D_{R_1}}$		
M & $M_{D_{R_2}}$		
M & $M_{D_{R_3}}$		
D		

Series Five

Entry		
B_{HW}		
D		

ENTIRE STAKE

Entry		
D		
$\overline{D}$		

Number of ties

(Possible) M = 4	(Possible) M & M = 3	(Possible) B = 4	
		LW = 1	HW = 3
(Observed)	(Observed)	(Observed)	

(Fall, 1967)

(Number: of 55.)

Figure 14-1.--Pontchippi Critique Form A, to be completed by a judge (himself) to assist in organizing data (from "his book") for one aspect of his post-evaluation (the week immediately following the trial) of his judging performance. [*Author's note*: Obviously, format must be adapted "to fit" each trial.]

Pontchippi Critique Form A is completed with the assistance of a competent, retriever-wise colleague and co-worker; (contrary to my ideals) these forms are not checked again--too much time is involved. In fact, I believe that if an RE is not prepared to spend ("a good bit of") time in post-evaluation the week immediately following the trial, then he should not judge the trial. For example, given 5 series and 11 birds, a judge can estimate that his post-evaluation of a single pair of performances will take from 5 to 10 minutes.

Instructions for using Pontchippi Critique Form A.-- This form is used to compare the performances of two retrievers. For convenience, only three symbols are used: −, 0, +; hence, for each line there will be one pair of entries (shortcomings of such a system are recognized). If there is not a noticeable difference in performances, indicate the tie by the ordered pair (0, 0). If one performance is slightly better than another, indicate by the ordered pair (+, 0) or (0, +). If one performance is far better than another, indicate by (−, +) or (+, −).

The use of this form can probably be most easily described in terms of an example; see Figure 14-2, where I compared the performances of two retrievers, A and B.

Series one.--I could tell no difference in the performances of A and B on the M; hence, I entered 0 for both A and B. On the M & M bird, B was better; hence, I entered + for B and 0 for A. B won the first series, so I gave + to B and 0 to A, the ordered pair (0, +).

Series two.--There was no obvious difference in performances on the mark; hence, the tie was indicated by (0, 0). Entry A performed better on the long blind; hence, the entry (+, 0). The fact that A won the series ("got the decision," D) is indicated by (+, 0).

Series three.--Entry A did better on the mark; hence, the pair (+, 0). Entry B performed better on the short blind as indicated by (0, +). Entry A whipped B on the long blind, so the entry (+, 0) is made. Entry A won the series: (+, 0).

Symbolism: M = mark; M & M = mark and memory; B_{HW} = blind, heavily weighted; B_{LW} = blind, lightly weighted; SB_{LW} = short blind (diversion), lightly weighted; LB_{HW} = long blind, heavily weighted; D_{R1} = first duck retrieved; D_{R2} = second duck retrieved; D_{R3} = last duck retrieved; D = decision; and $\bar{D}$ = no decision.

Series One

Entry	A	B
M	0	0
M & M	0	+
D	0	+

Series Two

Entry	A	B
M	0	0
B_{HW}	+	0
D	+	0

Series Three

Entry	A	B
M	+	0
SB_{LW}	0	+
LB_{HW}	+	0
D	+	0

Series Four

Entry	A	B
$M_{D_{R1}}$	0	0
M & $M_{D_{R2}}$	0	0
M & $M_{D_{R3}}$	0	0
D	0	0

Series Five

Entry	A	B
B_{HW}	+	0
D	+	0

ENTIRE STAKE

Entry	A	B
D	✓	
$\bar{D}$	X	X

Number of ties

(Possible) M = 4	(Possible) M & M = 3	(Possible) B = 4	
		LW = 1	HW = 3
(Observed)	(Observed)	(Observed)	
3	2	0	0

(Fall, 1967)

(Number: 1 of 55.)

Figure 14-2.--Pontchippi Critique Form A, to be completed by a judge (himself) to assist in organizing data (from "his book") for one aspect of his post-evaluation (the week immediately following the trial) of his judging performance. [*Author's note:* Obviously, format must be adapted "to fit" each trial.]

Series four. -- There were no differences in performances on any bird or on the series; hence, the four ordered pairs: (0, 0), (0, 0), (0, 0), (0, 0).

Series five. -- Entry A surpassed entry B on the water blind as indicated by (+, 0); since there was only one retrieve, A also won the series.

Entire stake. -- Entry A surpassed B over the entire stake; this is indicated by a check mark under A.

Number of ties. -- There were 4 marks; there were 3 entries of (0, 0); hence, 3 ties. There were 3 memory birds; there were 2 entries of (0, 0); hence, 2 ties. There were no ties on the blinds.

Comment one: One "+" in a series with three birds does not necessarily mean that the retriever with the + wins the series; the decision D remains "judgmental"; tabulations are merely mechanical procedures to assist the judge in making his decision.

Comment two: It is possible, say, in a triple, to indicate ties for all three birds and yet give the series to one of the entries; to explicitly state one case, on each and every bird one entry might have been just a bit more precise than the other entry.

Comment three: Minus signs are always treated as danger signals. Clearly, for retrievers who complete the trial, the minus quantity cannot be excessively large; however, a judge, in evaluating his own performance, will always consider the minus sign as being equal to or greater than -1. This is especially true in the decision box. In short, if an entry has a minus sign in the decision box, seldom will that entry win the stake over the entry which has no minus sign in a decision box.

Comment four: There may be a just noticeable difference (JND) between two different entries on a particular bird in a particular series. However, upon inspection of the entire series and referring to notes made at the time of the performances, a judge might make the decision that there is no difference between the entries for that series.

Comment five: The analyses of pairs of retriever performances should be made in a randomized order. It is convenient to overlap pages so that judging forms correspond with order of entries in Form A. To emphasize an earlier statement: The judge must have a dedicated, rigorously honest co-worker "checking" him when completing Form A.

Comment six: In your post-evaluation of your judging performance, force yourself to make a decision on every pair of entries. If you cannot make a decision, mark it "no decision" tentatively. Set it aside for a day or two. Come back and compare the entries on a completely new and independent form; compare the two forms. If you still cannot reach a decision, flip a coin.

Comment seven, more on ties: I find that on blinds, pairs which are difficult to discriminate between are likely to be those in which each entry had "poor" work; whereas, performances on marks which do not allow easy or clear differentiation are likely to be those for which each entry "pin-points" the fall.

Post-Evaluation, Licensed Amateur Stake, An Example

Ten retrievers were awarded ribbons in this trial; hence, there were $\binom{10}{2}$ or 45 comparisons to be made. Pontchippi Critique Form A was adapted as shown in Figure 14-3; 45 copies were prepared and numbered 1 of 45, 2 of 45, ..., 45 of 45.

Probability of a tie.--All possible paired comparisons were made and results recorded on a Form A for each pair. Then the results were summarized in Table 14-1. Clearly, the relative frequency (r.f.) (probability) of a tie is greatest on marked (M) falls, r.f. = 0.46, and least on the water blind (WB), r.f. = 0.04. The probability of separation is (1.00 − r.f.).

Circular triads.--Using methods presented in Chapter Six, an attempt was made to distinguish between the performances of each pair of ribbon winners (obviously, a heavy requirement). Decisions were

Symbolism: M = mark; M & M = mark and memory; SB = short blind, lightly weighted; LB = long blind, heavily weighted; B_w = blind, water; D = decision; and $\overline{D}$ = no decision.

Series One

Entry		
M		
M & M		
D		

Series Two

Entry		
SB		
LB		
D		

Series Three

Entry		
M		
M & M		
M & M		
D		

Series Four

Entry		
B_w		
D		

Series Five

Entry		
M		
M & M		
M & M		
D		

ENTIRE STAKE

Entry		
D		
$\overline{D}$		

Number of ties

(Possible) M = 3	(Possible) M & M = 5	(Possible) B = 3		
		SB = 1	LB = 1	B_w = 1
(Observed)	(Observed)	(Observed)		

(Number: of 45.)

(Spring, 1968)

Figure 14-3.--Pontchippi Critique Form A, to be completed by a judge (himself) to assist in organizing data (from "his book") for one aspect of his post-evaluation (the week immediately following the trial) of his judging performance.

Table 14-1. --Number of ties, by type of test, all possible paired comparisons of 10 entries which were awarded ribbons,
amateur stake, licensed trial, spring, 1968

Set		Type of test				
Number	ID	M	M & M	SB	LB	WB
1	A–B	1	2	0	0	0
2	A–C	2	3	0	0	0
3	A–E	1	2	0	0	0
4	A–F	1	1	0	0	0
5	A–G	1	3	0	1	0
6	A–H	2	3	0	0	0
7	A–J	2	3	0	0	0
8	A–D	3	1	0	0	0
9	A–K	1	3	0	0	0
10	B–C	1	1	0	0	0
11	B–E	0	0	0	0	0
12	B–F	2	3	1	0	0
13	B–G	2	2	0	0	0
14	B–H	0	1	0	0	0
15	B–J	2	2	0	0	0
16	B–D	1	2	0	0	0
17	B–K	1	1	0	0	0
18	C–E	1	1	0	0	0
19	C–F	0	2	0	0	0
20	C–G	2	2	0	1	0
21	C–H	1	2	1	0	0
22	C–J	2	2	0	0	0
23	C–D	2	1	1	0	0
24	C–K	2	1	1	0	0
25	E–F	0	1	0	0	0
26	E–G	1	2	0	0	0
27	E–H	2	5	0	0	0

(Continued)

Table 14-1.--(Concluded) Number of ties, by type of test, all possible paired comparisons of 10 entries which were awarded ribbons, amateur stake, licensed trial, spring, 1968

Set		Type of test				
Number	ID	M	M & M	SB	LB	WB
28	E-J	2	3	0	0	0
29	D-E	1	3	0	0	0
30	K-E	2	3	1	0	0
31	F-G	0	1	0	0	0
32	F-H	1	1	1	0	0
33	F-J	0	1	0	0	0
34	D-F	1	1	0	0	0
35	K-F	0	1	0	0	0
36	G-H	1	3	0	0	0
37	G-J	3	5	0	0	0
38	D-G	3	3	0	0	0
39	K-G	2	2	0	0	0
40	H-J	1	3	0	1	0
41	D-H	2	4	1	0	1
42	K-H	1	3	1	0	0
43	D-J	2	3	0	0	0
44	K-J	2	2	0	0	0
45	D-K	2	3	1	1	0
Observed total = O	...	62	97	9	4	1
Possible total = P	...	3×45 = 135	5×45 = 225	1×45 = 45	1×45 = 45	1×45 = 45
Relative frequency (of ties), r. f.	$\frac{O}{P}$	0.459	0.431	0.200 Land blinds: $13/90$ = 0.144	0.089	0.022
Probability of separation	$1 - $ r.f. (tie)	0.541	0.569	0.800 Land blinds: $1 - 0.144$ = 0.856	0.911	0.978

made as shown in Table 14-2. Then Table 14-3 was prepared to check for circular triads (circular reasoning).

When the number of ribbon winners to be compared is even, the maximum number of circular triads is

$$\frac{n^3 - 4n}{24}.$$

If we let a_t equal the sum of the entries in a given column in Table 14-3, then the number of circular triads, d, will be given by

$$d = \left(\frac{1}{12}\right)(n)(n-1)(2n-1) - \frac{1}{2}\Sigma a_t^2$$

$$= \left(\frac{1}{12}\right)(10)(9)(19) - \frac{1}{2}(283)$$

$$= \left(\frac{1}{12}\right)(1,710) - (141.5)$$

$$= 142.5 - 141.5$$

$$d = 1.$$

Clearly, there is one circular triad out of a possible

$$\frac{n^3 - 4n}{24} = \frac{1,000 - 40}{24} = 40.$$

When we define the coefficient of consistency as ζ (zeta),

$$\zeta = 1 - \frac{24(d)}{n^3 - 4n},$$

and substituting,

$$\zeta = 1 - \frac{24(1)}{960}$$

$$= 1 - 0.025$$

$$\zeta = 0.975,$$

where $\zeta = 1.000$ would indicate no circular triads.

[*Aside*: Early in my analysis, I assigned G as the highest

Table 14-2.--Worksheet for summarizing paired comparisons, ribbon winners, amateur stake, licensed trial, spring, 1968

```
A > B = 1     C > A = 1     E > A = 0     G > A = 0     J > A = 0
A > C = 1     C > B = 0     E > B = 0     G > B = 0     J > B = 0
A > D = 1     C > D = 1     E > C = 0     G > C = 0     J > C = 0
A > E = 1     C > E = 1     E > D = 0     G > D = 0     J > D = 0
A > F = 1     C > F = 1     E > F = 0     G > E = 1     J > E = 1
A > G = 1     C > G = 1     E > G = 0     G > F = 1     J > F = 1
A > H = 1     C > H = 1     E > H = 0     G > H = 0     J > G = 0
A > J = 1     C > J = 1     E > J = 0     G > J = 1     J > H = 0
A > K = 1     C > K = 1     E > K = 0     G > K = 1     J > K = 0
     ΣA = 9         ΣC = 7         ΣE = 0         ΣG = 4         ΣJ = 2

B > A = 0     D > A = 0     F > A = 0     H > A = 0     K > A = 0
B > C = 1     D > B = 0     F > B = 0     H > B = 0     K > B = 0
B > D = 1     D > C = 0     F > C = 0     H > C = 0     K > C = 0
B > E = 1     D > E = 1     F > D = 0     H > D = 0     K > D = 0
B > F = 1     D > F = 1     F > E = 1     H > E = 1     K > E = 1
B > G = 1     D > G = 1     F > G = 0     H > F = 1     K > F = 1
B > H = 1     D > H = 1     F > H = 0     H > G = 1     K > G = 0
B > J = 1     D > J = 1     F > J = 0     H > J = 1     K > H = 1
B > K = 1     D > K = 1     F > K = 0     H > K = 0     K > J = 1
     ΣB = 8         ΣD = 6         ΣF = 1         ΣH = 4         ΣK = 4
```

Table 14-3. --Comparative judgments for a judge with one circular triad, amateur stake, licensed trial, spring, 1968

Retriever (row)	Retriever (column)									
	E	F	J	H	K	G	D	C	B	A
E		1	1	1	1	1	1	1	1	1
F	0		1	1	1	1	1	1	1	1
J	0	0		1	1	1	1	1	1	1
H	0	0	0		1	0	1	1	1	1
K	0	0	0	0		1	1	1	1	1
G	0	0	0	1	0		1	1	1	1
D	0	0	0	0	0	0		1	1	1
C	0	0	0	0	0	0	0		1	1
B	0	0	0	0	0	0	0	0		1
A	0	0	0	0	0	0	0	0	0	
a	0	1	2	4	4	4	6	7	8	9
a^2	0	1	4	16	16	16	36	49	64	81

ranking JAM; had I stuck with that decision, there would have been no circular triad--but I changed my judgment.]

Another Example, Post-Evaluation of a Licensed Open Stake

Eleven retrievers completed this stake and were awarded ribbons. Form A was adapted to that shown earlier in Figure 14-1 and $\binom{11}{2}$ or 55 such forms were completed--55 comparisons made. Number of ties, by type of test, are shown in Table 14-4. Probabilities of separation are explicitly shown at the bottom of the table.

Ranking of those entries which completed the trial.-- Using methods of paired comparisons presented in Chapter Six, a score for each retriever was tabulated on a worksheet (Table 14-5). Clearly, Retriever A is the winner and Retriever H did not rank above any of those who finished.

Circular reasoning.--Continuing with the methods of paired comparisons described in Chapter Six, a test for circular reasoning can be made from Table 14-6. Because there are no 1's below the diagonal, it is obvious I did a perfect job. *Comment:* I was lucky!

OPERATIONAL STANDARDS

After a given judge has carefully analyzed his judging performance in a specified stake, undoubtedly, he would hope that his performance compared favorably with $\mathscr{J}$'s or his own ideal performance. An incomplete (an abridged) set of standards are set forth below for your consideration.

A.   The stake was conducted according to current ... *Field Trial Rules and Standard Procedures for ... Retrievers, ...* and *Standing Recommendations of the Retriever Advisory Committee.* AND

B.   The winner is a retriever that $\mathscr{J}$ would like to take home with him. AND

C.   The stake was conducted so that all entries who would be called back for the i + 1 series, if one were conducted, would de-

Table 14-4. --Number of ties, by type of test, all possible paired comparisons of 11 entries which completed an open licensed
stake, 1967

Set			Type of test		
				B	
Number	ID	M	M & M	LW	HW
1	A-B	3	2	0	0
2	A-C	4	2	0	0
3	A-D	4	2	0	1
4	A-E	1	1	1	0
5	A-F	4	2	0	1
6	A-G	4	3	1	0
7	A-H	2	1	0	0
8	A-J	4	1	0	1
9	A-K	4	2	0	1
10	A-L	3	2	0	0
11	B-C	3	2	1	2
12	B-D	3	2	1	0
13	B-E	2	2	0	1
14	B-F	3	3	0	0
15	B-G	3	1	0	0
16	B-H	3	1	1	1
17	B-J	3	2	1	0
18	B-K	3	3	1	1
19	B-L	2	2	1	0
20	C-D	4	2	1	0
21	C-E	1	1	0	1
22	C-F	4	2	0	0
23	C-G	4	0	0	1
24	C-H	2	2	1	1

(Continued)

Table 14-4.--(Continued) Number of ties, by type of test, all possible paired comparisons of 11 entries which completed an open licensed stake, 1967

Set		Type of test			
				B	
Number	ID	M	M & M	LW	HW
25	C-J	4	1	1	0
26	C-K	4	2	1	1
27	C-L	3	2	1	1
28	D-E	1	1	0	0
29	D-F	4	3	0	1
30	D-G	4	1	0	1
31	D-H	2	2	1	0
32	D-J	4	1	1	2
33	D-K	4	2	1	0
34	D-L	3	3	1	0
35	E-F	1	1	0	0
36	E-G	1	0	1	0
37	E-H	1	0	0	1
38	E-J	1	3	0	0
39	E-K	1	2	0	0
40	E-L	3	1	0	1
41	F-G	4	2	0	1
42	F-H	2	2	0	0
43	F-J	4	1	0	3
44	F-K	4	2	0	1
45	F-L	3	3	0	0
46	G-H	2	2	0	0
47	G-J	4	2	0	0
48	G-K	4	1	0	0

(Continued)

Table 14-4.--(Concluded) Number of ties, by type of test, all possible paired comparisons of 11 entries which completed an open licensed stake, 1967

Set		Type of test			
				B	
Number	ID	M	M & M	LW	HW
49	G-L	3	2	0	1
50	H-J	2	2	1	0
51	H-K	2	2	1	1
52	H-L	1	3	1	1
53	J-K	4	2	1	1
54	J-L	3	1	1	0
55	K-L	3	2	0	1
Observed total = O	...	159	97	23	30
Possible total = P	...	4×55 = 220	3×55 = 165	1×55 = 55	3×55 = 165
Relative frequency (of ties), r.f.	$\dfrac{O}{P}$	0.723	0.588	0.418	0.182

Note: Relative frequency of ties for
land blinds (HW) = $24/110$ = 0.218;
water blinds (HW) = $6/55$ = 0.109.

Probability of separation, $1 - $ r.f. (ties), for
land blinds (HW) = 0.782;
water blinds (HW) = 0.891.

Table 14-5.--Worksheet for summarizing paired comparisons, entries which completed an open licensed stake, 1967

A > B = 1	C > A = 0	E > A = 0
A > C = 1	C > B = 0	E > B = 0
A > D = 1	C > D = 1	E > C = 0
A > E = 1	C > E = 1	E > D = 0
A > F = 1	C > F = 1	E > F = 1
A > G = 1	C > G = 1	E > G = 1
A > H = 1	C > H = 1	E > H = 1
A > J = 1	C > J = 1	E > J = 1
A > K = 1	C > K = 1	E > K = 0
A > L = 1	C > L = 1	E > L = 0
ΣA = 10	ΣC = 8	ΣE = 4
B > A = 0	D > A = 0	F > A = 0
B > C = 1	D > B = 0	F > B = 0
B > D = 1	D > C = 0	F > C = 0
B > E = 1	D > E = 1	F > D = 0
B > F = 1	D > F = 1	F > E = 0
B > G = 1	D > G = 1	F > G = 0
B > H = 1	D > H = 1	F > H = 1
B > J = 1	D > J = 1	F > J = 0
B > K = 1	D > K = 1	F > K = 0
B > L = 1	D > L = 1	F > L = 0
ΣB = 9	ΣD = 7	ΣF = 1

(Continued)

Table 14-5. --(Concluded) Worksheet for summarizing paired comparisons, entries which completed an open licensed stake,
1967

G	>	A	=	0	J	>	A	=	0	L > A = 0
G	>	B	=	0	J	>	B	=	0	L > B = 0
G	>	C	=	0	J	>	C	=	0	L > C = 0
G	>	D	=	0	J	>	D	=	0	L > D = 0
G	>	E	=	0	J	>	E	=	0	L > E = 1
G	>	F	=	1	J	>	F	=	1	L > F = 1
G	>	H	=	1	J	>	G	=	1	L > G = 1
G	>	J	=	0	J	>	H	=	1	L > H = 1
G	>	K	=	0	J	>	K	=	0	L > J = 1
G	>	L	=	0	J	>	L	=	0	L > K = 0

$$\Sigma G = 2 \qquad \Sigma J = 3 \qquad \Sigma L = 5$$

H	>	A	=	0	K	>	A	=	0
H	>	B	=	0	K	>	B	=	0
H	>	C	=	0	K	>	C	=	0
H	>	D	=	0	K	>	D	=	0
H	>	E	=	0	K	>	E	=	1
H	>	F	=	0	K	>	F	=	1
H	>	G	=	0	K	>	G	=	1
H	>	J	=	0	K	>	H	=	1
H	>	K	=	0	K	>	J	=	1
H	>	L	=	0	K	>	L	=	1

$$\Sigma H = 0 \qquad \Sigma K = 6$$

Table 14-6. --Comparative judgments for a judge with no circular triads, entries which completed an open licensed stake, 1967

Retriever (row)	Retriever (column)										
	H	F	G	J	E	L	K	D	C	B	A
H		1	1	1	1	1	1	1	1	1	1
F	0		1	1	1	1	1	1	1	1	1
G	0	0		1	1	1	1	1	1	1	1
J	0	0	0		1	1	1	1	1	1	1
E	0	0	0	0		1	1	1	1	1	1
L	0	0	0	0	0		1	1	1	1	1
K	0	0	0	0	0	0		1	1	1	1
D	0	0	0	0	0	0	0		1	1	1
C	0	0	0	0	0	0	0	0		1	1
B	0	0	0	0	0	0	0	0	0		1
A	0	0	0	0	0	0	0	0	0	0	

serve and be awarded a JAM or higher. The greater number of such entries after thorough testing, the better the judging performance. AND

D. The stake was conducted so that the first four places were clearly separated; fourth place was clearly separated from the highest JAM; and the lowest JAM was clearly separated from the top entry who was not called back for the $i + 1$ series and, hence, did not receive a JAM. AND

E. The tests were set for proportion of callbacks to be in the neighborhood of the following (or better--higher):

	$\mathscr{J}$	(McMahan's estimates)
from first to second series:	π_{12}	(0.83)
from second to third series:	π_{23}	(0.71)
from third to fourth series:	π_{34}	(0.61)
from fourth to fifth series (in this example, $i + 1$ series):	π_{45}	(0.65).

Or about π (23 per cent according to McMahan) of the original entries enter the fifth series. AND

F. The probability of separation of any pair of entries (selected at random, of course) on each type of test of those entries who were awarded JAM's or higher was approximately as follows:

	$\mathscr{J}$	(McMahan's estimates)
marks:	π_M	(0.25)
mark and memory:	π_{MM}	(0.40)
land blinds:	π_{LB}	(0.75)
water blinds:	π_{WB}	(0.90).

In summary, in terms of set-builder notation,

$\mathscr{J}$'s ideal performance $= \{P : P = \{A \cap B \cap C \cap D \cap E \cap F\}\}$.

[Read the foregoing notation as "$\mathcal{J}$'s ideal performance is equal to the set of ideal performances such that that set of ideal performances is equal to A *intersect* B *intersect* C ... *intersect* F."] Hence, any judge whose performance meets the standards of ideal judge's ideal performance must have performed in such a way that his performance satisfied A *and* B *and* C *and* D *and* E *and* F. That is, symbolically,

$$(jp = \mathcal{J}P) \Leftrightarrow (jp \supseteq \{P : P = \{A \cap B \cap C \cap D \cap E \cap F\}\})$$

where jp = any judge's performance, and $\mathcal{J}P$ = $\mathcal{J}$'s ideal performance.

[Read the above notation as "any judge's performance is equal to $\mathcal{J}$'s ideal performance *if and only if* that judge's performance is contained in (or equal to) the set of ideal performances such that that set of ideal performances is equal to A *intersect* B *intersect* C ... *intersect* F."]

A pittance of practice may be worth a tome of theory.

NOTES TO CHAPTER FOURTEEN

1. A Judge's Self-Evaluation of His Judging Performance

Time after time I have asked questions of qualified judges (having five and/or eight points, some having many times eight points) concerning their ability to set up tests which discriminate using only tests of marking (M) and tests of marking and memory (M & M). In particular, did they believe that such tests, M and M & M, really discriminate among the best dogs in a trial? Repeatedly, I have been assured that such tests did discriminate. Yet I have devoted full-time to gallery judging, with all of its limitations, "concurrently with" these same judges; I have even arrived at essentially the same group of dogs which received places, and often the group which received a ribbon. When I analyzed the performance of every pair of entries, I find that the tests set by these judges (in my hands) did a relatively poor job of discriminating with tests other than blinds (with M tests and M & M tests). In fact, the continuum of discrimination may run about as illustrated below.

M	M & M	B
		(heavily weighted)

| L_____|_____J |

| $Pr(\text{tie}) \approx 8/10$ | $Pr(\text{tie}) \approx 7/10$ | $Pr(\text{tie}) \approx 2/10$ |

In other words, with really competent open retrievers, discrimination is obtained from tests which test for some attribute other than so-called natural ability; moreover, the more the test tends to test for abilities acquired through training, the greater the discrimination.

To elaborate, apparently the selection process (derby and qualifying stakes) for open retrievers is selective of those retrievers who can mark; in short, "most" open retrievers can mark and mark well. Hence, discrimination involving marks on a given day may be mainly due to "within animal variability" and to chance.

In view of the replies of experienced judges, I must conclude that most judges have probably never really evaluated their performances as judge. They think they know what they do, but actually "they know not what they do."

603

Moreover, I have never seen another judge have a systematic method (such as I use and have suggested) for comparing dog work at the end of a trial--bird by bird within series and then series by series--in combination with post-trial evaluation. [*Aside:* This is not to say that selected judges don't have such systematic methods; I merely state that I have never seen the evidence.]

The results presented on differential discrimination are likely to evoke a comment somewhat as follows: "Sure, that's obvious; every senior judge knows that you get your separation in open stakes on the blind." My comment is that it is obvious *once it has been pointed out*, but to date, as far as I've been able to determine, no one has organized a body of data to logically arrive at this conclusion. Moreover, a judge should know what his tests do, what type of mark does discriminate. By post-trial self-evaluation a judge might learn what he is doing. I think a judge should face up to rigorous self-evaluation of his judging performance(s).

2. **Illustration of Pontchippi Method for Pre-series Critique of a Test (Pontchippi Critique Form B)**

[*Instructions:* It is assumed that if you can't "call your shots in advance," then you should not expect your colleagues to respect your opinions and judgment. Since it is well-known that many of us have 20/20 hindsight, use only information available to the judges; that is, complete this form in ink before a test dog or the first dog runs. If the test is changed after the test dog runs but before the first dog runs, you may enter modifications in pencil on this form.]

1. Type of stake: (Derby) ✓ (Qualifying) (Amateur) (Open).

2. Series number in stake: (1) (2) (3) (4) ✓ (5) (6).

3. Number of starters or callbacks for this series: _21_ .

4. Number of retrieves in this series: _2_ .

5. Number and type of retrieves: M, _1_ ; M & M, _1_ ; B, _0_ .

6. Sketch of test: Label the problem areas on a sketch [sketch not presented here].

7. **Purpose of test:** *To test steadiness--dog must turn 160° to see mark; to test performance in mud and swimming water; largely, to test memory (M & M) since the mark appears to be relatively easy; to test eagerness and drive and special training--dog must run a considerable distance through mud before entering swimming water in going for the memory bird.*

8. **Ranking:** In your opinion, will there be a sufficiently wide variation in performances on this test to facilitate ranking? Yes __√__ ; No _____ .

9. **Separation of best dogs:** Because poorer dogs are of little concern to judges, in your opinion, will this test generate data for separating the top dogs of this stake? Yes __√__ ; No _____ .

10. **Clear view of Guns and birdboys:** In your opinion, can the dog see all the Guns and birdboys easily and clearly? Yes _____ ; No __√__ .
     It will be difficult for the dog to see clearly the personnel for the memory bird at the foot of the dike.

11. **Freeze:** In your opinion, will some dogs tend to "freeze" on one set of Guns? Yes __√__ ; No _____ .

12. **Major temptations:** Enter major pull and obstacles; considering type of stake, enter characteristics of this test which make it difficult.
     (1) The memory bird will appear to most entries to land on top of dike or beyond. (2) Mixed bag with dead pheasant on land: entries will be "expecting" a duck, some young derby dogs may, or at least may tend to, blink pheasant after retrieving duck. (3) Some dogs will not dive into swimming water after running a considerable distance on land through mud for second bird. (4) Some dogs will return via land (left bank).

13. **Workmanlike jobs:** What percentage of contestants do you think will do really workmanlike jobs? Estimated __25__ per cent.

14. **Failures:** In your opinion, what percentage of contestants will fail this test and have to be dropped? Estimated __50__ per cent.

15. Judges' kit of tools: Check your kit of tools. In your opinion, did the judges make effective use in this situation of available tools? Yes _____ ; No __✓__ .

16. Major errors of judges: List the major errors which you think the judges made here:

> *(1) Invited freezing on memory bird. (2) Provided poor view of Guns and birdboys for memory bird.*

17. Your test in this situation: Sketch below a test you might prefer to run at this location.

> *Objectionable as it is, I think that I would prefer to run into the wind from the dike (sketch not shown).*

18. Sport of "cussing judges": After a test is set up and you see it, you actually may have more information than the judges had when they set it up. To elaborate, assuming that the judges exercised their best judgment in setting the test, you have an operational indication of that judgment plus your own experience and know-how. Moreover, the judges of a licensed trial are under pressure; you are not. Therefore, before you "cuss 'em," demonstrate that you have better foresight. One method is as follows: Place your completed critique in an envelope; seal it; hand it to a knowledgeable but critical colleague; after the series is over, have your colleague check each item as to whether you or the judges exercised better judgment on certain points.

> Item _____ : ( ) Judges were better,   ( ) I was better.

In the course of the conduct of the test, if you hear someone in the gallery "cussing the test," ask him for his completed "Pontchippi Pre-series Critique Form." If he hasn't committed himself before the first dog ran, has he earned the right to criticize? Obviously, many damnfools "know" shortcomings and/or weaknesses of a test after 21 dogs have run it. Remember that McMahan thinks that shots must be called in advance if one expects his listeners to respect his judgment.

THE LAST BUT ONE

The author (arrow) judging the open stake with Roy J. Brinkman, First Licensed Field Trial, Atlanta Retriever Club, 1970. (Photo by and courtesy of JDO)

PROGRAM

FIRST
A.K.C. LICENSED RETRIEVER
DOG FIELD TRIAL

CALLAWAY GARDENS HUNTING PRESERVE
PINE MOUNTAIN, GEORGIA

May 8-10, 1970

ADDENDA

Throughout this book, many ideals are expressed. Oftentimes, back-up data are completely omitted; at other times only fragmentary data are presented. Failure to provide complete data reflects, for the most part, lack of space--money. Included in this addenda are selected back-up materials on the anatomy of all-age championship stakes.

To elaborate, in order to demonstrate the amount of work behind the set of assumptions put forth in this chapter (and elsewhere in this book) by the ideal judge, $\mathscr{J}$, it is worthwhile to point out that McMahan assumes that only the best judges are invited to judge national championship stakes. Moreover, he assumes that manpower, money, time, management, and other skills, plus birds and the like, are in sufficient supply to enable these judges to set up and conduct the trial the way they really desire.

Over the 5-year period 1963-1967, the (concensus) opinion of k (where k ≤ 15) top judges has been summarized in Tables 14-A-1 and 14-A-2. Note that these data generate an operational definition (in terms of what judges do, not in terms of what they say) of what should be contained in an open stake. These results (along with those shown in Table 14-A-3 and Table 14-A-4) were used to confirm the make-up of $\mathscr{J}$'s ideal stake.

Anatomy of an open stake with respect to marked (M), memory (M & M), and blind (B) retrieves.--$\mathscr{J}$ prefers a little more than one-fourth of the retrieves to be marks, about one-third to be blinds, and about four-tenths to be memory retrieves. He prefers only slightly more land retrieves than water retrieves; only rarely would he set tests containing more water retrieves than land retrieves. Ideally, although often time will not permit, $\mathscr{J}$ would like for those dogs which complete a stake that he judges to make at least 12 retrieves under his judgment. Realistically for an open stake, $\mathscr{J}$'s ideal numbers are 354--75 or 354--66, 3 marks, 5 memory birds, 4 blinds--7 retrieves on land, 5 on water, or 6 on land and 6 on water.

Comment: McMahan and his co-judge conducted such a trial in Florida, Fall, 1966, as follows: first series, triple on land; second series, triple on water; third series and fourth series combined, double on land and double blind; fifth series, double blind on water. Obviously, this is not the only way

Table 14-A-1.--Number and percentage of retrieves, by series, terrain, and type, [American] National Amateur Retriever Club Championship Trials, 1963-1967

Year	Series	Land				Water				Total (land and water)
		M	M & M	B	Total	M	M & M	B	Total	
1963	1			1	1				0	1
	2				0	1	2		3	3
	3	1	2		3				0	3
	4				0			1	1	1
	5	1	2		3				0	3
	6			2	2				0	2
	7				0	1	2		3	3
	8*		1	1	2	1			1	3
	9				0			1	1	1
	10				0	1	1	1	3	3
	Total	2	5	4	11	4	5	3	12	23
	Per cent of total retrieves	9	22	17	48	17	22	13	52	100
	Per cent of land retrieves	18	45	36	100	...	...	...	...	...
	Per cent of water retrieves	...	...	...	...	33	42	25	100	...

Per cent of total retrieves classified: M = 26;   M & M = 43;   B = 30.

*Mixed bag; blind classified as land; assumed duck retrieved first.

(Continued)

Table 14-A-1. --(Continued) Number and percentage of retrieves, by series, terrain, and type, [American] National Amateur Retriever Club Championship Trials, 1963-1967

Year	Series	Land				Water				Total (land and water)
		M	M & M	B	Total	M	M & M	B	Total	
1964	1	1	2		3				0	3
	2				0			1	1	1
	3			2	2				0	2
	4				0	1	2		3	3
	5*	1	2		3				0	3
	6**	1		2	3				0	3
	7				0	1			1	1
	8†		1		1		2		2	3
	9‡				0	1	1	2	4	4
	10	1	1	2	4				0	4
	Total	4	6	6	16	3	5	3	11	27
	Per cent of total retrieves	15	22	22	59	11	19	11	41	100
	Per cent of land retrieves	25	38	38	100	...	...	...	...	...
	Per cent of water retrieves	...	...	...	...	27	45	27	100	...

Per cent of total retrieves classified: M = 26; M & M = 41; B = 33.

* One dog walk-up.
** Plus fly-away.
† Mixed bag; assumed one duck retrieved first.
‡ Classified water somewhat arbitrarily.

(Continued)

Table 14-A-1. --(Continued) Number and percentage of retrieves, by series, terrain, and type, [American] National Amateur Retriever Club Championship Trials, 1963-1967

Year	Series	Land				Water				Total (land and water)
		M	M & M	B	Total	M	M & M	B	Total	
1965	1*		1	1	2	1			1	3
	2				0			2	2	2
	3	1		1	2				0	2
	4				0	1	2		3	3
	5	1	2		3				0	3
	6				0	1		1	2	2
	7	1	1	2	4				0	4
	8				0	1	2		3	3
	9				0			1	1	1
	10	1	2		3				0	3
	Total	4	6	4	14	4	4	4	12	26
	Per cent of total retrieves	15	23	15	54	15	15	15	46	100
	Per cent of land retrieves	29	43	29	100	...	...	...	...	...
	Per cent of water retrieves	...	...	...	...	33	33	33	100	...

Per cent of total retrieves classified: M = 31; M & M = 38; B = 31.

* Mixed bag, assumed duck retrieved first; blind involved land, water, land; hence, called land blind.

(Continued)

Table 14-A-1.--(Continued) Number and percentage of retrieves, by series, terrain, and type, [American] National Amateur Retriever Club Championship Trials, 1963-1967

Year	Series	Land				Water				Total (land and water)
		M	M & M	B	Total	M	M & M	B	Total	
1966	1	1	1		2				0	2
	2			2	2				0	2
	3				0	1	2		3	3
	4				0			1	1	1
	5	1	2		3				0	3
	6*		1	1	2	1			1	3
	7			2	2				0	2
	8				0	1	2		3	3
	9			1	1			1	1	2
	10	1	2		3				0	3
	Total	3	6	6	15	3	4	2	9	24
	Per cent of total retrieves	13	25	25	62	13	17	8	38	100
	Per cent of land retrieves	20	40	40	100	...	...	...	...	...
	Per cent of water retrieves	...	...	...	...	33	44	22	100	...

Per cent of total retrieves classified: M = 25;   M & M = 25;   M = 42;   M & M = 44;   B = 33.

* Mixed bag; assumed that duck was retrieved first.

(Continued)

Table 14-A-1.--(Concluded) Number and percentage of retrieves, by series, terrain, and type, [American] National Amateur Retriever Club Championship Trials, 1963-1967

Year	Series	Land				Water				Total (land and water)
		M	M & M	B	Total	M	M & M	B	Total	
1967	1	1	1		2				0	2
	2*				0			1	1	1
	3				0	1	2		3	3
	4				0			1	1	1
	5	1	2		3				0	3
	6			3	3				0	3
	7				0	1	2		3	3
	8				0			1	1	1
	9				0	1	2		3	3
	10	1	2	2	5				0	5
	Total	3	5	5	13	3	6	3	12	25
	Per cent of total retrieves	12	20	20	52	12	24	12	48	100
	Per cent of land retrieves	23	38	38	100	...	...	...	...	...
	Per cent of water retrieves	...	...	...	...	25	50	25	100	...

Per cent of total retrieves classified: M = 24;   M & M = 44;   B = 32.

* Reported combinations of land and water are tabulated under heading "water."

Table 14-A-2.--Number and percentage of retrieves, by terrain and type, [American] National Amateur Retriever Club Championship Trials, 1963-1967

Year	Land				Water				Total (land and water)
	M	M & M	B	Total	M	M & M	B	Total	
1963	2	5	4	11	4	5	3	12	23
1964	4	6	6	16	3	5	3	11	27
1965	4	6	4	14	4	4	4	12	26
1966	3	6	6	15	3	4	2	9	24
1967	3	5	5	13	3	6	3	12	25
Total	16	28	25	69	17	24	15	56	125
Per cent of total retrieves	13	22	20	55	14	19	12	45	100
Per cent of land retrieves	23	41	36	100	...	...	...	...	...
Per cent of water retrieves	...	...	...	...	30	43	27	100	...

Per cent of total retrieves classified: M = 26;   M & M = 42;   B = 32.

Table 14-A-3.--Number and percentage of retrieves, by series, terrain, and type, [American] National Retriever Championship Stakes, 1958-1967

Year	Series	Land				Water				Total (land and water)
		M	M & M	B	Total	M	M & M	B	Total	
1958	1	1	1		2				0	2
	2				0	1	2		3	3
	3	1		2	3				0	3
	4				0	1	1	1	3	3
	5				0			2	2	2
	6*	1	2		3				0	3
	7			1	1				0	1
	8				0	1	1	1	3	3
	9				0	1	2		3	3
	10	1	1	1	3				0	3
	Total	4	4	4	12	4	6	4	14	26
	Per cent of total retrieves	15	15	15	46	15	23	15	54	100
	Per cent of land retrieves	33	33	33	100	...	...	...	...	...
	Per cent of water retrieves	...	...	...	...	29	43	29	100	...

Per cent of total retrieves classified:　M = 31;　M & M = 38;　B = 31.

* Walk-up.

(Continued)

Table 14-A-3.--(Continued) Number and percentage of retrieves, by series, terrain, and type, [American] National Retriever Championship Stakes, 1958-1967

Year	Series	Land				Water				Total (land and water)
		M	M & M	B	Total	M	M & M	B	Total	
1959	1				0	1	2		3	3
	2			2	2				0	2
	3				0			2	2	2
	4	1	2		3				0	3
	5	1	1		2				0	2
	6				0	1	2		3	3
	7	1	1	1	3				0	3
	8				0	1		1	2	2
	9		1		1	1			1	2
	10	1*		1	2				0	2
	Total	4	5	4	13	4	4	3	11	24
	Per cent of total retrieves	17	21	17	54	17	17	12	46	100
	Per cent of land retrieves	31	38	31	100	...	...	...	...	...
	Per cent of water retrieves	...	...	...	...	36	36	27	100	...

Per cent of total retrieves classified: M = 33; M & M = 38; B = 29.

* Plus a fly-away cock pheasant; the dog saw only one fall; hence, a mark.

(Continued)

Table 14-A-3.--(Continued) Number and percentage of retrieves, by series, terrain, and type, [American] National Retriever Championship Stakes, 1958-1967

Year	Series	Land				Water				Total (land and water)
		M	M & M	B	Total	M	M & M	B	Total	
1960	1				0	1	1	1	3	3
	2	1	1		2				0	2
	3	1	1	1	3				0	3
	4				0	1		1	2	2
	5			1	1				0	1
	6				0	1	2		3	3
	7				0	1	1	1	3	3
	8				0			2	2	2
	9	1	2		3				0	3
	10	1	1		2			1	1	3
	11	1			1		1	1	2	3
	12*	1		1	2				0	2
	Total	6	5	3	14	4	5	7	16	30
	Per cent of total retrieves	20	17	10	47	13	17	23	53	100
	Per cent of land retrieves	43	36	21	100	...	...	...	...	...
	Per cent of water retrieves	...	...	...	...	25	31	44	100	...

Per cent of total retrieves classified: M = 33; M & M = 33; B = 33.

* Blind required first.

(Continued)

Table 14-A-3. --(Continued) Number and percentage of retrieves, by series, terrain, and type, [American] National Retriever Championship Stakes, 1958-1967

Year	Series	Land				Water				Total (land and water)
		M	M & M	B	Total	M	M & M	B	Total	
1961	1	1	1		2				0	2
	2				0			1	1	1
	3*				0	2	2		4	4
	4			1	1				0	1
	5	1	2		3				0	3
	6	1			1		2		2	3
	7	1		1	2				0	2
	8				0			1	1	1
	9	1	1	1	3				0	3
	10				0	1	1	1	3	3
	Total	5	4	3	12	3	5	3	11	23
	Per cent of total retrieves	22	17	13	52	13	22	13	48	100
	Per cent of land retrieves	42	33	25	100	...	...	...	...	...
	Per cent of water retrieves	...	...	...	...	27	45	27	100	...

Per cent of total retrieves classified: M = 35; M & M = 39; B = 26.

* Quadruple delayed mark.

(Continued)

Table 14-A-3. --(Continued) Number and percentage of retrieves, by series, terrain, and type, [American] National Retriever Championship Stakes, 1958-1967

Year	Series	Land				Water				Total (land and water)
		M	M & M	B	Total	M	M & M	B	Total	
1962	1*	1	1		2				0	2
	2*			2	2				0	2
	3				0	1	2		3	3
	4				0			1	1	1
	5	1	2		3				0	3
	6			1	1				0	1
	7				0	1	2		3	3
	8	1	1	1	3				0	3
	9				0			1	1	1
	10		1		1	1		1	2	3
	Total	3	5	4	12	3	4	3	10	22
	Per cent of total retrieves	14	23	18	55	14	18	14	45	100
	Per cent of land retrieves	25	42	33	100	...	...	...	...	...
	Per cent of water retrieves	...	...	...	...	30	40	30	100	...

Per cent of total retrieves classified: M = 27;   M & M = 41;   B = 32 .

* Series 1 and 2 run in conjunction with each other.

(Continued)

Table 14-A-3. --(Continued) Number and percentage of retrieves, by series, terrain, and type, [American] National Retriever Championship Stakes, 1958-1967

Year	Series	Land				Water				Total (land and water)
		M	M & M	B	Total	M	M & M	B	Total	
1963	1	1	1	1	3				0	3
	2				0	1	2		3	3
	3				0			1	1	1
	4	1		1	2				0	2
	5*	1	1		2				0	2
	6*			2	2				0	2
	7				0	1	2		3	3
	8				0			1	1	1
	9				0	1	1	1	3	3
	10	1	2	1	4				0	4
	Total	4	4	5	13	3	5	3	11	24
	Per cent of total retrieves	17	17	21	54	12	21	12	46	100
	Per cent of land retrieves	31	31	38	100	...	...	...	...	...
	Per cent of water retrieves	...	...	...	...	27	45	27	100	...

Per cent of total retrieves classified: M = 29; M & M = 38; B = 33 .

* Fifth and sixth series combined.

(Continued)

Table 14-A-3. --(Continued) Number and percentage of retrieves, by series, terrain, and type, [American] National Retriever Championship Stakes, 1958-1967

Year	Series	Land				Water				Total (land and water)
		M	M & M	B	Total	M	M & M	B	Total	
1964	1	1	1		2				0	2
	2			3	3				0	3
	3				0	1	2		3	3
	4				0			3	3	3
	5	1	2		3				0	3
	6	1	1	1	3				0	3
	7				0	2	1		3	3
	8				0			2	2	2
	9	1		1	2				0	2
	10				0	1		1	2	2
	Total	4	4	5	13	4	3	6	13	26
	Per cent of total retrieves	15	15	19	50	15	12	23	50	100
	Per cent of land retrieves	31	31	38	100	...	...	...	...	...
	Per cent of water retrieves	...	...	...	...	31	23	46	100	...

Per cent of total retrieves classified: M = 31; M & M = 27; B = 42.

(Continued)

Table 14-A-3.--(Continued) Number and percentage of retrieves, by series, terrain, and type, [American] National Retriever Championship Stakes, 1958-1967

Year	Series	Land				Water				Total (land and water)
		M	M & M	B	Total	M	M & M	B	Total	
1965	1	1	1		2				0	2
	2			1	1				0	1
	3*				0	1	2		3	3
	4*				0			1	1	1
	5	1	1		2				0	2
	6				0			3	3	3
	7**	1	1	1	3				0	3
	8			3	3				0	3
	9	1	2		3				0	3
	10				0	1	2		3	3
	Total	4	5	5	14	2	4	4	10	24
	Per cent of total retrieves	17	21	21	58	8	17	17	42	100
	Per cent of land retrieves	29	36	36	100	...	...	...	...	...
	Per cent of water retrieves	...	...	...	...	20	40	40	100	...

Per cent of total retrieves classified: M = 25; M & M = 38; B = 38.

* Combined, blind by invitation.
** Could have been classified as water (?).

(Continued)

Table 14-A-3.--(Continued) Number and percentage of retrieves, by series, terrain, and type, [American] National Retriever Championship Stakes, 1958-1967

Year	Series	Land				Water				Total (land and water)
		M	M & M	B	Total	M	M & M	B	Total	
1966	1	1	1		2				0	2
	2			2	2				0	2
	3				0	1	2		3	3
	4				0			1	1	1
	5	1	2		3				0	3
	6				0	1	2		3	3
	7			1	1				0	1
	8				0			1	1	1
	9	1	2		3	1	2		3	3
	10				3				0	3
	Total	3	5	3	11	3	6	2	11	22
	Per cent of total retrieves	14	23	14	50	14	27	9	50	100
	Per cent of land retrieves	27	45	27	100	...	...	...	...	...
	Per cent of water retrieves	...	...	...	...	27	55	18	100	...

Per cent of total retrieves classified: M = 27;   M & M = 50;   B = 23.

(Continued)

Table 14-A-3. --(Concluded) Number and percentage of retrieves, by series, terrain, and type, [American] National Retriever Championship Stakes, 1958-1967

Year	Series	Land				Water				Total (land and water)
		M	M & M	B	Total	M	M & M	B	Total	
1967	1	1	1		2				0	2
	2			2	2				0	2
	3		1		1			2	2	3
	4				0	1			1	1
	5	1	2		3				0	3
	6				0			2	2	2
	7	1		1	2				0	2
	8				0		1		1	1
	9				0	1	2		3	3
	10	1	2	1	4				0	4
	Total	4	6	4	14	2	3	4	9	23
	Per cent of total retrieves	17	26	17	61	9	13	17	39	100
	Per cent of land retrieves	29	43	29	100	...	...	...	...	...
	Per cent of water retrieves	...	...	...	...	22	33	44	100	...

Per cent of total retrieves classified: M = 26; M & M = 39; B = 35.

Table 14-A-4. --Number and percentage of retrieves, by terrain and type, [American] National Championship Stakes, 1958-1967

Year	Land				Water				Total (land and water)
	M	M & M	B	Total	M	M & M	B	Total	
1958	4	4	4	12	4	6	4	14	26
1959	4	5	4	13	4	4	3	11	24
1960*	6	5	3	14	4	5	7	16	30
1961	5	4	3	12	3	5	3	11	23
1962	3	5	4	12	3	4	3	10	22
1963	4	4	5	13	3	5	3	11	24
1964	4	4	5	13	4	3	6	13	26
1965	4	5	5	14	2	4	4	10	24
1966	3	5	3	11	3	6	2	11	22
1967	4	6	4	14	2	3	4	9	23
Total	41	47	40	128	32	45	39	116	244
Per cent of total retrieves	17	19	16	52	13	18	16	48	100
Per cent of land retrieves	32	37	31	100	...	...	...	...	...
Per cent of water retrieves	...	...	...	...	28	39	34	100	...
Per cent of total retrieves classified: M = 30; M & M = 38; B = 32.									

* Twelve series.

Note: Based on Table 14-A-3.

that ideal requirements for an open stake can be satisfied.

Number and percentage of callbacks are presented in Table 14-A-5 for 10 national championship stakes (1958-1967), and in Table 14-A-6 for 5 national amateur championship stakes (1963-1967).

[Source of the data in Tables 14-A-1 through 14-A-6 is selected issues of *(Retriever) Field Trial News*.]

If you're not proud of it, *then* don't peddle it!

Table 14-A-5. --Observed number and percentage of starters surviving each of nine series, [American] National Retriever Championship Stakes, 1958-1967

Year	Type of data	Starters	Called back for series								
			2	3	4	5	6	7	8	9	10
1958	(Number)	(46)	(46)	(42)	(42)	(26)	(17)	(16)	(12)	(12)	(12)
	Per cent of starters	...	100	91	91	57	37	35	26	26	26
1959	(Number)	(44)	(44)	(44)	(42)	(28)	(24)	(17)	(13)	(9)	(6)
	Per cent of starters	...	100	100	95	64	55	39	30	20	14
1960*	(Number)	(55)	(54)	(46)	(40)	(40)	(24)	(18)	(13)	(10)	(8)
	Per cent of starters	...	98	84	73	73	44	33	24	18	15
1961	(Number)	(50)	(50)	(41)	(39)	(31)	(26)	(19)	(19)	(10)	(8)
	Per cent of starters	...	100	82	78	62	52	38	38	20	16
1962	(Number)	(56)	(55)	(51)	(50)	(41)	(36)	(31)	(10)	(9)	(8)
	Per cent of starters	...	98	91	89	73	64	55	18	16	14
1963	(Number)	(57)	(55)	(45)	(36)	(30)	(30)	(21)	(20)	(14)	(9)
	Per cent of starters	...	96	79	63	53	53	37	35	25	16

* In 1960, 12 series were conducted; 6 back (11 per cent) for series 11, 4 back (7 per cent) for series 12.

(Continued)

Table 14-A-5.--(Concluded) Observed number and percentage of starters surviving each of nine series, [American] National Retriever Championship Stakes, 1958-1967

Year	Type of data	Starters	Called back for series								
			2	3	4	5	6	7	8	9	10
1964	(Number)	(59)	(57)	(48)	(42)	(27)	(19)	(15)	(14)	(8)	(7)
	Per cent of starters	...	97	81	71	46	32	25	24	14	12
1965	(Number)	(45)	(43)	(43)	(36)	(17)	(16)	(14)	(12)	(12)	(9)
	Per cent of starters	...	96	96	80	38	36	31	27	27	20
1966	(Number)	(57)	(57)	(51)	(49)	(34)	(23)	(20)	(15)	(9)	(8)
	Per cent of starters	...	100	89	86	60	40	35	26	16	14
1967	(Number)	(54)	(52)	(49)	(37)	(33)	(25)	(17)	(17)	(11)	(11)
	Per cent of starters	...	96	91	69	61	46	31	31	20	20
Total	(Number)	(523)	(513)	(460)	(413)	(307)	(240)	(188)	(145)	(104)	(86)
	Per cent of starters	...	98	88	79	59	46	36	28	20	16
Range of percentages		...	96-100	79-100	63-95	38-73	32-64	25-55	18-38	14-27	12-26

Table 14-A-6.--Observed number and percentage of starters surviving each of nine series and estimated true survival rates, [American] National Amateur Retriever Club Championship Trials, 1963-1967

Year	Type of data	Starters	Called back for series								
			2	3	4	5	6	7	8	9	10
1963	(Number)	(58)	(57)	(57)	(38)	(33)	(28)	(25)	(18)	(14)	(10)
	Per cent of starters	...	98	98	66	57	48	43	31	24	17
1964	(Number)	(51)	(46)	(46)	(46)	(30)	(28)	(21)	(17)	(12)	(7)
	Per cent of starters	...	90	90	90	59	55	41	33	24	14
1965	(Number)	(55)	(39)	(33)	(28)	(25)	(19)	(17)	(11)	(9)	(7)
	Per cent of starters	...	71	60	51	45	35	31	20	16	13
1966	(Number)	(62)	(61)	(60)	(57)	(48)	(29)	(19)	(15)	(10)	(10)
	Per cent of starters	...	98	97	92	77	47	31	24	16	16
1967	(Number)	(60)	(55)	(44)	(31)	(27)	(23)	(16)	(14)	(12)	(9)
	Per cent of starters	...	92	73	52	45	38	27	23	20	15
Total	(Number)	(286)	(258)	(240)	(200)	(163)	(127)	(98)	(75)	(57)	(43)
	Per cent of starters	...	90	84	70	57	44	34	26	20	15
Range of percentages		...	71-98	60-98	51-92	45-77	35-55	27-43	20-33	16-24	13-17

CHAPTER FIFTEEN

CONFERENCES FOR JUDGES

Throughout this book, much material has been presented that might be adapted for profitable use at judging clinics. I shall not repeat any of that material in this chapter, but I shall attempt instead to add a few new action items, and suggest other subject-matter that might be worthwhile considering.

It seems to me that judging conferences tend to attract those RE's already "committed" rather than the "uncommitted or unconverted." Hence, one might justifiably ask: Judging conferences for what? The answer to the question posed would seem obvious: The aim of judging clinics is to improve the judging process in retriever field trials. This answer appears incomplete, however, without the next question: What parts of the judging process need improvement? Even though there may be no concensus here, most judges would probably agree that retriever field trial judging calls for an expert, explicitly, one who knows how to evaluate a retriever's performance in the field.

Purpose

I have never seen nor heard the purpose of a "retriever conference" explicitly stated. As indicated above, I assume that a major purpose is to improve the "state of the art of judging retrievers in field trials." I assume an ultimate purpose is to benefit the sport by creating more qualified judges. Moreover, I suppose that such conferences provide opportunities for one to meet other people who are interested in judging; hence, I assume that most of us hope that these conferences will be enthusiastic gatherings which are not only informative, but also enjoyable to those who thirst for knowledge concerning judging. Once a conference is institutionalized, it amounts to an "annual get-together."

Methods

Again, never have I heard the "method of instruction" explicitly outlined. It seems to me that the underlying method is one of teaching by means of airing differences of opinions. The foregoing notwithstanding, I suppose the method could be labelled eclectic, in that theories, opinions, methods, solutions vary from person to person depending on who is putting them forward. At least, a judging conference is a great two days for exercising the jaws, and ideas do get aired. At each conference, some "contributors" seem to have so little to offer by way of sound argument and they are so patently off-base as to be absurd; in short, "they talk through their hats." In fact, in some conferences, innumerable pointless utterances are presented, and from time to time I fear that the conference is going to degenerate into a symposium of hot air.

It is my opinion that speakers in such conferences should distinguish clearly among (1) what they know or is known, (2) what they do not know, and (3) their opinions. Many speakers seem unwilling to admit that they do not know or that they really have not formulated a firm opinion on a certain topic. Instead, they tend to be cagey about committing themselves. Moreover, many participants attempt to discuss pros and cons of topics which had best be left alone.

Certain chapters in this book are presented as reliable knowledge. Until some scientist demonstrates that this material does not belong in that category, it could be considered as being known. Furthermore, many aspects of this book can be presented in much simpler form when cut down to "small doses." Certain aspects of the color-book and the field trial procedures are unambiguously clear. Furthermore, it is obvious that experience has given us much other knowledge for which there can be little doubt.

In a judges' conference, one would expect matters to be treated seriously, essential facts presented when available, and reasonable tolerance brought to bear on all matters. There is no place for cheap jibes about, say, what happened to one handler and his entry. Those participants of ill-informed or small mind who comment out of a blind desire for recognition should be "handled" courteously by a strong chairman and urged in private to take a dispassionate look at themselves.

Planning

For a retriever judging conference, one needs a planner of infinite skill. Good organization, well-chosen panels selected far ahead of time, panels assigned a specific objective, considerable exchange of information before the conference by panel members, carefully prepared (and planted) questions for use in case the audience does not evoke good responses from panels, all contribute to an exchange of views which should lead to greater understanding and uniformity in judging retriever trials.

If one sees misspelling and misprints in the program, the probability is high that the conference is poorly planned, because obviously attention has not been paid to details. If planning is done well, no one seems to notice; if planning is done poorly, it is conspicuous by its absence.

Speculations. -- One could consider utilizing "university centers of continuing education" for conferences for retriever judges. Use could be made of their know-how, their recording facilities, and the like. Moreover, they could serve as temporary institutionalized repositories of information generated at such conferences. Both the tried and the trying need access to materials before the conference begins; after all, one of the unique characteristics of man is that he can pass on information from one generation to the next--from the past. Each generation does not have to start from scratch. Why should each generation of judges not be able to stand on the shoulders of more experienced judges?

At these university centers of continuing education, with a little forethought, use could be made of computer assisted instruction. Even at this writing (1967), lectures, drills, examinations, problem situations, all can be administered by means of computers. Moreover, the student judge can be praised or reprimanded immediately. In short, the "what if ..." game can be exploited; a student judge can be put under pressure and allowed to judge a simulated trial, where paths to the fall, lines to the blind, breaking, ... , and the like, can be displayed on "screens" and/or typewriter terminals. The judge's performance can be evaluated in dollars and cents in terms of the influence of his errors on the expenses of a trainer and/or owner as well as in terms of critical comments and even derogatory remarks. In short, he can learn some aspects (only some) of judging in a situation where he doesn't "hurt anybody." (See 1970 PJ*J, page 17 .)

Justification and defense. -- Judging conferences could be planned and conducted to supply some "logic for" and "explanations of" judging procedures, not material to avoid criticism. After analyzing the contents of several judging conferences (so-called "content-analysis"), I am convinced that much subject-matter discussed is influenced by "fear of criticism" or "how do I (as judge) explain ... ." Even a statement in our "trade journal" several years ago indicated that the editor thought material presented in judging clinics was so controversial that he would not print the findings. I must assume that he too valued highly the "social approval" of the field trial fraternity. In the face of such convention, how did I dare to write the foregoing fourteen chapters and now Chapter Fifteen?

I faced squarely up to this problem on at least two occasions, the first when I decided to judge. In short, I explicitly decided that all I wanted from the rank and file member of the field trial fraternity was respect, earned respect. Where retriever competition was involved, by definition of the situation, social approval had to be of little import when I accepted the role of judge. I faced up to the problem a second time when I decided to publish this book. In short, I intended to plow

Her Majesty the Queen at the Retriever Trials, Balmoral, October 7 and 8, 1965. Her Majesty was photographed with the Hon. Margaret Forbes-Semphill, President of the Scottish Gun Dog Association. Photographed by Alex C. Cowper; courtesy Alex C. Cowper. Courtesy also Shooting Times and Country Magazine.

A general view of The Royal Kennels at Sandringham. (Photographed with permission of Her Majesty the Queen by Peter Moxon; photograph provided by Peter Moxon with special permission of Her Majesty the Queen.)

new ground where others feared to tread; there was no compulsion on my part for admiration from the group, but I did covet the respect of selected individuals who had earned my respect--individuals who would judge (exercise judgment) and let criticism and/or admiration be mere by-products of the process.

   Summing up: Critical analysis, yes; defense against criticism, no.

LITERATURE ON JUDGING

It seems to me that judging conferences could serve a useful purpose by providing guidance to the literature on judging. Throughout this book, some basic principles of exercising judgment have been outlined. Many of these principles have been treated many times in man's writings, from the philosophical point of view to the practical. The German philosopher, Immanuel Kant (1724-1804), even wrote a critique of judgment.

Material which is directly applicable to judging American retriever trials is not easy to locate. If one consults a card catalog in a large public library under such topics as judging, judgment, and judges, what will he expect to find? Undoubtedly, he will find a variety of publications on such topics as clinical and social thought, courts, ethics, ... , lonely men, judicial process, judicial statistics, justice, lawyers, psychology of thought and judgment, and other topics. One might even find books on judging under such headings as the following: architectural design, art, automotive design, beauty contests, beef cattle, decorations of various sorts, dog shows, essay contests, gardens, floats, flower shows, hair styles, horses, photography, pigeon shows, poultry shows, science exhibits, and other topics.

Even though the judging of American retriever field trials is a specialized topic, there exists some literature on judging field trials for various other breeds of dogs. Moreover, there are other types of contests in which judging has some common problems with the retriever game, e.g., boxing bouts, dancing contests of various sorts, diving contests, skating (to include ice) contests, music contests of various sorts, and more.

Reading Course

Before a retriever enthusiast attends his first judging conference, I think that he should pursue a course in reading about dogs, the field trial game, and judging in general. I think it must be mandatory that the material he covers should have been published before he became an active participant in the retriever field trial game.

Suppose a person became active in the retriever field trial game shortly before 1960. It seems to me that he should explore writings on other breeds and trials for other breeds (and groups), say, other sporting dogs, hounds, working dogs, published prior to 1960. I am assuming, naturally, that this person will explore current literature as well.

TOPICS

Topics to be discussed at judging conferences need to be selected with care; in particular, they ought to be relevant to the role of judge of licensed American retriever field trials. A topic may be of vital interest to each of us as citizen, hunter, ... , wildfowler, ... , clay pigeon shooter, and yet be more appropriately discussed and acted upon at the club level; otherwise, we may dissipate the time allotted to judging conferences.

Topics that might be useful at a judging conference can be found in many publications. As a mere suggestion, selected references are given to *American Field* as follows:

1. M. C. Jennings, "Bird Dog Handlers' Golf Championship and Seminar," Vol. CLXL, No. 27 (July 6, 1968).

2. W. Ray Shenk, "Flash Points," Vol. CLXL, No. 29 (July 20, 1968).

3. T. R. Harvey, "Championship Trends," Vol. CLXL, No. 33 (August 17, 1968).

4. Doyess D. Boyett, "Oklahoma Field Trial Seminar," Vol. CLXL, No. 35 (August 31, 1968).

5. Tom McNeal, "Judges--Today's Iron Men," Vol. CLXL, No. 36 (September 7, 1968).

6. Timely Thoughts, "Appreciate the Judge's Role," Vol. CLXL, No. 37 (September 14, 1968).

7. Timely Thoughts, "Anent Withholding Placements," Vol. CLXL, No. 47 (November 23, 1968).

8. A Guest Editorial: "Role of the Amateur Field Trial Clubs of America," by Dr. W. H. McCall, President, Vol. CLXLI, No. 4 (January 25, 1969).

9. T. R. Harvey, "The All-Age and Shooting Dog Myths," Vol. CLXLI, No. 34 (August 23, 1969).

10. Carl P. Wood, "The Preferred American Gun Dog," Vol. CLXLI, No. 41 (October 11, 1969).

11. Timely Thoughts, " 'First Time,' " Vol. CLXLI, No. 43 (October 25, 1969).

In order to illustrate the type of material which might be worthwhile calling to the attention of participants at judging conferences, I have reproduced selected excerpts from the literature.

Excerpt Number One

This first excerpt concerns my first-love, bird dogs. Why can't we motivate more of our distinguished retriever trainers to make their opinions matters of record? [*Aside:* Where could their thoughts be published if they were willing to write them?]

[Reproduced from *American Field*, April 13, 1968, page 444 (by kind permission of the publisher).]

PERFORMANCE IN OPEN CHAMPIONSHIPS

Highest Standards Essential for
Breed Improvement

By John S. Gates

First of all, let me assure the reader that I must feel deeply about the matter to attempt to put my thoughts into words. Conversation comes easy, but when one tries to put into writing his ideas--well, that's something else again. I make no pretense of being a writer, but do feel that there is something I might contribute toward a clear-cut definition of what should be looked for in open field trial championship performance.

What prompted me to take pen in hand at this time is no decision by any judge or set of judges in any field trial; it is because there have been articles and considerable talk about handling technique, about showing dogs to judges, about what judges should be looking for ... and it is my sole purpose to emphasize that dog and handler are a team and that the ideal field trial performance is an exhibition that brings out brilliantly all the superior qualities of the brainy, bold, tireless bird dog.

My credentials are not writing skill, but the fact that I have handled more dogs to more championships than any other professional in the records of field trials. This is not said boastfully, but to lend credibility to the fact that I might know a little something about championship performance. You hear so much about the credibility gap in national administration affairs, that it seemed worthwhile to mention my background and experience in making bold to write about what standards are essential in open field trial championship performance if it is our hope to continue the improvement of the bird dog breeds.

I hold no brief for a handler who rides wildly and constantly over a course. Nor do I want to see glorified a dog to which handling response is foreign to his nature. But there has been such a trend to shooting dogs in the last decade that there is the worry that the great principles on which field trials were built may be lost if all of us do not think soundly on the purposes of field trials.

I remember reading the late Dr. William A. Bruette's article on "The Real Purpose of Field Trials," and it made such an impression on me that I have referred to it frequently.

Basically, the real purpose of bird dog trials is improvement of the pointing breeds, the elevation of bird dog performance in the hunting field. There are other objectives also, but some of the latter will cause novices, particularly those with only shooting dog experience, to be confused by particular standards applied to exhibitions in field trial competitions. Too many bird shooters do not seem to have the right conception of the purpose of field trials.

To revert to Dr. Bruette, he stressed that field trials were not instituted for the purpose of bringing to the front a dog or a class of dogs eminently suited to the wants of the average gunner whose primary object in using a dog afield is to swell the game bag, regardless of the manner in which the dog performs, but rather for the purpose of bringing to the notice of the public a class of performers best suited to perpetuate the most desirable qualities possessed by the high-class field trial dog.

These dogs are not at all times the most desirable to shoot over, for the reason that their individuality is such that it cannot be dominated by the handler's use of "foot-rule" methods whereby a dog of subservient temperament is forced to range so many yards to the front or to the right or left without consulting his inclination or judgment. In some cases, a high-class field trial performer may run "too big," so great is his ambition to find birds, and while it is by no means the wish to encourage the development of too-wide running, nevertheless it is certain that more harm will attend breeding from sires of soft, deferential dispositions than will come from the use of those whose independence is so great that it is with some difficulty they are persuaded to work to the gun in a manner satisfactory to the average sportsman. The best field trial dogs, given the proper preparation and type of work, are actually the best shooting dogs. But you can't pick the really brilliant individuals on the basis of shooting dog performance.

Those who have had the greatest success with breeding say that strong individuality and the possession of prepotent bloodlines are the basic requirements in a successful sire, and 'tis known that the really and brilliant field trial champions have been instrumental in perpetuating and improving the qualities most desired in the high-class field dogs. Breeders look for sires who have tremendous nervous energy and virility, independence of spirit and endless determination to hunt for and find birds.

The high-class field trial performer, in order to show his natural qualities to the best advantage, is developed and intensified to the highest degree, which is something different than making an ordinary shooting dog subservient to the gun. Handlers who have had the most success in developing field trial champions, virtually allow these dogs to train themselves, applying only such restrictions as are necessary in steadying of a dog on point and back, but allow the dog almost absolute freedom in other respects so that he is not hampered in the development of his natural qualities (which are all that can be perpetuated).

By the use of proper methods in training, any dog which possesses mentality of a high order (which is one of the prime requisites of the ideal field trial performer) can be developed or subjugated in a manner which will make him eminently suited for a gentleman's shooting dog. But in order to develop a dog's natural qualities to the utmost, so that they may be exhibited in trials and thus afford the breeder opportunities to make intelligent selections of the highest class individuals, a special course of training is instituted which, while it accomplishes its purpose in admirable fashion, does not render the dog fit for use in general shooting until he has undergone further training.

Major circuit field trials are not intended to be trials for shooting dogs nor for the wild running dog, heedless of handling, which displays little brains. Placing either harms the interests of bird dogs.

Let us mold our major championships so that only the most fit and finest compete. These are not for shooting dogs, but if too much stress is put on mere pointing of game, you find this type entered. It makes the starting fields too large, causes the trials to take too long for completion, literally starves a handler because of the amount of time that must be consumed and the number of dogs that must be carried.

We want a dog that will run, but a dog that will use his country and cut it up to hit birdy objectives, a dog that may reach out boldly on a searching cast, but one that will come around. There will be times when a handler has to ride, not to curb the going inclinations of the dog or herd him around, but to know which direction the dog's hunting may head so that in case he does find birds, he can be found more readily. There will be times, also, when a judge has to ride up to watch a dog's pattern or to be able to witness a dog's manner of going to game. Different situations call for different techniques; you cannot generalize. The handler's role is to enable his dog to display his natural qualities to fullest advantage and there has never been a successful trainer of a topflight performer who did not at some time during a field trial performance feel nervous--*you always do*--and it intensifies your desire to be as helpful as possible to the dog.

Let me say again, it is a handler's job to know his dog, his predispositions, his capabilities ... and the expert's training methods are designed to show a dog's qualities to best advantage. The fact that a hard driving dog has a consuming desire to find game is best portrayed by allowing the exercise of the dog's independence, and the experienced handler rides alertly where conditions require it. The class performer's initiative, his ambitious range, his spirited search and his courage in completing casts of thrilling proportions cannot fail to set one's pulse to pounding. It builds tension when you are witnessing such a grand opera performance, as Dr. T. Benton King was accustomed to describing it. One doesn't sit back complacently. When a reporter says the galleryites were riding high in the saddle it describes the reaction to a spectacular effort, or to use a favorite word of reporters, a scintillating race. The adrenalin begins to flow faster and reflexes are quickened also. If a bird dog fan isn't moved by such an exhibition, he has no real appreciation of class.

When a dog reaches out into birdy country, a handler likes to know the dog's direction. In the 1968 Free-for-All, a finalist was lost and found on point more than an hour later in the same neighborhood where he was headed when last seen. Think how a handler feels when his dog *on point* is not found in time? If the terrain is rolling or hilly, alert forwarding riding is an intelligent part of proper handling procedure. It is not something to be indulged in constantly-- none of us condone that--but where it may enhance the excellence of a dog's pattern, who can be critical of it? Like Jim Avent used to say, the time to turn a dog is when he nears the end of his cast to a birdy objective, and if the handler is under a hill at such time, precious minutes can be lost. All of this is not contrary to Clyde Morton's recommendations; it is said merely to describe approved technique that Clyde himself used with such great success.

There have been many great sportsmen in field trials who have been outstanding judges and their contributions have been of greatest importance in setting performance standards. They never overemphasized the mere pointing of game. They were quick to reward the bold, brilliant dog for meritorious bird work. It would serve no useful purpose to include names, but the sport owes a debt of gratitude to these for the enhancement of bird dog excellence.

It might be well for me to list the qualities looked for in the high-class field trial dog. All of the natural qualifications, to be sure, such as speed, range, intelligence and stamina. A dog must have the instinct to hunt and the desire to find birds. A good nose is of great importance, able to detect the faintest scent and to locate game quickly and accurately. Pointing is instinctive, and character, intensity, style and loftiness on point are essential, as well as stanchness. A champion is expected to have bird sense, wisdom which enables him to select likely objectives and to pattern the course intelligently for greatest effectiveness. His pace and his range should be adaptable--in a sense adjusted to the terrain and type of cover, but always on the ambitious side reflecting the capacities of the performer, ever conscious of his handler but not dependent on him to take the dog places to hunt. A dog should have a strong constitution, and imperturbability also, an ability to orient himself quickly, any amount of stamina and highest courage in facing all sorts of cover or conditions. Carl McKinney, the colored retainer on the Ames Plantation who worked for years with James M. Avent, used to say the most important quality of a field trial dog was that he had to be nervy, and Carl meant by that ambition, nervous energy, courage--in a word, gameness, for that's what keeps a dog working and trying and doing, still reaching out when another is looking to be picked up.

The class bird dog in open championship competition should show great speed and cover a large amount of country ... and when he does this, the handler can't be dilatory or sluggish in his actions. What some refer to as mental telepathy enters the picture, for there is no doubting the records--handlers with the greatest intelligence, alertness and general know-how have developed the most champions. No one would say that Clyde Morton was a handler to sit calmly on his horse--he got nervous like the rest of us--but his energies were always directed toward assisting his dog and toward showing the dog's superior qualifications. He never rode out merely for the sake of riding fast; it was always to accomplish something, and in this sense that is what a handler is supposed to do. When a dog is staying in front in flashy form, the handler has merely to keep him in sight and may ride comfortably with the judges and field trial party, but when the ambitious performer reaches over yonder hill and sights a likely objective far beyond, and possesses the initiative, independence and courage to go to it, it is the duty of the handler to keep contact with his dog, a dog which if he does not find game will come around, but if he does point, the handler wants to have some idea of where to look. Ed Farrior, Dewey English and others did not hesitate to ride and handle aggressively when circumstances dictated such.

Some of our greatest sires, both pointers and setters, would never have been heard of if a wise handler had not noted the brilliant class of the dog, and applied training methods and handling technique so that the natural qualifications of the individual were brought to the attention of breeders.

It is of the utmost significance that in our open field trial championship stakes judges apply the highest standards to performance, not just a dog with nice speed, range and style that handles easily, but the brilliant individual, exuding class, showing the intensified qualities of the prepotent sire. For unless such dogs are developed by handlers and shown by them, and selected by wise, experienced judges, breed improvement will grind to a halt because of commonplace "ideal shooting dogs."

Excerpt Number Two

To illustrate that retriever enthusiasts do not have a monopoly on judging problems, some of the criticisms, problems, and complaints of exhibitors and judges of livestock are presented.

[Reproduced from *The Field*, May 25, 1967, page 954 (by kind permission of the editor).]

JUDGING THE SHOW JUDGES

By Ralph Whitlock

How those in the hot spot in the livestock rings come to be there

One might think that refereeing a friendly football match is the only activity to approach show judging as a passport to unpopularity. Hear what uncomfortable words are said about the adjudicators:

No. I'm not entering any of my cattle in the Barsetshire Show this year. Old Dodderby is judging. He's 85 if he's a day, and he was set in his views about the

breed when he was 40.

Did you notice the inter-breed champion was lame? Still, he belonged to the judge's own breed, so what can you expect?

No, the main ring is not vacant yet. Old Dragge is still judging cattle there, though he's half an hour behind schedule already.

No, I didn't agree with the judge's placings at all, but that isn't to be wondered at. He doesn't give himself time to do the job properly. He was through the entire list in less than an hour.

Yes, we know that he isn't the best judge of the breed, but he was the only one we could get at this late date. We tried six others, and three of them never even replied.

Where the awards for Classes 8 to 10 are, heaven alone knows. The judge has gone wandering off with the cards in his pocket.

Then there are those who think that in livestock classes records count for everything and conformation nothing, and those who consider there is too much paper. Judging, indeed, appears the most thankless task under the summer sun. Yet standards there must be. Someone must set them and match the parading beasts against them, and every year the job is done.

There are at least 60 major summer agricultural shows and innumerable lesser ones. Some leading breeds of livestock stage several classes at the more important shows. For all contests judges are found and, despite such criticism, their work meets with general satisfaction. Though all appreciate the honour of judging at a big show, many are also happy to assist smaller shows free of charge.

Two authorities are concerned in the appointment of livestock judges. One is the council of the society staging the show, the other the council of the breed society whose animals are being judged.

The first move lies with the breed society, which has the task of guiding the development of the breed and ensuring that standards are maintained. Each breed society prepares a list of approved judges, and this is sent to any show society asking for it. A few breed societies prefer to nominate the judges for more important events, but most show societies insist on making their own selection.

*   *   *

Among judges in the major livestock classes, farmers and breeders predominate. In the dairy cattle classes they are supreme, and rightly so. Most beef cattle judges are also breeders, with a tendency towards the country estate owner rather than the strictly commercial farmer. Auctioneers and dealers sometimes appear in the lists.

Sheep classes are judged almost exclusively by farmers, who are usually men with mud on their boots. With pigs, however, the customer is more frequently represented. The occasional butcher interposes. In carcase classes, breeders retire into a minority. Managers of bacon and meat factories, Ministry officials and scientists, and Pig Industry Development Authority officers come into their own.

Heavy horses, though now few, are generally judged by breeders, but riding horses are the province of country gentry, with retired colonels and majors featuring prominently and ladies well to the fore. In the Suffolk Show last year three of the hunter judges were Masters of Hounds. Masculine preponderance is challenged in many pony classes, though the trend is balanced in some breeds of native ponies, where tough old mountain farmers still cast their practised eye over the contestants.

For the judges of lesser categories of livestock, we move into city streets. This is because the multimillion pound poultry industry with its vast intensive units is remote from the poultry which appear at shows. Shows remain chiefly the domain of the poultry, pigeon and rabbit fanciers, not of commercial tycoons, and the experts are men with years of experience in breeding. As for goats, the policy is to try to get judges from as far away as possible.

The principle of selecting judges from lists provided by breed societies has its difficulties. Most larger show societies have on their judges' selection committee a member of each of the major breed societies. Smaller shows, lacking this advantage, are presented with lists of up to 200 names. Some inevitably include dead wood, older men who retired from breeding 10 or 20 years previously and still judge by standards operative then--not that old judges are necessarily bad. Experience is invaluable.

For smaller show societies, an obvious solution is to select someone well known. With justification, they argue that advertising a popular judge who has appeared at the Royal will bring in extra entries. But, if a judge obliges too freely, he may find himself at several shows in the same district where often he will see the same animals. Naturally, the losers at the first show think it hardly worth while to attend the others, which thus experience a drop in entries. Recently show societies, to secure the services of the most popular judges, have been issuing invitations several years in advance. This competition will continue as long as show societies make direct contact with judges.

As a recruiting experiment, the pairing of a young judge with an older one in class and championship judging at shows has given rise to much controversy. Some judges, who have an altruistic interest in the future of their breed, take endless trouble in coaching the young man; others have no patience with the arrangement. In general, the judging of the senior judge counts, while the junior is merely invited to mark his card privately, so that his assessment of the animals can be compared with the senior's. Whatever the honours attached to their services, most judges operate at some cost to themselves, even if only in time and inconvenience. The breeds and shows owe them a great debt.

Judges also have their problems and complaints in the show ring. Let us conclude with some uncomfortable words from their side:

I got into trouble for consulting the show catalogue when judging in the ring. Someone objected that I was supposed to be judging 'the best of the day,' not taking into account past performances. But I had not been given any detailed instructions, and the catalogue was the only place where I could find the necessary information.

When I finished my judging the steward was missing and so I had to take my cards back to the awards secretary myself. On the way I met and talked with friends, with the result that the awards secretary worked himself up to a fine state thinking the lists were lost.

At some inconvenience I started early and arrived at the showground at nine o'clock, as originally advised, only to find that my judging had been postponed till 11.

After having been held up in traffic, I needed half an hour to find the secretary's tent, no-one having bothered to send me a plan of the showground. So, I was late in starting my judging.

When I judged at Marlshire County Show, the show society paid my wife's hotel expenses as well as mine and provided her with meals on the ground and a grandstand ticket. At Chalkshire County Show in the following year, I had to pay not only my wife's hotel bill but even for her admission to the showground.

At Marlshire I was invited to meet the Press and give them my comments. At Chalkshire I was reprimanded for talking to them.

Why should I hurry over my judging of these beautiful animals just in order to clear the ring for an Army circus?

Why does the rain always bucket down when I judge at Barsetshire?

So the compliments are tossed to and fro, and harassed secretaries try to soothe ruffled feelings. Yet in this, as in other contexts, the show goes on. Though all, from breed societies to show secretaries to judges to stewards, are convinced that there is still vast room for improvement, they never stop trying. The offices are filled, the classes are judged, the standards maintained, and both breed and show societies are encouraged to plan for next year.

Excerpts Three and Four

The following letter appeared in the October 28, 1965, issue of *Shooting Times and Country Magazine* (reproduced by kind permission of the publisher):

SCORING AT FIELD TRIAL

■ □ Sir, --Can any one enlighten me on the rules and regulations used in field trials for Labrador retrievers and also the method of awarding points?

I have attended a number of trials this season as a spectator and I have been amazed to see dogs which have been slow, showing no interest and failing to retrieve a number of birds, finishing well up in the top scores, many of them being placed in the first three. On the other hand, dogs which have been stylish, fast and making some excellent retrieves on runners, perhaps failing on one bird only, have been awarded low scores and in many cases put out of the trial halfway through the day.

MYSTIFIED,
South Yorks.

This letter is referenced in the following article which is reproduced to help describe a British retriever field trial as well as to provide material for discussion. The article is reproduced by permission of the author, Mr. P. R. A. Moxon, and the publishers of the official organ of the Wildfowlers' Association of Great Britain and Ireland and the Clay Pigeon Shooting Association.

PITY THE POOR JUDGE!

Like "MYSTIFIED," whose letter was published in issue October 28, many spectators (and sometimes competitors) are often puzzled by the apparently obscure decisions of field trial judges, and when the awards are announced at the end of a stake find that their own forecasts as regards placement were miles out. This leads to a lot of bitter criticism from the uninformed but, it must be admitted, is sometimes justified on those rare occasions when judges have slipped up (and no judge is infallible), or, even more rarely, when one or more of the judges is inexperienced or biased. Let there be no mistake about it, judging field trials for any breed of gundog is not an easy task, but is fraught with pitfalls for the unwary and calls for not only a sound knowledge of the requirements of a gundog, but of the various Kennel Club rules and regulations governing field trials, as well as the valuable guide to judges issued by that body. Indeed, most experienced triallers would far prefer to run a dog than to judge, although it is always considered a compliment to be asked to adjudicate and it is churlish to refuse without good reason. Trial judges require powers of concentration, tact, diplomacy and a sense of humour if they are to be successful, as the vast majority undoubtedly are. A fellow judge once remarked that, in his opinion, the job is one of the quickest ways of making an enemy that he knows!

It may come as a surprise to many readers, "Mystified" included, that at field trials proper (as opposed to most tests) there is no actual system of "scoring." By this, I mean that points are not allocated (as they are at the Game Fair tests, for example), and the question of scores does not enter into the reckoning. The system of judging is entirely at the discretion of the judges so long as they keep to the Kennel Club rules. It should be noted, the advice in the guide to judges is not intended to be rules but, for all that, most judges do now follow it, although their interpretations of various aspects of it may differ.

I cannot detail in the space of an article the full lists of rules and regulations governing trials, nor reproduce the guide to judges. These are available upon application from the Kennel Club, 1 Clarges Street, London, W.1., and are also reproduced in full in the appendix of my book "GUNDOGS: Training and Field Trials" (Popular Dogs Ltd., 25s.). All I can hope to do is to give readers a broad outline of the tactics adopted by the majority of judges at retriever trials stakes.

Most organising societies appoint three judges, each of whom has two dogs down under him in the line at one time. If four judges are appointed, then they officiate in pairs, each pair having two dogs down in the line at one time. No dog can be discarded from the stake until it has been under two judges unless it has been guilty of one of the "eliminating faults," such as hard mouth or unsteadiness. Dogs are tried in numerical order, numbering from the right, and no dog may be called up for trial a second time until every dog in the stake has been tried once. After all the dogs have been tried once, judges may call up for trial any dog at their discretion. Usually, each judge has two guns working for him, and a bird shot by one of these is tried for first by the lowest-numbered dog down under him. If this fails, the other dog is then tried. If this also fails, the retrieve can be offered to one of the other judges for his dogs. Every dog has the right of first try on a shot bird, so that even if one is collected by the second dog down, this dog still has the first chance on the next bird shot, which is only fair and reasonable.

During the course of the trial the judge makes notes on the performance of each dog that comes under him. The usual practice (and the one recommended in the guide) is to place the runners in categories A, B, C, and so on, with plus or minus if thought fit, so that when the time comes to compare notes it is possible to sort out the top dogs, which are then seen again by one of the judges under whom they have not been down previously. After all the dogs have been under two judges (except those discarded for a major crime), those which pleased the judges most can be run-off for placement, when *all* the judges will watch the work of each dog until a unanimous, or a majority, decision can be made.

The element of luck

Strange things can, and frequently do, happen at field trials, and it is not by any means impossible for a mediocre dog to win a stake against much more brilliant animals merely because it went through the event without making a mistake or having a failure, "keeping its nose clean" as it is termed in field trial parlance. The aim of most judges of wisdom is to discover the best gamefinder and bag filler, even though this dog may turn out to be one which they would not give house room to, due to lack of pace, style, drive or what have you. A dog wins on the day, and luck plays a very big part as everyone who knows trials will admit. Some dogs get the opportunities, take them and succeed. Others never get the opportunities, and still others fail when opportunity is presented. Because our trials are run as nearly as possible like a normal shooting day, it is impossible to provide each competing dog with absolutely equal circumstances of fall, cover, wind direction and scenting conditions. Brilliant dogs can fail on a bird, especially if it is a stronger runner, and a failure as first dog down may, and often does, eliminate from top placings. For all that, most judges try to obtain an *overall* picture of the dog work and give their awards to the most consistent worker. If game is sufficient and shooting accurate, nine times out of ten it is possible for the judges to leave a trial feeling that they have found the best dogs *on the day's work.*

Some dogs may be lucky and have every bird shot stone dead and straightforward for them, whilst others get put on to strong runners. A dog *may* blunder into a bird by accident, thus wiping the eyes of one or more competitors. "Eye-wipes" are regarded very seriously by judges but, at the same time, the value of that incident must be taken into account. By this I mean that if a dog picks up a bird after a failure by a very indifferent dog, too much emphasis should not be placed upon it. On the other hand, if it wipes the eye of another good dog (or dogs) on a difficult bird, great credit must be accorded. Very often a good try is as valuable as an eye-wipe, even if unsuccessful.

In some stakes the dogs seem to sort themselves out naturally, whilst in others they are running neck to neck. If judges are "helped" by cases of unsteadiness, hard mouth or whining by several dogs, the field is narrowed, naturally. If two or more dogs are running equal, then the judges have to fall back for final placements upon what may be termed "minor refinements," such as delivery, strict steadiness at heel or even the way the dog looks at its handler. Other things being equal, pace, style and courage in cover, to say nothing of the ability to be handled and willingness to please, will give a dog the edge over a rival, but gamefinding ability must always be the main consideration.

One reason, probably the most important, why spectators and some handlers so frequently violently disagree with the decisions of trial judges is because they are not fully aware of the facts about each dog's performance under each judge. It is usually quite impossible, even from the centre of the line, to watch *all* the work of *every* dog in the stake. Very often the outstanding good or bad actions of a competitor may be obvious to all, but only in the most exceptional circumstances of ground can any one man hope to see *everything* that goes on. Only the judges can, by comparing carefully taken mental and written notes, hope to arrive at a final, fair and accurate assessment of the work of each individual dog throughout one or perhaps two days of field trialling. Even judges can be wrong, as I have stressed, for human nature being what it is, none of us is perfect. A dog may do something wrong unsighted by the judge, yet in view of the public gallery, or he may be distracted by a message from a steward at a critical moment, quite unintentionally. A judge can only judge on what he *sees*--hearsay evidence must never be listened to, but only the opinions of his fellow adjudicators.

I have not left myself a lot of space to deal with spaniel trials, but much of what I have written about retriever stakes applies to spaniel events as well, insofar as the judging procedure is concerned. However, only two judges officiate, each with one dog down *questing* at a time, but a referee is appointed to keep a general eye on things and is called in if the judges cannot agree. In practice the referee can be a dead loss, for he cannot see all the work of every dog under both judges and may, therefore, have missed the very point in the performance of a particular dog on which the judges are in doubt. In some respects spaniel trials are easier to judge than retriever events, because not only retrieving but, naturally, questing ability is considered and, indeed, this aspect of the work is rightly considered of major importance. As there are only two dogs down at a time, it is often possible for a judge to see much of the work of the dogs down under his colleague as well as his own but, again, the ground may be against this and, in any case, he must concentrate upon his own dog.

Usually the judging books are marked A, B, C, according to the performances of the dogs. Retrieves may be exchanged, and if the dog under one judge fails, the other judge brings his dog and handler over to try for it. It is invariably arranged for each dog to go under both judges, unless put out of the stake for an "eliminating fault," and after consultation the judges arrange for a run-off between those which have shown up best, running them close together in order to compare hunting ability, courage in cover, ground treatment, pace and style. As in the case of retrievers, the number of retrieves given to each dog depends upon the game supply, and judges endeavour to share them out fairly, but until the first round is completed it is not usual to call a dog into the line for a retrieve after the two already operating under the judges have failed, as can (and does) happen in retriever trials. Long, blind retrieves are not the usual rule (as they may be for retrievers), but marking ability is highly regarded. Gamefinding, both of unshot game and that on the ground after a shot, is of supreme importance, whilst steadiness to flush, shot and fall are a must. The spaniel judge has more to take into consideration than the retriever judge, and is liable to just the same human errors.

As one who has competed in both retriever and spaniel trials, judged a good many and spectated and reported at countless events, I can quite honestly say that, in my opinion, the majority of judges are both capable and fair, arriving at their decisions only after most concentrated effort and careful deliberation among themselves. Field trials are not perfect, and I do not see how they ever can be but, by and large, I believe that the most worthy dogs usually come to the top. Luck, good and bad, plays a tremendous part, but this element should be accepted by anyone who interests himself in field trials and helps considerably, to my mind, to make the sport more interesting and open.

P. R. A. MOXON

[Source: *Shooting Times and Country Magazine*, December 2, 1965, pages 1582-1583.]

Excerpt Number Five

Judges need to understand and know what to expect regarding variability in field trial performance. In the article which follows, Mr. Moxon reports on a field trial in which 20 out of 24 entries were awarded ribbons.

[From *Shooting Times and Country Magazine*, December 15, 1966, page 1656 (by kind permission of the publisher and Mr. Moxon).]

GOLDENS GO GREAT GUNS

It is a pity that some of the more violent critics of retriever field trials could not have been present at Westhide, Hereford, recently, when the Northern Golden Retriever Association staged its 24-dog all-aged stake by kind invitation of Mrs. J. M. Fraser. If they had been, they would surely have been impressed not only by the gamefinding ability and control of the dogs, but by their courage in some of the toughest cover imaginable.

Judging this event with my friends and colleagues Andrew Wylie and Jimmy Scott was a pleasure indeed, especially as our views upon the shooting man's requirements in a gundog coincide, thus enabling us to assess the dogs in virtually complete agreement. In the latter stages the dogs sorted themselves out; walking-up and driving, with birds sometimes falling in very thick brambles and other woodland cover or, at the other extreme, on fairly bare ground, alternated throughout the two days, and we were able to obtain an overall picture of the ability of each dog and handler. Only a water test was lacking.

Accurate shooting

The game supply was so good, and the shooting so accurate that there was never any question of our having to resort to what I term "negative" judging--the seeking of faults rather than qualities in the dogs. Of course, some retrieves were easier than others--even Mrs. Fraser and Westhide cannot eliminate the element of luck which plays such a big part in any trial--but, on the whole, conditions were as nearly level for each dog as I have ever known at a stake of this nature.

As so often happens, the incidence of game was at times higher on one side of the line than the other, with the inevitable result that some dogs had longer "downs" than others before being given a retrieve; despite this every dog had been down under at least two judges by the end of the first day and no handler present could possibly complain that they had not been given a fair crack of the whip.

Failures were conspicuous by their absence and the complete elimination of only four of the two dozen competitors on the completion of the second round would, on less favourable ground, have given the judges a considerable headache and driven them nearly frantic with worry as to how they could ever arrive at a convincing conclusion. Not that every dog left in was considered top quality, by any means, but each had proved itself a capable gamefinder and steady, able to deal with rough cover and thus well worthy of further consideration on the second day.

The game supply was even better, and the cover even

tougher the next morning, when in brilliant sunshine the dogs were walked-up on a heavily wooded hillside. The shooting was very accurate and all three judges were kept busy. How the guns managed to shoot so well between the trees I shall never know, but nearly every bird came down stone dead. Despite the difficult walking and the jungle-like conditions, both handlers and dogs marked very accurately in most cases and retrieves were speedily concluded.

None eliminated

The time had come for the judges to take more serious note of the finer points of gundog work, as well as of sheer gamefinding ability. Inevitably, some dogs slipped up because of lack of drive or style, poor heel-keeping or slovenly delivery of game, but even at this stage no dog could be completely eliminated from some form of recognition.

A drive when pheasants fell on the bare ground of a hop-garden proved both interesting and instructive, and here handlers were able to demonstrate the abilities of their dogs as regards direction and control, something which could not be effectively assessed in the woods. Of the previously leading dogs, one proved restless, one switched birds when retrieving, and another failed on a runner and had its eye wiped. Lack of drive and punch in some not very thick rough grass and weeds downgraded a fourth.

Five dogs contested the run-off, at the start of which there was not a great deal to choose between them on previous showing. However, one proved reluctant to handle into a wood on a blind retrieve, although ultimately succeeding, and another was rather sloppy in the delivery of a hare. And so on to the final drive, when four dogs lined out in a ride below a wood and young plantation and above a grassy bank leading to a ploughed field. Here one dog was restless and inclined to voice its opinion (albeit very quietly!), and another had its eye wiped on one of the shot birds which fell on the plough below. The last two birds required fell in the very thick young plantation above us, and though both dogs sent to retrieve were successful, one made very heavy weather of the cover and retrieved more slowly and sloppily than even the conditions warranted.

The winner, Mrs. June Atkinson's Holway Lobo, was an "A" dog with all three judges throughout, doing everything asked of him in effortless fashion, handling beautifully and at all times going with style, drive and precision. At the run-off he wiped the eye of another dog and dealt with a blind retrieve from thick cover in a masterly manner.

Not so "comfortable"

The runner-up was Miss Pilling with Westhyde Zenith, another fast and stylish gamefinder who handled nicely and built himself up throughout the stake, very forceful in cover, an excellent heel-keeper and a spot-on marker and clean retriever. At the run-off drive he stood rather than sat, and was not quite so "comfortable" as the winner.

In third place was Eric Baldwin with F. T. Ch. Palgrave Holway Harmony, which, after giving a very good account of himself in the body of the stake, fell from grace somewhat at the run-off, by reason of slovenly delivery and lack of forcefulness. A grand marker and probably the most impressive and slick handling dog present, unfortunate not to have been higher.

Fourth prize went to E. Crowther-Davies with Belway Bingo, a really useful gamefinder with terrific guts in cover and great gun-sense, handling adequately when necessary except during the all-important run-off, when the winner wiped his eye on the bird on plough and he proved restless during the course of the drive.

Fifteen Certificates

Reserve and certificate of merit was given to Dr. Nancy Laughton with Claverdon Holway Willow, another unanimous "A" dog which fell away somewhat during the concluding stages, taking a long time to find a not-too-difficult bird in the hop-garden and proving somewhat reluctant to handle into a wood on a blind retrieve, but otherwise put up a first-rate performance in all departments.

The judges had no alternative but to recognise 15 other dogs by awarding them certificates of merit, a fact that was as gratifying to us as it must have been to the owners and handlers. All the certificate dogs gave most adequate examples of true solid gundog work and gamefinding and exhibited no major faults which could eliminate them. Several of otherwise very high quality, although facing the thick cover, lacked drive and punch and others did not handle on to blind retrieves as convincingly as might be desired, or slipped slightly from grace for minor technicalities. Many an open stake has been won on performances in no way inferior to that put up by some of these dogs, all of which *found their game.*

    .   .   .   .

P. R. A. MOXON

Excerpt Number Six

We have the problem of large numbers of entries in our American licensed retriever trials. This sixth excerpt concerns the problem in Britain.

[Reproduced from *The Field*, November 9, 1967, page 857 (by kind permission of the editor).]

LIMITATIONS IN GUNDOG TRIALS

In the excellently produced news-letter of the United Retriever Club the field trial secretary, Mr. F. K. Bazley, makes with tact and understanding a plea which certainly does not come too soon. Briefly, it is an appeal to newcomers to the more ambitious ranks of gundog owners not to enter in field trials until they have real knowledge of what is demanded. It is not good enough merely to have a capable, properly trained dog by the standards of an average shoot or training class. For competition at this level an animal must be exceptional by normal standards.

Few informed people will doubt that Mr. Bazley's initiative is a timely one. But something more than exhortation is likely to be needed if the desired result is to be obtained. This is the elimination from the entries of that familiar proportion of runners in nearly every trial which have no business to be there at all.

Their presence has three effects. First, it simplifies the task of the judges, who find that though there are, say, 12 names on their card, only six need be seriously considered. Secondly it keeps others more trial-worthy, and perhaps some potential winners, out of the competition altogether. Thirdly, by inflating the pressure on the obtaining of nominations it obliges the would-be field trial competitor to apply for several events in the hope (not always realized) of being lucky enough to run in one of them; the consequence of this is to add greatly to the burdens of promoting societies.

The passengers

Since field trials depend on the generosity of those who provide the ground, and since the Kennel Club is very properly determined that their value shall not be diluted by over-frequency, it is unlikely that there will ever be enough trials to absorb all who would like to take part. The problem, therefore, is to ensure that as far as possible only those really fit to participate enter the trials which do take place.

It is here that exhortation unbacked by regulation may prove inadequate for an easily understandable reason.

Not many, if indeed any, experienced field trial competitors could say with hand on heart that they have never run a below-standard (as opposed to an off-form) dog in a field trial, either unwittingly because they did not know the form; or wittingly to give themselves, or their servants, experience in competitive handling. What past generations have done, present and future generations will assuredly continue to do unless something is done to stop them. And something is urgently necessary because the presence of 'passengers' in field trials now causes increasing unfairness to others in proportion to the increasing interest in top-class gundog work.

Three steps
Promoting societies could take three steps towards this end. All are free to do so. By acting themselves, instead of having action thrust upon them, they would preserve the opportunity for each to adapt its measures to individual or local needs.

First, consider as to whether field trial society membership is too easily obtained. At present, a proposer and seconder are the sole qualification for membership in nearly every case, and a person so 'qualified' thereby obtains the right to run a dog in a trial. Perhaps systems could be devised under which membership would be a first step to qualification for a nomination, some measure of competence constituting a second step (as is the practice in some of the chief coursing events).

Priorities
Secondly, in Open and All-Aged stakes priority should surely always be given to dogs which are already winners before opening the draw to those which have yet to prove themselves. It is illogical that whereas Non-Winner Stakes are closed by definition to winning dogs, some of the most important events are open to dogs which have never won, and quite evidently never will. Furthermore, their presence may (and often does) prevent the entry of animals richly deserving a chance to earn further distinction and deprived, because of previous victories, of doing so in lesser and easier stakes.

Thirdly, and more controversially, the running of Novice Dog-Novice Handler Stakes might with advantage be discontinued. The idea is to bring more people into field trials; the problem is that there are too many in already, most of them

dependent on other people's hospitality. To make things easy
for beginners is a means to this end. As a policy, it seems
half-baked. The really keen competitor will get in some-
how--whatever the disappointments, however long the trail.
Those who have been spoonfed are the ones who get the form
wrong, and who complain with an outraged sense of injustice
when they learn just how tough field trials are, and ought to
be.

Excerpt Number Seven

Since it's getting pretty close to "layin-by" time for this chapter,
I reckon I ought to try to place this series of excerpts (and the entire
book for that matter) in the proper perspective for McMahan, the
down-to-earth gundog man. This final excerpt concerns learnedness
and common sense. I suppose my underlying question as far as retriever judges is concerned might be worded as follows: Is knowledge
separate from wisdom?

[Reproduced from *Shooting Times and Country Magazine*, November
3, 1966, page 1417 (by kind permission of the publisher).]

SCIENTISTS AND LAYMEN

It is, perhaps, a pity that it is, nowadays, becoming almost a "fashion" for laymen to denigrate and deny the work
and findings of scientists. If, however, we are to be strictly
fair, it could hardly be disputed that scientists have, themselves, contributed to this state of affairs. In his own field
(which may often be severely limited) a trained scientist
possesses certain qualifications not shared by the average
layman but he is not infallible by virtue of them.

The scientist might be justified in arguing that the main
trouble is that the layman cannot understand him but, unless
he is both prepared and able to talk in ordinary language, this
is inevitable, however undesirable. Many scientists have a
habit, not necessarily bad in itself, of writing learned papers,
many of which are embalmed in equally learned publications
enjoying an insignificant circulation. Even if the layman had
ready access to these journals most of the writings, with tabular statistics, graphs and formulae, would be little more
than gibberish.

Again, it might be argued that scientists cannot put their views over in plain language. This is nonsense.

. . . .

Many scientists, perhaps inadvertently, tend to act and speak as if they were infallible. This, too, is nonsense. Those of us with grey hairs will know that, according to various astronomers over the past 40 years, we have been living in a universe which is sometimes said to be contracting, at others to be expanding with incredible speed. So far as the layman is concerned, this particular aspect of the universe around us may be only of academic interest but it is rather confusing, all the same.

Scientists are not necessarily right in any conclusions which they may decide to draw from the facts at their disposal. They constantly have to revise their conclusions in the light of fresh evidence. But they are professionals in their own right. Most of them got their various degrees by virtue of brains, hard work and .... . Most of them know a lot about very little, which is no mean feat and surely deserves at least a salute from the majority of us--the laymen--who usually only know a little about a lot of things. But the little we do know may well have inclined us, rightly or wrongly, to the belief that an ounce of commonsense is sometimes of more practical value than a ton of learning.

ACTION ITEMS

For purposes of illustration, I have prepared several items which are presented over the next several pages. In my opinion, some would be more appropriate for club meetings as compared to judging clinics; others merit no more consideration than on an individual basis, if that.

Item 1.--Such a topic as follows might literally devour the entire time devoted to a judging clinic: Are you willing to hang the following sign on your front door?

THERE ARE NO GUNS IN THIS HOUSE.

It is my opinion that this type of topic is better omitted from the program of a conference devoted to judging retrievers in the field.

On the other hand, I think it is a great topic for discussion, and action, at a club meeting. On second thought, I might even be willing to set the stage at a club meeting for a "red hot discussion." As a starter at the club meeting, I might begin by quoting King George VI who made the following statement: "The wild life of today is not ours to dispose of as we please. We have it in trust. We must account for it to those who come after." It seems to me that we not only have responsibility for the genes that have been entrusted to us in our retrievers, but also for the privilege to shoot shotguns in America. I would suggest that the latter should have high priority in gatherings of field sports enthusiasts.

Repeatedly during my lifetime, anti-firearms legislation (regulatory to prohibitory) has been introduced into Congress; at least two well-known regulatory acts (1934 and 1938) have been passed since I have been sensitive to the subject.

Over the last several months (as of April, 1968), I have followed the passing and implementation of "shotgun legislation" in Britain (see the excerpts which follow).

Shooting Times and Country Magazine   April 6, 1968

IF YOU HAVE A SHOT GUN
YOU MUST HAVE A CERTIFICATE

From 1st May you must have a shot gun certificate from the police if you 'possess, purchase or acquire' a shot gun. If you don't, you'll be breaking the law. There are a few exceptions but the police will tell you about them.

You can get an application form from the police, your gunsmith, shooting society or organisation. You should take it with the 5/-fee, to your local police station. Don't wait until 1st May. APPLY NOW.

If you do not wish to keep your shot gun, you may sell it to a gunsmith or anyone aged 17 or over, or hand it in to any police station before 1st May, 1968.

Firearms Amnesty. It is already a serious offence to possess many other kinds of firearm, including war souvenirs, without a Firearm Certificate. If you have in your possession any illegally held firearms or ammunition, hand them into the police immediately. No proceedings will be taken if you do this before 1st May, 1968.

Issued by the Home Office.

Shooting Times and Country Magazine   April 20, 1968

SELLING A SHOTGUN

On and from May 1 it will be an offence for anyone to transfer the possession of a shotgun to a person who does not produce a shotgun certificate. The only exception is that a person can transfer it to a firearms dealer who is in possession of a dealer's certificate.

A person advertising a gun for sale commits no offence by merely advertising; but before actually parting with possession to a purchaser he must have the purchaser produce a valid shotgun certificate. Even sending a shotgun on approval to a person who does not hold a shotgun certificate will be an offence on the part of the sender. Mail order firms will commit an offence if they send guns to persons without first having a valid shotgun certificate produced to them by the purchaser.

The regulations as to parting with shotguns will be just as strict as they are now as regards parting with the possession of pistols and rifled firearms under Section XI of the Firearms Act 1937. The provisions of that Act will now apply to shotguns.

My grateful thanks to Woodman for providing this information.

JACK SNIPE

Shooting Times and Country Magazine   April 6, 1968

THE FIREARMS AMNESTY

Sir, --The WAGBI page of March 23 mentioned that few people appreciate that the present amnesty in fact permits a man to sell his gun or firearm to the trade and that the general belief is that they must be handed in to the police.

This brief mention is not, in my opinion, enough. This is a point which should be elaborated upon and which the Home Secretary and the police have not made at all clear. Just why, I cannot imagine, as surely this is a big incentive for people to rid themselves of firearms and at the same time to get a fair price for them from licensed firearms dealers as opposed to receiving nothing from the police.

I am told that most licensed dealers will accept the weapon without any formality, whilst others require a Provisional Firearms Certificate, which the police must issue subject to the prospective vendor having no criminal record. This Provisional Certificate assures that the dealer can purchase, should he wish to do so without fear of recriminations from the police for either party.

What happens to valuable firearms handed in to the police? I suspect that many are sold by the police and the proceeds applied to a police charity. As charity over these sort of matters most certainly starts at home, I suggest that more publicity is given to this way of legitimately selling firearms during the amnesty.

K. E. G. CHEVENIX-TRENCH,

PRO, WAGBI

The Field   April 18, 1968

THE FIREARM CERTIFICATE

Sir, Mr. Luker [4 April] will derive small comfort that his experience with the renewal of his firearm certificate is by no means unique. The Firearms Act of 1965 gives chief constables wide powers to endorse certificates to limit the use of arms to specific places, but, like so much legislation passed through Parliament in the last few years, it might well defeat its object and drive more arms underground or lead to utter contempt of the law.

My certificate, which I had held since 1942, was due for renewal last July. The local police constable brought me the usual form to complete and asked me to state where I was to use these arms; I pointed out that this was virtually impossible to say, as I use my rifles for deer-stalking and, since I did not own or lease a forest, it would depend on what stalking I could rent through letting agents.

I also mentioned that the certificate would be renewed for three years and I could not say where I would be stalking in three years' time. It was suggested that I put in the places where I had stalked in the past and so I mentioned three estates. I wanted my .22 rifles for vermin destruction on the banks of a small river in Scotland, which adjoins a deer forest, and for similar use on an estate in England where I had been requested to shoot by the owner.

Over the next 10 days I had several telephone calls from police headquarters asking questions as to who owned the various estates, what area did these deer forests cover, was I ever asked to stalk as a guest and so on. These questions I was able to answer but I thought it would be easier to explain the position personally and therefore had an interview with the police where I produced maps and the particulars of the various forests.

In September I rented some stalking in Argyll, and, as I had not received my certificate back I told the local police where I was to stalk and unless I was told in writing I was not allowed to do so, I would proceed with my holiday. On 18 December I received a letter from the chief constable. I quote, "At my request enquiries have been made by the local police in respect of each of the estates and forests submitted by you. The result is that in each case, with one exception the land is either considered unsuitable, or no shooting rights are available to you." The certificate was returned endorsed for the one estate.

My investigations showed that in one case the local police had gone to the wrong estate in Scotland, and the owner
of another estate confirmed to me that he had assured them
that I stalked with his consent and invitation.   The owner of
the land in England had never been asked.

If I wished to continue deer-stalking I was told I would
have to appeal to Quarter Sessions; the law allows only three
weeks in which to lodge such an appeal and one's solicitor
has to brief counsel. When the notice of appeal had been settled my solicitor explained to the chief constable what I had
explained to a constable in July.

The chief constable then saw his way to vary my certificate to include any estate where I had shooting rights and also the .22 rifles for vermin destruction on the two places
mentioned.   Like Mr. Luker I cannot legally shoot vermin
anywhere else although I can shoot on any deer forest I rent
or am invited as a guest.   I am told that this example is by
no means unusual and all police forces are adopting this attitude.

If one wants to continue to shoot one must not treat this
law with contempt, for, if one transgresses, the chief constable would be quite within his rights to withdraw one's certificate.   Fortunately, in my case I did not have to go to the
court but the legal charges were well in excess of the   5s
fee required for renewal.

It is also of interest that if an appeal is successful the
appellant pays his own costs and costs cannot be awarded
against the chief constable, whereas if the appeal fails and
the court thinks the application frivolous the police costs can
be awarded against the appellant.

In my view the police have always been reasonable but at
the present time they are just obeying the orders of their
political masters.   I expect quite soon that it will be just as
difficult to obtain a shotgun certificate.

M. B. THOMPSON
Ashbourne, Derbyshire.

The foregoing excerpts were selected to reflect my personal opinion; I hold strong views against any additional governmental power to

control shotguns in the hands of American sportsmen. Where do we stop? What is the other side of the argument?

Item 2.--Through the years, stereotyped sayings develop and new-comers to the game seem to pick them up quickly. It seems that it might be a worthwhile project to ask an experienced retriever enthusiast to make a collection of these trite phrases and elaborate on their real meanings at judging conferences. To illustrate just a few:

1. "I like to allow a retriever two mistakes before I drop him." *[Aside for discussion:* This statement requires careful definition; clearly this whole book could be devoted to "mistakes."]

2. "Out of sight, out of control." *[Aside for discussion:* No, it depends on the situation, the time out of sight, the action taken by the handler, the response by the retriever, ...]

3a. "Handle on a mark and you're dead."

3b. "Handle on the first bird you send for in a triple and you're dead."

3c. "Handle on two birds in a triple and you're dead."

And there are many other "phrases" that could be catalogued.

[Warning: The young judge must be ever on the alert not to consider trite phrases, cliches, platitudes, and the like, as hard and fast rules.]

Item 3.--Routinely, within 3 days after each licensed stake he judges, judge X writes a critique (of less than 200 words) on each of the 4 retrievers "he placed." What useful purposes would such a practice serve? Discuss.

Item 4.--Opinions on trainers of retrievers: Do many trainers (amateur and professional) have inflated reputations? Even among experienced retriever people, much nonsense is peddled about the relative ability of individual trainers. How much of the "pooled opinion" is based on close day-to-day observation at the trainer's kennels and training sessions? Much opinion is based on current results. How sure are you that "ol' ... can't train ivy to grow up a wall"?

Even in the most confidential circumstances, some wise experienced RE's never give an opinion on the ability of a specified trainer. Newcomers to the field trial game are oftentimes "so certain" of their opinions. As we grow older and gain experience along the way, most of us have been proved wrong so often (by both men and retrievers) that we are more guarded in expressing our opinions. Discuss the following assertion: Good retrievers can make good trainers; because of luck, those trainers in the limelight currently may not always be the best.

Item 5.--In retriever training, there seems to be more than one "right way." In fact, "dog management," training, handling, kennelling, exercising, and the like, vary from handler to handler and kennel to kennel; they all seem to be based on some basic principles, but techniques and applications differ among those who are equally successful in practicing the art.

Some retriever enthusiasts get along better with one breed than another. I assume that any RE will be more successful with a variety (breed) of retriever that he genuinely admires than with one which he does not; moreover, I assume that all experienced RE's have some degree of "kennel blindness" and "variety or breed blindness."

A newcomer to the retriever field trial game was fortunate enough to secure an outstanding young Labrador bitch. At a trial in Houston, he informed me that American retriever field trials were tailor-made for the Labrador; all other breeds were doomed to something less than "first place."

I asked him the following questions: Have you ever owned another breed of retriever? *Answer:* No. Have you first-hand knowledge of the Cheasapeake? Golden? Flatcoat? Curlycoat? Irish water spaniel? His reply was "no" to each of these questions.

How could he possibly know? With practical experience, RE's do change their minds. Discuss.

Item 6.--Set forth the "pros and cons" of a visiting judge judging two stakes on a single weekend with the same co-judge versus with two different co-judges. Secondly, discuss inviting a judge to judge two stakes on a weekend.

Item 7.--Is a sportsman an amateur handler if he runs a "pro's dog" in an amateur stake? Discuss.

Item 8.--Comment by your co-judge: "That retriever didn't mark that bird; he winded it." What enters your mind? Do you penalize the retriever for using "the wind"? Discuss.

Item 9.--Part one: A pheasant is badly shot up, not only unusable as food for the table, but "blood and guts showing." A derby fails to pick up the bird and make a retrieve of any part of the pheasant. Do you give him a rerun or do you drop him? Discuss.

Part two: A shot pheasant falls in a bed of "fire-ants." A retriever in an open stake would not pick up the bird (neither would either of the judges). Would you have given the retriever a rerun or would you have dropped him? Discuss.

Part three: Compare your decisions in parts one and two, then discuss.

Item 10.--How could he possibly know? Given a retriever just slightly less than three years old; this retriever had compiled an enviable record in licensed trials as a derby. Inquire of a veteran RE and renowned trainer, handler, and judge who has daily first-hand knowledge concerning the progress of this retriever.

Reply by the veteran RE: This retriever has developed some real problems; handler X ruined his ability to mark by "pulling him off of marks" just as soon as he became two years old. *Questions:* What did the teaching of hand signals and other enforced control have to do with confusing this young retriever? Does the veteran RE have enough first-hand knowledge to know *why* the young retriever can no longer mark well? Might his marking achievement have deteriorated if he had never been "pulled off" of marked falls? What kind of evidence would one like to have before agreeing that the veteran RE knew what he was talking about?

Item 11.--What does a dog see (marking problems)? Given a body of water, with cover, along with a dike (levee, dam), where there is a road on top of the dike. Set gunners and birdboys on top of the levee to throw (at 45 degrees to the line with running dog) so that the fall hits at the bottom of the dike ("between" the dike and the dog). Conduct enough training sessions using different locations and dogs so that you can form an opinion on the following hunch: In this situation, the dog tends to mark the fall as being on top of (in the road) or beyond the dike.

Discuss (with your supporting evidence composed of carefully collected observations). Discuss also from the dog's (your) point of view--if you can.

Item 12.--As a dog delivers to hand, the handler appears to drop the bird; it's close. Should the handler be asked to have the dog pick it up? Suppose that the dog goes immediately for another bird, what then? If this happens in a junior stake, will your decision differ from your decision in a stake where championship points are awarded?

Item 13.--Mixed bag, duck and pheasant, derby stakes: Given a double in a licensed derby stake, where a thrown dead pheasant is the memory bird and a shackled duck is the mark. How many derby dogs out of 20 would you expect to hesitate to retrieve ("pick up") the pheasant after retrieving the duck? Does it make a difference if the dead pheasant is thrown "close to water" as compared to having the dead pheasant thrown far from the edge of the water--say, where the dog has to cross the water and then run over a considerable body of land? If care is not used in the mixed bag for derby stakes, might a judge be starting a blinking problem? Discuss.

Item 14.--How does a judge rank performance on such a test as the one described on the following page? In a licensed open stake in the fall of 1967, I *observed* a land series somewhat like the one outlined and sketched. Instructions to the handlers amounted to the following: (a) First pick up the shot flying pheasant, number ① ; (b) then pick up the blind; (c) do not pick up bird number ② at all.

Handlers were not informed as to "how" the judges intended to evaluate performances.

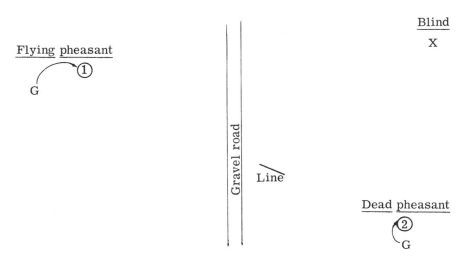

Before you read any further, write down how you would evaluate this series; explicitly state why you would evaluate it in that way.

[*Aside:* McMahan prefers not to set up a test like this one, because often he creates problems for himself in ranking the performances on such a test.]

Now every senior RE knows the following (approximate) quote: "... On 'marked' retrieves, the order in which birds are to be retrieved should not be specified by the judges, unless it is to be considered a test of control, i.e., a 'handling test.'" Furthermore, in view of the judges' instructions, is the concept of "area of the fall" involved in this series at all? If what precisely constitutes the "area of the fall" defies accurate definition, then is this not one way to avoid that problem? Discuss. In short, in view of the judges' instructions, retrieve of fall number ① cannot be graded as a marked fall. Discuss. Isn't the possibility of a penalty for "conspicuously intensive lining" in such a test eliminated? Discuss. Moreover, how do you rank the performance of an entry who hunts close and finds the fall as compared to the performance of an entry whose handler lines the entry accurately, hits the whistle quickly, and handles sharply to the fall? Discuss.

To provide further topics for argument, almost by definition, this becomes a test of "handling" over "lining." Discuss. In such a situation, how do you rank "excellent lining" performances in comparison with "sharp excellent handling" performances?

Fall number ② was never collected (by an entry). Is this a sound procedure to follow in a public demonstration? Would this "... simulate ... the conditions in an ordinary day's shoot"? Discuss. Would each retriever who was "pulled off" fall number ② , and who later picked up the blind, "think" that he had picked up fall number ② ? How do you know what a retriever thinks? Moreover, some handlers say that "retrievers like fliers better." Would the retriever "know" there was a dead bird at fall number ② ? If true, would the retriever wonder how a dead bird could run? Discuss. Finally, is this treating a top retriever correctly in that he was not allowed to complete his task--obtain closure and, thus, satisfaction? Discuss.

In written form, summarize your procedures for grading this test.

Item 15. -- Is this a test of control? In the open stake of the 1968 Louisiana State Championship (which I judged), two series had been conducted on land. The third series was a tough water blind. This item concerns the fourth series conducted at the same location as was the third series.

The first bird down (fourth series) was a shackled drake thrown from an island, across water, into swamp grass (water); the second bird down was a shackled drake into a pothole; the entry number was called. After picking up the last bird down (number ② fall), the handler had his retriever sit. He signalled the judge when ready, and a third mark (a shackled duck) was thrown over decoys into open water. Again the number was called and the handler sent for fall ③ , and then for the long memory bird (number ① down). Schematically, the test looked essentially as shown in the sketch on the following page.

This test, with the pull of the old blind, proved to be a discrimi-

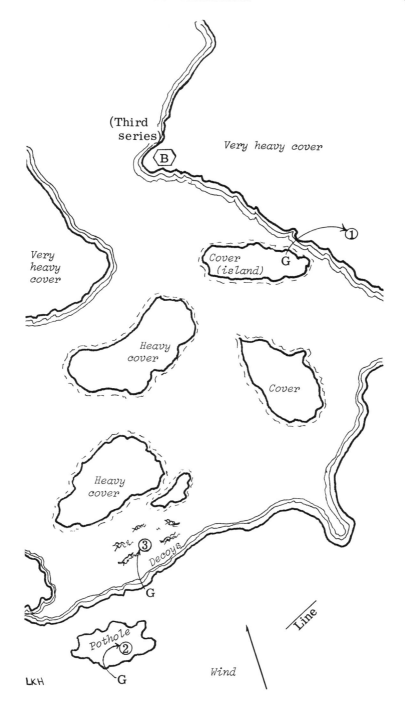

(Third series)

Very heavy cover

B

①

Very
heavy
cover

Cover
(island)   G

Heavy
cover

Cover

Heavy
cover

③
Decoys
G

Line

Pothole
②
G

Wind

LKH

nating test of ability; the judges obtained excellent separation. No explicit verbal instructions were given to the competing handlers. The handler of the test dog was told (privately) what was desired and he ran the test accordingly.

Questions: Was this a test of marking and memory or was it a test of control? Could a judge consider excessive lining in this situation? What action should the judges have taken if a handler picked up number ① bird (the long retrieve) first? What should the judges have done if a handler picked up number ② bird, then had his retriever sit while number ③ was shot, pulled his entry off number ③ and sent his retriever for number ① ? Would sharp handling outrank a slight hunt in the test? Suppose a retriever picked up number ② fall, delivered to hand, and then "took off" for number ① fall spontaneously. What action then on the part of the judges? Discuss.

Would a simpler version of this test be useful in training a derby retriever to remember a "tough double"?

Item 16.--Discuss the importance of members of the field trial committee being on the field trial grounds during the conduct of the trial. Outline the great responsibilities of that committee and procedures for instructing the members of the committee before the trial. Consider the advantages and disadvantages of having the marshal assist in a stake while being concurrently a member of the field trial committee.

Distinguish clearly between the responsibility of the judges and the field trial committee regarding selected topics, say, suspension, abuse of a dog by a handler, arguments between judges and handlers, training on the field trial grounds, a retriever watching blinds being planted for a test he has not run, whether a handler is an amateur or not, whether a particular retriever broke or not, others.

Members of the field trial committee should be familiar with at least three documents: the color-book, the recommendations ... , and the guide for dealing with misconduct at field trials.

Item 17.--On rare retrieves: Request some distinguished handlers to "tell about" some of the greatest retrieves they have ever witnessed.

*Item 18.--*Request some distinguished RE's to comment on the following assertion: "Only millionaires and fools go in for American retriever trials."

*Item 19.--*What is the probability that a single marked retrieve will be used as a test in the next national championship stake? Assume (better yet, verify) that there were 10 series in each of 15 national championship stakes investigated (see Chapter Fourteen), a total of 150 series. What is the relative frequency of series composed of a single marked fall?

Item 20.--Tragedy at H(...): To get lots of attention, it's hard to beat a "good big mistake." Have you *(personally)* ever seen a conventional weekend licensed trial "continued over" from Sunday until Monday and completed on Monday? Have you ever requested such a continuation? Did you succeed in having the request granted?

Given "50 entries" to run in an amateur stake on a cloudy Sunday (in the South) in February, starting time at 8:00 a.m. What is the maximum average time you would allow per dog in planning your first series (or your first and second series combined on one trip to the line)? What do you think of the following test as the "first series"? On a single trip to the line, run a tough single land mark on a flying pheasant; then run a blind angling across a body of water, where the line has been set back 50 yards from the water's edge. Would your philosophy of judging allow you to set this test?

Item 21.--Reference blind retrieve: Straighten out the concept of cast refusal. That is, when and how do you use the following rule? "As long as the dog is getting closer to the blind, it is not a refusal."

Item 22.--Example of the exercise of (good or bad) judgment: Given a licensed open stake, where the first series was a tough land triple with one flier. A male entry had performed in a workmanlike manner on the test and was leaving the line with his handler. The retriever "reared and attempted to mount" his handler in front of the judges; apparently on impulse, the handler hit the retriever under the chin with his "open hand."

Questions: Is there a specific "rule" which applies to this situation? In an ordinary day's shoot, how would you have handled the situation if you had been handling this retriever?

From the point of view of the judges, discuss the action which you would have taken.

Action which was taken: Not being afraid to do something unorthodox, and yet attempting to exercise common sense (in a situation which I had not encountered before), the dog was not called back for the next series. The incident was not mentioned to the handler, who (being a professional) continued to participate in the trial in a routine manner.

Item 23.--Given a young judge: For series one, he suggests a triple mark, say, such as is sketched below. For series two, the

②

①   Flier
                                     ③

X̄ Line

young judge suggests that the same test be repeated at the identical location, but that a blind be added (as shown on the following page). If you follow his suggestion, what would you expect to get for your money in terms of information?

Item 24.--In 1967, at the spring trial of the ... Amateur Retriever Club, 31 entries were officially listed as being entered in the qualifying stake, to be run on Saturday, February 18; starting time was listed as 8:00 a.m. Saturday was a mild day with only a

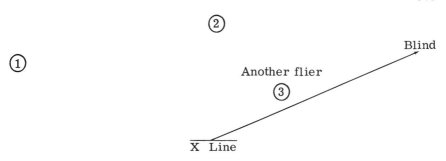

few scattered clouds; temperature ranged from a morning low of 51°
(F) to a high of 68°. Some rain did fall in the area on Saturday, measuring 0.01 inches, but I do not recall that it rained at the trial
grounds.

It was reported that the judges conducted three, and only three
series as follows: At area one, a double marked land series with one
live pheasant; a land blind at a second area; and a triple on water with
three live shackled duck. No water blind was conducted.

By operational definition, the judges of a qualifying stake certify
that the first and second place retrievers in such a stake are qualified
to run in limited all-age stakes--are qualified retrievers. *Questions:*
Is it sound procedure in general to certify retrievers as being qualified without having the entries demonstrate that they can and will pick
up a simple unseen retrieve on water?

Item 25.--On a single blind, say, a water blind, some handlers
make a practice of walking to the line "on a line to the blind." Is this
procedure advantageous? Discuss.

Item 26.--One purpose of this item is to see how much an RE
knows about handling a retriever under actual "hunting or shooting"
conditions. Assume there are several Guns, each with one retriever,
at a shoot, say, a dove shoot. Assume that each Gun agrees that when
a bird is down, it is a sound idea to get the retriever to the area of the
fall as quickly as practicable.

Assertions for discussion: (1) The probability of a retriever
making a find is decreased if a man is "standing on the fall"; hence,

do not walk to the area of the fall--(stay back yourself and) send the retriever instead. (2) Allow only one retriever (at a time) to hunt for a downed bird; that is, do not allow multiple retrievers to search for the same bird at the same time. (3) If your retriever is hunting for a bird that is down, and if another handler brings his retriever over to "assist you," then you should "pick up" your retriever and quietly walk away.

If you agree with assertions 2 and 3, explicitly state your reasons for agreeing. Are the foregoing assertions in conformance with the way American retriever trials are conducted? ... the way British trials are conducted?

Item 27.--Hands: Request an experienced trainer to give a talk on "hands of the handler" from the viewpoint of the retriever. Ask him to cover such topics as stroking, patting, holding the lead, pressure, conveying of messages, signals, snap of fingers, wrist movement, raised hand, clap of hands, sudden movement of hands, the hand providing both reward and punishment, heeling and the hands, hand-shy, eating out of hand, and other topics.

Item 28.--For discussion by a panel of experienced retriever judges: Invite three distinguished officials from three different sports, say, professional football, professional boxing, and diving. Ask each one to discuss the art of officiating in his particular sport. Request the panel of experienced retriever judges to select aspects which are applicable to our retriever game and get the pertinent points down on record so that we might possibly add to the body of knowledge on judging retriever trials.

Item 29.--A tall tale for discussion: Most experienced RE's have first-hand knowledge of and/or can spin tales that are worth relating to new RE's and novice judges. I shall fabricate such a tale for purposes of illustration.

A young greyhound was lucky enough to win a couple of schooling races; he was so proud of himself--just like many a young owner-handler who wins a derby stake with his very first retriever. Moreover, this greyhound "knew it all, " even though he didn't even know the rules and procedures of dog racing.

Unfortunately, this youngster strutted in front of a car and was splattered before he found out the facts of life. It so happened he was reincarnated as a (two-legged) joiner of clubs, one of which was a retriever club; in short, he became a "reincarnated retriever enthusiast" (RRE). True to his way of life, he was lucky enough to obtain a pretty fair derby dog. Now because he had little experience, was not familiar with the rules applying to retriever field trials (FT), was not familiar with recommendations from committees, it came to pass that he determined it was time to corner an experienced RE or an officer of a licensed trial-giving club to inform him of how trial procedures should be changed and judging revised.

He professed that a running commentary should be employed to make the FT more enjoyable to spectators; he used a televised golf tournament as an analogy. *Comment:* This RRE did not realize that retriever trials are an amateur sport; they are not a spectator sport; hence, not "self-supporting."

Not realizing that, at most, FT judges are required to make use of ranking scales, our RRE suggested that judges assign an interval score independently on each performance, that these scores be added, and the winner, places, and ribbons be assigned based on totals.

His greyhound lines not completely forgotten, he further suggested that each retriever's performance be timed and, other things being equal, the performance with the shortest time be declared superior.

Discuss.

Item 30.--Invite an experienced eight-point judge to set forth a logical argument why the advice volunteered below is or is not "sound advice" to a beginning judge. [*Aside:* It must not be sound advice, because many judges do not follow the policy.]

If you expect to obtain the correct answers (that is, to rank the retrievers accurately), decide ahead of time (before the series starts)

what you are looking for, then keep your eyes on the retriever you are
judging while he is under judgment.   Do not take your eyes off of that
retriever "a-toll."   Look at each retriever as if you never saw him
before--no matter how well you may know that retriever.   Do not permit what you saw that retriever do "last week" (or what you have read
about him) to even enter your mind.   Do not consider who the handler
is or who owns the retriever under judgment.   Remember that initially you must judge him, independently of the other judge, on what you
witness yourself in this particular stake.

Item 31.-- Request a graduate veterinarian to address himself to
the following question: Why do dogs eat grass?   Then ask for comments from experienced RE's.

Item 32.-- When I first began to train retrievers in the Bonnet
Carré Spillway ("the Spillway"--see diagram on the next page), around
1957, the area was practically devoid of human litter. *Prediction:* It
won't be many years until the Spillway will be an open sewer. It seems
to be a paradox that the cleaner we make ourselves, the dirtier the
environment in which we run our retrievers becomes.   Human litter
seems to be a national and international problem.   What positive action can we take to prevent our field trial RE's from being "litter-
bugs"?   How can we get them to use litter bags and litter barrels?
Discuss.

Item 33.--Consider the source: How could he possibly know? Given
a young trainer-for-pay who has been in the business "long enough to
know"; identify him as A .

Given also a "non-trainer-for-pay" senior RE , identify him as
Z . Let the relative frequency (R) with which ribbons are picked up
in licensed trials be defined as follows:

$$R = \frac{\text{number of ribbons collected}}{\text{number of actual starts}} .$$

Furthermore, let R_A refer to the relative frequency with which A

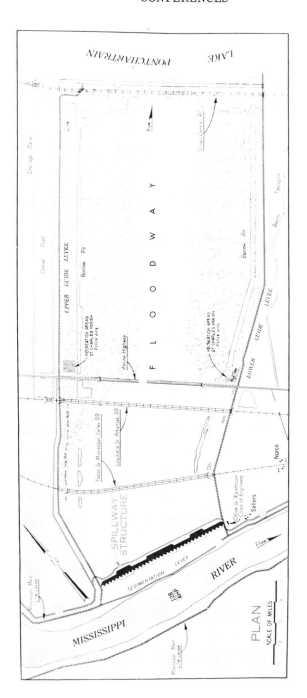

BONNET CARRÉ SPILLWAY

(From Mississippi River Commission, U.S. Army Engineer District, New Orleans, Corps of Engineers, 1969.)

collects ribbons and R_z denote the relative frequency with which Z collects ribbons.

Assertion by A: "Z is the most stupid one in the field trial game."

Consider a classification whereby one might operationally define stupid as being "dull and slow-witted" relative to the retriever game (see below).

Classification of retriever trainers and enthusiasts	Profits noticeably from		
	his own mistakes	mistakes others make	his own and others' mistakes plus insight
Enterprising, quick-witted	Nearly always	Often	Sometimes
Middling	Often	Sometimes	Rarely
Dull and slow-witted	Not often	Rarely	Never

Additional information to be considered: Z has personally trained and personally campaigned more than one retriever; Z has judged a score of licensed "point-giving" stakes plus many licensed junior stakes; each and every retriever which Z has entered in licensed stakes (and can be classified as Z-owned, Z-trained, Z-handled) has obtained a first place, sooner or later; and $R_z > R_A$ ("is better than"--collects ribbons with greater relative frequency) for derby stakes, qualifying stakes, and open stakes.

In contrast, A is recognized as "a nice guy, but with somewhat below average acumen." *Questions:* How could A possibly classify Z correctly? Is he merely a gossipmonger repeating what he heard some disappointed field-trialer assert? In short, when we hear such assertions made, do we as sportsmen have an obligation to ask the question: How could A possibly know? Is there a general problem outlined and implied here or does this merely reflect people? Discuss.

Item 34. -- What do we mean by labelling an RE as also being a true sportsman? Would you agree with the following? The true sportsman has an unselfish attitude. He knows, perhaps unconsciously, that the "best" enjoyment of the sport comes from trying to put into it a little more than he takes out; he identifies with the group to such an extent that he recognizes when it is best not to claim one's rights. Explicitly state other characteristics of the true sportsman.

Item 35. -- At a judging conference, I prefer to call it a judging clinic (July, 1966, Monroe, Louisiana), the actual performances of four retrievers were judged by the conferees. On Saturday afternoon, those registered for the clinic were divided into pairs of judges by "pulling names out of a hat."

On Sunday morning "at the lake," two experienced judges set up and conducted four tests on water: (1) a double marked retrieve and leave the line; (2) after all entries had run, a double blind from the previous line over the old marked falls; (3) a triple mark (4) in combination with a long blind (between two of the falls).

After the four series were completed, those registered for the clinic returned to the conference table. Shortly after noon, a seminar and panel discussion was held for which I served as moderator. The panel was composed of the two judges who designed and conducted the tests and two other experienced judges.

I numbered each pair of judges which had been selected on Saturday; then using a table of random numbers, I selected two pairs of judges to discuss each test and evaluate the performance of each entry; after the presentations by the two pairs of judges, the panel members made comments (the two judges who set up the test making the final remarks).

The point to note here is that the process of assigning judges to pairs by "drawing names out of a hat" is not a satisfactory randomizing procedure in general; however, the pairs selected to discuss each test were selected by a process which is considered to be a sound randomizing procedure.

Request a competent RE to discuss the randomizations above; ask him also to discuss the 1940 and 1969 "draft lotteries."

Item 36.--If, and only if, a retriever has generations of working ancestors is it highly probable that he will develop to where he is really competitive in open stakes. A retriever which will take a line, stick to it, face heavy, rough cover, swim in icy water with all his heart without hesitancy, retrieve a wounded duck or stray runner tenderly, is the final product of careful breeding--the result of untold man-years of effort. An owner who happens on a retriever with courage, great mouth, nose, and speed, and first-rate temperament is indeed privileged to stand on the shoulders of men of the past.

What are retriever field trials? Are they the public demonstration of the results of the efforts of those who breed a gundog for a particular function on a shooting day? Is training secondary to breeding? Should a judge have a clear-cut philosophy regarding the purpose of American field trials?

Breeding and sale of top class retrievers constitutes big business. Does big business mean mass production? Since mental and physical abnormalities can be perpetuated by human mismanagement, what is the responsibility of the retriever owner? What responsibility does the seller of the retriever have for training the new owner?

Item 37.--Probability and odds were discussed at considerable length in Chapter Seven. In 1783, because of the possible impact on his grandchildren "to be," Thomas Jefferson was concerned about the education of his 11-year-old daughter, Martha. He reasoned that because schools in Virginia were scarce at that time, "the chance that in marriage she will draw a blockhead I calculate at about 14 to 1."[1]

We are little concerned in the retriever field trial game with marriage and, for the moment, blockheads. We do hear our peers in the game abused, however. Suppose that you prepare an operational definition of a stereotyped vicious rumormonger. If a retriever club were selected strictly at random and if a member from that club were randomly selected, from those members who actually handle retrievers in licensed field trials and have been a member of the club for more than 2 years, I estimate that the odds are about 3 to 2 that a backbiting gossipmonger (beebeegee) will be selected. (What odds would you set forth?)

Given these odds, what is the probability of randomly selecting a beebeegee?

Ask someone to check history as to whether or not Martha married a blockhead. Did Mr. Jefferson change the original odds he quoted by the action he took? Should an eight-point qualified judge behave in such a manner as to qualify as a beebeegee? Should some type of special code of ethics be prepared for qualified judges?

What actions can we as RE's take to change the odds for selecting a beebeegee from among our colleagues in the retriever field trial fraternity?

Item 38.--Webster defines *futurity race* as "a horse race usually for two-year-olds in which the competitors are nominated at birth or before." There are a good many "pointing breed futurities," say, the quail (dog) futurity, the pheasant dog futurity, the grouse futurity, the national shooting dog futurity. Is it true that the quail futurity has existed for nearly 70 years? Does the explanation of no "retriever futurity" lie in "no money prize" allowed?

Item 39.--Some "unconventional methods of scoring at field trials" are set forth from time to time. Ask a senior judge to discuss some of these methods. Suggest that he discuss the following ones which have appeared in print during the last decade: (1) *Field Trial News*, January-February, 1964, pages 15 ff.; (2) *Field Trial News*, July-August, 1964, page 3; (3) *Retriever Field Trial News*, Volume V, Number 7, October, 1969, page 3.

Item 40.--In the main, there is considerable land area between opposite lanes of traffic in New Orleans; much of this land area is planted and landscaped, providing the many lovely boulevards for which New Orleans is famous. Because rainwater does not drain naturally from New Orleans but must be pumped out of the city, many of these beautiful "traffic islands" are the result of converting open drainage canals to large land-covered culverts. In many other sections of the United States, a traffic island or land area between traffic lanes is designated as the *median*. Not so in New Orleans; here these areas are referred to as *neutral ground*.

In contrast, there seems to be no "neutral ground" in retriever field trial judging, either in New Orleans or elsewhere. Yet, judging disputes need to be reconciled or resolved if the judging of American retriever field trials is to be improved. The question is "how"--can judging disputes be settled by argument? The following quotation from Thomas Jefferson appears in Fleming's *The Man from Monticello:* "I never saw an instance of one of two disputants convincing the other by argument."[1]

Discuss methods (other than argument) of settling disputes concerning judging retriever field trials.

Item 41.-- Reference item 22, page 672. Take the position that the judges made an incorrect decision. Use (material in paragraph 39) ... *Field Trial Rules* ... to prepare a logical argument to support your position.

Item 42.-- Consideration for judges of the derby and qualifying stakes by the judges of stakes in which championship points are awarded: Given a field trial where suitable land and/or adequate water may be limited. Judges of the open stakes may say: We may use area A or we may use area B; reserve both of them for us. ... Judges of the amateur stake may ask that water C and water D both be reserved. (Priorities are clearly stated and are well-known.)

Under such circumstances, choices must be made; if the judges of the "priority stakes" will not make decisions and live with those decisions, what practical methods are available to assist the judges of "junior stakes"? What routine planning procedures should apply?

Request a panel of experienced judges to discuss.

Item 43. -- Assertion for discussion: The probability is high that an investigation into the background of a "better judge" would disclose that he has had first-hand experience with breeds of gundogs other than retrievers. Experience with (several) breeds of gundogs (such as bird dogs, spaniels, hounds) other than retrievers not only broadens the explicit considerations of an RE, but also improves his ability "in depth" to evaluate retrievers in the field. Discuss. [*Aside:* The variety of "retrievers" and other gundogs pictured in this book is (intended to be) operational evidence that this author holds such an opinion.]

Item 44. -- Reference *A Review of the Flat-Coated Retriever* by Nancy Laughton, published by Nancy Laughton, the Bungalow, Buckley Green, Henley-in-Arden, Warwickshire, England, 1968. See also the references on pages 151-152 of that book. Use both Laughton's book and her references to lead you to the literature on retrievers in Great Britain; however, you should not focus on the flat-coated retriever.

Item 45. -- "Pressure" on the judges: I feel a tremendous amount of pressure on the day prior to a trial when my co-judge and I are setting up tests and preparing a general protocol for the stake we have agreed to judge. Repeat: Under those circumstances, I always feel the stress. *Hypothesis:* There is tremendous pressure on the three judges who must "set up" a national championship stake. Request several RE's who have judged such a stake to describe the "pre-trial tension" and how the stress of preparing for a national championship stake differs from the stress of preparing for a "routine" licensed trial. Is it merely stretched out over a longer period of time prior to a "national"?

Item 46. -- Assertion for discussion: American retriever field trials have become increasingly more "artificial" since World War II. What does *artificial* mean in the context of this assertion? Request a panel (of RE's) to discuss the foregoing assertion and its implications.

Item 47.--New Orleans Mardi Gras: An RE who has combined field trial activities with attendance at "the greatest free show on earth" might attempt to describe Shrove Tuesday and the week or so of parades and other activities previous to "Fat Tuesday." Ask such an RE to give you the "details" on such topics as Boeuf Gras, "If Ever I Cease to Love," School of Design, Mardi Gras, Rex's reign, selection of his Queen, flambeaux, "purple and green and gold," financial support of carnival krewes, selection and identities of other kings and queens, and/or other topics. How much information versus misinformation did this RE find out about the carnival balls that extend from Twelfth Night (January sixth--the twelfth night after Christmas) to Comus (Mardi Gras night)? *Hypothesis:* A visiting RE can learn no more about "how it really is" with New Orleans Mardi Gras and the society behind it than a first-timer at a retriever field trial can learn about the training and judging of retrievers, much less about the "ins and outs" of the retriever field trial fraternity--and that it's a complex structure not to be toyed with.

Item 48.--Each judge should routinely be supplied with a chair to which a large towel is attached. Observe the frequent use of the towel. Report at the next club meeting why you hadn't provided such a convenience before. Discuss.

Item 49.--A possible next step: Theory follows facts; it is well-known that a theory summarizes a body of consistent facts. Now that a little theory has been worked out for our American retriever field trial game, it's timely to collect a set of applied papers illustrating the design and setting of tests. Then we can conduct new experiments, obtain new results, and formulate more comprehensive theory. To write those applied papers, we shall need, say, five judges selected from those who have judged a championship stake and .... . Discuss.

The Day That Seldom Was

Wasn't the judging terrible at this trial? You know, my retriever won the open up at "N" last year; the judging and trial mechanics were just perfect. I'm going back this fall; they run the best trial on the southern circuit. .... .

Geese came over in thousands; duck darkened the sky and I just stood up in my blind and "shooed" them away; dove came in droves and they kept coming back all afternoon. Camp operators, motel and hotel proprietors, operators of launch facilities, lessors of shooting rights or ponds, guides, and even our field trial colleagues seem to repeatedly advise in superlative terminology that ... last week or yesterday.

Woodcock yesterday, woodcock next week, but seldom woodcock today.

Snipe yesterday, snipe next week, but seldom snipe today.

Dove yesterday, dove tomorrow, but seldom dove today.

Duck yesterday, duck tomorrow, but seldom duck today.

Geese yesterday, geese tomorrow, but seldom geese today.

[Even (grouse) (partridge) (pheasant) (quail) yesterday, ...]

My retriever handled superbly last week in the open; he'll handle well in the amateur Sunday; I just can't understand why he wouldn't handle today.

Sound and capable judging yesterday under ... , sound and capable judging tomorrow under ... , but seldom sound and capable judging today--unless you win of course.

ACTION ITEM

A "good" dog today.--Ask the following question of handlers at a picnic trial, a sanctioned trial, or even a licensed trial: How's your dog doin'? Then tabulate the replies in some such manner as suggested on the following page.

Item i	Reply	Hash marks	Frequency f_i
1.	Not too good, he hasn't been trained much lately.	⫲⫲ ... ‖	f_1
2.	Not too good, he's off form today.	⫲⫲ ... ‖	f_2
3.	Not much, there's a raw bitch here that upset him.	⫲⫲ ... ‖	f_3
4.	Not much, he's got his mind on a bitch at home.	⫲⫲ ... ‖	f_4
5.	Not too good but he's young--he's going to be good.	⫲⫲ ... ‖	f_5
6.	Not too good, he's past his prime.	⫲⫲ ... ‖	f_6
7.	Not too good, he's been worked hard in cold water and he's a little sour.	⫲⫲ ... ‖	f_7
8.	Not too good, I've been getting on him pretty hard trying to make him handle ... ; hence, he's not marking well.	⫲⫲ ... ‖	f_8
9.	Not much, we bred him twice last week and you know	⫲⫲ ... ‖	f_9
10.	Good.	⫲⫲ ... ‖	f_{10}
11.	Excellent.	⫲⫲ ... ‖	f_{11}
⋮			
k.	Really great.	⫲⫲ ... ‖	f_k

REFERENCE

1. Fleming, Thomas. *The Man from Monticello*, New York: William Morrow and Company, Inc., 1969.

A pittance of practice may be worth a tome of theory.

An "illustrated story" by a 7-year-old boy submitted in response to the following assignment to a class of second grade students: Write about the funniest thing you can think of. (Traced from the original and reproduced--courtesy LBMcM.)

CHAPTER SIXTEEN

TAIL-PIECE

Ah, the sweetness of anticipation. But if we who are senior retriever judges today do not take action wisely, willynilly we shall soon have some good reasons to look back to the 1960's as the good ol' days. Even though at the moment we are concerned with "back-end" problems, this final chapter is not a summary; neither is it a conclusion. As the title of the chapter implies, it is a challenge.

Old Battleground

Is there one single "sport" in which each competitor and spectator agrees with the "referee" invariably on every occasion? Clearly, the judging of retriever field trials is not a new battleground. In the main in this book, I have merely revived questions which, as in other fields, have been raised in the past; moreover, some of them may have been soundly answered, even though the answers may have been long forgotten.

In the field trial game, much pleasure and joy comes from stumbling upon insights, as well as from the war of words. When all the controversy has been settled by established procedures and facts, there will be a certain "deadness" about the game. In short, when we bring our judging of retriever field trials to a state of practical perfection, we shall say good-bye to a lot of fun.

Since we have not yet reached that state of perfection, a new judge must clearly recognize that owners and handlers of retrievers have an inescapable curse upon them; that curse holds for each and every trial they enter. They all dream of winning, yet all but one are fated to suffer the death of that dream. Moreover, a new judge must recog-

nize that an American retriever field trial is (1) an elimination contest, for the purpose of (2) selecting the "best dog" in the stake,
within (3) limitations of time, money (birds and "shells"), conditions
available and/or prevailing for the particular stake.

Even if an RE were perfectly knowledgeable (according to any
criteria whatsoever) regarding retrievers and the retriever field trial
game, he would still find it difficult to play the role of judge.

Analogy.--When youngsters play school, one youngster may
play the role of teacher for one period, then later he may play the role
of pupil; an RE may play the role of handler in one stake and the
role of judge in another, both roles being played on the same weekend.
Clearly, I intend "role" to include the ideas, attitudes, and habits of
the part played or assumed.

Populations and Generalizations

In the main, generalizations about judging retrievers are unsatisfactory; for the most part, there seem to be exceptions to most any
general rule. In spite of the foregoing, a substantial part of this book
has been devoted to methods for generalizing to the "population of retriever trials" or to the "population of judging performances."

Analogy.--The clinician deals with patients; the epidemiologist
deals with populations. The amateur RE deals with individual retrievers; the professional handler deals with multiple retrievers on
an individual basis. The judge of a trial deals with groups of retrievers, explicitly, relative to rank within one group at the time. This
book has been concerned not only with multiple groups of retrievers,
but with multiple (stakes) trials--thousands of them--all possible performances.

The individual amateur handler is limited in his picture of judging retrievers; even the professional handler is limited in his picture.

All handler experience is likely to be incomplete; all individual
judging experience is likely to be incomplete. This book is concerned
with selected aspects of the population of judging experiences, and

methods of systematically examining it. Another way of saying somewhat the same thing is that this book is concerned with selected aspects of the "judging process."

Even if an individual has judged enough to accumulate several
points and even if he has become glib and has learned to "cut ruth-
lessly" after each series, this experience alone may not necessarily
mean that he understands the judging process which he is not only attempting to apply, but of which he is part and parcel. He may be like
the surgeon who has skillfully performed the procedure of removing
malignant tumors many times; such experience alone does not necessarily imply that this surgeon knows much about, or even remotely
understands, the growth process underlying cancer.

Knowing It All

The really great RE, the really successful gundog trainer, each
has the attitude that no one ever knows it all; in particular, he is still
learning. Nevertheless, he observes that many novice gundog fanat-
ics graduate to the "expert" category overnight. He knows that the
probability is high that the fellow who is pleading ignorance today and
picking his brain will be telling him how to ... , how it should be
done, by next week.

Trial Purist

Before this book was written, there was a great gap between genuine knowledge and guess-work in the judging of American retriever
field trials. Now that this book has been written, there still remains
a great gap between knowledge and guess-work in the judging of American retriever field trials.

For any one individual (as was indicated in the preceding analogy),
much observation of retriever activity and wildlife is purely acciden-
tal. Any one person's experience is only partial and grossly inadequate. Nevertheless, this book has emphasized that one has to be
careful about even "dismissing lightly" something he was told or read

as being "unsupported by critical evidence" or "highly improbable" or "approaching zero probability--impossible."

This is the computer age. Retriever field trials has its own ends like a business in a materialistic world. Some of the findings of this book, disgorged as "hard facts" from the computer, bear out some theories and suggest others.

It is well-known that all of us own brilliant dogs when they are home in their kennels; field trials provide an opportunity for those very same dogs to demonstrate their superiority in competition with other dogs. However, field trials were never intended to produce the final answer. Most experienced gundog enthusiasts will admit that trials do severely test the combination of drive and control.

For the most part, in American and British field trials, the man with the dog is not the man with the gun. Furthermore, there is a difference in outlook between the ordinary shooting man and the retriever field trial purist. The ordinary shooting man requires a retriever trained in self-discipline and trained to work without constant supervision. In contrast, field trials are selective of a particular type of dog; a type of dog which may require the entire concentrated attention of a handler.

Some of the organizers and supporters of field trials are fully aware of "apparent weaknesses" of field trials even though they are unable to correct them. In particular, there is always a shortage of time and awards are frequently made on the skimpiest of information. Moreover, the element of luck is one of the strongest appeals of field trials. Additionally,

1. Field trials are inevitably artificial.

2. Individual field trials do not provide comprehensive tests under all types of country and conditions.

3. Judges may pay too much attention to refinements rather than "finding."

4. Field trial dogs may be over-trained in the eyes of some retriever enthusiasts.

5.   Other "weaknesses."

The foregoing notwithstanding, as long as retriever field trials are conducted under all conditions, the shooting man should have a reliable source from which to obtain his gundog.

In the main, the winner of a licensed open stake is a first-class shooting dog. By and large, in my opinion, he is superior to the retriever who has been labelled "first-class shooting dog" (outside the framework of licensed trials) with regard to control, drive, nose, and steadiness.

Challenge

Each and every dedicated retriever enthusiast is challenged to make careful observations, to collect data, and to demonstrate that McMahan is "wrong," that *Retriever Theory* won't stand up under critical scrutiny. This is as it should be because one can't prove that McMahan is "right." Hypotheses need not be proven in closed deductive systems, say, one such as that set forth in Chapter Eleven. In fact, hypotheses are usually formulated to be rejected; after all, we can't wait until "all the apples of all time have fallen ... ."

Derogatory remarks, smear tactics, whispering campaigns, "loud talk," and other unsupported criticisms do not provide data to justify rejection of hypotheses. If we ever expect to generate a reliable body of knowledge concerning the American retriever field trial game, use must be made of institutionalized procedures for eliminating hypotheses as possibilities. Let those who have data or information for eliminating a specific hypothesis step forward with the evidence, marshalled in such a way as to demonstrate beyond a reasonable doubt $(P < 0.05)$, that said hypothesis is not tenable.

Where only opinion is involved, let him who has a different opinion express it in written form, unambiguously clear, so that members of the retriever field trial fraternity will have it for consideration.

One can spot immediately the mistakes of the secretary, the other handlers, the judges, the marshals, the gunners, the birdboys, and others associated with a retriever field trial. Moreover, it is easy to write about the mistakes that others can and do make. It is never quite so easy to go through exactly the right motions at exactly the right moment in preparation for a trial or under trial conditions.

The old-time retriever field-trialer may be taken aback by the explicit recognition of some of the problems outlined in this book; he may be even more perplexed, perhaps dismayed, by the use of symbolism in the attempt to formalize these problems and to obtain solutions to some of them. The reactionary may deplore retriever field trials' being computerized, but technology is as applicable to the field trial game as it is to various aspects of business, government, industry, and agriculture. However, one must avoid contributing to the halo of modern formulas or to the beliefs that 1966 model computers can think, and that only computers are intellectually capable of doing many tasks. After all, modern applied mathematics is only a tool; let it be clearly understood that 1966 model computers also are merely tools that perform certain operations efficiently, after being programmed properly by man. In short, a man did the thinking on these retriever problems, not the applied mathematics nor the computer. In fact, in order to keep up my motivation so that I would continue plugging away, I have asked myself the following question many times: Is it not better to think a little and maybe push a few buttons, with all the associated limitations, than to continue having the chain pulled on one or more of us in practically every trial?

Epilogue and Prologue

Epilogue.--Make the assumption that McMahan, in *Retriever Theory*, has written down all that he knows about judging American retriever trials. Now suppose that we are given a complete list of judges who have eight or more points. Let J_i indicate the ith judge, where i goes from 1 to k + 1. Further, let McMahan be identified as J_{k+1}. All other things being equal, if each judge, J_i where i < k + 1, were to master the material in this book, then each and every judge, J_t,   would know everything McMahan knows plus what J_t knows himself. If each and every J_t were to assimilate and apply these principles, under stringent ethical standards, it would follow logically that McMahan would be the least qualified of all so-called eight-point judges.

Prologue.--That being the case, it would be unwise for any individual or club to consider McMahan for further judging assignments. This logical conclusion brings to mind an associated idea. In almost every trial which I have judged, at least one or more handlers, while on the line, has attempted to "assist" me in evaluating the work of his retriever. The following thought has occurred to me repeatedly and I (like other judges) have actually made such a remark on occasion: "You run 'em; I'll judge 'em." In view of the conclusion above which we deduced by logical methods, now and in the future, I shall be able to say: "I merely run 'em; you judge 'em."

If a reader, even a most dedicated retriever judge or would-be judge, has been with me from the preface, by this time he must be thinking somewhat as I am, namely, words, symbols, formulas, statistics, statistics, formulas, symbols, words, if only they could produce honest, competent retriever field trial judges. Let this dedicated retriever fan also remember that this whole undertaking has been conducted merely as a bare indication of what lies ahead and what can be achieved.

A pittance of practice may be worth a tome of theory.

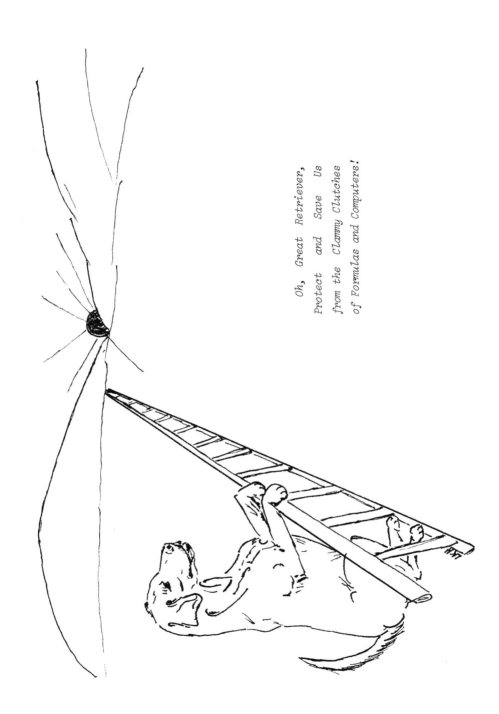

Oh, Great Retriever,
Protect and Save Us
from the Clammy Clutches
of Formulas and Computers!

APPENDIX A

ASSUMED READER WISDOM

For the most part, this appendix is written in conversational mode directly from "me" to "you," but before we get deeply involved some background facts should be set forth. First of all, the reader should know that this book was written as a leisure time activity--for sheer enjoyment; I assume that the reader will keep this in mind. The embryonic stage of this book involved more or less unrelated activities in which the author made many abortive attempts to clarify his own thoughts about narrow aspects of the retriever field trial game. In fact, it may be helpful for the senior retriever enthusiast (the reader) to keep in mind throughout that in the main this book was written to the author, for the author, by the author. As a consequence, even if every other retriever enthusiast (RE) "knows" everything that's in this book, the reader can assume that at least one RE (the author) found out part of what every other senior RE "knows."

The foregoing implies that the writing of this book has been play. As a matter of fact, it is my belief that play has preceded work throughout the history of mankind in the development of complex societies. Moreover, I don't mind admitting that I'm a boy at heart; I haven't grown old and I guess I can't really grow up. I suppose that's why I like the puppy so much; he's the most playful animal it's been my pleasure to know.

I assume that the reader is wise and considerate enough to know that my comments apply to conventional trials--if such exist; obviously, comments may not apply to special all water trials or all land trials; and there may be other exceptions. With these preliminaries out of the way, I have many things to say to the reader in a direct sort of way, so let's be on with the monologue.

695

If you have trained your own retriever as a derby, handled him or her in a licensed trial and completed the stake and have no further "retriever experience," then only small portions of this book are likely to be meaningful to you. If you yourself have trained and handled this same retriever to a ribbon in a licensed qualifying stake, then far more of this book should be meaningful to you. If you yourself have trained and handled an all-age retriever all the way from a puppy to the derby stake, through the qualifying stake, and on to the point-giving all-age stakes, and if your entry has been awarded at least a judges' award of merit (JAM) in a licensed all-age (open or amateur) stake, and further, if you will put forth considerable intellectual effort, there is no excuse for your not being able to read and understand most of this book (except perhaps selected highly technical portions). On the other hand, if you have only handled retrievers which others have trained, do not try to understand this book; it is to be expected that you will fail to appreciate its implications. And yet, if you will read and try to understand the implications with the intention of meeting these criteria in the future, you should be able to benefit from the implications and possibly realize an appreciation for the book at that future time.

As alluded to earlier, I assume that you are familiar with the literature on retrievers and retriever field trials. Of course, even at the moment, you continue to read books and "trade journals" on retrievers and field trials; in addition, you read popular columns on dogs, kennels, and other such topics. However, in view of your vast experience, I assume that you do wonder why so much space (in the aforementioned materials) is devoted to subject matter which appears so obvious to you.

In addition to a background with sporting dogs, and explicitly with retrievers, the reader must put forth intellectual effort in order to understand this book. It is mandatory that the reader often work slowly with paper and pencil in hand. Each example (with exceptions as noted) should be verified in detail. The reader should feel free to skip topics which appear complicated on first reading; the subject matter of that particular topic might be cleared up by remarks made a few pages later.

Undoubtedly, one or more practiced and competent mathematicians and/or statisticians will chance upon this volume. It is assumed that such a reader also is wise and considerate enough not to be destructively critical of the apparent lack of rigor in this book; it is further assumed that he will obtain some subject-matter knowledge (retriever knowledge) before he makes assertions from the point of view of the "symbol- or number-fumbler" only. When a reader does find a slip or error that may make a difference to our retriever game, it is assumed that he is wise enough to know that the author will appreciate his attention being called to such an error.

If you habitually bore your field trial colleagues by giving excuses for why your retriever did poorly (he had three fly-aways, his pheasant fell in water or in a hole, the judge forgot to call his number, every entry got a quacker except my retriever, the bird fell practically behind the gunners, a lady stealthily led her retriever into the ready box and startled my entry, the bird flew directly into the sun, ... , it was so near dark he could scarcely see the fall, ... , the judges just didn't like him, ... , it was a typical McM test, ... , he went within six inches of the bird on the up-wind side, he really had tough luck because he stayed close in the area and hunted "tight," Lady Luck was just against me, his duck dived and stayed down, his bird was killed far from the Guns and all others fell 30 yards closer, ... , he froze on the near Guns, ... , the wind changed to dead calm just as I went to the line, ...), then you are not mature enough regarding retrievers to get much out of this book.

If when you are one of the Guns at a trial, and you miss a cock pheasant because you let his long tail divert your swing from his head, and then you break the rule of "never making an excuse when you miss," then you need more seasoning before you read this book.

If you still think that licensed retriever field trials as conducted in the United States are not a game, then you are too naïve to assimilate the principles set forth here. By game, I mean specific "amusement" which involves competition under specified rules. If you think that sportsmanship is paramount in the field trial game, then you do need additional experience. By sportsmanship, I mean qualities and behavior befitting a person who can take loss or defeat without complaint and accompanying excuses, or take victory without gloating, and who treats game, judges, retrievers, Guns, and his opponents with humaneness, consideration, generosity, and courtesy. In the United States, I assert that *game* is descriptive of organized retriever field trial activities.

If you think that you can expect the best retrievers to be ranked "correctly" and thus to get the appropriate ribbons in a particular trial, then you are ignoring not only judging aptness, but favoritism, politics, and plain dishonest human behavior. If you think that over the long-run the best retrievers (according to American rules) get the ribbons and trophies, you are probably right; for this it is clear that no excuses need be offered.

If you feel compelled to go into detail about a test which your retriever failed or if you need to make excuses for why your entry was dropped after a particular series, then you need to walk to the line with a few more entries, or mature more before attempting to read this book. This is especially true if you repeat your excuses to person after person, to any and all who will listen to you.

If you have matured enough and if you have enough experience to have made the following rule for yourself and if you do not feel compelled to break it, then read on, for indeed you are a disciplined and sensible person. The rule is this: An unsatisfactory performance in a stake is the handler's fault or the retriever's fault or a combination of both, although there may be extenuating circumstances. If you have in truth arrived at the point in your career in the retriever field trial game where you never risk being a bore by making excuses, then this book has something to offer you. If you brag, and if you have something to brag about, you will be tolerated; in contrast, one who makes excuses will gain nothing from this book, and I do hope that he won't read it.

In short, there's no excuse for making an excuse; not only does each of us probably think that our retriever is more capable than he really is, but perhaps most of us think that we're better birdboys or handlers or Guns or marshals or judges than we really are.

I assume that the reader knows that trouble spots seem to develop in the life cycle of retriever clubs, either in the whelping process, ... , or in the conduct of a trial. Goldbricks, social climbers, and the like are always around for the free ride from reliable and dependable workhorses. The latter, who likewise happen to be true sportsmen, are the backbone of the game. Most clubs have one or more; I assume that the wise reader is grateful to each of these for conducting trials which provide him enjoyment.

The wise reader must have been in the retriever field trial game long enough to know that pinpoint marking is a game of inches. Moreover, this wise reader knows that "disappointment" is a name of the retriever field trial game; even the veteran professional or amateur of half a century expects the retriever field trial game to be just one disappointment after another. (See Addenda: *Disappointment* ... .)

Amateur-Professional Relationships

It is assumed that the reader is knowledgeable concerning the many ramifications and implications of the statement, "the amateur pays the freight." Moreover, it is assumed (as of this writing, 1965) that he knows that in many trials the amateur all-age stake is a "rush job," run on a "short Sunday," with weary judges (who may have flight schedules to meet) and supported by still wearier personnel.

Another assumption is that the reader knows that once the amateur becomes involved with a professional trainer, the series of steps he must take to accomplish certain objectives appears to be almost endless. It is further assumed that the reader knows client-professional financial relationships are many and varied. Not only may fees vary from professional (pro to pro), but the derivation of total charges also may vary.

Judging is Controversial

The reader to whom this book is addressed does not have to be reminded that there is much argument concerning the conduct of field trials for retrievers in America. In fact, he "knows for sure" that there is not only considerable but real controversy over the evaluation of retriever performance, and there is still no sign of general agreement about the methods to be used.

The competent retriever-wise reader is expected to recognize early that materials in this book run the gamut from rigorous scientific material composing new knowledge even in the field of mathematics, to applications of probability and statistics, to essays based on mere personal opinion; the continuum extends from science to anecdotes. There are essays on selected topics; I say essays because many subjects are analyzed and presented from a limited or personal point of view.

Provocative versus Controversial versus Sermonic

Provocative.--This book is written to stimulate thought and action; hence, it is provocative.

Controversial.--In order to be provocative, repeatedly my opinion is made an explicit matter of record; however, opinion has been clearly separated from reliable knowledge (where practicable).

Sermonic.--No part of this appendix nor of this book is a rebuke, nor is it addressed to one's conduct or duty. No part of this book is designed to inculcate either morality or rigid rules; moreover, I am not a preacher, nor is this discourse being delivered in a pulpit. In short, I am not sermonizing.

After a reader examines the contents of this volume, I assume that he will recognize early that this is a book about the dogs of one man and some abstractions (of that one man) relating to retriever field trial activities. Moreover, I expect the reader to recognize that the theory is advanced only on a relative basis, although some points may push back the bounds of mathematical knowledge.

Reasonable Care

Since reasonable care has been exercised from start to finish in the writing and preparation of this book, it should not be full of errors; moreover, if the reader begins at the beginning and follows suggestions and if he has the wisdom assumed in this appendix, then I not only hope but believe that he will not encounter many misleading statements and obscurities.

Invited papers.-- Each and every reader is invited to write to me on any topic either included or omitted from this book. I request that the manuscript follow the format of some well-known recognized manual of style. Only papers sent via registered mail, return receipt requested, will be read. The author should give permission to edit and print his paper with proper acknowledgment.

It is expected that each paper will have been rewritten at least four times, with at least a month's intervention between each writing. After, say, the fourth version, the paper should be set aside for at least three months. It is further expected that such papers would then be re-read, revised if required, then checked by a person who is competent in English grammar and structure. I shall look forward to receiving such a paper. For that reader who submits material or makes comments without such careful thought and preparation, I shall assume that he is like the field-trialer who had a nice 300-page book published entitled as follows:

What I *Know* About Retrievers

by

A. Bullshooter.

When one opens the book, he finds 300 blank pages.

In short, material which has been prepared according to the foregoing procedures will be genuinely appreciated.

Another Assumption

I assume that the wise reader explicitly recognizes, obviously, that after reading this book he will never "see" the retriever game again as he has "viewed" it in the past. In fact, I shall be looking over his shoulder each and every time he judges; I assert that he cannot escape the influence of *Retriever Theory* even if he tries (to hide his ...). The foregoing has forced me to recognize the great responsibility that I have in writing this book; consequently, as many of my acquaintances know, I have been somewhat reluctant to release it. However, I do have one great consolation, namely, if the wise reader will master the methods presented in *Retriever Theory*, then apply them correctly, he will turn out with wise decisions and "right answers" over the long run--not because of the author, but in spite of the author. In short, I assume that the wise reader recognizes that he too must share with me this great responsibility we have to the American retriever field trial game.

GLOSSARY OF RETRIEVER FIELD TRIAL TERMS

In view of the experience assumed of the reader, no attempt is made to provide a complete list of terminology; however, the reader should be cautioned that I have assigned explicit meaning to selected words and phrases. (Many references clearly set forth the "technical" terms; for example, see James Lamb Free, Chuck Morgan, or the annual membership roster, Hennepin County Amateur Retriever Club, Inc.)

A pittance of practice may be worth a tome of theory.

NOTES TO APPENDIX A

1. Two Series Back-to-Back

I was one of the judges of a derby stake in the spring of 1967 at Mobile. The first two series were back-to-back (that is, the entry came to the line once to run both series). Before the final test dog ran, the judges (at some risk of criticism, no doubt) announced that each and every entry would be allowed to run the second series (get a shot flying pheasant) regardless of whether or not that entry completed the first series, with but one exception; that exception being when the entry broke on the dead bird of the second series (the first bird of a double land mark). (As it turned out, although I do not recall positively, I believe all entries did get a shot flying hen.) The two series were separated by a line of cars parked bumper-to-bumper with a single exception where there was room for a man to walk. The entry came to the line on one side of the cars where he could not see the gunners for the second series, and the first series was run on that side using a thrown dead pheasant; it was a sound, well-selected test across a road, through light cover, up a small valley or draw, with good background. There were vast differences in performance on this single land mark; excellent separation was obtained. When the retriever returned with this bird, the handler heeled his derby entry accompanied by the judges through the one opening in the line of cars. Here series two was conducted involving a double mark on land throwing a dead pheasant first and lastly shooting a flying hen pheasant. For series two, the terrain and cover were different from series one; here the dead hen was beyond a slight knoll in the flat and the flying hen was shot on a hillside across a draw, at the bottom of which ran a small ditch. In this double, there were several pine trees between the two falls. Both birds were thrown from left to right; the judges preferred to throw both birds outward, but wind conditions prevented that set up. Again, excellent separation was obtained. In short, time was conserved, excellent separation obtained on a single, each entry got a flying pheasant, and the two tests were designed to obtain different types of information. For the record, the third series was a double on water and the last series was a land double using a live cock pheasant. Seventeen entries out of slightly more than 40 ran all 4 series getting 2 flying pheasant. At the conclusion of the stake, the judges had an overwhelming winner; second and third places were obvious; further deponent sayeth not.

2. Shotgun Analogy

This analogy was deliberately selected because I am not an expert on shotguns, yet I intend to ruffle tempers somewhat, since each user of the "scatter gun" seems to be strongly opinionated concerning shotguns; in short, each shooter looks for different "things" in a shotgun. In fact, one might justifiably assert that "wisdom flows" on topics of shotguns and scatter gun shooting.

I fired my first shotgun on Christmas day, 1926; it was a 12-gauge Holland and Holland, side-by-side, hammer gun owned by my father. To this day, I prefer the side-by-side double. Moreover, I prefer this hammerless double with box locks, double trigger, ejector, 26-inch barrels (both barrels bored improved cylinder, thus sacrificing instant choice of choke).

I suppose that my economic background and "great depression" experiences still influence my preference for the less expensive (yet "best made") box lock. My preference holds even though "by what they tell me," back action side locks are a bit stronger mechanically than bar action side locks.

In my lifetime, I must have shot a heap of shells at a passel of upland game and water fowl; moreover, not only am I basically a wingshot, but additionally I try never to take long shots, and more than that, I also claim to be a sportsman. Clearly then, I am not interested in firepower; furthermore, I am not interested in cheapness (economy) of the manufacturing process. These facts, combined with my opinion that the best made side-by-side double is a most beautiful sporting weapon, lead me to (be so bold as to) say that a major advantage I see to a "pump" or automatic is that they can be fitted with variable choke devices. Yet, with a double, one does have instant choice of choke if he has selected a shotgun with each barrel bored differently (as is conventional). As compared to automatics in particular, it is my opinion, based on many experiments and much experience, that the side-by-side double is more reliable and more flexible.

Bespoke guns.-- In 1940, I had Lefever manufacture a side-by-side hammerless, 16-gauge double for me. This was the first gun that I had made to my individual order.

It is well-known that through the years, America has gone "pump and automatic." The manufacture of best made side-by-side double guns has been

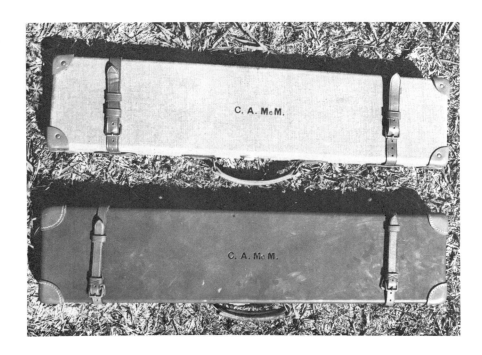

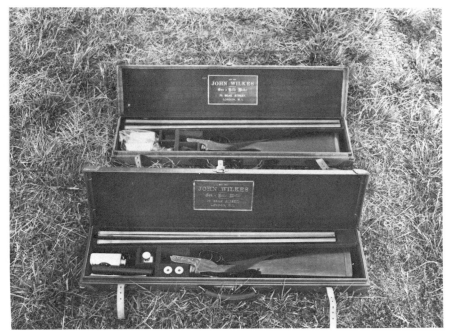

The Webley and Scott and the John Wilkes (bottom).

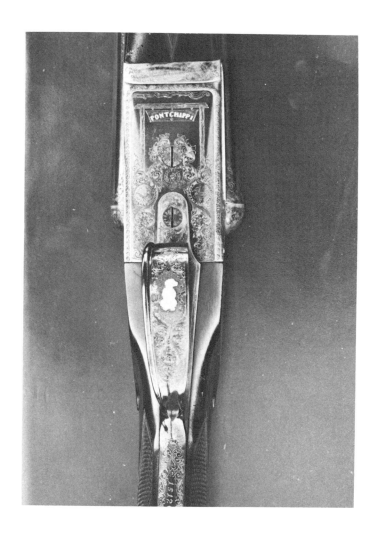

This "best-made" John Wilkes side-by-side double-barrel shotgun was engraved by M. A. Appleby, from a picture of the Pontchippi "emblem" (reference the frontispiece of this book). New Orleans is wedged in between Lake Pontchartrain to the north and the Mississippi River, hence, PONTCHIPPI (inlaid in gold). Although not clearly visible in this picture, the quail, the pigeon (reversed), and the dove are engraved on the "metal of the fore-end" (forestock). The southshore of the lake is visible above the Pontchippi sign. The pheasant and the mallard are below the uprights, and the coat-of-arms is just below the screw head. Kube is engraved in gold bas-relief on the trigger guard. The frontispiece, including its borders of demographic and statistical symbols, was adopted many years ago as the author's bookplate: Ex Libris, C. A. McMahan.

THE AMERICAN KENNEL CLUB

This Certifies That The Kennel Name Prefix

PONTCHIPPI

Has Been Registered For The Use Of

CHALMERS A. MC MAHAN

For A Five Year Period Expiring JANUARY 14, 1969

Secretary

After using the prefix for many years, application was made in 1963 to make it a matter of record.

practically phased out in the United States; reportedly, Winchester does still manufacture (in Japan) the Model 20. In contrast, British gunmakers are reputed to continue to manufacture best quality (to include durability, handling and shooting qualities, and reliability) side-by-side shotguns. Accordingly, in 1965, I discussed and inspected side-by-side double shotguns with personnel at several firms: Churchill (Gunmakers) Ltd. (London); Cogswell and Harrison Ltd. (London); Gallyons (Cambridge); John Dickson and Son (Edinburgh); James Purdey and Sons Limited (London); and John Wilkes, Gun and Rifle Manufacturer, 79 Beak Street, Regent Street (London). On the good advice of two of my English friends who are also flat-coated retriever enthusiasts, Mr. D. C. G. Jessel and Captain Wilson Stephens, I placed an order (fall, 1965) with John Wilkes for a best made shotgun as follows: box lock, side-by-side, hammerless, ejector, double trigger, 12-gauge, 26-inch barrels, both barrels bored improved cylinder. (See excerpt below which appeared two years later in 1967 .)

(Reproduced by kind permission of the publisher.)

SHOTGUNS AND SHOOTING

A Fortnightly Commentry by Turnstone

Although this gun lives within a mere 30 miles of the Smoke, I make it my stern and inexorable duty, despite the blandishments of an M road and an allegedly smooth diesel service, to make as little contact with it as possible. Nevertheless, when, duty bound, I am compelled to enter this vast arena of mini-skirts and pallid faces, I always try to call on at least one gunmaker with a view to catching up on the latest tit-bits of news in the gun world.

Churchill's, Purdey's, Holland's and Boss are, perhaps, the names which immediately spring to mind when one mentions London gunmakers, with Cogswell's, Rigby's and Atkin, Grant and Lang all straining for the post. One, however, that does not is John Wilkes. Little discredit to you if the name is not familiar, for they tend to shun the harsh light of publicity. You want to know where they are? Turn off Regent Street and down the esoteric wonders of Carnaby Street, left into Beak Street and there at the end, with no concession to window displays or such fripperies, is John Wilkes. A plain shop window in need of a lick of paint. A superficial glance might even lead you to suppose the premises empty. But let us look a little closer.

One of the nicest things about Wilkes's is that they still retain an aura of being *real* gunmakers. Tools are to hand, barrels line the walls like miniature organs, and in the back office a stock is, perhaps, being delicately strained and bent as the hot linseed slides over it. There is a feeling of craftsmanship in the air and one is reminded of the days when gunmakers were proud to have their workmen before the public gaze.

They are, too, a genuine family firm, and the name Wilkes is still borne by two sons, a father and an uncle, all of whom strive to maintain the highest traditions of British gunmaking.

The firm was, in fact, started in 1830 in Birmingham, though Wilkes's had been gunmaking way back into the 18th century. In those early days they were chiefly concerned with military arms with some sporting guns as a sideline. It was not until the 1880's that they moved to St. James's Street in London, and there John Wilkes, son of the founder, partnered a Mr. Dougal. The latter after some time took over Short's Powder Factory, leaving John Wilkes to run the firm. Due to legal complications the Dougal part of the team was dropped about 1900, but there still occasionally comes to light a gun with the name Wilkes and Dougal engraved on it.

Just before the First World War another shop was opened in Broad Street, Birmingham, which lasted until 1927. The firm came to its present site in 1924.

They are still making their own guns, and though you will have to wait two years for a sidelock and deplete your bank balance by some £850, it will be worth it. On the other hand, if you are impatient, you may be prepared to make do with a boxlock for about £300 to £400 which can be delivered in a twelve-month.

Rifles are one of their specialities. I was shown a 7 mm. magnum embellished with some of the finest engraving it has been my pleasure to see and a gold kudu, every detail superbly depicted, set beneath the action. This was destined for America. An unusual sight these days was a new falling block rifle in .264 calibre and I was told that the demand for these highly accurate single-shot weapons has increased of late.

Good quality engravers are these days at a premium, and when they are also young and obviously have a brilliant career before them, they are worth much to any gunmaker in terms of prestige and standards of presentation. The Wilkes family are, perhaps, particularly fortunate in having the services of Malcolm Appleby, only 21 and ostensibly still an apprentice, yet producing a quality of work which is quite astounding. His mastery of line and delicate touch combined with an unusually mature sense of restraint indicate his great future. At present he is studying at the Royal College and it is hoped that when his term there is over he will return to Beak Street.

The next time you are in London and have an hour to kill, call in at John Wilkes the gunmakers. You may not buy anything, but you will be recieved courteously, and will leave enriched by the knowledge that old-fashioned standards still apply on this humdrum world.

*   *   *

Incidentally, while I was in Wilkes's I was told that a day or so

M. A. Appleby.

"THE SPIRIT OF FIELD SPORTS"

As interpreted in an engraving by Malcolm A. Appleby, engraver for John Wilkes. Original in the author's private Pontchippi Collection by way of John Wilkes, 1965.

before two outrageously garbed, apparent members of the male sex, swayed in from Carnaby Street and asked to purchase a cartridge extractor. What gauge was it required for? they were asked. Twelve-bore or, perhaps, sixteen? That didn't matter, they said. They just wanted a cartridge extractor. Well, did they require one with a ring and hook or just the simple ring extractor? They indicated the latter. On being shown several gauges they tried them on their fingers, finally selecting two, which fitted perfectly, and pranced out of the shop, highly delighted with their latest "mod jewellery." Ah, well!

(Source: *Shooting Times and Country Magazine*, March 2, 1967, p. 266.)

While in London, I also purchased a Webley and Scott, box lock, double trigger, hammerless, 12-gauge, side-by-side double through the Wilkes. Young John Wilkes accompanied me to the West London Shooting Grounds where he had made an appointment for me with the world-renowned "shot and coach," Mr. Percy Stanbury. Mr. Stanbury spent the morning with me and we used a try-gun. Moreover, under his supervision and coaching, I shot at a white-washed steel plate; I shot at clay pigeons from conventional traps, and I shot at clay pigeons from "high towers." After Mr. Stanbury was convinced that he had collected the necessary "fitting data," the firm of John Wilkes reset the stock on the Webley and Scott according to Mr. Stanbury's instructions; then the gun was shipped to me later. Of course, John Wilkes used these same specifications for the shotgun that they manufactured for me. (See picture of the shotgun made by John Wilkes.) During the fall of 1967, Mr. Tom Wilkes met a tragic death; then in March of 1968, Mr. John Wilkes, Sr., died.

Concluding statement regarding the shotgun analogy.-- From the foregoing, it must be clear that over the years I have delved into various topics related to shotguns; to list just a few: proof; safety; original form of the double, the over-and-under (which is centuries old); history and development, from the flint locks of the eighteenth and nineteenth centuries to the perfection of the modern side-by-side double around the turn of the twentieth century; ... ; killing power (penetration) of shotgun pellets; ... ; master eye and cross-eyed stocks; ... ; heavy, high velocity loads as compared to others; ... ; fire-arms regulations; fit (pitch, cast-off, ... , comb-height, comb-thickness); ... ; fine craftsmanship and artistry, to include balance, weight, engraving, style; choke dimensions, shot size, length of barrels, and many other matters. When such varied subjects of discussion have been well-considered, it seems that finally I always end up with just two standards by which I judge a particular shotgun: (1) Do I like the shotgun?   (2) Do I shoot well with this particular shotgun?

How does this analogy relate to the judge of retriever field trials? I wish the judge who evaluates my retriever's performance to be just as biased and opinionated about retrievers as I am prejudiced and bullheaded about shotguns; however, I want him to know retrievers in depth and the judging process far, far better than my superficial knowledge of shotguns and shooting.   Does the judge like the retriever which he placed first?   Would this retriever be useful in a day's shooting?

3.   DF Questions and Answers

Sometimes I am tempted to think that the path of life is rough, rocky, and bumpy; in short, that getting older is terrible, until I consider the only alternative.   Even as I travel along the retriever highway, many people ask me what I consider tough but legitimate questions; I always try to answer these questions to the best of my ability and when I don't know, I so state because I take pride in knowing what I don't know. Often, however, a questionner poses a query and provides his own answer in the same breath before I can reply. People who know me well know that for that individual I use the following rule: Ask me a foolish question and I'll provide a damn fool (DF) answer.   To illustrate, flat-coated retrievers have long hair and an appearance somewhat similar to "black setters." If someone asks me a question such as "what kind of retrievers are those, Doc, a cross between a setter and a Labrador?" I may just grin, remain quiet, and oftentimes the questionner appears to infer "yes." If I have had just the right amount of toddy for the body, I then might even neologize for him and state: They belong to a new breed called "setradors."

Since I mentioned the setrador, this is a good place to discuss the flatrador (flatcoat × Labrador--McMahan style) and to explicitly state what I mean by certain degrees of (dog) inbreeding.   Basically, I assume that all matings of dogs involve some degree of inbreeding; in short, I assume there is a continuum of inbreeding. Depending upon the context, I also reserve (use) the term inbreeding for brother × sister matings and parent × offspring matings.   To summarize and continue under the foregoing assumptions, when I use the term inbreeding, I shall refer to sib matings and/or parent to offspring matings ("close inbreeding"); all other "inbreeding" (matings of known close relatives) I shall refer to as line breeding.   Selection within a closed

Pontchippi Chance and Pontchippi Choice, flat-coated retriever males, whelped June 5, 1969 (Wynk ex Wave).

A "flatrador" puppy at Pontchippi, 1968.

UNITED   RETRIEVER

CLUB

RULES

"One" of the finest retriever clubs in the world.

A collection of references consisting of well-selected programs
and other articles, 1941-1970. (For example, the entry fee for the
National Championship Stake was $125.00.)

Note South Carolina County Hunting License, Oconee 1415, purchased in my name by my father, while I was away in the Army, Christmas Eve, 1941.

kennel or closed community would be the next degree of inbreeding (on my hypothetical continuum), but I would not speak or think of such matings as inbreeding or line breeding; obviously, matings within breed or variety would be even farther removed from close inbreeding. Even though the best flat-coats were used in the making of the "modern" Labrador, the cross between a flatcoat and a Labrador (1960 style) would be the next degree of inbreeding, namely, the crossing of breeds within species. And for completeness, there could be other even lesser degrees of inbreeding on our hypothetical continuum.

4. Tribulations of Clubs

No retriever club has a monopoly on growing pains and disputes; McMahan has seen these problems first-hand from Florida to Texas, from Louisiana and Alabama through Tennessee to Wisconsin and Minnesota, in New York and New England, and in Canada and Great Britain as well. Moreover, he has seen similar problems in bird dog and beagle clubs and show-giving clubs-- including clubs in Georgia.

5. Dog Versus Retriever

In many places throughout this book, the word dog is used interchangeably with retriever. In other places, dog is used correctly in contradistinction to bitch. I shall expect the context of usage to make clear the meaning to the wise and experienced reader.

6. Charged with Emotion

I expect the reader to recognize that the subject of judging American retriever field trials may be charged with emotion, and seems to excite particularly those who know least about it; more pointedly, degree of excitement might be described as being inversely related to true knowledge of the judging process.

7. Dilemma of the Author

The wise reader is expected to recognize the dilemma in which the author has found himself repeatedly in trying to write this book. That is, in order to be unmistakably clear, this book is written in a limited mathematical notation for senior retriever enthusiasts who in the main cannot read mathematical shorthand. Carefully note, however, that I do not expect a reader to cram his brain with irrelevant gibberish to the exclusion of worthwhile know-how--and I assume that he will not.

8. Mistakes Won't Hurt

When I was a boy in South Carolina, I often heard the expression "by what they say to me.'" This meant that the speaker did not quite believe it all himself and he was not quite sure whether or not his listener would challenge him; but on he would go because he thought someone said it. I assume that the new judge knows that many RE's don't go to the trouble of prefacing their remarks by some such statement as "... to me."

In the main, young judges are hampered by lack of quantitative information about judging retriever trials. By necessity, conclusions have been based upon nothing better than personal hunches, even though there might have been some lion-hearted attempts to obtain quantitative data. Even though this book does not purport to provide definitive answers, there are enough selected materials in it so that a new judge can seriously consider many specific situations before he encounters them in a trial. It is like a driver (automobile) training course in a classroom; it does not teach you how to drive, but it does enable one to be presented problem situations where a mistake doesn't hurt anyone.

9. Reader

What RE will be capable of reading this book? What RE will be sufficiently motivated to read it? These are the types of questions raised by my 23-year-old son when he glanced at drafts of the chapters during the days of Christmas, 1967. At that time, this young man was already a graduate engineer (B.S., 1966) and a second year graduate student in nuclear physics at Rice University and a holder of an Atomic Energy Commission Fellowship. Not only was he somewhat sophisticated with regard to symbolism, but he had completed a first-rate course in mathematical statistics. Moreover, he was knowledgeable retriever-wise, having been a birdboy for years, having attended trials (to include an "amateur national") from Florida to Texas, to Minnesota, Wisconsin, and Michigan, to New York, and other areas up east. His comment was that he could not read it without having pencil and paper at hand.

Reply.--As stated elsewhere in this treatise, I expect the reader to have paper and pencil at hand. Nevertheless, I do recognize that this book may still be 30 years ahead of its time (1968). Field-trialers of the year 2000 can read it easily; many field-trialers of 1970 can only criticize it but even they can't afford not to try to read it. I reckon there will be about four levels of readers: (1) the statistician who is interested in new methods who will stand on my shoulders as I have stood on the shoulders of others; (2) the dedicated reader with considerable mathematical and statistical background who one might expect to contribute to new knowledge; (3) the reader who can follow through the worked examples and who is interested in furthering his understanding of the game; and (4) the reader who will not struggle through the gobbledeegook, but who will accept the statements on faith. For the latter reader, he will find "rules of thumb" for his further consideration where I suggest that for each such rule of thumb, he clearly identify as follows: "Back, tweet-tweet, and pop" and use the form on the next page to improve on those rules.

Moreover, he should distinguish among the rules of thumb that are supported by logic or empirical evidence, in contrast to those based solely on the author's opinion.

10. A Bit of Chronology, and More

Samuel Eliot Morison once stated: "... History is like that, very chancy." Under the assumption that a discerning reader might exercise even greater reach of thought if he knew about some early events and something of my "early thinking," material in this section is reproduced from old notes and "memoranda for the record."

In 1956, I made an off-hand remark in the presence of my 12-and-16-year-old sons that someone ought to dedicate the entire life of at least one retriever to the understanding of the judging process in American retriever field trials. The quick retort came back: Why don't you do it? I closed my mouth and quietly slipped away, but I continued to think about it.

Such an undertaking, I reasoned, should be addressed to many questions that most retriever enthusiasts have never asked. Complicated problems would necessarily have to be attacked with simple models; even so, interesting aspects could be studied over limited ranges. Nowhere must the treatment (be intended to) be dogmatic (even though it may appear dogmatic for convenience in getting along with the study).

It is assumed that the wise reader will recognize any such categorical, positive assertion and treat it properly--merely as a handy instrument. After all, a retriever enthusiast, or a scholar, who is both dogmatic and wrong should be an easy target; the author knows that well. Like the topics of our fathers and grandfathers, much of what we believe about retrievers boils

Back, tweet-tweet, and pop

B
a
c
k

t
w
e
e
t
-
t
w
e
e
t

a
n
d

p
o
p

Rule(s) of thumb for those who have Pontchippi faith:

Reader's "better" rules:

where reader defines "better" as follows:

B
a
c
k

t
w
e
e
t
-
t
w
e
e
t

a
n
d

p
o
p

Back, tweet-tweet, and pop

McMahan, in the process of clearing a place for the boat dock, Pontchippi-on-Canal,1958 (both the canal and levees provide convenient training areas).

With Kube in the Tchefuncte River Nr. Bogue Falaya State Park, 1958 or 1959.

The renowned Cork (Kube's sire), with Tony (his distinguished trainer) and Mac, at Del-Tone Kennels, St. Cloud, Minnesota, 1961. (Cork demonstrated on this occasion also that he would not heel.)

Training in Illinois (1961). The distinguished trainer "Cotton," (out front of) Kube, and the author ("on rope").

down to personal experience versus personal experience; hence, we should not expect a final verdict. Nevertheless, I can make a start toward consolidating experiences and making them available to others.

About two years later (1958), I decided to take action necessary to ... understanding the judging process and hope that I would be lucky enough to get a capable retriever who would be blessed with good health and a decade or so of "productive" life; so, I selected a Labrador bitch (for obvious reasons).

I further decided that the entire endeavor must be fun; nevertheless, I would attempt to share what knowledge and insights I gained with other interested individuals via a written "report." At the outset, I made up my mind that for the duration of the venture, first priority must always be on understanding the judging process; "club life," participation in "retriever social activities," "popularity" and recognition in the field trial game, must have low priority; winning and points must always be important, but likewise have lower priority than the quest for knowledge of the judging process. Moreover, *the* report must not be released during the lifetime of *the* retriever; "sales appeal" must be disregarded out-and-out in order to allow myself great freedom regarding what to include; and firstly, it must not yield personal monetary profit. [*Aside, 1970:* After all, I have never sold a retriever.]

Hence (in 1958), I went to Michigan and purchased a big, clumsy, lovable bitch puppy sired by Cork. In tune with the times, the boys labelled her a "square in 3-D"; so I called her Kube. When this project is terminated, I hope I shall be able to say the following: Kube influenced "for the good" the judging process (and the understanding of the judging process) of American field trials more than any retriever who ever lived; dedication of her life to this venture appears to have been worthwhile. If I can say this, then shortly before the report is released, I shall write the following and fill in the blanks:

The retriever is dead; long live the retriever.
Kube [1958-19_ _] is dead; long live her influence.

11. Afterthought, 1970

This lucubration really amounts to a "set of exercises" I went through in order to understand the process of judging dogs in the field, particularly American retrievers in field trials. Where others speculated, I attempted to measure and evaluate. Rather than merely assert conclusions, I have tried to show how I arrived at those conclusions. Only lately, before I turned over the results of these attempts to others, have I provided the details of the methods used. I do not feel compelled to explain why this book is necessary nor how it differs from those that already exist. As of (Spring) 1970, as far as I can ascertain, this treatise on the application of mathematics, probability, and statistics to American retriever field trials is a "sole source." Most retriever enthusiasts probably feel that we do not have good tools for evaluating retriever performance in the field. This application of the mathematics of uncertainty to judging trials for fetching specialists was further motivated by my own compulsion to do a better job of evaluation; after all, half the skill of life lies in making poor tools do good work.

I am an achiever; I am not a protestor. It is not a purpose of this book to set the world on fire, but merely to create a williwaw within the American retriever field trial fraternity.

12.   May, 1970

According to plan (1958-1970), this book can now go to press; I shall continue field trialing but with one ever-present absence.

ADDENDA

"And the same to you."--Each spring, as a university professor I am forced to lecture to second year medical students at the Louisiana State University Medical Center; to say the least, my subject is not a popular one; moreover, students are required to work and to think, both of which appear to be objectionable to many people. This, combined with the fact that grades must be assigned--judgment exercised--generates antagonism in selected students toward the course and toward me. In short, I "know" what these students think about me. Hence, I tell students that I appreciate their speaking to me when our paths cross, but each time I return the salutation they should explicitly infer and know that I am actually returning their "kind thoughts" by saying "and the same to you." The situation is somewhat analogous in the role of judge versus owner and/or trainer and/or handler. Each time one or more of those has kind thoughts or makes kind remarks about my judging or even calls me "great names," each and every one of them knows for sure that my "good morning" includes "and the same to you (whatever your thoughts or whatever you have said)." I assume that the wise reader likewise will not soon forget this as he examines and reacts to the products of my leisure time activities. Obviously, even the best will not suit everyone.

Disappointment (danger! Analogy).-- American football enthusiasts have been brainwashed by radio and TV announcers through such terminology as blitz, bomb, effort, and second effort; some well-known coaches are quoted as naming the game "fumble or knock or hit." The above notwithstanding, all seem to recognize that American football is a game of inches.

Analogy, danger.-- If one asks a pro what he charges per month to train a retriever, he may receive a quick reply of, say, 100 per month. The inquirer then may calculate rapidly that he could get his retriever trained for 6 months for a total outlay of only 600 dollars. This figure may be far from factual, even though the pro offered reliable information. It may be similar to asking an automobile salesman to quote the price of a popular make car and receiving a reply of "only $2298." Later you may find that the quoted price is f.o.b. factory, stripped (no radio, heater, extra tire, ... , air cleaner, ...), without taxes, servicing charges, ... , *ad nauseum.*

715

Throughout this book, I have assumed knowledgeable readers. This is a good place to demonstrate the depth of knowledge that I assume on each subject. To repeat, in order to illustrate the depth of knowledge which I expect my reader to possess on every subject, it seems worthwhile to write down some policies which I "hear" (second-hand) exist on this, an obvious topic.

A. Fees for training and boarding may be included in a single fee, say, 90 dollars per month.

B. When an owner pays the entry fees, a fixed charge may be made for each trial in which a pro handles a dog, say, 15 dollars.

C. Board may be a fixed amount, say, 50 dollars per month, and training may be added on separately.

D. Training for field trials may be charged separately and may vary from, say, 50 to 150 dollars per month.

E. Ammunition and birds may or may not be included in fixed fees. If they are not included in a single amount, charges may be made for birds separately, say, from 25 cents to 75 cents per pigeon (imagine the bookkeeping problems under such a system!), from 2 to 4 dollars per pheasant or duck.

F. Some pros explicitly state a charge for pickup and delivery services to railroad stations and airports; others "hide" the charge.

G. The senior trainer at one training kennel may welcome visitors and assist them "for free"; others charge (explicitly) for their services. The trainer may charge differentially for assisting with a dog which belongs to a client but which is "not with the trainer, " as compared to assisting a person who requests assistance but who has not placed a dog with the trainer.

H. Training fees may differ from training to shooting dog standards as compared to training to field trial standards.

I . Other.

Clearly, I could have chosen another topic to suggest that I expect the reader to have knowledge in depth.

A medical student's operational definition: The professor is a practitioner of applied probability (color slide courtesy of a student presentation at a student-faculty banquet, circa 1961).

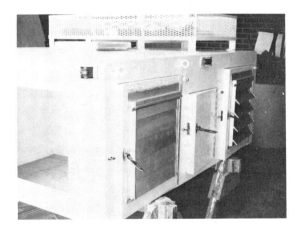

Evidence of McMahan as a practitioner of the "manual arts." Kennel compartments under construction, 1968 Pontchippi Shooting Brake. Note thick fiberglassed (insulated) roof and walls, cross-ventilation, and powered roof ventilator to assist in "beating the heat" in the deep South.

AMERICAN BRITTANY CLUB
This Certifies That

Capt C A Mc Mahan

IS A MEMBER OF THE AMERICAN BRITTANY
CLUB, AND A SPONSOR OF ITS IDEALS.

This Card Expires

4/30/45

J L Whitworth
Secretary

Service

He was a major but the club records still showed captain.

APPENDIX B

MY IDEAL JUDGE

Definition of $\mathcal{J}$

The symbol $\mathcal{J}$ refers to my theoretical model of the idealized (nonexistent) judge of American retriever trials, 1969.

BACKGROUND MATERIAL

Personality and Character of the Judge

In 1951, I wrote an essay in which I pointed out that "a great [amount] of research concerning personality has accumulated, but many of the concepts are not operational and do not lend themselves to scientific study." I further stated that "almost every writer on the subject ... defined the term in his own manner ... ." Personality, like amateur handler, is difficult to define. In this framework, I wrote the following:[1]

> It is assumed that man is a mass of protoplasm; that he does not do anything unless he is "pushed" ... . Life amounts to a process of problem solving--that is, of adjusting to one situation after another. In this process of living, each individual solves his problems rather consistently. Of course he does not behave as consistently as do some of the comic-strip characters, such as Alley Oop, Nancy, or ... . It is possible to predict how each of these characters will "get out of" the predicament in which he finds himself, as he regularly solves his problems by the same patterns. Even though actual individual behavior is less predictable, people in general behave fairly uniformly. This uniformity of behavior enables us to point out certain traits in individuals, to describe them, and to develop patterns of expectancy.

717

Human personality.--In that same essay, I wrote that [one author] tentatively defined personality as "the more or less organized ideas, attitudes, traits, and habits which an individual has built up into roles for dealing with others and with himself." In this book on retriever-ism, clearly, we are concerned with the *role* of judge of an American retriever field trial.

What personality is not.-- In order to clarify the term further, I wrote as follows:[1]

> (1) Personality is not an evaluative term. [One author] holds that "character is personality evaluated, and person-ality is character devaluated." Although according to the val-ues of our society some personality traits and characteristics are more desirable than others, in the main the term is not used with the idea of value attached. Therefore, within this framework, the following type of statement has no meaning: "he has a dynamic personality"; "she has a negative person-ality"; or "... has a magnetic personality." To say of a child that he has a "good," "bad," or "average" personality is meaningless.

> (2) One person does not have "more" personality than another. In the technical sense, one person has just as much personality as another, the important point being that the per-sonalities are different from one another.

Judge's personality and character.-- In selecting a judge, it seems to me that we desire a judge with a consistent method of problem-solving (personality) which we approve or value (character).

Wise Reader

Clearly, possession of ideal traits of character is a necessary condition for our ideal judge, $\mathcal{J}$, but this is not a sufficient condition. It is assumed that $\mathcal{J}$ not only has ideal character traits (to include those of a patriotic citizen), but he also possesses all the attributes and experience of the "wise reader" sketched in Appendix A.

Analogy (danger) and an assumption.-- Some games can be learned in ways other than actual participation and experience. It is well-

known that some of the "best" "old-time" football coaches never actually played competitive football. Contrariwise, some of the best
football players do not make the best coaches; neither do some of the
best retriever trainers and handlers make the best judges. *Assumption:* The above notwithstanding, $\mathcal{J}$ believes that the competent retriever field trial judge must be an experienced trainer, and must
have demonstrated training and handling competence in field trials.

Assumption. -- Admittedly, social status, wealth or lack of it,
"personality," and dress of a handler and/or owner could be used as
the basis for selecting the best field retriever from a group of retrievers. Private judgments, opinions, lies, debates, unforgettable
retrieves, fancies, one or more of these likewise could be used as the
basis for selecting the best retrievers for field work. One might even
supply many sorts of evidence and information on (each retriever in)
a group of retrievers to one of these modern high-speed electronic
imbeciles and invite it to select a winner. Aside from the fact that
computers lie from time to time, such a system would make us fore-
go the many pleasures of speculation. Undoubtedly, there are other
bases that could be used for selecting the best retrievers. The above
notwithstanding, $\mathcal{J}$ makes a fundamental assumption. $\mathcal{J}$ assumes
that institutionalized public competition is the best method for deciding which is the best retriever(s) in a given class.

DISCUSSION BETWEEN $\mathcal{J}$ AND A LESS
EXPERIENCED JUDGE

In order to crystalize some ideas concerning the ideal judge, $\mathcal{J}$,
I have chosen to discuss several topics to indicate the scope and depth
of thinking that is required to develop such a model. As points of departure, $\mathcal{J}$'s responsibility to the young judge is discussed; then some
of his ideas on training and treatment of game are presented; finally,
some considerations for selecting judges, plus other ideal characteristics of $\mathcal{J}$, are outlined.

[*Aside:*   As used in this discussion, "young" refers to the other judge, called the "young judge, " who has less judging experience than $\mathcal{J}$. Depending on the context, young may also indicate a lower chronological age or both less experience and lower chronological age.]

Senior-Junior Judge Relationship

One judge is not supposed to be senior in authority to another judge, but in practical situations, one judge often has more experience than the other, especially in junior stakes. $\mathcal{J}$, being the ideal, often has more knowledge and experience than the person with whom he judges, and $\mathcal{J}$ believes that this should always be the situation in junior stakes. Since an obvious prerequisite to judging is knowledge of retriever work, it is disturbing to $\mathcal{J}$ to see young judges being indoctrinated into the role of judge by other judges who do not know retrievers and retriever trials.

$\mathcal{J}$ thinks that one need not be pessimistic in any sense when he envisions the possible difficulties of obtaining an adequate supply of good judges in the future; he thinks the supply will be found all right. At the moment, inculcation of enthusiasm, sportsmanship, and knowledge of retrievers among the young judges is of vital importance.

As a "senior" judge, $\mathcal{J}$ realizes that licensed retriever trials are the showcase for American retrievers; they are not training sessions. Consequently, $\mathcal{J}$ accepts responsibility for setting and demanding high standards, not only for performance of the retrievers in the field, but for selected other activities connected with the conduct of the trial. $\mathcal{J}$ is the kind of a man to whom one would like to assign responsibility for indoctrinating his son or grandson into a sport of sportsmen. $\mathcal{J}$ recognizes that the entire field trial fraternity is dependent upon responsible, experienced men to introduce young and/or less experienced judges properly to the game. $\mathcal{J}$ knows that he must ascertain that the young judge has completed his basic training before the young judge and his peers take over.

According to my definition, judging is the process of forming an opinion or of making an evaluation by discerning and comparing. $\mathcal{J}$ impresses upon the young judge that each judge is expected to exercise his powers of judgment with perception and acumen.

To illustrate, if a judge routinely and/or invariably is a party to conducting a stake where only 6 dogs or less complete out of, say, 35 starters, then $\mathcal{J}$ is inclined to suspect that this judge is evading his responsibility to exercise judgment. In short, he suspects that this judge is acting merely in an executive role for the trial-giving club. That is, he is setting tests which the dogs can barely complete and, thus, he avoids making judgments. $\mathcal{J}$ also impresses upon the young judge that although the judges have full authority, neither judge is simply a referee nor is he simply an umpire; that setting up tests requires the combined skill and judgment of both judges--each must contribute to the utmost; that once a test is set, each judge should exercise *his* powers of judgment independently of the other judge; that the retrievers must be tested until each judge is convinced that he has witnessed a winning performance; and that both judges must agree independently (see definitions in Chapter Seven) that the winner is obviously the winner. In short, the conclusion must be completely satisfactory to each judge; otherwise, additional series must be conducted. Moreover, $\mathcal{J}$ knows that when there is not a wide difference between first and second places (but yet the first place entry is a clear and obvious winner), the handler (owner and/or supporter) of the second place dog will almost invariably say: "I was surprised when you stopped; I thought you would run another series."

In his discussions with less experienced judges, $\mathcal{J}$ makes explicit efforts to pass along his thoughts on pertinent subjects. Some of those thoughts are presented in the paragraphs which follow.

Ideal retriever.--$\mathcal{J}$ insists that a judge must have a clear idea of what he is looking for in a retriever, because his tests must be set up to select that ideal retriever. $\mathcal{J}$ wants the winner of the stake he judges to be a retriever which he would like to take home with him after the trial; this is one criterion of his performance as a judge. If the winner is not that type of retriever, then 𝒥 feels that he failed in setting his tests for that stake. Deep down, 𝒥 realizes well that good retrievers can turn an ordinary shoot or hunt into a major occasion. Ideally, 𝒥 wants to breed, own, train, handle, campaign, and shoot over a retriever with a superior nose-brain combination, with drive under control (where drive means determination to deal with all situations, including different types of cover, effectively but without wildness), and with a soft mouth; he wants the retriever to have great marking ability and memory, an even and kindly temperament with a will to please; 𝒥 wants to see decisive and polished retrieving combined with resistance to temptation when the pressure is on; in all-age stakes, the retriever must be attuned to long-distance remote control; and 𝒥 desires to have all this ability packaged in a good-looking, classy retriever with style. [*Aside:* Even though 𝒥 does not think pedigrees are all-important, he does study them before he breeds a litter. 𝒥 is not particularly interested in his retriever's sire's sire's sire; 𝒥 is more interested in what his retriever can sire (or whelp). Consequently, 𝒥 occasionally, after diligent and careful study, breeds a litter; however, 𝒥 assumes satisfactory conformation to "breed standards" and is not overly concerned with it on the day that he judges a field trial.]

ACTION ITEMS

Item 1.--In an ordinary stake, 𝒥 assumes that retrievers have stamina; he admits that he cannot test for stamina in the usual circumstances under which American trials are conducted. Discuss.

Item 2.--Read Routledge: 𝒥 thinks that each and every man who even considers judging, but before he judges his first trial, should read *The Ideal Retriever and How to Handle Him* by Vincent Routledge, published in 1929. As reprinted, it can be purchased for slightly more than a dollar from Mr. Guy Routledge, Ewshot Hall, near Farnham, Surrey, England.

Pontchippi Demo (1965) demonstrating the "fire and style" that I admire (photo by VPA).

Difficult to Judge Derby and Qualifying Stakes

$\mathcal{J}$ thinks that (except for the physical ordeal) a national championship stake would (in some ways) be the easiest of all stakes to judge. $\mathcal{J}$ believes that the derby and qualifying stakes are not easy to judge. Hence, $\mathcal{J}$ thinks that judges are obligated to be as careful, do as much homework, and to spend as much time preparing for derby and qualifying stakes as for all-age stakes--to expend even greater time and effort. In the junior stakes, cover, water, wind, light, terrain, and other factors should be exploited with care, special care, and allocated time should be utilized and contestants allowed to participate as much as practicable. $\mathcal{J}$ considers these junior stakes as the all-important training grounds of retrievers, handlers, judges, and others. Work-life expectancy is relatively short for club members, handlers, and open retrievers (see Chapter Eight); junior stakes serve as the source of both "retriever-power" and critical specialized retriever manpower. To repeat an earlier suggestion, $\mathcal{J}$ thinks that it follows logically that at least one member of each pair of judges in junior stakes should be a qualified judge.

On Disciplining Retrievers

In the course of the time that they spend together, $\mathcal{J}$ and his co-judge discuss disciplining of retrievers. $\mathcal{J}$ reasons that it is neither polite nor does it reflect good judgment to administer routine discipline to children in the presence of visitors; he thinks it should be avoided if at all practicable. Likewise, $\mathcal{J}$ does not think it good practice to use selected (retriever) training aids where people gather. $\mathcal{J}$ is prudent; $\mathcal{J}$ uses sound judgment; $\mathcal{J}$ does not think that even ... and the like should be used at training sessions involving a sizeable group. $\mathcal{J}$ would never, repeat never, condone using such training aids, not even "a foot, glove, or short leash," even at picnic trials. Scolding? Yes! Slight shaking? Yes! ... ? Never! $\mathcal{J}$ is careful, considerate, and sagacious; he is ever mindful of the "good name" and future of the retriever game.

ACTION ITEM

Discuss techniques that judges can use to prevent derby dogs on-leash from being "yanked" on the way to and at the line. How can a "stake marshal" be used here?

Avoidance of Inspecting List of Entries to be Judged

𝒥 admires the field trial enthusiast whom he can label "breeder, owner, trainer, and handler." However, he is careful never to look at the list of entries for the stake he is judging (as shown in the program--card, to my British friends) until that stake has been completed. He merely asks someone for the number of entries in the stake which he is to judge.

Agreement Concerning Controlled Breaks, Creeping, and Wild Game

In judging junior stakes, 𝒥 discusses controlled breaks with the other judge. 𝒥 points out that these seem invariably to lead to problems, but he does not have strong feelings about how they should be handled. However, he does believe that false starts in any sport should be penalized, even though 𝒥 does not have a clear-cut policy relative to controlled breaks.

𝒥 and the young judge discuss how they will handle wild game, if encountered. Also, the young judge learns that 𝒥 does not have a unique policy concerning creeping. 𝒥 invariably discusses these topics with his co-judge and the policy for that particular stake is determined, with consideration to the expected quality and number of entries.

Haste and Caution

"Waiting time" can be defined as the interval of time from the instant the running dog passes behind the line of judges until the next dog leaves the ready box and starts to the line. During the course of a stake, this may be a considerable time period. 𝒥 uses this time wisely, and suggests that other judges-in-waiting do likewise.

𝒥 neither hurries nor does he keep others waiting. 𝒥, through long experience, has learned to expect the unexpected. When faced with a problem, 𝒥 knows that it is often simpler to think up panic measures than to suggest balanced solutions. 𝒥 cautions the young judge against panic; moreover, he cautions the young judge against consulting handlers or by-standers about a test which he is setting up, or has set up, or is conducting. In addition, the young judge learns that 𝒥 is not concerned very much about the complainer, but he also learns that 𝒥 knows how to handle the complainer.

𝒥 follows a policy of never initiating, repeat, initiating, discussion of a handler's, trainer's, and/or owner's entry which he has judged. To elaborate, after a trial 𝒥 never initiates discussion of why an entry was dropped, why one entry was placed above another, why one entry received fourth place and another entry a JAM, why one entry received a JAM and another entry did not, and the like. 𝒥 believes that if any such discussion originates, it should originate with the owner, handler, and/or trainer concerned.

Selected Preferences, Beliefs, and Little "Rules"

𝒥 never allows a retriever which has not worked to honor. 𝒥 tries to avoid a dog fight; he carefully selects the location for the honoring dog; he does not want the position of the honoring dog to interfere with the running dog; he prefers to excuse the honoring retriever as soon as the working entry has passed a certain point on his way to the "first retrieve." He is careful, however, not to release the honoring retriever too soon; he does not want a loud "heel" to distract the working retriever. In fact, 𝒥 expects to set his test and conduct it in such a manner as to assure that the honoring retriever and his handler do not distract the working retriever.

If a retriever must be handled on a marked fall, 𝒥 desires the handler to handle onto the fall; 𝒥 prefers not to see a handler blow the whistle, give one or two hand signals, and then allow the retriever to hunt for an extended period of time, eventually perhaps chancing on the bird.

In a test where there are multiple falls, $\mathcal{J}$ believes that it is the retriever's choice which bird he picks up first. But if the retriever should choose a bird other than the last one down, $\mathcal{J}$ prefers (even expects) that he pick up his first choice quickly.

Designing Tests

$\mathcal{J}$ has perfected the art of listening. $\mathcal{J}$ consults and heeds the local field-trialers concerning peculiarities of the terrain, such as briars, sand burrs, scenting conditions, usual or expected direction of the wind, location of the sun, and other such factors. Moreover, since field trial grounds are of critical importance to the retriever field trial game, $\mathcal{J}$ thinks that the landowners' and/or farmers' interests should be a serious consideration of all retriever field trial judges and enthusiasts.

Amount of game available is always a basic consideration in planning tests. $\mathcal{J}$ tries to test dogs thoroughly with a reasonable amount of game.

Circumstances permitting, in any derby stake, $\mathcal{J}$ prefers to run at least four series, more preferably five; in a qualifying stake, $\mathcal{J}$ prefers to run at least four series and include a simple land blind and a simple water blind.

In stakes where championship points are awarded, $\mathcal{J}$ prefers about a dozen retrieves; he prefers to run the same number of series on land as on water, but he recognizes that some series are mixed and/or difficult to classify. In addition, $\mathcal{J}$ prefers to have only slightly over half the retrieves on land, and thus nearly half on water. He prefers one-fourth to three-tenths of the retrieves to be "pure marks" (as defined herein), one-third to be blind retrieves, and the remaining 40 per cent retrieves to be "memory" birds. If the ideal score on a retriever's performance (RP) in the field is divided into two parts, performance on blinds (RP_B) and $(RP_{\bar{B}})$, then $\mathcal{J}$ assumes that

$$RP = RP_B + 2(RP_{\bar{B}}). \qquad (1)$$

Since RP_B is the score on non-marking performance, Eq. (1) takes into consideration the dictum that "marking is of primary importance," where, obviously, marking includes memory.

$\mathcal{J}$ does not know clearly what is meant by "trick tests"; he does try to set up fair tests which are sound. To illustrate, he prefers not to shoot guns when a retriever is on the way to a fall; he prefers not to give marks when a retriever is returning with a pheasant where a wing may be over the retriever's eye; he does not think it wise to throw two marks from one location at a great distance from the line; neither does he like to use over-and-under (or under-and-over) marks. $\mathcal{J}$ prefers to avoid running a blind directly into the wind (although he uses this device in training). $\mathcal{J}$ prefers not to pull a retriever off a marked fall to pick up a blind first.

$\mathcal{J}$ believes that tests must not only be standard, straightforward, and sound, but that serious consideration must be given to problems of ranking (grading or scoring) the performances. The judge must not set tests for which he cannot distinguish grades of performance. To illustrate, if the test is a water blind, $\mathcal{J}$ makes sure that the retriever must get (at least) his feet wet.

$\mathcal{J}$ gets great satisfaction when someone makes a comment such as: "He can't get rid of dogs." $\mathcal{J}$ likes to set tests that entries can complete (C), that lend themselves to the grading process (G), and yet which can separate (S) entries, and are not tricky ($\overline{T}$?). In other words, a test should satisfy the criteria

$$C \text{ and } G \text{ and } S \text{ and } \overline{T}?.$$

$\mathcal{J}$ believes that he must be able to see the performance from essentially the same physical area or position as that of the handler; $\mathcal{J}$

believes that it is discourteous to the handler for a judge to be permitted more freedom of movement than a handler or to be given a better vantage point from which to view the performance of the handler's retriever.

$\mathcal{J}$ invariably sets up his marking tests from the viewing point of the retriever; $\mathcal{J}$ actually gets down on his knees on the line. Ideally, $\mathcal{J}$ would like for the retriever to be able to see changes in cover from his sitting position. On a marked fall, $\mathcal{J}$ always considers the sun, wind, and the background from the eye-level of the retriever; $\mathcal{J}$ prefers to have a bird thrown high enough to break the horizon. $\mathcal{J}$ prefers that duck be shackled rather than taped since the dog can probably see "more motion"; likewise, he prefers that the working retriever see the bottom of the fall--see the bird hit the ground. $\mathcal{J}$ never angles a bird at (toward) either the working retriever or the honoring retriever.

$\mathcal{J}$ believes that, to a major extent, switching is an outgrowth of poor tests. To illustrate, in a double for the derby stake, $\mathcal{J}$ exerts great effort to prevent a retriever from switching birds; he does not even want to tempt these young dogs to switch. Hence, he prefers to have both birds or duck thrown outward; if this is not practicable, he prefers to throw both falls at least in the same direction, say, both left to right; only as a last resort, will he condescend to have both birds thrown toward each other.

In water tests, $\mathcal{J}$ always wants to see not only entry into water, but also re-entry into water. $\mathcal{J}$ attempts to avoid setting up a water test which tempts retrievers to run the banks; he makes special efforts to avoid bank-running in derby and qualifying stakes.

$\mathcal{J}$ believes that marks in a qualifying stake should be sound, solid marks; that mark-blind combinations should not be employed in such a stake, that is, that blinds should not be run over old falls, nor near the marks; he prefers to move to a new location and make the blinds relatively easy yet "qualifying blinds."

$\mathcal{J}$ earnestly attempts to set tests so that he will be able to obtain information on each and every retrieve--no "free birds." For illustration, in an open or amateur stake, he tries to prevent setting up an easy triple mark where each fall is "easily and automatically" picked up; then after having consumed valuable time, he as judge has to justify (to himself and/or to others) the test on the basis that it was used to set up a blind. $\mathscr{I}$ thinks it is inexcusable to justify a marking test solely on the basis that it was needed to set up a blind. On the other hand, $\mathscr{I}$ does know that occasionally every entry will perform practically perfectly (say, with perfect scores) on a test which he is convinced has not only a satisfactory degree of difficulty, but is sound. However, $\mathscr{I}$ expects this to happen rarely; in fact, under certain assumptions, $\mathscr{I}$ knows about how often to expect it to happen over the long-run (see Chapters Twelve and Thirteen).

In every qualifying and "point-awarding" stake, $\mathscr{I}$ believes that there should be a water blind involving swimming water (if available); moreover, the water blind should provide more information than merely that a retriever can swim, for that is well-known.

In handling tests, $\mathscr{I}$ wants to determine how well an entry will handle some distance from the line. ($\mathscr{I}$ expects capable retrievers other than derbies to take a reasonable line for a reasonable distance.) On land, $\mathscr{I}$ walks the ground and carefully checks the cover in setting up handling tests; in lieu of a test dog, he ties a white patch below an assistant's knee and observes that assistant as the assistant walks the area. $\mathscr{I}$ wants to be sure that a handler will be able to see his retriever and that the retriever will be able to see the handler. $\mathscr{I}$ always uses a test dog in planning his water blinds. In the interest of conserving time, $\mathscr{I}$ always considers the method and needed assistance in planting blinds. $\mathscr{I}$ prefers to have no pieces of cloth tied out to locate blinds for the handler.

For each marked fall and memory bird, $\mathscr{I}$ explicitly (but obviously silently and to himself) makes a decision whether he thinks handling is or is not required (SH $\equiv$ should handle); he makes it unmistakably clear to himself that he must not wait for a handler to make that decision for him.

In setting up his tests, *J* is always concerned about paths developing to birds, particularly for unseen retrieves. He instructs the birdboys to avoid dropping birds, setting them on the ground, dragging them through cover, in such a way as to create "highways to the blind." In order to reduce the problem of trailing and to avoid creating highways to blinds, *J* often instructs a handler to receive the bird at a different location from the line. However, *J* walks with the handler to that location.

J considers moving the line and Guns to reduce trailing and to leave fouled ground behind. *J* prefers to "move" only under ideal conditions, say, essentially constant terrain, cover, and particularly unchanging background. *J* thinks that when each move is made, it should be for a meaningful distance, say, 30 yards after 6 dogs have run, rather than 5 steps after each dog runs.

J attempts to make the marks in a particular series as alike as practicable--never as alike as possible. *J* knows that he can control the difficulty of a test to some degree by consulting with the gunners with regard to angle of flight and how far they should "ride out" a flier--say, particularly in a land double with pheasant in a derby stake.

J believes that in derby stakes, the retriever should demonstrate ability on the way to the fall, at (near) the fall, and on the return--not necessarily on the line. *J* is aware that many handlers think there may be a tendency for retrievers, especially young ones, to overshoot a mark which is run downhill.

In *J*'s hunting and shooting experience, by far the majority of his kills have involved single falls. Hence, *J* believes that a well-chosen single mark is appropriate for all stakes, especially the derby stake and occasionally for point-giving stakes. Moreover, *J* believes that every entry in a licensed trial should be given at least one shot flying bird.

In selecting the location for the decoys, *J* is not overly concerned when retrievers, particularly entries in a derby stake, "check decoys." He reasons that if a derby entry checks a couple of decoys and then is able to mark well and/or remember, then this animal probably has some of the attributes which 𝒥 is seeking in his ideal retriever.

In setting up a triple with duck, 𝒥 may request drakes for the first two falls and a hen for the third bird down. In reply to a query from the young judge, 𝒥 comments that in general drakes make less noise than hens; in fact, 𝒥 does not object to having a squawker on the last bird down.

[*Aside:* This is another example which may appear obvious but the query has come from a young judge on more than one occasion.]

In order to conserve time, 𝒥 keeps a pick-up dog handy for water tests.

𝒥 uses retiring Guns with special caution and care, always assuring that they can be completely hidden at all times after retiring and they do not retire "upwind of the fall."

𝒥 assures that a handler stands out clearly, is easily and obviously visible to the working retriever. He checks to see that neither the gallery nor the background interferes with the handler-retriever working relationship.

𝒥 does not assume responsibility for assisting handlers, but he does follow a philosophy of trying to avoid eliminating dogs on technicalities. In short, he will suggest to a handler not to block his dog when honoring, to put a visible chain in his pocket, ...

To mark the line, 𝒥 prefers to outline a box on the ground with the heel of his boot; he prefers to avoid using a rag, rope, tree limb, board, and the like.

When the line is stationary, in order to make tests more comparable, 𝒥 "scents the area of the fall" before the first entry runs; he accomplishes this by allowing the game of choice to be shot or thrown in that area.

Instructions

At a given trial, 𝒥 prefers to handle communications and instructions through one or two individuals.

𝒥 knows from experience that many assistants at trials (assistant marshals, birdboys, gunners, and the like) are inexperienced or have half-forgotten vital details.   Hence, the young judge observes that 𝒥 routinely holds a training session before a series begins and gives sharp, clear, detailed instructions.

Often in derby stakes, after a failure, the handler asks that a bird be thrown; when 𝒥 grants the request, in order to avoid scenting an area away from the fall, he instructs the birdboy to throw the bird in the exact, repeat, exact, spot of the fall. 𝒥 insists that game not be thrown anywhere else.

When throwing a dead bird or shackled duck, 𝒥 prefers the bird-boys to be on the near side, next to the working dog; that is, he places the gunner (popper) on the opposite side of the birdboy from the working retriever.

𝒥 instructs the gunner (popper) to shoot no later than a short interval of time before the dead bird or shackled duck reaches the apex of the path of the throw. He further instructs the popper to attempt to shoot consistently and to invariably point his gun in the direction of the fall. On occasion, 𝒥 requires two shots.

𝒥 attempts to prevent retrievers from freezing on marks (and/or Guns) and thus not seeing other falls.   In addition to care in order of shooting, realizing that many retrievers appear to be trial-wise and focus on the suspected location of the live game, 𝒥 attempts to have four persons at each location, whether the game is dead or alive. 𝒥 asks that at least two people stand up at the location of the gunners. If an assistant intends to sit down, he is requested to sit while each and every retriever works.

𝒥 instructs his gunners and other assistants carefully concerning quietness. In particular, he requests gunners not to open and close gun mechanisms when an entry is running and to minimize movement and talk. (*Aside:* 𝒥 even prefers that his poppers use double-barrel shotguns.) He requests all other persons to remain quietly in position. If the gunners see a runner or wild game, 𝒥 requests that one of them quietly raise his hand; if the retriever is returning with a bird other than the one thrown or shot, *J* requests to be notified in a similar manner.

J requests the gunners and birdboys to wear "bright" clothes so that the working retriever can locate them easily. In case of changes in weather, he is careful that apparent changes are not made in the clothing visible to the working dogs.

J emphasizes that field trials are to select the best retrievers; far down the list is to provide pleasure for gunners.

Luck of the Draw and Evaluation

J believes that order of running influences the probability of completing a trial. As a consequence, *J* wants to be assured that the drawing is strictly random (Chapter Five) and he desires that entries come to the line in that order as far as practicable.

J comments to his (junior) co-judge regarding consistency of evaluation. Our ideal retriever field trial judge, *J*, has strong feelings, he is also opinionated regarding the retriever and the retrieving performance. Note that this implies clear-cut criteria; in such a framework, *J* can make judgments based solely on what he witnesses in a stake, hopefully "free of bias." Moreover, *J* believes that if each retriever field trial judge is not mulish, he will not stick to his standard; hence, he cannot possibly judge consistently. The foregoing notwithstanding, *J* exerts explicit effort to be consistent, but he realizes that it is difficult to evaluate performance according to the same principles over a series; for example, should two "identical" performances occur, one early in the series, the other, say, 30 entries later, he realizes that the probability is large that he will not evaluate both performances identically. Moreover, *J* realizes the great danger of being inconsistent from series to series. *J* keeps these difficulties constantly in mind and not only suggests but uses a system for callbacks and ranking which he hopes will keep unfairness to a minimum (see Chapters Ten through Thirteen).

The young judge learns that $\mathcal{J}$ notes and records so-called "minor faults" but that $\mathcal{J}$ is not particularly concerned with them unless there is repetition.

In assigning "grades" to expedite callbacks.--In order to establish a relative ranking scale, as each dog runs, $\mathcal{J}$ assigns a grade (category); then, after the first three dogs run, $\mathcal{J}$ may re-evaluate and re-assign the grades. After the first five dogs, $\mathcal{J}$ may re-assign grades again. Then routinely, $\mathcal{J}$ goes back to these first few dogs' performances to keep his categories in line with categories assigned to performances of early entries.

$\mathcal{J}$ thinks there is no substitute for qualitative description; just because a judge attaches a letter or a number to a performance doesn't mean that a judge knows much about that performance. After all, $\mathcal{J}$ knows that a letter or a number is an abstraction which may be farther removed from the performance itself than is qualitative description. In passing, the young judge learns that $\mathcal{J}$ will not give a sheet containing data on an entry ($\mathcal{J}$'s judge's sheet) to a handler. Since $\mathcal{J}$ uses many abbreviations, he will considerately explain what he witnessed, but he prefers not to let a handler try to interpret his shorthand.

[*Aside:* Abbreviations, codes, shorthand, and the like which one of my colleagues and I use would be meaningless without a translator (to illustrate, AA, BL, $\overline{\text{BL}}$, ... , HTG, ... , MW, ... , PD − 1, ... , PS, PW, $\overline{\text{PW}}$, ... , TG, ΣT_t, ... , WM, ...).]

The young judge asks the question: "On a blind, suppose that a handler doesn't 'try the test,' but he attempts to circumvent it." $\mathcal{J}$ replies: "If enough handlers do try the test and perform in a workmanlike manner, a handler who doesn't try it gets classified 'Oh!'; in short, he who flagrantly avoids the test falls in the subgroup 'eliminated' and is not even involved in the comparisons which I make later."

Conducting the Test

$\mathcal{J}$ thinks that each and every judge must know the mechanics of a retriever field trial as well as know retrievers.

Killed by mechanics.--ℐ attempts to keep entries from being penalized because of mechanics; he feels that it happens all too often.

ℐ always runs one or more test dogs; he runs the test dog mainly for himself, secondarily for handlers, although he desires that they benefit from it. He demands a capable test dog in capable hands, although he may not be particularly concerned with the performance of the test dog. He is always seriously concerned with the mechanics of the test and he may run two or even three test dogs to perfect those mechanics. Even though he may be focusing upon mechanics, if two capable test dogs fail the test, then it must follow that probably the test dogs were not really capable or the test was faulty; in either case, corrective action must be seriously considered.

Even though he thinks it should not be necessary, ℐ is ever on the alert for sounds or acts which amount to threatening gestures or unsportsmanlike behavior on the line--chain rattling, excessive hissing, exposing training equipment (even a crutch) and/or other.

ℐ supervises the conduct of a test constantly; he is always alert to try to prevent any occurrence which may change a test; he provides relentless supervision over the test. To elaborate, ℐ not only gives instructions, but he also follows through; that is, in conducting a test, he supervises and checks to see that the details of his instructions are carried out. This requires tact. Moreover, ℐ has tremendous respect for the individual; he does not want to hurt anyone's feelings or embarrass anyone, particularly a worker at a field trial. Hence, ℐ tries to obtain cooperation; he knows that he is completely dependent upon the gunners, birdboys, and others, if an efficient stake is to be conducted. ℐ does not instruct persons out from the line or at gun locations by yelling or by using a loudspeaker. If necessary to instruct personnel at gun locations, ℐ walks (or sends a marshal) out to that location by a circuitous route, downwind from where the working retriever is expected to travel. In fact, he tries to prevent anyone from walking the path or even walking upwind of the path to a fall or a blind. He inquires as to how birds are to be replenished for

marks or blinds; if obviously unsatisfactory, he makes alternate suggestions. Always, however, $\mathcal{J}$ sees that his suggestions, adjustments, corrections, and specific requests are made quietly and in private to the individual concerned.

In passing, the young judge takes note concerning running a test
and calling numbers on the line. He notes that $\mathcal{J}$ usually calls a one-
digit number. To illustrate, "one" is the call for entry number 11;
... , "nine" is the call for entry number 29; and so on. When there
is an off-leash retriever on-line observing, $\mathcal{J}$ glances to assure that
this honoring retriever is sitting and ready. $\mathcal{J}$ signals for each bird
in turn. Then $\mathcal{J}$ glances instantaneously and momentarily at the retrievers as the final bird is down; if either retriever is moving, he
refrains from calling the number. If all is well, he calls the number
immediately; he does not delay nor "hold" the working retriever.

ACTION ITEM

Given a land double in a licensed junior stake where a controlled
break may be allowed. The judge signalled for bird number one. Before he signalled for the second bird, the dog was on the way to retrieve bird number one; the judge failed to call for bird number two.
The handler stopped his dog four steps from the line. In short, the
judge interrupted the cadence with which he was calling for the second
bird; obviously, the judge does not know what would have happened had
the test been "shot" according to plan. Discuss the following comment: The judge should attempt to signal for both birds in essentially
the same manner for each and every dog; on the other hand, the number should not be called if a dog is in motion toward a fall.

More Discussion

During the course of their discussions, the young judge also questions concerning amateur handlers versus professional handlers. He

finds out that $\mathcal{J}$ believes one difference between the average professional handler and the average amateur handler on tests of control is the following: Professional handlers tend more to control than to hope, while many amateur handlers tend more to hope than to control.

The young judge asserts that from time to time he hears of experienced field-trialers who are going to "quit running" but continue to judge a little. $\mathcal{J}$ replies that he believes that if they quit running, then they ought to quit judging.

Brief Sketch, No Catalog

This section has presented only the briefest sketch of the model of an ideal judge; there are additional but incomplete specifications in the remainder of this Appendix. To be concise at this point, let it be known that $\mathcal{J}$ is a remarkable man; he is perfection and he is a perfectionist. He dislikes next-best; he knows when he makes mistakes; he may become annoyed at his own failures, but he does not blame others for them. Neither is $\mathcal{J}$ a credit-snatcher (from the other judge); for example, when his co-judge suggests a well-conceived, sound test, $\mathcal{J}$ gives him credit.

In the practical situation, $\mathcal{J}$ does not exist unless you are willing to agree that the ideal judge, called $\mathcal{J}$, is ... . In short, the judge is a fallible human in every real trial.

Responsibility.--The retriever field trial judge has grave responsibility not only to the individual retriever and his breed, but also to many people as well. When $\mathcal{J}$ is paired with a junior judge, he feels tremendous pressure and responsibility. $\mathcal{J}$ believes that we are not seeking do-gooders as judges, but that we want enlightened judges. Just because a problem has been solved a particular way down through the years doesn't mean that we should not stop and consider it carefully. We need judges with deeper insights, who are honest, who have courage (guts) to go with their convictions, and who will concentrate on the job at hand when judging.

Motivation to judge.-- Initially, $\mathcal{J}$ thinks that he probably judged to learn more about training, handling, and evaluating retrievers. In the main, however, $\mathcal{J}$ thinks that he continues to judge because of the challenge. Explicitly, what he thinks of himself is at risk each time he accepts an invitation to judge a stake; beyond this, his reputation with himself is at risk of being damaged for each test he sets up and conducts in that stake. In addition, $\mathcal{J}$ judges because he thinks what he is doing is worthwhile; $\mathcal{J}$ believes that he renders a service by guiding a complex operation which takes place during the leisure time of an important segment of society. $\mathcal{J}$ is motivated to a trifling degree by the respect and admiration which he has earned in the eyes of those few particular peers whom he respects. $\mathcal{J}$ prefers that even that admiration be granted grudgingly; in fact, $\mathcal{J}$ is not concerned at all with his outright critics and enemies, but he is concerned with his friends.

Training

Throughout his lifetime, whether it be short or long, $\mathcal{J}$ has tried to learn all he can about gundogs, particularly retrievers, and their work. He picks the brains of every good amateur and professional trainer he meets. Moreover, $\mathcal{J}$ reads every available book and magazine on the subject of training dogs and other animals. He makes it a point to train with some of the best professional and amateur trainers in the world; he works with them and for them--as a popper, birdboy, thrower, or the like.

$\mathcal{J}$ understands training methods and training problems thoroughly. He knows what is difficult and what is less difficult and when he can't distinguish. In fact, $\mathcal{J}$ not only has a working knowledge of the laws of learning, but $\mathcal{J}$ also appreciates and really understands the process of training the individual retriever. He has knowledge of many alternate methods for accomplishing the same end result; he knows that one method will work with one retriever and another method must be used for the second retriever. He knows that he can over-do any particular aspect of training. To illustrate, he can "over-train" an open retriever to avoid points of land on a water blind to the extent that he can't even pick up a blind on a point in a trial.

In fact, $\mathcal{J}$ has more than slight acquaintance with some of the fundamental processes of learning on the part of the retriever. Basically, he believes that a foundation of learning for a future top-grade retriever is motivation; he believes that basic motivation is highly dependent upon heredity. $\mathcal{J}$ considers the adult "personality" of the retriever (since p is the first letter of personality and to distinguish it from the human personality), call it P' (P-prime), to be a product of heredity, H', and environment, E': $P' = H' \times E'$. Clearly, the retriever's personality is not a summation; if either H' or E' becomes zero, the retriever's personality ceases to exist. Thus, a retriever-man must not conclude that heredity is more important than environment, or vice versa, for one cannot exist without the other. Heredity probably does determine the limits of the raw materials from which the retriever's personality is molded (i.e., temperament, a basis for intelligence, marking and the retrieving instinct, physique, and maybe "something else").

$\mathcal{J}$ realizes that a puppy whelped in one's own kennel is a puppy for a much longer time (in $\mathcal{J}$'s mind) than if he purchased the puppy at 6 to 8 months of age. Hence, given the ideal protoplasm, $\mathcal{J}$ understands thoroughly that he must wait for certain levels of maturation to take place in the young retriever and he understands the inefficiency of overcrowded practice. Since $\mathcal{J}$ understands the intimate relationship of motivation to learning, he likewise understands the use of reward and punishment.

$\mathcal{J}$ is familiar with conditioned response experiments and accompanying principles. $\mathcal{J}$ attempts to show and show and show the retriever in order to allow it to associate ideas (condition its reflexes to perform certain acts on command) and exploit its retrieving instinct. Then he repeats with enforcement, if necessary.

$\mathcal{J}$ knows the importance of memory in the retriever. When $\mathcal{J}$ begins to think of the nature of learning, he has already started considering remembering. Failure to remember implies forgetting; hence, $\mathcal{J}$ realizes that memory and forgetting are part of the same process of learning. Moreover, $\mathcal{J}$ knows that over-learning may aid retention, but he attempts not to bore his retriever.

$\mathcal{J}$ does not assume that a retriever has more "reasoning power" than it has. He bases most if not all his training on memory and repetition.

$\mathcal{J}$ is consistent, fair, and just in training of his retrievers. In fact, $\mathcal{J}$ is tough on occasion, but he is always considerate.

From long experience, $\mathcal{J}$ knows that the novice trainer tends to over-train his retriever. [The reader should differentiate clearly between over-learn and over-train.]

$\mathcal{J}$ believes that early training should consist of a series of carefully graded exercises, that the retriever should master the previous exercise before attempting the next. $\mathcal{J}$ prefers to use as many different types of dummies as is practicable.

ACTION ITEM

From the behavior of some experienced RE's, I infer that they don't understand the meaning of nonslip. Some experienced RE's seem to be embarrassed to be seen in public using a slip. In contrast, I probably use a slip too often simply because I observe situations developing where, had a slip been used, far greater consideration would have been shown for others (both other retriever enthusiasts and other retrievers). *Questions:* How many RE's do you know who appear to be apprehensive of being seen using a lead? Although I prefer to use a lead (slip) made of small nylon rope, what else is a choke chain collar with a short piece of leather attached but a slip? (For the type of dog that I keep in my kennel, I like the light, compact, snarl-free nylon slip because it is easily tied and has almost endless lasting ability.) How many RE's really know how to use a nylon slip (not chain), tug of war versus shock action?

Game

Our ideal judge, $\mathcal{J}$, periodically takes stock and reflects. One of his concerns is the opposition to field sports to which he applies the iceberg theory. Nine-tenths of an iceberg is said to be submerged and as a consequence is extremely dangerous; periodically, $\mathcal{J}$ wonders if only a tenth of the opposition to field sports is visible. As an aftermath of this pondering, $\mathcal{J}$ predicts that upland game shooting and waterfowling will be increasingly threatened by anti-field-sports elements because they present a biased and over-emotional picture of shooting as a whole. He is seriously concerned about retriever field trials as they are conducted in America.

$\mathcal{J}$ recognizes that the dominant factor in the balance of nature is man. As a result, the zealous sportsman $\mathcal{J}$ is a keen conservationist. $\mathcal{J}$ believes that we who shoot and hunt must control conservation; we must never allow it to be controlled by those who do not themselves shoot and yet would prevent others from shooting. $\mathcal{J}$ believes that the true sportsman avoids and prevents all cruelty.

$\mathcal{J}$ believes the following: We must take seriously the great responsibility we have for the treatment of "game" used in connection with retriever training and trials. If we do not establish and enforce a satisfactory code of behavior, certain practices will be outlawed, as has been done in Canada and England. No matter what the circumstances, live game must be handled not only humanely, but kindly. Birds should not be left shackled for long periods of time or allowed to remain in crates under a hot sun. Wings of pigeons should not be "locked"; pigeons should not be tossed on hard ground; rather than throw shackled live pigeons on hard ground, $\mathcal{J}$ uses dead pigeons. Shackled duck should be thrown only in water--never on land. A handler should not toss live game on the ground after it has been retrieved.

ACTION ITEMS

Item 1.--$\mathcal{J}$ thinks that the competitive spirit is out of place when shooting in the field. Discuss.

Item 2.--On water tests in stakes where championship points are awarded, use dead duck for controlled falls and shoot duck for other falls. To avoid divers on shot duck, if feasible, request Guns to shoot the "shot duck" again after it hits the water. Discuss.

J believes that one should never attempt shots beyond the certain killing-range of his gun. In cases of error, whatever the circumstances, it is inexcusable not to make every effort to retrieve wounded game. Here is where we who train and campaign retrievers in field trials live our code and often claim that both our pleasure and bag are increased by capable retrievers. One of *J*'s greatest shooting thrills comes from a retrieve to hand of a bird which he has given up for lost.

J has some thoughts about "the law of nature." For man as well as the game he shoots, the one inescapable outcome of the marvel of birth is death: The primary rule of nature is to kill or be killed. Whether man does the killing or not is irrelevant, but when man does kill, *J* believes that there must be no unjustified cruelty. When we, sportsmen, kill, death should be no more painful and involve no more fear than occurs naturally. (Note carefully that comparison of the degree of suffering by denial of freedom as compared to being physically hurt is beyond the scope of this particular discussion.)

J may or may not be a hunter (rough shooter or wildfowler in Britain). If *J* is a hunter, then he is a sportsman (not in the derogative sense); he feels affection, respect, and responsibility for his quarry and he has a chilvalrous attitude toward it; this attitude calls for strict self-discipline and demands study and understanding of the creatures he hunts and their habitats. In fact, by diligent study, *J* can properly identify the wild species he hunts.

ACTION ITEMS

Item 1.--In a group discussion or club meeting, see how many hunters you can list who express affection for the game they pursue by keeping collections of quail, pheasant, wild geese, wild duck, and/or other wild game.

Item 2.--In the spring of the year, do hen pheasant have less scent than cock pheasant? Discuss.

ℐ believes that one should only take fair shots, but the following question immediately comes to his mind: What is a fair shot, where fair implies that the quarry had a sporting chance? To be explicit, is it fair for a wildfowler to shoot a sitting duck? On the other hand, there is no question in *ℐ*'s mind that it is not fair to shoot bobwhite quail on the ground--not even for a boy to take such a shot.

Since the subject of fair and unfair shots is complex, *ℐ* recognizes that there are arguments and counter-arguments. Opinions and interpretations differ as to whether game is moving or not, quantity of game available, speed if moving, time, place, weather, and other characteristics. For example, *ℐ* believes that some sitting shots are fair and not all flying shots are sporting.

ℐ 's tentative definition of fair shot.-- The shot must have high probability of killing, in combination with small probability of only wounding; it must not help fill an over-the-limit excessive bag; it must not be harmful in any respect over the long-run; and the quarry must have a reasonable chance of escape either because of difficulty in the act of approaching near or of speed and/or angle of flight.

ACTION ITEMS

Item 1.--*ℐ* makes a careful distinction between domestic animals and birds versus wild animals and birds. How do we Americans justify throwing a pheasant into the air and shooting it at our retriever trials?

Item 2.-- A retriever conference, club, or association might consider developing a code for human beings in the treatment of game. This is a grave responsibility and requires clear thinking. Discuss.

Item 3.--Consider the practicability of using shackled duck once in a stake; then immediately unshackle and rest them. Discuss.

More Specifications for *J* and the Practical Task of Selecting a Judge

Innumerable pitfalls may follow over-simplification, but from the background material presented earlier, it follows that the making of a judge begins with "the gleam in his father's eye." Those who select the judge must probe deeply to assure that beneath that outer shell there reposes the basic personality and character of a man, a gentleman, and a sportsman. One can tell much about a judge by the way he uses his spare time; the interests he exhibits (which we witness) allow us to make inferences concerning his character.

First of all, has he arrived to the point that he can see the good points of another man's retriever? *Opinion:* This is a fundamental prerequisite for judging; he must have "arrived."

Is he currently training and running an entry himself in licensed trials? *Opinion:* He should be. Does he enjoy competing more than judging? *Opinion:* He should derive greater enjoyment from competing; he should regard judging as a chore, but he should be willing to take his turn, say, once or twice a year. In short, he should not be over-anxious to judge. To be even more specific, does he himself train, handle, and compete in, say, at least six times as many trials as he judges? *Opinion:* He should. Did he train and handle an entry to a place in a licensed derby stake before he attempted to judge a licensed derby? *Opinion:* He should. Did he train and handle an entry to a place in a licensed qualifying stake before he attempted to judge a licensed qualifying stake? *Opinion:* He should. Had he handled an entry of his own training to completion of a licensed all-age "point-giving" stake before he attempted to judge a licensed all-age stake? *Opinion:* He should and more.

IMPERIAL CANCER RESEARCH FUND
DIVISION OF CHEMISTRY & BIOCHEMISTRY

Telephone No:
CHAncery 9901

Lincoln's Inn Fields,
London, W.C.2.

RDB/DCC

7th September 1966.

Prof. C. A. McMahan,
Dept. of Biostatistics,
Louisiana State University Medical Centre,
1542 Tulane Avenue,
New Orleans,
Louisiana 70112, U. S. A.

Dear Prof,

. . .

I've just found out that a Norman Knight called Fitz Urze used to live in the next village to us. He was one of the murderers of St. Thomas a Becket. He must have found local reaction a bit hostile because he went off to Ireland and changed his name to McMahan! So you might be a direct descendant.

All the best.

Yours sincerely,

/ [Mick] /

R. D. Bulbrook, M. Sc., Ph.D.

P. S.   Evidence enclosed.

THE

Festival of Flowers

St. Peter and St. Paul, Teston, Kent

Friday, 9th September	3 p.m. - 7.30 p.m.
Saturday, 10th September	10 a.m. - 7.30 p.m.
Sunday, 11th September	8 a.m. - 7.30 p.m.

**Teas at the Village Hall Friday and Saturday
3.30 p.m to 5.30 p.m.**

The Parish of St. Peter and St. Paul

Teston

Our Parish Church stands in a beautiful setting beyond the Village Green--a focus of our history, and of the life of our village. The site is mentioned in the Domesday Survey of 1086. Bareham Court, near-by, was the home of Hugo Fitz Urse, one of the four knights who murdered St. Thomas à Becket. It is said that Fitz Urse fled to Ireland where he adopted the name of MacMahan. He made over his property to relatives who took the name Bereham. Their descendants occupied Bereham Court until the 16th century.

[*Aside:* Clearly, there are exceptions, but each such exceptional case must be considered as an individual case.]

Does this judge have "rabbit-ears"? That is, does he want to hear what handlers, "gallery judges," and spectators have to say about him, his judging, and the working retrievers? *Opinion:* A judge should not have "rabbit-ears." *ℐ* knows that American retriever trials have practically a zero spectator component; participants have clearly biased views and views of non-participants are of little import. After all, it is the judge's job to rank the performances independently of the biases of the proud owners or handlers and/or their supporters and detractors.

Did this judge recently attend a recognized retriever judging clinic or conference? If he attended such a conference, did he make an effort to learn, or did he just "exercise his jaws"? *Opinion:* Anyone who is asked to judge must have attended a recognized retriever judging conference within the, say, YY months immediately preceding a licensed judging assignment.

Does the judge have good field trial manners? Does the judge realize that good field trial manners are as important as table manners? Does the judge understand hunter (field-trialer)-landowner and/or farmer relationships? *Opinion:* Good field trial manners are as important as good table manners; otherwise, one might get "his eye put out with a fork or have a trigger-finger cut off." The judge should not only be courteous, but should understand hunting and shooting in relationship to the landowner and/or farmer; he should set the tests, conduct the trial, and insist on behavior such that the club will be invited back to again utilize the field trial grounds.

Has the judge mastered, *mastered*, the color-book and supplement? Does the judge re-read the entire color-book and supplement immediately before (within two days of) each trial he judges? Has the judge prepared and taken an open-book comprehensive examination on the color-book and supplement? Would the judge be willing to spend $25 to take an examination administered by a nationally recognized testing

service? *Opinion:* *J* knows the color-book and the supplement thoroughly; *J* thinks that a testing program should be initiated and that
passing of the test should be a mandatory condition, but not a sufficient
condition, for judging in a licensed trial.

ACTION ITEM

Consider the possibility and feasibility of including a quiz with
answers as a regular feature in the *Retriever Field Trial News.* The
series could be initiated with questions on the *Registration Rules and
Field Trial Rules and Procedures* and *Standing Recommendations of the
Retriever Advisory Committee.* Actual judging situations which arise
in practice could be used also. Discuss.

Does the judge know the administrative organization of the licens-
ing and sanctioning body for American retriever field trials? Does
the judge know how policies are made and rules established and
changed, the details of registration, the posting of titles, and other
details? *Opinion:* He should.

Does the judge believe that the only reason for participating in retriever field trials is for enjoyment? *Opinion:* One who judges should
have this underlying belief.

Will the judge make all "cuts" and the final placings solely on
what he witnesses? *Opinion:* Callbacks and placings should be based
solely on what the judges witness "that day under those conditions."

Does the judge know that criticism of the judge is not only inevitable, but the warp and woof of the sport? Does the judge recognize that
most criticism probably has at least an element of truth in it? *Opinion:*
J knows that gossip is a major activity of the field trial fraternity; he
knows that a large segment of the fraternity is not only antagonistic to
the judge, but also jealous; he knows that "sour grapes" is an often-
used mechanism; moreover, he recognizes that a segment of a segment
of the fraternity fights like ... , by means of malicious gossip. The

foregoing notwithstanding, *J* should and does recognize that his judging is open to criticism and that he may well benefit from it; *J* believes that those who write for the retriever field trial follower as well as those who judge must recognize that there is no alternative but to live with stinging criticism--even a poisoned pen. Common sense and reality dictate accepting it when it is reasonable, rejecting it when it is unwarranted, and ignoring it for the most part. *J* knows that in observing a retriever's performance, one judge may note action which indicates a desirable (natural or other) quality, whereas another equally qualified judge may conclude that the performance merited no special attention.

In any sporting endeavor, a good beginning may be a great help. Is the judge concerned with the novice to the sport? *Opinion:* He should be. *J* realizes fully that as each of us learns more and more about the retriever game, as we mature retriever-wise and trial-wise and thus better appreciate the more subtle aspects of our favorite game, we tend to forget that once as novices we did not know protocol either. In fact, *J* knows that if one wishes to needle a less experienced friend a bit, just remind him of some of his capers and actions as a handler or birdboy at one of the first club trials in which he participated; he probably would not believe that he could possibly have behaved in the asserted manner. *J* knows and appreciates that as a judge, hence, self-styled old-timer (but still with a first retriever), all of this tends to be forgotten all too soon.

After many years of personally training retrievers and personally handling entries in licensed trials, *J* is confident. His confidence stems from recognizing his own limitations and knowing full-well that he must and will judge within them. Moreover, he knows that he will have to make decisions separating entries on fine points--too fine for anyone to assess who was not actually judging. This competent judge, *J*, is ever mindful that luck plays a great part in retriever field trials; hence, he realizes that it is his responsibility to conduct the trial so that there is no doubt but that the winning handler has a good dog and knows how to work him. Moreover, he must know that his methods of judging will sort out the top retrievers over the long-run.

Is the judge a student of the "dog's mind"? Can the judge "think like a dog"? *Opinion:* $\mathcal{J}$ should not only be a student of the "dog's mind," but he should be able to "think like a dog."

Basically, $\mathcal{J}$ recognizes that retriever field trials should be fun; they should be enjoyed for their own sake, win or lose. Within such a framework, $\mathcal{J}$ is still able to comprehend that the object of retriever trials is to provide outlets for the competitive spirit and, at the same time, to improve the retriever breeds, their training, and their handling. $\mathcal{J}$ assumes that the hardcore of retriever field trial people are good sportsmen, yet he knows that some contestants cannot accept bad luck and defeat with "good grace." From experience, he knows that those who win only awards of merit have friends galore, but that many of these same contestants, when they begin to earn places, wonder where their friends have gone--but $\mathcal{J}$ knows and understands this process. All of the above notwithstanding, $\mathcal{J}$ retains a certain simplicity of outlook he had as a novice; he is not too critical; he enjoys what happens.

$\mathcal{J}$ is a true sportsman. He is reluctant to believe one-sided stories because he knows the "trials and tribulations" of retriever field trial clubs.

$\mathcal{J}$ thinks that judges of retriever field trials either contribute favorably to the sport or spoil it. The judge must find the best dog that day, but even the poor dogs must be given a chance to demonstrate that they are below par in this trial. Dogs must be thoroughly tested; if a dog cannot do the job on a given day, each competitor must feel that at least he was given the opportunity.

$\mathcal{J}$ believes that the shooting of upland game (wing shooting) and/ or waterfowling and/or hunting is a sport, from the point of view of an individual, only when that individual (himself) puts something into it other than hard cash.

$\mathcal{J}$ recognizes that officials of retriever clubs sometimes attempt to gain prestige for themselves and the local club by "bringing in judges" from long distances and/or judges who are well-known; $\mathcal{J}$ also knows that selected judges, including older men, continue to accumulate points whether they understand the judging process or not, and whether or not they are physically up to the task. Boxing, in a similar vein (an analogy--beware), sometimes utilizes "small older men" to referee a bout involving giants; with his size and physical infirmities, he cannot even shove back the contestants when they clinch, much less see what really goes on. In short, $\mathcal{J}$ sometimes asks, do our "expert" field trial judges do as poorly as some of our boxing referees?

$\mathcal{J}$ knows that the sport of retriever field trials is gaining in popularity year by year.

ACTION ITEMS

Item 1.--With the growing population of the United States in combination with this increasing popularity of retriever trials, the average number of entries per trial may be expected to increase as well as problems of excessively large numbers of entries to develop on many occasions. What alternatives are open? To initiate discussion, selected possibilities are put forward.

(a) Require that a series of local sanctioned club trials be conducted to qualify retrievers for licensed trials. (b) Limit the number of entries for a particular stake; if more than the allowable number of applications are received, number the entries, furnish that number with the name of the entry, the handler, and the owner to the national governing body, and have the actual entries plus alternates selected randomly; when the host club is notified, it can in turn notify each handler. This could be expedited, if required, by teletype and/or by telephone. (c) Establish new clubs and conduct a greater number of trials; this may lower the average number of entries per trial but will not necessarily prevent excessively large stakes. (d) Conduct regional championships (patterned after bird dog trials). (e) Utilize the system practiced in the British Isles. (f) Revise the assignment of trial dates or adopt some other procedure.

Item 2. -- Early in a qualified judge's career, it is useful to learn how the game is played with regard to the selection of judges. This item can be altered in many ways to provide insight into the retriever field trial game.

[In the next paragraph, the reader will encounter the symbol J_A. Read J_A as "J sub-A." The subscript is merely a convenient identification tag; it is similar to an adjective. J is used because it is the first letter of the word judge, and A is used because it is the first letter of the word aspiring. Thus, J_A is convenient shorthand for indicating the "aspiring judge." A few lines later, the reader will encounter the symbol J_V; read J_V as "J sub-V." Again, J is used because it is the first letter of judge, and V is used because it is the first letter of the word visiting. Clearly, then J_V is a way of indicating symbolically that we mean the "visiting judge"; again, it is merely convenient shorthand.]

Given an aspiring judge, J_A, who has demonstrated to himself and to his peers in his geographical region of residence that he is not only a gentleman, but a qualified trainer, handler, and a competent "five-point plus" all-age judge. He desires an invitation to judge in another geographical region.

a. Let J_A, or better yet some of his respected friends, confer with a visiting judge, J_V, from another region; further let it be known concerning the desire and availability of J_A. *Prediction:* J_V will assure that he will be glad "to do what he can"; my more realistic hypothesis is: The relative frequency (see Chapter Seven) with which J_A will receive an invitation is small.

b. Let J_A, or better his distinguished supporters, confer concurrently with two "distinguished field-trialers" from another region where both are five-point open judges. Again, let the desires and qualifications be aired with appropriate recommendations. *Prediction:*

The relative frequency of firm encouragement for J$_A$ will be small; J$_A$ will not receive the cordial assurance he (or his friends) received in the conference with a single judge. Moreover, J$_A$ will receive "excuses" such as "it's strictly a matter of finances." If J$_A$ (or his friends) counter that argument with "J$_A$ will be in the region on business," J$_A$ is likely to endure a lecture on whether or not it is ethical for a person to bear his own expenses in order to judge.

Clearly, there are approaches which yield a higher relative frequency of successes (invitations) for J$_A$; state some of your suggestions explicitly and in detail. Do you think that this whole subject is worth airing? Some aspiring judges know how the game is played; do you?

Item 3.--$\mathcal{J}$ believes that most fathers were started off erroneously when they went to retrievers. Discuss the pro's and con's of starting a boy off with a well-trained retriever and training the boy under a professional handler also.

Item 4.--Discuss the three judge system used in some British retriever trials. What are its assets? What are its limitations?

Item 5.--Many British retriever authorities forecast that American retrievers will deteriorate simply because of the way we conduct our trials. Discuss to include the use of force in training. Do we bore our retrievers by our methods of training? Will our methods lead to the selection of large, tough retrievers?

Item 6.--List by name the RE's who judge field trials in your area who consider themselves expert RE's and/or who may be considered as being retriever-wise enthusiasts by some (at least one) other RE. Record the number of RE's on this list who have had one and only one "good retriever."

The major focus of this action item is the owner-trainer-handler (OTH) retriever enthusiast. Assume for the purposes of this action item that an RE on this list who has not solely trained at least one of his own retrievers from puppyhood to at least completion of a licensed open stake cannot possibly understand retriever work, handlers, and retriever-man relationships. Eliminate from your list any RE who does not meet the specified criteria of OTH even though an RE may have won with or placed a trained retriever which he purchased, or even if he had a retriever trained by someone else, professional or otherwise, or even if this RE had handled and/or competed in a national stake. From those remaining on your list, identify those OTH's (RE's) who have trained more than one retriever from puppyhood all the way to completion of a licensed open stake. Operationally define those RE's to be retriever-wise or knowledgeable RE's.

All other RE's on your list are those OTH's who have solely trained one and only one retriever from puppyhood to completion of a licensed open stake. *Assertion for discussion:* These RE's have not demonstrated that they understand retriever work, handlers, and retriever-man relationships; further evidence is required. Discuss.

What do you think of such a statement as follows about those RE's on your list who trained only one retriever up to high standards? He's "been through" several puppies and he can't seem to get another good one. Is this *prima facie* evidence that this OTH does not have sufficient know-how and experience to train a second retriever of different personality up to field trial standards? Don't be misled by such a statement as follows: Each man in his lifetime is entitled to one good retriever and one good .... I guess Mr. X has had his good retriever. Discuss.

Is it likely that some OTH's who have trained several retrievers, none of which became field champions, may be more knowledgeable than an OTH who has trained only one retriever, who lucked up on an exceptional retriever puppy, and who made him a field trial champion? Discuss.

Item 7.--Read the complete, repeat, complete, monograph entitled *Registration and Field Trial Rules and Standard Procedures for Basset Hounds, Pointing Breeds, Dachshunds, Retrievers, Spaniels* (or equivalent title), New York: The American Kennel Club, latest edition. A short title is *Registration Rules and Field Trial Rules and*

Procedures . Also read the latest edition of *Standing Recommendations of the Retriever Advisory Committee*. Also read "Guide for Field Trial Committees in Dealing with Misconduct at Field Trials."

For each of the above documents, underscore the following words: may, must, shall, should, and will. Then study the text (and context) where they occur. Next, write a careful definition of each of the above five words. Indicate where you as a judge (or handler) have a choice and where you do not. Specify the action (expected) (required) of you as judge of an open stake if you, say, failed to "honor," if you failed to use decoys.

Item 8.--Reference Ralph C. Craig, *Elementary Spaniel Field Training*, New York: American Spaniel Club, 1947, and *The Conduct and Judging of Spaniel Field Trials*, English Springer Spaniel Field Trial Association, 1963. After you have read these materials (and others) ask a knowledgeable RE to discuss the judging of spaniel field trials.

CONCLUDING STATEMENT

At the end of a licensed trial, invariably *J* seems to feel that he conducted an imperfect trial and he solemnly promises himself to do better on his next judging assignment.

REFERENCE

1. Smith, T. Lynn and McMahan, C. A. *Urban Life*, New York: Dryden Press Inc., 1951, pp. 748-760.

A pittance of practice may be worth a tome of theory.

A judge in training pants!

APPENDIX C

PONTCHIPPI SURVEY OF RETRIEVER
FIELD TRIAL JUDGES, 1968†

Basic Question

What evidence can be brought to bear on the following proposal? The mail questionnaire might be employed (profitably or unprofitably) as an adjuvant method for accumulating reliable knowledge about the American retriever field trial game. In an elementary attempt to answer this question, the Pontchippi Survey of Retriever Field Trial Judges, 1968, was conducted; it consisted of questionnaires sent by U.S. mail to 144 judges of American retriever field trials. From a historical point of view, the survey was designed with the possibility in mind of providing a benchmark. In particular, it was anticipated that responses to the questions might provide a cursory description of the 1968 "qualified" judge (of American retriever trials) to whose hands has been entrusted a major responsibility for the breed and for the retriever field trial game. In addition, the survey could provide estimates of certain parameters relating to this population of judges. In the short-run, however, this survey was undertaken as a pilot study; hence, the immediate purposes were to obtain estimates of response rates and a concept of special problems associated with polling the particular group to which the questionnaires were submitted. Not exclusive of the foregoing, this survey was conceived with the hope of increasing interest in certain aspects of the art of judging American

† A preliminary report was mailed in 1968 to 139 of the 144 qualified judges; the contribution of each judge who returned a carefully completed questionnaire is gratefully acknowledged.

retriever field trials, of providing additional material as food for thought and controversy, of motivating selected individuals to comment about such an undertaking (as a mail questionnaire), and of affording judges an opportunity to classify themselves operationally.

Population of "Qualified" Judges

"Qualification" of each judge was determined by the presence of the judge's name on a listing of "eight-point judges" (judges who had judged eight or more stakes in which championship points were awarded) as of December 31, 1967, furnished by the American Kennel Club (AKC). The listing included 160 eight-point judges; 144 of those judges were listed as having judged a stake which carried championship points in 1965, 1966, or 1967; these 144 judges comprised the Pontchippi Survey population and, hence, the sampling frame.

Methods

See Technical Note to this appendix. At this point, it is sufficient to state that "modern, well-accepted" survey methodology was used, including probability sampling; the entire population was utilized in a design involving replicate subsampling; bias was explicitly estimated; sampling error was computed; and confidence intervals were computed and were noted to be wide.

Why a Mail Questionnaire

If you want to know what an experienced judge of retriever trials thinks, why not ask him? .... If you want to know some of the procedures he uses in judging a trial, why not ask him? .... If you want to know whether or not a group opinion exists, why not ask members of the group? In each of these cases, without other evidence, one has to accept the answers as being straightforward and responsible.

How does an individual go about asking experienced judges of American retriever field trials (relatively inexpensively and within a relatively short period of time), when they are geographically disbursed from Canada to southern Florida, and from the Atlantic coast to the Pacific coast? Sooner or later, a letter or questionnaire is suggested as a possible solution; however, it is well-known that many persons do not reply to questionnaires. When we resort to a mail questionnaire, we are faced with the widely publicized problem of nonresponse and all the bias associated with it.

Response

In view of the problems of nonresponse, this survey was planned and conducted as a pilot study to estimate the proportion of a group of experienced judges who would respond to a mail questionnaire and who would not balk at using simplifying assumptions, even though individual members of this group might find the assumptions objectionable. This really amounted to a crude attempt to explore the feasibility of finding out something about those experienced persons who judge American retriever field trials, some of their opinions, ... , and practices regarding certain well-chosen subjects. The design made it as painless as possible for a judge to refuse to answer. All he had to do was independently make no entry on the questionnaire, place it in the white envelope which was furnished, seal it, and mail it in the brown envelope provided. No one else could possibly know that he as an individual had refused to respond.

Response to the survey is reported on the following page in tabular form for convenience and clarity.

It is clear from this tabulation that the response rate was about 84 per cent (even though better than 90 per cent replied). Inasmuch as it is well-known that organizationally sponsored surveys (questionnaires) yield a better response rate on the average than do questionnaires sent out by individuals, I should expect that the true response rate is no worse than that which I, as an individual, obtained.

Even though the survey population was restricted to judges who had judged within the last three years, two judges indicated they had

Observation	Number	Per cent
Returned a questionnaire	121	84.0
Before reminder	(78)	(54.2)
After reminder but before registered letter	(26)	(18.1)
After registered letter	(17)	(11.8)
Replied, but did not return a questionnaire	9	6.2
Returned by post office--not delivered*	4	2.8
No information returned	10	6.9
Total to whom questionnaire was sent	144	100.0

* *Note:* Had the methodology included (permitted) use of the telephone, at least one of the "correct addresses" probably could have been obtained.

retired from retriever field trials completely, and at least one judge was reported to be deceased. In addition, four questionnaires sent via U.S. registered mail, return receipt requested, were not delivered and were returned by the post office. No reply was received from 10 judges; in addition, 6 judges declined or refused to complete a questionnaire (although only 2 of the 6 took advantage of the "anonymous refusal" opportunity). Nevertheless, 144 eight-point judges were active in judging stakes which awarded championship points (at sometime) during the period 1965-1967.

Bias.--As this survey was designed and analyzed, it was impossible for a judge to escape "participating" in the study--no matter what he may assert; he had to contribute either positive information or contribute to the bias of the study. The 23 judges from whom no response (in the form of answers to questions posed) was obtained are among those who influenced the retriever field trial game during the three-year period, and perhaps for an indeterminable period theretofore and thereafter. The lack of response from those 23 judges, no matter the reason or justification, contributes toward biasing estimates of the parameters under consideration, especially in the case of the 18 judges who declined to complete a questionnaire, because, undoubtedly, their opinions (on the retriever field trial game) differ from those of the 121 judges who submitted a completed questionnaire.

Known Performance of the Survey Instrument

How accurate were the estimates which were obtained from this mail questionnaire? *Answer:* In general, we do not know, but two checks were explicitly provided.

Physicians, dentists, and veterinarians.--By utilizing certain assumptions, 26 judges could be identified on the roster as being either a physician, a dentist, or a veterinarian; hence, the "true proportion" of physicians, dentists, or veterinarians was defined to be 26/144 or 18.1 per cent.

Questionnaire results.--The item, "your occupation," was included on the questionnaires solely to provide data for a check of accuracy, and for that reason only. Based on 118 respondents, 23 judges reported the occupation of physician, dentist, or veterinarian. Hence, the estimated proportion of physicians, dentists, or veterinarians among all judges is 23/118 = 19.5 per cent.

Comment: Intuitively, this gives evidence that the questionnaire method is capable of providing a pretty good estimate of facts; that is, the estimate, 19.5, is fairly close to the true answer, 18.1--in fact, ... close! This questionnaire did well on this particular estimate.

Experience in judging a national championship.--This item was included on the questionnaires solely to provide data for a second check of accuracy (of factual data), and for that reason only. After all, *The National Retriever Field Trial Club, 1941-1960, The Handbook of Amateur Retriever Trials, Ten-Year Edition, 1951-1961,* and selected issues of *Field Trial News* and *Retriever Field Trial News* contain such information. From these sources, the "true proportion" of the 144 judges who have judged either a national championship or a national amateur championship or both was computed to be 46/144 or 31.9 per cent.

Questionnaire results.--Based on 121 respondents, 38 judges reported that they had judged at least one national championship or national amateur championship stake; the estimated proportion is 38/121 or about 31.4 per cent.

Comment: Intuitively, this estimate gives further evidence that the questionnaire method is capable of providing a pretty good estimate of facts; that is, the estimate, 31.4, is fairly close to the true answer, 31.9. Thus, in spite of the fact that a 95 per cent confidence interval based on these data would be wide, the point estimate itself almost coincides with the parameter (true value). Such findings tend to increase confidence in the other results of the survey.

RESULTS

Age

In 1968, the average judge was 53.5 years of age; this arithmetic mean is based on 120 responses. The range for year of birth was from 1894 to 1933, or 39 years. In 1968, only 10 per cent of the judges were 44 years of age or younger; one-half of the judges were 52 years of age (the median) or younger; three-fourths of the judges were not more than 60 years of age; and 90 per cent of the judges were aged 66 or younger. In terms of conventional 5-year intervals, a greater number of judges (25) was concentrated in the interval 50-54 than in any other such interval.

Hypothesis.--In view of the rapid expansion of the American retriever field trial game during the 1960's, the mean age of eight-point judges will probably decline during the next decade. Explicitly, it is hypothesized that the mean age will be lower in 1978 than it is in 1968.

Year Registered First Retriever

Each and every one of the 119 judges who answered this item registered his first retriever before 1960. On the average, more than 18 years (the mean) had elapsed since the eight-point judge registered his first retriever; however, the reported range was 43 years, from 1916 to 1959. Fewer than 10 per cent of the judges registered their first retrievers during the decade prior to 1968; on the other hand, 10 per cent of the judges registered their first retrievers 28 or more years ago. One hundred of the judges (84 per cent of the 119 judges) registered their first retrievers between 1945 and 1959 inclusive; in terms of 5-year intervals, 1950-1954 (with 38) was the most popular (the modal class interval).

Active Participation as Handler, 1967

Only about 2 out of each 3 judges reported that they handled a retriever in a licensed trial in 1967 (121 judges responded to this item).

Example of sampling error.--As summarized, the overall estimate of active participation was 66 per cent; the group which received Form A (see note to this appendix) reported 64 per cent, the group which received Form B reported 65 per cent, and the group which received Form C reported 70 per cent. If one assumes that the failure of these three percentages (64, 65, 70) to be the same reflects sampling error (in the main), clearly, there is lack of evidence here that more than 7 out of 10 eight-point judges actively handled retrievers the previous year.

Retriever Club Membership

One-half of the 120 judges responding to this item reported belonging to 2 or fewer clubs, although the mean was about 2.6 clubs per judge. Thirteen of the judges reported holding membership in 5 or more clubs; in contrast, 35 judges reported membership in a single club.

Retrievers Trained in 1967

More than 13 per cent of the judges (of 113 respondents) reported that they did not train retrievers in 1967. The median number of retrievers trained was two (one-half the judges trained two or fewer retrievers); moreover, the training of two retrievers was most popular (the mode was two). Three judges reported that they each trained five or more retrievers in 1967.

Experience

By 1968, the average judge reported that he had judged more than 27 stakes in which championship points were awarded. The range of judging points (of the 120 judges reporting) was greater than 92, from 8 to more than 100. About 90 per cent of the judges reported between 10 and 50 judging points; one-half of the judges reported 20 (the median) or fewer points.

Triple Mark on Land with Pheasant

The total number of possible responses to this item was 48, because only one-third (144 ÷ 3) of the judges received Form A; there were 41 respondents.

About 95 per cent of the responding judges were willing to use two fliers; of those who were willing to use two fliers and gave a preference, 78 per cent preferred two fliers.

Fewer than half (46 per cent) of the 41 judges were willing to use three fliers; moreover, among those judges willing to use three fliers, 11 out of 15 (about 73 per cent) reported that they preferred two fliers.

Downwind Fall

Only about one-half of the judges (51 per cent, that is, 21 out of 41 respondents) indicated that a downwind fall was required to test marking ability in puppies. Clearly, there is no group opinion here; we would expect to get about the same results flipping pennies when *heads* equals yes and *tails* equals no.

Attempts to Count "Refusals"

About 93 per cent of the judges (38 out of 41 respondents) indicated that they attempt to count refusals in judging performance on blind retrieves.

Differential Difficulty in Judging Stakes

There appears to be no group opinion concerning which stake is the easiest to judge, the derby or the open. Out of 38 judges responding, 17 stated that the derby was easiest to judge and another 17 stated that the open was the easiest to judge.

On the other hand, one must infer from the group of respondents (38) that the qualifying stake is the most difficult of the three to judge (P < 0.01). Results were as follows: 8 judges thought the derby was most difficult; 23 judges thought the qualifying was most difficult; and 7 judges thought the open was the most difficult to judge.

Scoring or Grading System Used

About 5 out of 6 judges (on the average) used some type of numerical scoring system (33 out of 40 respondents), either alone or in some sort of combination. There remains only about 1 judge in 6 to state that he does not use a numerical system.

On the average, 7 out of 8 judges assigned an overall grade or score to each series. Of the 35 judges who assigned an overall grade or score, 17 reported that they graded or scored performance on a per bird basis. (Note, explicitly, that "assigned overall grade or score" does not necessarily imply that the judges averaged three scores, nor that they summed three scores.)

First Licensed Trial and First Retriever Registration

Only about 1 judge in 6 entered and handled his first retriever in a licensed trial less than 10 years ago. In fact, one-half of the judges had already entered and handled their first retrievers in a licensed trial before the end of 1953. The foregoing is based on 39 responses out of a possible 48 responses, where the range was 21 years (1940-1961) as to when a judge entered and handled his first retriever in a licensed trial. Moreover, every one of these judges had entered and handled in a licensed trial by 1961.

As one might suspect, one-half of the judges reported an elapsed time of 2 years or less between the time he registered his first retriever and the time he entered and handled his first retriever in a licensed trial.

Retriever Identity

Nearly 3 out of 4 (of the 37 judges who responded) reported that when judging they identified the retriever by entry number only.

Best Separation and Type of Test

Only 31 out of 48 judges responded to this item. Of the 31 respondents, nearly 3 out of 4 reported that best separation was obtained with water blinds and/or water blinds and another type of test.

Mark(s)-Blind Combination (Qualifying Stake)

There were 36 respondents out of a possible 48 on this item. Among the respondents, only 1 judge in 9 preferred the combination mark-blind on one trip to the line. One judge in 4 preferred the same line but with two trips, one trip to the line for the mark and a later trip to the line for the blind. About 64 per cent of the responding judges preferred to run the blind in a new area, away from the marks.

Without Comment (Last Item, Form C)

Selection of Poorest Job, A, B, or C:

Number who responded to this question: 34.

Number who selected Retriever A: 4 (11.8 per cent).
Number who selected Retriever B: 26 (76.5 per cent).
Number who selected Retriever C: 4 (11.8 per cent).

Selection of Best Job, A, B, or C:

Number who responded to this question: 34.

Number who selected Retriever A: 13 (38.2 per cent).

Number who selected Retriever B: 4 (11.8 per cent).

Number who selected Retriever C: 15 (44.1 per cent).

Number who reported A and C
        "equal":   1 (2.9 per cent).

Number who reported B and C
        "equal":   1 (2.9 per cent).

FINAL COMMENTS

The response rate obtained in this feasibility study provides evidence that a large proportion (84 per cent) of this group of experienced judges can be expected to respond to a mail questionnaire. Beyond and aside from this evidence, this venture appears to have been received favorably for the most part. In view of this, one is tempted to assert that, in general, the 1968 qualified American retriever field trial judge is interested in generating a reliable body of knowledge concerning the art of judging field trials, that the 1968 judge is willing to contribute to that body of reliable knowledge, and that the 1968 judge might be willing to educe from that body of knowledge ideas and concepts which may improve his own methods and techniques, increase his understanding of some aspects of the art of judging, and assist him in clarifying or formulating his own opinions and those of his colleagues.

The problems encountered in this study were no more than were anticipated, and ran the gamut, from "Who wants to know?" to "Why ... ?" to "So what?" to the financial requirements of such an undertaking. To emphasize a matter of record, I shall state explicitly what has been implicitly noted earlier: This survey was entirely an independent endeavor, invented, designed, conducted, analyzed, and financed by a single individual.

Not only did this survey exhibit evidence that each judge could be encouraged to classify himself operationally, it verified that information could be collected on a number of diversified topics. More important, it clarified a methodology, an adjuvant technique, for generating a reliable body of knowledge relative to the judging of American retriever trials.

Since it was assumed that each eight-point judge would know the limitations of a one-page mail questionnaire (especially one in which words were not carefully defined), obviously, no one, especially the author, expected a great wealth of information from this survey.

Both the scope and breadth of subject matter covered were necessarily made narrow because the survey was exploratory; nevertheless, the breadth was not as narrow as it might have appeared to an individual judge if he completed the questionnaire independently (according to the request). In short, the three sets of items provided more knowledge than one might suppose.

The Pontchippi Survey, 1968, was not designed to alter nor to confirm judges' opinions; rather, to record them. However, if the questions, and/or the task of answering those questions, provoked introspection or motivated re-evaluation concerning certain aspects of judging practices and procedures, then is it likely that the survey itself may have been instrumental in influencing the art of judging American retriever field trials?

And finally, were the purposes of this study served further? Although there is no "reliable knowledge," is there considerable hearsay evidence that this survey did provide material as food for controversy, and did motivate selected individuals to expound personal opinions concerning aspects of the questionnaires and of the individual who was "so bold as to ... "?

ACTION ITEMS

Item 1.--What other reliable body of knowledge based on carefully assembled, experienced opinions do you know of on judging American retriever field trials? What reliable (body of) knowledge have you contributed to judging American retriever field trials that is equal to or better than the product of these 144 judges?

Item 2.--How many eight-point judges from your state of residence were listed in the sampling frame used for the 1968 survey? For example, there were only two from Louisiana, McMahan and Wood.

Tables

It is well-known that information can be packed into a table like clay pigeons in a carton; however, it is not so well-known that ordinary reading ability is not effective in reading a table.

Nevertheless, under the assumption that an RE might prefer to make his own interpretation of data, and in order to economize the reader's time, selected tables (Tables C-N-1 to C-N-31) containing additional results are provided (following the Notes to Appendix C) for the dedicated retriever enthusiast. For example, tabulations by experience judging amateur national and/or national championship stakes were obtained as a by-product of one of the checks of accuracy.

If an RE doesn't know how to read a table, it is assumed that he will learn by asking someone or by consulting a worthwhile book, say, Wallis and Roberts.[1]

REFERENCE

1. Wallis, W. Allen and Roberts, Harry V. *Statistics, A New Approach*, Glencoe, Illinois: The Free Press, 1957, pp. 270-290.

A pittance of practice may be worth a tome of theory.

NOTES TO APPENDIX C

At the time this survey was designed, a purpose of the project was to explore the potentialities (for the American retriever field trial fraternity) of a well-designed, well-conducted mail questionnaire (complete with protocol and technical notes although the protocol is not reproduced here). If by chance this evidence should support further positive action, even an additional survey, it was and is intended that such action be initiated by some "other body," say, even an institutionalized retriever body. (If such be the case, questionnaire items should be prepared carefully by a panel of experienced judges and pre-tested as is routine with well-conducted surveys.) Clearly then, the 1968 survey was a ground-breaking ceremony for somebody else-- not for me.

To avoid influencing the survey before the initial mail-out date, it was not discussed with any other RE (retriever enthusiast); in fact, it is highly unlikely that any other RE could have possibly known that it was in preparation until some qualified judge actually received it through the mail.

In view of the nature of the group, I thought it would be wise for the survey period to include a national gathering. After all, it is well-known that some RE's won't leave a point until they feel "number eights." Moreover, a national gathering provides an opportunity for an RE to get his neck stuck (way) out. Since the 1968 National Amateur Championship Stake (NACS) was scheduled for June 18-21, the survey was planned as follows:

Initial mail-out (Exhibit A); date: May 22, 1968.

Reminder (Exhibit B); date: two weeks later, June 5, 1968.

Registered letter (Exhibit C); date: one month after initial mail-out date and on day following termination of NACS, June 22, 1968.

Envelopes postmarked May 23-June 22, 1968, opened by certified public accountant; date: June 26, 1968.

Closing date for data collection period: July 22, 1968.

Envelopes postmarked June 23-July 22, 1968, opened by certified public accountant; date: July 30, 1968.

Three different questionnaire forms were employed, each of which was sent to two subsamples of the survey population. Each questionnaire con-

6356 Bellaire Drive
New Orleans, Louisiana 70124
May 22, 1968

Mr. R. F. T. Judge
554 Quail Lane
Mallard Nᵣ McNeil, Mississippi 39457

Dear Mr. Judge:

This is a personal request from one retriever enthusiast to another, explicitly, a request that you participate in a survey of (American) retriever
field trial judges by completing the enclosed questionnaire and returning it to
me.

According to my count, the 1968 "official list of retriever field trial
judges" contains one hundred forty-four (144) "8-point judges" having judged
a stake carrying championship points as recently as 1965. Your name, my
name, and 142 other names appear on that list. I am writing 143 individual letters, such as this, in an attempt to obtain some reliable knowledge regarding the attitudes and opinions of these judges as a group. The sole purpose of this survey is to provide data for making inferences about this group
of judges; consequently, I do not want to be able to identify your attitude as an
individual.

Without discussing the enclosed questionnaire with anyone else, please
complete each and every item on the form. Then, place the completed questionnaire in the blank white envelope (enclosed), and seal the envelope. (Observe that neither your questionnaire nor this white envelope contains any
identification whatsoever.) Lastly, place the sealed white envelope containing your questionnaire in the (enclosed) brown, numbered, self-addressed,
stamped envelope, and seal this envelope.

Please sign your name under the identifying number at the top left of the
brown envelope, and mail the envelope to me.

When the brown envelope is received, it will be logged in to indicate that
you have replied. When all replies have been received, the (hopefully) 144
unopened envelopes will be taken to a firm of certified public accountants.
This firm will open the brown envelopes, destroy them, and return the unopened white envelopes to me for processing and analyzing of the questionnaires. Hence, I cannot possibly identify your reply, nor can anyone else.

Thank you for participating in this project.

Sincerely,

/s/

C. A. McMahan

CAMcM/at

Enclosures as stated.

[Exhibit A]

[Exhibit B]

[Mail - out date + 2 weeks: June 5, 1968.]

6356 Bellaire Drive
New Orleans, Louisiana 70124
June 22, 1968

Mr. R. F. T. Judge
554 Quail Lane
Mallard N. McNeil, Mississippi 39457

Dear Mr. Judge:

Reference invitation of May 22, 1968. Enclosed is an unsigned, retyped letter which was posted to you by regular mail in May. Since it was not returned to me, the sender, it seems reasonable to assume that it was properly delivered.

Reference reminder two weeks later. On June 5, a pencil sketch was mailed (via AIR) routinely to jog the memories of those judges from whom no reply had been received.

Final opportunity to participate in this pioneering exploration. Recall that the survey design ensures that no individual reply can be identified; in fact, no one but the judge himself can know whether he responded or not. Returns have been far better than our experiential data for mail questionnaires had lead us to expect; in fact, better than 50 per cent of the judges answered in the first two weeks after the initial mail-out. (The "riposte rate" now exceeds 75 per cent; for those who have experience with returns from mail questionnaires, that's a "high" rate.) Our records indicate that your reply has not been received as of this data. In view of the above, I am sending this letter by registered mail to be certain beyond question that you are afforded an opportunity to share in this venture.

In the event that you have misplaced the original materials or did not receive them, I am enclosing another form and set of envelopes for your convenience.

Sincerely,

/s/

C. A. McMahan

CAMcM/at

Enclosures (5)

[Exhibit C]

tained eight "basic items," the first eight items of each form (see Figure C-N-1). In addition to these basic items, a different set of items was included on each form (see Figures C-N-2, C-N-3, and C-N-4).

By a strictly random process, each form was assigned to two subsamples. The randomization resulted in the following assignments:

Form A was assigned to samples 2 and 5;

Form B was assigned to samples 1 and 6;

Form C was assigned to samples 3 and 4.

By means of this design, theoretically, 144 replies would be generated for each of the eight basic items. In addition, there could be 48 replies to each of the other items on each of the three forms; in other words, generalizations would be based on responses of 48 judges. Clearly, estimates of sampling error would be available for the eight basic items because they were replicated in the three forms; moreover, there was a possibility of obtaining an unbiased estimate from one or more of the subsamples of 24.

[Tables are numbered as follows (for convenience only): Tables C-N-1 through C-N-8 refer to information requested in the eight basic items of the survey questionnaires (refer again to Figure C-N-1); Tables C-N-9 through C-N-14 refer to information requested on Form A (Figure C-N-2); Tables C-N-15 through C-N-17 refer to items included on Form B (Figure C-N-3); and Tables C-N-18 through C-N-31 refer to items included on Form C (Figure C-N-4). Note that in tables in which "number of stakes judged" is reported in (only) two categories ($\geq$ 20 and < 20), the category $\geq$ 20 (stakes judged) is reported first.]

Survey of Retriever Judges

PONTCHIPPI

Your occupation: _____ (Please print)

Year of your birth: _____

Year in which you formally registered your first retriever in your own name as owner: _____

Regarding calendar year 1967:
Indicate for one retriever which you own and which you personally entered and handled in a licensed stake during 1967: _____ (Please print)

Stake: _____

Date of trial: _____
(If you did not enter a trial, write "NONE.")

To how many retriever clubs did you pay membership dues in 1967?
One ☐   Two ☐   Three ☐   Four ☐   Five + ☐

How many different retrievers did you yourself actually train and handle during 1967?
One ☐   Two ☐   Three ☐   Four ☐   Five + ☐

How many licensed amateur and open stakes have you judged?
_____ (Estimated)
(By actual count)

Have you ever judged an amateur national championship stake or a national championship stake (or both)?
Yes ☐   No ☐

Figure C-N-1.--Basic items, Pontchippi Survey of Retriever Field Trial Judges, 1968.

Triple mark on land with pheasant:
Assume that you (as judge) are going to conduct a series in a licensed open stake with 18 excellent retrievers called back (to run this series). Further assume more than adequate terrain, an unlimited supply of pheasant, and adequate time.

Would you be willing to use two fliers?   Yes ☐   No ☐

If "yes," which would you prefer?   One ☐   Two ☐

Would you be willing to use three fliers?   Yes ☐   No ☐

If "yes," which would you prefer?   One ☐   Two ☐   Three ☐

Assertion:
In setting a test (in training sessions) of marking ability in puppies, a downwind fall is required.
Do you   Agree? ☐   Disagree? ☐   Have no opinion? ☐

In judging performance on a blind retrieve in a licensed open stake, do you (as judge) attempt to record and count the number of whistles, the number of whistle refusals, and the number of cast refusals?
Yes ☐   No ☐

Consider the following three stakes in a licensed trial: Derby, Qualifying, Open.

Which stake is the most difficult for you to judge? _____ (Please print)

Which stake is the least difficult for you to judge? _____ (Please print)

Figure C-N-2. --Items included on Form A, in addition to eight basic items, Pontchippi Survey of Retriever Field Trial Judges, 1968.

On the back of this sheet, please sketch (in a crude sort of way) a land triple mark on pheasant, using one flier (last bird down). Then, by means of the type of grading (or scoring) system which you routinely employ, please indicate how you might describe the following performance.

(1) "Perfect" work on the first bird retrieved (the flier, last bird down).

(2) "Good" work on the second bird retrieved (the second bird down).

(3) "Fair" work on the last bird retrieved.

Did you use a numerical scoring system, a letter grade, or some other classification system when evaluating the above series?

Numerical ☐   Grade ☐   Other ☐

Did you score (or grade) on a per bird basis?

Yes ☐   No ☐

Did you assign an overall grade (or score) to this series?

Yes ☐   No ☐

If "yes," what grade (score) did you assign? _____

For the very first retriever which you entered and handled in a licensed trial, please indicate:

Name of club: _____   Fall ☐   Spring ☐   Year 19 _____

Figure C-N-3. --Items included on Form B, in addition to eight basic items, Pontchippi Survey of Retriever Field Trial Judges, 1968.

When judging a field trial, do you identify a retriever in your notebook other than by number ?

Yes ☐   No ☐

In a triple land mark, consider the first bird retrieved as the "mark," the other two retrieves as "memory" birds.

In judging open stakes, do you get the best separation with marks, memory falls, land blinds, or water blinds ?

Marks ☐   Memory ☐   Land blinds ☐   Water blinds ☐   Don't know ☐

Suppose that in a licensed qualifying stake (1) the first series is a land double mark, (2) the second series is a land blind. Do you prefer to conduct

____ the blind at the same location as the marks, on one trip to the line ?   ☐

or ____ the blind at the same location as the marks, but on a second trip to the line ?   ☐

or ____ the marks, then change to a new location for the blind, away from the marks (entirely new area) ?   ☐

Assume: Open (stake) land blind, 140 yards; all conditions equal except the following:

Retriever A takes good line to blind, stops and "pops" at 60 yards; takes cast in workmanlike manner.

Retriever B takes good initial line, drifts; sits on whistle at 60 yards (about 20 yards off the line), fails to take first cast and moves in direction away from blind; takes next whistle and cast in workmanlike manner.

Retriever C takes poor initial line (a little less than 20 degrees off, say, 18 or 19 degrees); stops on whistle at 60 yards; takes cast (back to the line to the blind) in workmanlike manner.

With this obviously limited information, select: Poorest job ____   Best job ____

Figure C-N-4.--Items included on Form C, in addition to eight basic items, Pontchippi Survey of Retriever Field Trial Judges, 1968.

Table C-N-1.--Number of judges, by age interval and by whether or not entered and handled a retriever in a licensed stake during 1967, Pontchippi Survey of (Qualified) Retriever Field Trial Judges, 1968

Age interval	Entered and handled a retriever during 1967		Total
	Yes	No	
< 40	4	1	5
40-44	13	3	16
45-49	12	11	23
50-54	16	9	25
55-59	14	5	19
60-64	12	5	17
65-69	7	2	9
≥ 70	4	2	6
Not reported	1	0	1
Total	83	38	121

Table C-N-2.--Number of judges, by number of retrievers personally trained and handled during 1967 and by broad age group, Pontchippi Survey of (Qualified) Retriever Field Trial Judges, 1968

Broad age group	Number of retrievers trained and handled during 1967							Total
	0	1	2	3	4	5+	Not reported	
35-44	1	6	9	5	0	0	0	21
45-54	7	7	16	6	5	3	4	48
55-64	6	11	9	7	1	0	2	36
≥ 65	1	2	8	1	2	0	1	15
Not reported	0	0	0	0	0	0	1	1
Total	15	26	42	19	8	3	8	121

Table C-N-3.--Number of judges, by number of retrievers personally trained and handled during 1967 and by number of licensed amateur and open stakes judged, Pontchippi Survey of (Qualified) Retriever Field Trial Judges, 1968

Number of stakes judged	Number of retrievers trained and handled during 1967							Total
	0	1	2	3	4	5+	Not reported	
< 15	2	9	12	5	1	2	2	33
15-19	4	5	7	2	2	0	1	21
20-24	1	2	7	1	1	1	1	14
25-29	2	4	5	2	0	0	1	14
30-34	1	3	1	0	1	0	1	7
35-39	0	0	3	2	1	0	0	6
≥ 40	4	3	7	7	2	0	2	25
Not reported	1	0	0	0	0	0	0	1
Total	15	26	42	19	8	3	8	121

Table C-N-4.--Number of judges, by number of licensed amateur and open stakes judged and by number of retriever clubs to which judge paid membership dues in 1967, Pontchippi Survey of (Qualified) Retriever Field Trial Judges, 1968

Number of stakes judged	Number of retriever clubs to which judge paid membership dues in 1967							Total
	0	1	2	3	4	5+	Not reported	
< 15	0	10	10	7	2	4	0	33
15-19	0	10	3	4	4	0	0	21
20-24	0	2	2	3	3	4	0	14
25-29	0	4	3	2	3	2	0	14
30-34	0	3	1	0	3	0	0	7
35-39	0	0	1	2	1	2	0	6
≥ 40	0	6	6	4	7	1	1	25
Not reported	0	0	0	0	1	0	0	1
Total	0	35	26	22	24	13	1	121

Table C-N-5.--Number of judges, by age interval and by number of retriever clubs to which judge paid membership dues in 1967, Pontchippi Survey of (Qualified) Retriever Field Trial Judges, 1968

Age interval	Number of retriever clubs to which judge paid membership dues in 1967							Total
	0	1	2	3	4	5+	Not reported	
< 40	0	3	0	0	0	2	0	5
40-44	0	7	4	1	1	3	0	16
45-49	0	8	3	5	6	1	0	23
50-54	0	6	9	3	6	1	0	25
55-59	0	4	5	5	3	2	0	19
60-64	0	2	2	6	3	4	0	17
65-69	0	4	1	0	4	0	0	9
≥ 70	0	1	2	2	1	0	0	6
Not reported	0	0	0	0	0	0	1	1
Total	0	35	26	22	24	13	1	121

Table C-N-6.--Number of judges, by age interval and by whether or not he judged an amateur national championship stake or a national championship stake, Pontchippi Survey of (Qualified) Retriever Field Trial Judges, 1968

Age interval	Judged an amateur or national championship stake		Total
	Yes	No	
< 40	0	5	5
40-44	3	13	16
45-49	6	17	23
50-54	11	14	25
55-59	5	14	19
60-64	7	10	17
65-69	3	6	9
≥ 70	2	4	6
Not reported	1	0	1
Total	38	83	121

Table C-N-7.--Number of judges, by age interval and by number of licensed amateur and open stakes judged, Pontchippi Survey of (Qualified) Retriever Field Trial Judges, 1968

Age interval	Number of stakes judged								Total
	< 15	15-19	20-24	25-29	30-34	35-39	≥ 40	Not reported	
< 40	2	2	0	0	0	1	0	0	5
40-44	4	3	4	2	1	0	2	0	16
45-49	8	5	2	3	2	1	2	0	23
50-54	5	3	2	3	2	2	8	0	25
55-59	6	6	2	2	0	1	2	0	19
60-64	5	1	3	2	0	1	4	1	17
65-69	1	1	0	1	2	0	4	0	9
≥ 70	2	0	1	1	0	0	2	0	6
Not reported	0	0	0	0	0	0	1	0	1
Total	33	21	14	14	7	6	25	1	121

Table C-N-8.--Number of judges, by age interval and by year registered first retriever in his name as owner, Pontchippi Survey of (Qualified) Retriever Field Trial Judges, 1968

Age interval	Year registered first retriever								Total
	Before 1930	1930-34	1935-39	1940-44	1945-49	1950-54	1955-59	Not reported	
< 40	0	0	0	0	0	1	4	0	5
40-44	0	0	0	0	2	7	7	0	16
45-49	0	0	0	0	7	10	6	0	23
50-54	1	0	1	1	8	8	6	0	25
55-59	0	0	0	2	6	5	5	1	19
60-64	2	0	4	2	4	3	2	0	17
65-69	0	0	1	2	3	3	0	0	9
≥ 70	0	0	0	3	2	1	0	0	6
Not reported	0	0	0	0	0	0	0	1	1
Total	3	0	6	10	32	38	30	2	121

Table C-N-9.--Number of judges, by most difficult stake to judge, by number of licensed amateur and open stakes judged, and by whether or not judged an amateur national championship stake or a national championship stake, Pontchippi Survey of (Qualified) Retriever Field Trial Judges, 1968

Experience		Most difficult stake to judge				
Number of stakes judged	Judged amateur or national championship	Derby	Qualifying	Open	Not reported	Total
≥ 20	Yes	1	6	0	3	10
	No	5	2	2	1	10
< 20	Yes	0	1	0	0	1
	No	2	14	5	2	23
Total		8	23	7	6	44

Note: The first two rows of this table contain information from judges who have judged 20 or more such stakes (≥ 20).

Table C-N-10. --Number of judges, by least difficult stake to judge, by number of licensed amateur and open stakes judged, and by whether or not judged an amateur national championship stake or a national championship stake, Pontchippi Survey of (Qualified) Retriever Field Trial Judges, 1968

Experience		Least difficult stake to judge				
Number of stakes judged	Judged amateur or national championship	Derby	Qualifying	Open	Not reported	Total
≥ 20	Yes	4	0	3	3	10
	No	2	3	4	1	10
< 20	Yes	0	0	1	0	1
	No	11	1	9	2	23
Total		17	4	17	6	44

Table C-N-11.--Number of judges, by whether or not the judge agrees with
the assertion that a downwind fall is required as a test of
marking ability in puppies and by number of licensed amateur and open stakes judged, Pontchippi Survey of (Qualified)
Retriever Field Trial Judges, 1968

Number of stakes judged	Downwind fall required				Total
	Agree	Disagree	No opinion	Not reported	
≥ 20	9	10	0	1	20
< 20	12	9	1	2	24
Total	21	19	1	3	44

Table C-N-12.--Number of judges, by whether or not the judge agrees with
the assertion that a downwind fall is required as a test of
marking ability in puppies and by age interval, Pontchippi
Survey of (Qualified) Retriever Field Trial Judges, 1968

Age interval	Downwind fall required				Total
	Agree	Disagree	No opinion	Not reported	
< 40	2	0	0	0	2
40-44	2	4	1	1	8
45-49	5	2	0	0	7
50-54	4	3	0	0	7
55-59	1	4	0	1	6
60-64	3	6	0	0	9
65-69	3	0	0	0	3
≥ 70	1	0	0	0	1
Not reported	0	0	0	1	1
Total	21	19	1	3	44

Table C-N-13.--Number of judges, by number who attempt to count and record "refusals" on a blind retrieve in a licensed open stake
and by number of licensed amateur and open stakes judged,
Pontchippi Survey of (Qualified) Retriever Field Trial Judges, 1968

Number of stakes judged	Counts and records "refusals"			Total
	Yes	No	Not reported	
≥ 20	18	1	1	20
< 20	21	2	1	24
Total	39	3	2	44

Table C-N-14.--Number of judges, by number who attempt to count and record "refusals" on a blind retrieve in a licensed open stake
and by age interval, Pontchippi Survey of (Qualified) Retriever Field Trial Judges, 1968

Age interval	Counts and records "refusals"			Total
	Yes	No	Not reported	
< 40	2	0	0	2
40-44	8	0	0	8
45-49	7	0	0	7
50-54	6	1	0	7
55-59	3	2	1	6
60-64	9	0	0	9
65-69	3	0	0	3
≥ 70	1	0	0	1
Not reported	0	0	1	1
Total	39	3	2	44

Table C-N-15. --Number of judges, by type of scoring system used, by number of licensed amateur and open stakes judged, and by whether or not judged an amateur national championship stake or a national championship stake, Pontchippi Survey of (Qualified) Retriever Field Trial Judges, 1968

Experience		Type of scoring system used			Total
Number of stakes judged	Judged amateur or national championship	Numerical	Letter grade	Other	
≥ 20	Yes	11	2	2	15
	No	8	0	1	9
< 20	Yes	1	0	0	1
	No	13	1	1	15
Total		33	3	4	40

Table C-N-16.--Number of judges utilizing a numerical scoring system, by method of computing over-all score for a series, by number of licensed amateur and open stakes judged, and by whether or not judged an amateur national championship stake or a national championship stake, Pontchippi Survey of (Qualified) Retriever Field Trial Judges, 1968

Number of stakes judged	Experience: Judged amateur or national championship	Numerical grade assigned to the series				Total
		By adding score on each bird	By not adding three scores on individual birds	Not reported	Not applicable	
≥ 20	Yes	1	10	0	4	15
	No	1	6	1	1	9
< 20	Yes	0	1	0	0	1
	No	2	11	0	2	15
Total		4	28	1	7	40

Table C-N-17.--Number of judges, by year entered and handled first retriever in a licensed trial and by age interval, Pontchippi Survey of (Qualified) Retriever Field Trial Judges, 1968

Age interval	Year entered and handled first retriever in a licensed trial						Total
	1940-44	1945-49	1950-54	1955-59	1960-64	Not reported	
< 40	0	0	0	1	1	0	2
40-44	0	1	1	0	1	0	3
45-49	0	1	4	3	1	0	9
50-54	0	3	1	4	0	0	8
55-59	0	1	3	2	1	2	9
60-64	0	0	0	1	0	0	1
65-69	0	1	3	0	0	0	4
≥ 70	1	1	2	0	0	0	4
Total	1	8	14	11	4	2	40

Table C-N-18.--Number of judges, by number of licensed amateur and open stakes judged and by method of identification of retriever in a field trial, Pontchippi Survey of (Qualified) Retriever Field Trial Judges, 1968

Number of stakes judged	Method of identifying retriever		Total
	Number only	Other	
≥ 20	16	6	22
< 20	10	4	14
Not reported	1	0	1
Total	27	10	37

Table C-N-19.--Number of judges, by whether or not judged an amateur national championship stake or a national championship stake and by method of identification of retriever in a field trial, Pontchippi Survey of (Qualified) Retriever Field Trial Judges, 1968

Judged national stake	Method of identifying retriever		Total
	Number only	Other	
Yes	8	3	11
No	19	7	26
Total	27	10	37

Table C-N-20.--Number of judges, by type of test producing best separation in open stakes and by number of licensed amateur and open stakes judged, Pontchippi Survey of (Qualified) Retriever Field Trial Judges, 1968

Number of stakes judged	Test producing best separation						Total
	Marks	Memory	Land blind	Water blind	Don't know	Not reported	
≥ 20	0	3	0	14	3	2	22
< 20	0	2	0	8	0	4	14
Not reported	0	0	0	1	0	0	1
Total	0	5	0	23	3	6	37

Table C-N-21.--Number of judges, by type of test producing best separation in open stakes and by age interval, Pontchippi Survey of (Qualified) Retriever Field Trial Judges, 1968

Age interval	Test producing best separation						Total
	Marks	Memory	Land blind	Water blind	Don't know	Not reported	
< 40	0	0	0	0	0	1	1
40-44	0	0	0	5	0	0	5
45-49	0	1	0	5	0	1	7
50-54	0	1	0	6	2	1	10
55-59	0	2	0	1	0	1	4
60-64	0	0	0	5	1	1	7
65-69	0	1	0	1	0	0	2
≥ 70	0	0	0	0	0	1	1
Total	0	5	0	23	3	6	37

Table C-N-22.--Number of judges, by method of identification of retriever in a field trial and by type of test producing best separation in open stakes, Pontchippi Survey of (Qualified) Retriever Field Trial Judges, 1968

Test producing best separation	Method of identifying retriever		Total
	Number only	Other	
Marks	0	0	0
Memory	4	1	5
Land blind	0	0	0
Water blind	18	5	23
Don't know	2	1	3
Not reported	3	3	6
Total	27	10	37

Table C-N-23.--Number of judges, by preference for conducting the blind at the same location or a different location from the marks in a combination (land) double mark-single blind (first and second series combined, licensed qualifying stake) and by number of licensed amateur and open stakes judged, Pontchippi Survey of (Qualified) Retriever Field Trial Judges, 1968

Number of stakes judged	Prefer to move to completely new location after (double) marks			Total
	Yes	No	Not reported	
≥ 20	14	7	1	22
< 20	8	6	0	14
Not reported	1	0	0	1
Total	23	13	1	37

Table C-N-24.--Number of judges who prefer to conduct a combination (land) double mark-single blind (first and second series combined, licensed qualifying stake) at a single location, by number of trips to the line and by number of licensed amateur and open stakes judged, Pontchippi Survey of (Qualified) Retriever Field Trial Judges, 1968

Number of stakes judged	Number of trips to the line				Total
	One	Two	Not reported	Not applicable	
≥ 20	3	4	1	14	22
< 20	1	5	0	8	14
Not reported	0	0	0	1	1
Total	4	9	1	23	37

Table C-N-25.--Number of judges, by method of identification of retriever in a field trial and by selection of retriever which did the poorest job in an open (stake) land blind, Pontchippi Survey of (Qualified) Retriever Field Trial Judges, 1968

Poorest job in open (stake) land blind	Method of identifying retriever		Total
	Number only	Other	
Retriever A	2	2	4
Retriever B	19	7	26
Retriever C	4	0	4
Not reported	2	1	3
Total	27	10	37

Table C-N-26.--Number of judges, by method of identification of retriever in a field trial and by selection of retriever which did the best job in an open (stake) land blind, Pontchippi Survey of (Qualified) Retriever Field Trial Judges, 1968

Best job in open (stake) land blind	Method of identifying retriever		Total
	Number only	Other	
Retriever A	8	5	13
Retriever B	4	0	4
Retriever C	12	3	15
Not reported	3	2	5
Total	27	10	37

Table C-N-27.--Number of judges, by number of licensed amateur and open stakes judged and by selection of retriever which did the poorest job in an open (stake) land blind, Pontchippi Survey of (Qualified) Retriever Field Trial Judges, 1968

Poorest job in open (stake) land blind	Number of stakes judged			Total
	≥ 20	< 20	Not reported	
Retriever A	2	2	0	4
Retriever B	16	9	1	26
Retriever C	1	3	0	4
Not reported	3	0	0	3
Total	22	14	1	37

Table C-N-28.--Number of judges, by number of licensed amateur and open stakes judged and by selection of retriever which did the best job in an open (stake) land blind, Pontchippi Survey of (Qualified) Retriever Field Trial Judges, 1968

Best job in open (stake) land blind	Number of stakes judged			Total
	≥ 20	< 20	Not reported	
Retriever A	9	3	1	13
Retriever B	1	3	0	4
Retriever C	8	7	0	15
Not reported	4	1	0	5
Total	22	14	1	37

Table C-N-29.--Number of judges, by age interval and by selection of retriever which did the poorest job in an open (stake) land
blind, Pontchippi Survey of (Qualified) Retriever Field Trial
Judges, 1968

| Age interval | Poorest job in open (stake) land blind | | | | Total |
	Retriever A	Retriever B	Retriever C	Not reported	
< 40	0	1	0	0	1
40-44	2	3	0	0	5
45-49	0	3	3	1	7
50-54	1	7	0	2	10
55-59	0	3	1	0	4
60-64	0	7	0	0	7
65-69	0	2	0	0	2
≥ 70	1	0	0	0	1
Total	4	26	4	3	37

Table C-N-30.--Number of judges, by age interval and by selection of retriever which did the best job in an open (stake) land blind,
Pontchippi Survey of (Qualified) Retriever Field Trial Judges, 1968

| Age interval | Best job in open (stake) land blind | | | | Total |
	Retriever A	Retriever B	Retriever C	Not reported	
< 40	1	0	0	0	1
40-44	2	0	2	1	5
45-49	1	2	2	2	7
50-54	4	1	3	2	10
55-59	1	1	2	0	4
60-64	3	0	4	0	7
65-69	1	0	1	0	2
≥ 70	0	0	1	0	1
Total	13	4	15	5	37

Table C-N-31.--Number of judges, by selection of retriever which did the best job in an open (stake) land blind and by selection of retriever which did the poorest job in an open (stake) land blind, Pontchippi Survey of (Qualified) Retriever Field Trial Judges, 1968

Best job in open (stake) land blind	Poorest job in open (stake) land blind				Total
	Retriever A	Retriever B	Retriever C	Not reported	
Retriever A	0	12	1	0	13
Retriever B	1	0	3	0	4
Retriever C	2	13	0	0	15
Not reported	1	1	0	3	5
Total	4	26	4	3	37

The action is BACK!

1968 Plus or Minus (±) 32 Years

Thirty-two years hence some persons active in the retriever field trial game today (1968) undoubtedly will still be active--at the turn of the twenty-first century. It is not, however, the purpose of this survey to forecast the opinions of the group of judges active in 2000 A.D., but merely to describe selected aspects of the group as it is in 1968. Moreover, it is not the purpose of this survey to undertake the problems of short-term forecasting, such as 32 years ago when the *Literary Digest* mailed out ten million ballots (questionnaires), yet failed to correctly forecast the outcome of the 1936 Presidential Election. Nor is this survey purported to catalog the legends and traditions associated with judging American retriever field trials. More explicitly, this survey is designed to increase interest in generating a reliable body of knowledge concerning certain aspects of the art of judging American retriever field trials. Since many a true word is spoken in jest, this survey might be expected to stimulate some useful comments along this line also. The foregoing notwithstanding, this study certainly concerns unwillingness--unwillingness to respond to a mail questionnaire and/or unwillingness to make simplifying assumptions.

Simplifying Assumptions

Each and every eight-point judge knows "for sure" that how one performs a specified judging function, or how one arrives at a specific decision depends upon (among other things) a specific combination of many variables which happen to be operating and are considered at the moment. Little (or much) may be contributed to a seminar or bull-session by such a statement as, "it depends on the quality of the entries, ..., the mechanics, ..., the cover, ..., the wind, ..., the game supply, the light and background, ...," for well it may. Yet after a retriever enthusiast (an RE) is asked to defend a position he has taken, or has been pushed into taking, oftentimes he may resort to the assertion that "you must remember that judging retriever trials is not a science; it is an art." He may get off the hook since few of us may have sound reason to disagree with this statement. What *is* shocking is that such a speaker often appears to think that he has settled the issue at hand, seeming to (conveniently) forget that principles, methods, and techniques of an art can be studied and learned in a manner similar to learning those of a science (see Chapter Two).

In order to obtain some elementary general principles of an art, it often may be helpful, at least at the start, to make some simplifying assumptions. This leads to the first question: What proportion of experienced judges of American retriever trials is willing to make some simplifying assumptions regarding the retriever game with the expectation of producing some generalities? It seems logical that if you want to know what an experienced judge of retriever trials will do, "put him in a situation" and observe his actions. When confronted with a situation which requires that one or more simplifying assumptions be explicitly made, we shall expect all judges to encounter difficulties; we shall even expect some judges to experience "blocks" such that they are bewildered and cannot make a decision or choice. We shall assume that the action taken by the judge reflects not only his basic personality, but especially his background and experience with the retriever field trial game.

Problem of Nonresponse

Suppose that I, as an individual, were to try to estimate the magnitude of the problem of nonresponse in a group of selected judges. Since it is well-known that organizationally sponsored surveys (questionnaires) yield a better response rate on the average than questionnaires sent out by individuals, I should expect that the true response rate is no worse than that which I, as an individual, could obtain.

Experiment versus Survey

In order to assure that we are talking essentially the same language, it is convenient to recall a rough and ready guideline, namely, that in an experiment, assignment of "treatments" is under control of the investigator; contrarily, in a survey, the investigator does not assign the treatments ("nature" has assigned them). In a survey there are four major methods of collecting data: documentary source, observation, personal interview, and mail questionnaire. For the most part, the data were collected in this survey by means of a mail questionnaire.

Timing

In 1961, I attended the National Amateur Championship Stake (Park

Rapids). Ever since that summer, I have been laying-off to seriously consider methodology for putting selected questions to the group of qualified judges. In 1967, I finally realized that there would be no convenient time, and
there were other compelling reasons for not delaying the conduct of the survey.

Explicitly, after the manuscript for *Retriever Theory* had been completed
(for the most part, except for editing) in the spring of 1968, this particular
survey was conducted to explore one more practical approach to obtaining reliable knowledge concerning selected aspects of judges and judging. Results
of the survey have not been incorporated in any manner whatsoever into
Retriever Theory ; hence, the author's opinions may not agree with those of the
survey.

Background

For purposes of this study, it was assumed that retriever field trial enthusiasts make up a well-informed, special-interest group within an affluent
portion of American society; moreover, that those judges who operationally
qualified as "eight-point judges" (8-J) make up a highly select group within
the group of RE's. It was assumed that each "thinking 8-J" knows that
"fact-collecting, " *per se*, on the retriever field trial game (and those who
judge it) is no substitute for hard thinking (nor for any on-going activity to
improve the art of judging, such as judging seminars, ... , and laboratory
field exercises at judges' clinics).

In addition to the foregoing, it was assumed that the 8-J is not totally
unfamiliar with the use of mail questionnaires ... from ... to market research ... , to ... , to opinion polls, to measuring popularity of political
candidates. It was assumed that if an 8-J has special interests in the methodology of the mail questionnaire (say, the advantages and disadvantages), he
has access to a library which he knows how to use. It was assumed that the
8-J is familiar with and understands the meaning of such sayings as "you
can get good statistics, bad statistics, and damn lies from mail questionnaires, " ... , "you can prove anything with statistics generated by mail
questionnaires." It was explicitly assumed that some of the limitations of the
mail questionnaire would be obvious to each and every 8-J , e.g., mail
questionnaires are inflexible because answers are final (probing is out), questions (items) may be vague and/or misunderstood, answers may be influenced
by discussions with others, ... , answers on the questionnaires are not in-

dependent, and judges who do not return questionnaires are likely to differ from those who do return questionnaires.

Description of the Sampling Problem

Suppose we have a well-defined population of N individuals whose names and addresses we can list. We wish to gather information on selected facts, practices, attributes, and opinions of this population. The attributes might be of the type, judging experience, age, and the like, and answers can be easily obtained, whereas, the opinions can be answered through multiple choice (and other) type answers provided the individual is willing to express such an opinion. It should be mentioned at this time that for the set of N individuals, each question posed creates a distinct population of size N. For example, there will be a population of ages, a population of judging experiences, ... A single questionnaire can be sent to all N individuals requesting information on all the attributes as well as opinions on all issues of interest. However, it is well-known that the longer the questionnaire and the more difficult the questions to answer (in this case, opinions to commit one's self to) the greater the likelihood of both nonresponse to the questionnaire and refusal to make an expression on some of the opinions. This condition, in reality, leaves us with a sampling of opinions from the population of size N. Such being the case, we might prefer to sample from the population of N individuals and send shorter questionnaires.

In the present study, the decision was made to prepare three separate one-page questionnaires, A, B, and C, each consisting of two parts. Part I, covering basic items such as age and experience judging a national championship, was made identical for A, B, and C, while Part II, dealing with opinions and practices, was different for A, B, and C. The questionnaires, which we will refer to simply as A, B, C, were then sent to different sampling groups.

Re-assignment of husband-wife (household) "teams."--After forms had been assigned to samples, the roster of each sample was inspected to determine if a "known" husband-wife appeared in the same sample. In addition, a check was made to determine if the team had been assigned the same form even though the individuals were in different samples. Two such teams were identified and re-assignment of husband-wife to different forms was accomplished as follows:

    1. A coin was tossed to determine which member would be "moved"

(heads = husband; tails = wife).

2. A number (1-6, excluding present sample number and/or present sample number of other member) was selected from a table of random digits to determine "new" sample assignment.

3. A second number (01-24) was selected from a table of random digits to determine which member of the ("new") sample would replace husband/wife in his/her original sample.

4. Identifying code (see next topic) numbers were simply "swapped" between the two judges.

Sampling frame.--In the terminology of sampling, we first required a sampling frame which is a listing of the sampling units for the population. For our study (i.e., survey) this consisted of 144 names and addresses (N = 144).

To elaborate, the "List of Retriever Trial Judges" (LRTJ) "as of January, 1968," was obtained from the American Kennel Club. It was assumed that the list was both complete and accurate, although past personal experience leads the author to believe that the assumption may be unjustified. Only persons who were listed as having judged 8 or more stakes carrying championship points (through December 31, 1967) were considered; the number of such persons was 160. The list was reduced by eliminating persons who reportedly had not judged a trial carrying championship points since 1964; as a consequence, 16 names were eliminated. Thus, the sampling frame for the survey consisted of the names of 144 (N = 144) "eight-point judges" who were reported as having judged stakes (where championship points were awarded) during 1965, 1966, and/or 1967.

Each of the 144 names was identified by a six-digit code number as follows: The first two digits indicate year of survey (68 = 1968); the third digit indicates sample number (1-6); the fourth, fifth, and sixth digits indicate number within N = 144. For example, 682-030 = year, 1968; sample number, 2; sequence number 30 (sixth member of sample 2, thirtieth member in N = 144).

Simple random sampling.-- For purposes of discussion, we could assert (although it is not true) that the next step was to select the groups of individuals who were to receive questionnaires A, B, and C; each group could have been selected in a completely random manner following conventional randomizing procedures described elsewhere in this book. In this method of selection each possible sample of n individuals from the population of N individuals has an equal chance of being selected. The method is known as "simple random sampling."

In estimating some characteristic (i.e., parameter) of a population of size N using a sample of size n (n < N), we cannot expect the estimate from the sample to exactly equal the parameter of the population. A difference will (probably) exist which we call a "sampling error." If we select three groups, one for each of the different questionnaires A, B, C, and let π_A be the parameter in the population corresponding to the proportion who have an opinion asked for by A and let p_A denote the corresponding proportion in the sample receiving A, we expect p_A to differ from π_A due to sampling error. Similarly, we would expect p_B to differ from π_B due to sampling error. However, p_A can be expected to differ from p_B for two reasons: sampling error and the fact that Forms A and B may not be equally easy to fill out.

Interpenetrating samples.--Actually, in the present study the population of N = 144 individuals was randomly divided into 6 samples of 24 individuals each. (Note that the entire population was used.) Samples number 2 and number 5 were assigned Form A, 1 and 6 were assigned Form B, while 3 and 4 were assigned Form C. (Hence, the same end result is obtained as if simple random sampling had been used.) Obtaining replicate samples for Forms A, B, and C is referred to as "interpenetrating samples." The method is frequently used to obtain an estimate of "between-interviewer" variation (when data are collected by the interview method) when more than one interviewer is used in making a survey. However, in this study replicate samples were used for a different purpose. Each subsample produces an independent estimate of the population characteristics and a subsample with no nonresponse present yields an unbiased estimate. With more samples we have a better chance of obtaining unbiased estimates.

Analysis

Type 1.--Estimate of proportion of population responding (π) from individual samples using p_i, i = 1, 2, 3, 4, 5, 6:

$$p_i = \frac{a_i}{n_i} = \hat{\pi},$$

where a_i is the number responding in sample i. Estimated variance of p_i

$$v(p_t) \quad = \quad \frac{N - n_t}{N(n_t - 1)} \; p_t q_t ,$$

where $q_t = 1 - p_t$.

Confidence interval for π (using the normal approximation) is

$$p_t \quad \pm \quad \left[t \sqrt{\left(1 - \frac{n_t}{N}\right) \frac{p_t q_t}{n_t - 1}} + \frac{1}{2n_t} \right] .$$

Type 2.--Testing for independence in contingency tables: Use the conventional χ^2 tests.

In the event of significant results, continue with tests covered in Cochran's paper.[1]

Type 3.--Estimating a population parameter when there is nonresponse involved: Suppose in a population of size N that $N*$ individuals will properly respond to a questionnaire. Let

$$W* \quad = \quad \frac{N*}{N}$$

equal the proportion of the population who will respond. Let

$$\overline{W}* \quad = \quad \frac{N - N*}{N} \quad = \quad 1 - W*$$

equal the proportion of the population who will not respond. Let

$$\pi \quad = \quad \frac{M}{N}$$

equal the proportion of the population with a particular attribute, where M = number in the population with this attribute. Let

$$\pi* \quad = \quad \frac{M*}{N*}$$

equal the proportion of those individuals in the population who will respond who do have the particular attribute with $M*$ representing the number in the response group who have the attribute in question. Let $\overline{\pi}*$ equal the proportion of the population in the nonresponse category who have the attribute in question.

It is clear that $\pi = W^* \pi^* + \overline{W}^* \overline{\pi}^*$ since $\overline{\pi}^* = (M - M^*)/(N - N^*)$.

Note: In the foregoing notation, $*$ (star) used alone refers to response group while $\bar{\;}$ (bar) refers to the nonresponse group.

We want to estimate the parameter $\pi = M/N$ and also find a confidence interval for π.

Suppose that we send the questionnaire to a sample of n individuals in the population and n^* of the individuals respond with m^* of the n^* individuals having the attribute in question.

Now $p^* = m^*/n^*$ is an unbiased estimate of π^* and, hence, an unbiased estimate of π provided $n^* = n$. If $n^* \neq n$, it is a biased estimate of π and the amount of bias is

$$E\left(\frac{m^*}{n^*}\right) - \pi = \frac{M^*}{N^*} - \pi = \overline{W}^*(\pi^* - \overline{\pi}^*).$$

For "fair sized" n^*, an approximate 95 per cent confidence interval can be obtained for π^* as follows:

$$p^* \pm 2\sqrt{\left(1 - \frac{n^*}{N}\right)\frac{p^* q^*}{n^*}},$$

where $q^* = 1 - p^*$.

However, we desire a confidence interval for $\pi = W^* \pi^* + \overline{W}^* \overline{\pi}^*$ and we have no information (i.e., estimate) on $\overline{\pi}^*$.

One procedure[2] is to take $\overline{\pi}^* = 0$ when estimating the lower confidence limit $\hat{\pi}_L$ and take $\overline{\pi}^* = 1$ when estimating the upper confidence limit $\hat{\pi}_U$.

This procedure gives conservative estimates of the confidence limits as follows:

$$\hat{\pi}_L = W^*\left\{ p^* - 2\sqrt{\left(1 - \frac{n^*}{N}\right)\frac{p^* q^*}{n^*}} \right\},$$

$$\hat{\pi}_U = W^*\left\{ p^* + 2\sqrt{\left(1 - \frac{n^*}{N}\right)\frac{p^* q^*}{n^*}} \right\} + \overline{W}^*.$$

Further modification should be considered here.

Absolute limits on π are easily seen to be

$$\frac{m^*}{N} \le \pi \le \frac{m^*}{N} + \left(1 - \frac{n^*}{N}\right) = 1 - \left(\frac{n^* - m^*}{N}\right).$$

Consequently, choose for the lower limit, $\hat{\pi}_L$, the larger of the two quantities m^*/N and

$$W^*\left\{p^* - 2\sqrt{\left(1 - \frac{n^*}{N}\right)\frac{p^*q^*}{n^*}}\right\},$$

and choose for the upper limit, $\hat{\pi}_U$, the smaller of the two quantities

$$\frac{m^*}{N} + \left(1 - \frac{n^*}{N}\right)$$

and

$$W^*\left\{p^* + 2\sqrt{\left(1 - \frac{n^*}{N}\right)\frac{p^*q^*}{n^*}}\right\} + \overline{W}^*.$$

Note that since

$$\frac{m^*}{N} = \frac{m^*}{n^*} \cdot \frac{n^*}{N} = \frac{n^*}{N}p^*,$$

the lower limit can never be less than $(n^*/N)p^*$. That is, it must be at least the fraction n^*/N of the sample estimate, where n^* is the number in the sample who respond.

Example 1.--$N = 144$, $N^* = 120$, $W^* = 120/144 = 5/6$, $\overline{W}^* = 1 - W^* = 1/6$, $M^* = 40 = $ number with desired attribute. $\pi^* = M^*/N^* = 40/120 = 1/3 = $ proportion responding who had desired attribute.

Note: $n = N = 144$, $n^* = N^* = 120$, $m^* = M^*$.

Since $n = N$, we have no sampling error and compute the absolute limits on π, namely,

$$\frac{m^*}{N} = \frac{40}{144} = \frac{5}{18}, \quad \frac{m^*}{N} + \overline{W}^* = \frac{5}{18} + \frac{1}{6} = \frac{8}{18};$$

therefore,

$$\frac{5}{18} \le \pi \le \frac{8}{18},$$

i.e.,

$$0.28 \le \pi \le 0.44.$$

(*Note:* "Sample" estimate is $1/3 = 6/18$.)

Example 2.--N = 144, N* = 120 = number responding in population, n = 48 = sample size, n* = 40 = sample response, m* = 12 = number responding with desired attribute, W* = 120/144 = 5/6, $\overline{W}$* = 1/6, p* = m*/n* = 12/40 = 0.30 = estimate (unbiased) of π* .

The absolute limits for π are

$$\frac{m^*}{N} = \frac{12}{144} = \frac{1}{12}$$

and

$$\frac{m^*}{N} + \left(1 - \frac{n^*}{N}\right) = 1 - \left(\frac{n^* - m^*}{N}\right)$$
$$= 1 - \frac{40 - 12}{144} = \frac{29}{36}.$$

We are certain that

$$\frac{1}{12} \leq \pi \leq \frac{29}{36}$$

i.e.,

$$0.08 \leq \pi \leq 0.81.$$

The conservative 95 per cent confidence limits for π are

$$\hat{\pi}_L = \frac{5}{6}\left\{0.30 - 2\sqrt{\left(1 - \frac{40}{144}\right)\frac{(0.30)(0.70)}{40}}\right\}$$
$$= 0.25 - 0.10 = 0.15$$

$$\hat{\pi}_U = \frac{5}{6}\left\{0.30 + 2\sqrt{\left(1 - \frac{40}{144}\right)\frac{(0.30)(0.70)}{40}}\right\} + \frac{1}{6}$$
$$= 0.25 + 0.10 + 0.17 = 0.52.$$

We are confident (at the 95 per cent level) that π lies in the interval 0.15 to 0.52 . Carefully note the width of the interval with only 1 out of 6 failing to respond.

Example 3.--Let us use the data of Example 2 to estimate M*, the total number in the population of potential responders who possess the desired attribute. The "ratio estimate" is one possible technique. For each individual in the sample, two measurements (say, X and Y) are obtained. First, does the individual respond to the questionnaire? Second, if he does respond, does he have the desired attribute? Let x_i = 1 if the ith individual either responds or would respond if questioned and let $x_i = 0$ otherwise. Also let $y_i = 1$ if the ith individual who responds has the desired attribute and $y_i = 0$ otherwise. Then

while

$$\sum_{i=1}^{N} x_i \;=\; N^* \;=\; \text{number in the population who will respond if questioned,}$$

and

$$\sum_{i=1}^{n} x_i \;=\; n^* \;=\; \text{number in the sample who do respond,}$$

$$\sum_{i=1}^{n} y_i \;=\; m^* \;=\; \text{number of responders in the sample who have the desired attribute.}$$

The appropriate ratio estimate of M^* is

$$\hat{M}^* \;=\; \frac{\sum_{i=1}^{n} y_i}{\sum_{i=1}^{n} x_i} \cdot \sum_{i=1}^{N} x_i \;=\; \frac{m^*}{n^*} \cdot N^* \;=\; p^* N^*$$

$$=\; \frac{12}{40}(120) \;=\; 36 .$$

Let us now return to our expression for 95 per cent confidence limits for π^* and denote the half-width of the confidence interval by

$$H \;=\; 2\sqrt{\left(1 - \frac{n^*}{N}\right)\frac{p^* q^*}{n^*}} .$$

Then

$$H \;=\; 2\sqrt{p^* q^*} \cdot \sqrt{\frac{1}{n^*} - \frac{1}{N}} ,$$

which means that

$$H \;\leq\; \sqrt{\frac{1}{n^*} - \frac{1}{N}}$$

since $p^* q^* \leq 1/4$ for all p^* and q^*. The maximum H occurs when $p^* = q^* = 0.5$.

Suppose we hold p^* constant and vary the number responding in the sample, n^*, and note the effect on H as shown on the following page. For example, with $m^* = 7$, $n^* = 24$, $p^* \approx 0.3$, the 95 per cent confidence interval for π^* is 0.30 ± 0.17 or 0.13 to 0.47, where our response rate in the sample is only 50 per cent. With $m^* = 14$, $n^* = 48$, $p^* \approx 0.3$

Response rate in sample (in per cent)	n^*	m^*		$H \mid p^* = 0.5$ $\left(H = \sqrt{\dfrac{1}{n^*} - \dfrac{1}{N}}\right)$	$H \mid p^* = 0.3$
		$p^* = 0.5$	$p^* = 0.3$		
50	24	12	7	0.186	0.171
62.5	30	15	9	0.162	0.149
75	36	18	11	0.144	0.132
87.5	42	21	13	0.130	0.119
100	48	24	14	0.118	0.108

the interval is 0.30 ± 0.11 or 0.19 to 0.41. This is the situation with 100 per cent response. With the sample proportion p^* fixed, we observe that the confidence interval width decreases as the response percentage increases (i.e., as n^* increases).

It might be of some interest to see what happens when m^* is held fixed and n^* increases.

We can write the half-width 95 per cent confidence interval as

$$
\begin{aligned}
H &= 2\sqrt{\left(1 - \frac{n^*}{N}\right)\frac{p^* q^*}{n^*}} = 2\sqrt{\left(1 - \frac{n^*}{N}\right)\frac{p^*(1 - p^*)}{n^*}} \\
&= 2\sqrt{\left(1 - \frac{n^*}{N}\right)\frac{m^*(n^* - m^*)}{(n^*)^3}} \\
&= \frac{2}{n^*}\sqrt{\left(1 - \frac{n^*}{N}\right)\frac{m^*(n^* - m^*)}{n^*}} \\
&= 2p^*\sqrt{\left(1 - \frac{n^*}{N}\right)\left(\frac{n^* - m^*}{m^* n^*}\right)} \\
&= 2p^*\sqrt{\left(1 - \frac{n^*}{N}\right)\left(\frac{1}{m^*} - \frac{1}{n^*}\right)} .
\end{aligned}
$$

Suppose we take $m^* = 16$.

n^*	p^*	H
24	2/3	0.176
30	8/15	0.162
36	4/9	0.143
42	8/21	0.126
48	1/3	0.111

We observe that the confidence interval decreases in width as the number of responders increases.

Let us now examine our conservative 95 per cent confidence interval for π. We have $\hat{\pi}_U - \hat{\pi}_L = 2W^*H + \overline{W}^*$ which indicates that regardless of the response rate in the sample, the confidence interval will be increased in width by an amount equal to the proportion of the population who will not respond. This means that if the population nonresponse rate is large the confidence interval may be so wide as to produce practically worthless information.

REFERENCES

1. Cochran, William G. "Some Methods for Strengthening the Common χ^2 Tests," *Biometrics 10* (4): 431 (December, 1954).

2. Cochran, William G. *Sampling Techniques* (Second Edition), New York: John Wiley and Sons, Inc., 1963, pp. 355-359.

APPENDIX D

ON TOSSING A DUMMY

This appendix is focused on both the practical and the theoretical--from tossing a dummy in the field to maximum range of a projectile. A practical retriever man like me may, on occasion, disdain the theorist and claim interest only in facts. My professional friends and colleagues who *know* already know that I have dedicated a lifetime to obtaining solutions to practical problems. In fact, I have often thought that better progress might be made in many endeavors if the movements behind the idea were less subject to overdoses of theory.

The body of this appendix is a report on a pre-pilot study--an empirical study. An experiment was designed and conducted on the spur of the moment (because manpower was available) even though I had contemplated conducting such an experiment for a long time. A purpose of the study was to generate some data for further consideration.

After I had made many careful observations on birdboys in action, my intuition led me to hypothesize that neither size of the dummy nor weight of the dummy nor "length of the rope" makes much difference in the length of time that a dummy (of the type that I routinely use) remains in the air on the average. (Does the birdboy "count"?) Moreover, I believe that a capable, practiced birdboy, should be able to "show" a retriever a dummy for 3 seconds or more in 9 or more throws out of 10 over the long run.

Throwers.--Always, "it seems" difficult for me to obtain assistance in conducting an experiment for which several people are required; of course, one can call on his kinfolk as a last resort. I did just that. During the days of Christmas, 1969, both my sons (and their families) were at home at Pontchippi, the older on leave from the army and the younger on vacation from the university. In spite of the fact that these young men had not thrown a dummy for years (at one time each was considered a first-rate birdboy), with the assistance of my younger son's wife, we conducted a "Pontchippi dummy-tossing experiment."

Design of the Experiment [Q and D (Undefined)]

Two observers, three throwers, three types of dummies (two of each type, a total of six dummies), and two stopwatches were used. The basic experiment consisted of each thrower tossing each dummy once; two observers independently clocked each toss. One "observer position" was filled by the same person during the entire experiment; however, the other "observer position" was occupied by two different persons (one at a time).

Assumed estimates of measurement error.--In Chapters Six and Ten, for convenience, error associated with measuring "flight time" of a shot pheasant or a thrown shackled duck was estimated by the failure of two observers to record the same (value of) elapsed time (airborne) on a specified mark. Attention was called to the fact that instrument (stopwatch) variability was confounded with observer variability. In the present experiment (really a "quickie," as stated earlier), more than two observers were involved; clearly, it is not easy to assume away "observer effect." Even if the same two watches were used and one observer made an observation on each toss of each dummy, we might expect (because two other persons were involved) the standard deviation of the pair of measurements (made on each dummy) to be near 0.2 seconds. Undoubtedly, it would be larger than 0.10 and 0.15 seconds as estimated earlier.

Assumption: We shall assume a standard deviation for measurement error of 0.15 seconds for this experiment. Moreover, in this experiment, we shall disregard variability among observers--throw away such information.

The dummy-tossers ("three each of one type") for the dummy-tossing experiment, Pontchippi-on-Canal, December 26, 1969.

Six training dummies, two each of three types, used in dummy-tossing experiment, Pontchippi-on-Canal, December 26, 1969.

Heat, heart worms, handling (hhh). *View toward the levee and canal. These backyard kennels were designed to force a "lazy man to handle" his dogs at least twice each and every day. Although insulated sleeping quarters, complete with breezeway, are available at the end of each run, the retrievers are lodged in screened quarters from late evening until after daylight.*

View of runs facing the levee.

View facing The Lake; the Lodge is "insect proof."

*View of the dog pens from the levee, Pontchippi-on-Canal, 1970
(see blow-up below of sign at arrow).*

Pontchippi Lane at Millard, Mississippi.

PONTCHIPPI AT MILLARD

Lake Pontchippi (view facing east).

Lake Pontchippi (view facing north).

Observations.--We made two observations on each toss of each dummy, one observation by observer A and one by "observer B." For purposes of reporting and analysis, we shall combine these observations into a single observation (a *weighted average*). Hence, (for analysis) we shall have only one observation for each toss of each dummy.

Number of observations: Given 3 throwers, 6 dummies, 1 observation per toss, we generated $3 \times 6 \times 1 = 18$ observations in the basic experiment. We replicated the experiment; hence, we have a total of $18 \times 2 = 36$ observations or 35 degrees of freedom "for error."

Each thrower was asked to "toss well" each dummy so that each and every dummy would break the horizon and fall about 20 yards from the feet of the (thrower) birdboy in a well-defined area between 2 trees. The data, in form for analysis, are shown in Table D-1.

Description of the Dummies

Because this experiment was a "quickie," the 6 dummies were selected haphazardly from dummies "on hand." The large white plastic dummies are often specified as being 3 inches in diameter and 15 inches long, 3" × 15"; the large canvas dummies have reported specifications of $3\frac{1}{2}$" × 15"; the small plastic dummies nominally are 2" × 12".

Length of the "throwing rope."--No attempt was made to hold constant the length of the rope (attached to the dummy). However, the length of each rope was measured, as illustrated in the snapshot at the top of page 813.

The length of rope attached to a specified dummy, measured to the nearest one-eighth inch, represents the consensus of two observers. The mean length of rope ($\bar{x}$) was approximately 12.83 inches, with a standard deviation (s) of approximately 3.47 inches.

Weights of dummies.--Each dummy was weighed independently by each of two observers, each using a different "balance" (spring

Table D-1.--Elapsed time in seconds (time airborne) between release of dummy from hand of birdboy on up-swing (event E) and dummy hits ground initially (event F), and selected statistical measures, three throwers, three types of dummies (six dummies), two replications, Pontchippi-on-Canal, December 26, 1969

Thrower and replication		Identification number of dummy					
		1	3	4	6	2	5
1	Rep I	3.3	3.0	2.6	2.9	3.2	2.9
	Rep II	3.0	3.2	3.1	2.5	4.1	3.2
2	Rep I	3.3	3.0	3.0	3.4	3.4	3.3
	Rep II	3.5	3.3	3.6	3.5	3.8	4.1
3	Rep I	2.9	2.7	2.9	2.5	2.9	3.5
	Rep II	3.2	3.7	3.1	2.7	2.8	2.9

Note: Observations were made by two observers, A and B, independently to one-fifth second using two stopwatches; no attempt was made to estimate measurement error; each entry shown in this table is a weighted mean of the two observations made by observers A and B. Dummies 1 and 3 were "large" plastic dummies, dummies 4 and 6 were made of canvas; and dummies 2 and 5 were "small" plastic dummies.

Identification number of dummy	Length of rope in inches
1	$9\frac{1}{8}$
2	$14\frac{1}{8}$
3	$7\frac{3}{4}$
4	$15\frac{1}{4}$
5	$15\frac{1}{4}$
6	$15\frac{1}{2}$

scale). Original measurements were made in grams because two sets of balances (gram scales) happened to be conveniently available. The mean of the two observations was computed and then converted to ounces by multiplying by the factor 0.0352740. The weight of each dummy is shown in Table D-2.

Selected calculations.--For convenience, we shall use some "computing formulas" to make several calculations for use later. Let x be a best estimate (an observation in seconds) of how long a specified tossed dummy was airborne; let n = number of observations.

$$n = 36; \quad \Sigma x = 114.0;$$
$$\bar{x} = \frac{\Sigma x}{n} = \frac{114.0}{36} = 3.17;$$

Table D-2.--Observed weight of each dummy in grams, two observers, and mean weight in grams and in ounces, six dummies, dummy-tossing experiment, Pontchippi-on-Canal,
December 26, 1969

| Identification number of dummy | Observed weight in grams | | Mean weight in grams | Approximate weight in ounces † |
| | Observer | | | |
	C	D	(C + D)/2	
1	518	520	519	18
2	374	377	376	13
3	504	506	505	18
4	372	376	374	13
5	353	356	354	12
6	414	416	415	15

† The mean and standard deviation of the approximate weights in
ounces of the n = 6 dummies are as follows: $\bar{x} \approx 14.8$, $s \approx 2.64$.

$$\Sigma x^2 = 366.46; \quad (\Sigma x)^2 = (114.0)^2 = 12,996.00;$$

$$\frac{(\Sigma x)^2}{n} = \frac{12,996.00}{36} = 361.00.$$

$$s^2 = \frac{\Sigma x^2 - (\Sigma x)^2/n}{n-1} = \frac{366.46 - 361.00}{35} = 0.1560;$$

$$s \approx 0.395 \approx 0.40.$$

Type of dummy.--Calculations of selected statistics regarding airborne time, by type of dummy, are shown on the following page.

Variability among throwers.--Calculations of selected statistics
regarding airborne time, by thrower, are shown on the following page.

Observed elapsed time in the air.--Over all 36 tosses, the dummy "averaged" being in the air for 3.17 seconds; the standard deviation for these 36 observations was about 0.4 seconds.

Observed elapsed time in the air, by type of dummy.--The small
plastic dummies (numbered 2 and 5) were observed to be airborne

Statistic	Type of dummy		
	Large plastic (1 and 3)	Large canvas (4 and 6)	Small plastic (2 and 5)
n	12	12	12
Σx	38.1	35.8	40.1
$\overline{x}$	3.18	2.98	3.34
Σx^2	121.79	108.36	136.31
$\dfrac{(\Sigma x)^2}{n}$	$\dfrac{1451.61}{12} = 120.97$	$\dfrac{1281.64}{12} = 106.80$	$\dfrac{1608.01}{12} = 134.00$
s^2	$\dfrac{0.82}{11} = 0.0745$	$\dfrac{1.56}{11} = 0.1418$	$\dfrac{2.31}{11} = 0.2100$
s	0.27	0.38	0.46

Statistic	Thrower		
	1	2	3
n	12	12	12
Σx	37.0	41.2	35.8
$\overline{x}$	3.08	3.43	2.98
Σx^2	115.86	142.50	108.10
$\dfrac{(\Sigma x)^2}{n}$	$\dfrac{1369.00}{12} = 114.08$	$\dfrac{1697.44}{12} = 141.45$	$\dfrac{1281.64}{12} = 106.80$
s^2	$\dfrac{1.78}{11} = 0.1618$	$\dfrac{1.05}{11} = 0.0955$	$\dfrac{1.30}{11} = 0.1182$
s	0.40	0.31	0.34

for the longest average $(\overline{x})$ time interval, 3.34 seconds per throw. The canvas dummies (numbered 4 and 6) were airborne the least time on the average, $\overline{x} \approx 2.98$ seconds. The large plastic dummies, the two heaviest dummies (numbered 1 and 3), were airborne on the average 3.18 seconds.

Weight of dummy and length of rope, confounded. -- Note that

the two large plastic dummies, the two heaviest dummies (numbered
1 and 3) also had the two shortest ropes.

Observed elapsed time in the air, by thrower. -- Dummies thrown
by thrower 2 averaged 3.43 seconds in the air. Dummies thrown
by thrower 1 averaged being in the air just under 3.1 seconds.
Airborne time for dummies thrown by thrower 3 averaged nearly 3
seconds ($\overline{x}_3$ = 2.98).

Analysis of variance (ANOVA). -- According to my criteria, this was
not a well-conducted experiment. Statistical tests and inferences beyond the data are unjustified. In particular, dummies were not selected randomly; length of throwing rope was not controlled. However, dummies were thrown in a strictly randomized order (using
random permutations of 6).

For purposes of description, a rough and ready ANOVA follows:

Source	df	ss	ms
Total	35	5.46	
Among throwers	2	1.34	0.67
Among types of dummies	2	0.77	0.38
"Experimental error"	4	0.43	0.11
"Sampling error"	27	2.92	0.11

Conclusion. --With these figures, we can say straight away that
these particular birdboys did not show the retriever "the dummy" for
the same average time. Moreover, average time in the air was not
the same for each type of dummy used here.

A pittance of practice may be worth a tome of theory.

NOTES TO APPENDIX D

Much of this book is operational evidence that I think the retriever field trial game in America needs a little theory grounded on sound facts. Moreover, many ideas which we accept as "purely practical" are based on many assumptions.

In practice, the birdboy is not concerned with the maximum horizontal distance that he can toss a dummy. On the other hand, the officer laying out a firing range must necessarily be concerned with the maximum range of projectiles to be fired. Undoubtedly, the officer has experiential tables to guide him. Tables could be prepared for birdboys, by age and size of the boy, type of dummy, and the like.

Birdboys, as school boys, often study theoretical problems. They learn in physics or calculus that, in a vacuum, the greatest range of a projectile on a horizontal plane is obtained by firing at 45 degrees to the horizontal. In contrast, a school boy in the role of birdboy, learns early that to throw a dummy the maximum distance, he should "throw at an angle" which is less than 45 degrees.

For convenience, let's focus on the somewhat more "exact instrumentation," say, the gunner in the field. The practical gunner "knows" that for maximum range, the gun should be elevated at an angle of about 35 degrees. What the practical gunner doesn't usually think about is how that "35" is arrived at, what the assumptions are, and that if he fires many rounds, how much variability there will be. In order to clarify our analytical thinking, both problems, with and without air resistance, are shown as worked examples. Note the value of k used for air resistance; how theoretical can you get in a practical problem?

[*Aside:* Those readers who have not had calculus and differential equations should omit the two worked examples; no continuity will be lost.]

First, we shall review some basic principles. In studying the performance of a shotgun (or rifle), one may be interested in how long it takes something to happen. Calculus is concerned with how fast certain phenomena change.

Average rate. -- If a projectile travels a distance y in the y-direction in

817

time t,   the average rate is y/t; it may be expressed in so many feet per
second.

Velocity.-- By velocity of a projectile, one means the rate at which it
passes over a very, very small distance. For example, if one is interested
in the rate at which the projectile passed over the distance dy during the
element of time dt,   then the velocity

$$v \; = \; \frac{dy}{dt} \, .$$

Moreover, v can be constant, or increasing (positive acceleration), or decreasing (negative acceleration).

Acceleration.-- The rate at which a velocity is changing is called acceleration. For example, if, at a particular instant of time, one is interested
in the additional velocity dv gained in a small interval of time dt,   then at
that instant the acceleration a is

$$a \; = \; \frac{dv}{dt} \, .$$

Inasmuch as $v = dy/dt$,

$$a \; = \; \frac{d\left(\frac{dy}{dt}\right)}{dt} \, ,$$

which may be written

$$a \; = \; \frac{d^2 y}{dt^2} \, .$$

Moreover, acceleration is expressed as a change in velocity per unit of time,
or in this case, so many feet per second per second.

No Air Resistance

Consider first the motion of a projectile in the atmosphere with the assumptions that there is no air resistance and the path is a plane curve traced
out by the center of gravity $P(x, y)$ of the projectile. $P(x, y)$ is the location of the center of gravity of the projectile in the plane at any time t.

Let

v_o = initial velocity (muzzle),

θ = angle of inclination with the horizontal,

w = weight of the projectile, and

g = acceleration of gravity.

[*Note:* Weight is used in place of mass because it may be more appealing intuitively to the retriever enthusiast.]

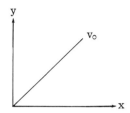

Now we know that in order to accelerate a mass, force must be applied. The force necessary to accelerate a mass is (1) proportional to the mass and (2) proportional to the acceleration which is being delivered.

If t is time (measured in seconds) then dx/dt and dy/dt are the components of velocity in the x and y directions (which we will take as horizontal and vertical, respectively) and d^2x/dt^2 and d^2y/dt^2 represent the components of acceleration. Also, let x and y be measured in feet, and let w (lbs) be the weight of the projectile and g (ft/sec^2) be the gravity constant. Using these units, in order to measure force in pounds we shall have to make use of a constant of proportionality k, where $k = 1/g$.

From Newton's second law of motion, we know two things: (1) The rate of change of momentum of a projectile is proportional to the force acting on it and (2) is in the same direction as the force. Hence, (after the projectile leaves the muzzle) the force f in the y-direction can be expressed in three ways:

$$f = (w) \text{ (acceleration in the y-direction) } (k),$$

$$f = kw \frac{dv_y}{dt},$$

and

$$f = kw \frac{d^2y}{dt^2}.$$

The force in the x-direction is zero; hence,

$$0 = \frac{1}{g} w \frac{d^2x}{dt^2}.$$

The only force acting on the projectile in the y-direction is the force of gravity, w; hence,

$$-w \;=\; \frac{1}{g} \, w \, \frac{d^2y}{dt^2}$$

$$-w \;=\; \frac{w}{g} \, \frac{d^2y}{dt^2} \;.$$

Therefore, using Newton's second law of motion we get the following system of differential equations:

$$\frac{w}{g} \, \frac{d^2x}{dt^2} \;=\; 0$$

$$\frac{w}{g} \, \frac{d^2y}{dt^2} \;=\; -w \;. \qquad\qquad\qquad (1)$$

Subject to certain conditions, namely at time zero, the center of gravity of the projectile is located at

$$x \;=\; 0\,, \qquad\qquad\qquad (a)$$

$$y \;=\; 0\,. \qquad\qquad\qquad (b)$$

Moreover, if v_0 is the initial velocity (ft/sec) and θ is the angle which the projectile makes (at the start) with the horizontal (as shown below) at time

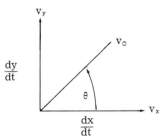

0, $\sin\theta = (dy/dt)/v_0$, $dy/dt = v_0 \sin\theta$; and $\cos\theta = (dx/dt)/v_0$, $dx/dt = v_0 \cos\theta$. Hence, at $t = 0$,

$$\frac{dx}{dt} \;=\; v_0 \cos\theta\,, \qquad\qquad\qquad (c)$$

and

$$\frac{dy}{dt} \;=\; v_0 \sin\theta\,. \qquad\qquad\qquad (d)$$

Continuing with the x equation in Eqs. (1), we have $d^2x/dt^2 = 0$ and integrate to get $dx/dt = C_1 = v_0 \cos \theta$ by use of (c). Integrating again $x = C_1 t + C_2$ and since by (a) $x = 0$ when $t = 0$ we get $C_2 = 0$. Therefore, $x = (v_0 \cos \theta)t$. From the y equation,

$$\frac{d^2y}{dt^2} = -g, \quad \frac{dy}{dt} = -gt + C_3 \quad \text{and} \quad C_3 = v_0 \sin \theta,$$

by use of (d). Integrating again, $y = -(1/2)gt^2 + C_3 t + C_4$ and by (b) $C_4 = 0$. Hence, $y = -(1/2)gt^2 + (v_0 \sin \theta)t$.

The solution for x and y in terms of t is

$$\left. \begin{array}{rcl} x & = & (v_0 \cos \theta)t \\[2mm] y & = & (v_0 \sin \theta)t - \dfrac{1}{2} gt^2 . \end{array} \right\} \tag{2}$$

This is called a "parametric form" for the solution because both x and y are expressed in terms of the parameter t.

We can obtain a "rectangular form" of the solution by eliminating the parameter t. From Eqs. (2),

$$t = \frac{x}{v_0 \cos \theta},$$

so

$$y = (v_0 \sin \theta) \frac{x}{v_0 \cos \theta} - \frac{1}{2} g \left(\frac{x}{v_0 \cos \theta} \right)^2$$

$$y = x \tan \theta - \frac{g}{2v_0^2} (\sec^2 \theta) x^2,$$

and the path of the projectile (with no air resistance) is a parabola.

To find the range, we set $y = 0$ and solve for t in Eqs. (2).

$$0 = (v_0 \sin \theta) t - \frac{1}{2} gt^2$$

and

$$t = \frac{2v_0 \sin \theta}{g}.$$

Then the range is the value of x when $t = (2v_0 \sin \theta)/g$. Thus,

$$\text{range} = v_0 \cos \theta \left(\frac{2v_0}{g} \sin \theta\right) = \frac{v_0^2}{g} \sin 2\theta$$

$$\text{range} = R(\theta) .$$

The range is a function of θ, say, $R(\theta)$. That is, its value depends on θ. Because the largest value of the sign of an angle is 1, it is clear that the maximum value of $R(\theta)$ occurs when $\sin 2\theta = 1$, i.e., when $2\theta = 90°$ or $\theta = 45°$. This may also be obtained by setting $R'(\theta) = 0$ and solving for θ. With no air resistance, the maximum range is v_0^2/g.

Air Resistance Proportional to Velocity

Next consider the case where the air resistance is assumed proportional to velocity of the projectile. Now the component of velocity in the x-direction will no longer be constant; it will be dx/dt multiplied by the constant k (where k is not the k used earlier), or $k(dx/dt)$. Moreover, there will be an additional force in the y-direction of $k(dy/dt)$. Combining these elements with Eqs. (1), the system of differential equations by Newton's second law of motion is

$$\left. \begin{array}{l} \dfrac{w}{g} \dfrac{d^2x}{dt^2} = -k \dfrac{dx}{dt} \\[3mm] \dfrac{w}{g} \dfrac{d^2y}{dt^2} = -w - k \dfrac{dy}{dt} . \end{array} \right\} \qquad (3)$$

For x we have

$$\frac{d^2x}{dt^2} + \frac{kg}{w} \frac{dx}{dt} = 0,$$

which is a "linear, homogeneous, second order differential equation with constant coefficients." It is linear because the derivatives of x with respect to t are raised to the first power only. [For example, $(d^2x/dt^2)^{3/2}$ is not linear.] It is homogeneous because the right side of the equation is zero. It is second order because the highest derivative is the second derivative. Further, the coefficients (say, kg/w) are constants.

A solution for this type is $x = C_1 + C_2 e^{zt}$, where m is the non-zero solution of $m^2 + (kg/w)m = 0$; $m = -(kg/w)$. Thus,

$$x = C_1 + C_2 e^{-(kg/w)t}$$

and

$$\frac{dx}{dt} = -\frac{kg}{w} C_2 e^{-(kg/w)t}.$$

Now using (a) and (c), namely, $x = 0$ and $dx/dt = v_o \cos \theta$ when $t = 0$, we find

$$0 = C_1 + C_2,$$

$$v_o \cos \theta = -\frac{kg}{w} C_2 ;$$

$$C_1 = -C_2 = \frac{w}{kg} v_o \cos \theta .$$

Hence,

$$x = \frac{w}{kg} v_o (\cos \theta)(1 - e^{-(kg/w)t}).$$

For the y equation of Eqs. (3),

$$\frac{d^2 y}{dt^2} + \frac{kg}{w} \frac{dy}{dt} = -g .$$

This equation is not homogeneous because the right member, $-g$, is not zero. The solution consists of two parts, one part, say,

$$y_c = C_3 + C_4 e^{-(kg/w)t},$$

as before with the x, and a second part, $y_p = C_5 t$, such that

$$\frac{d^2 y_p}{dt^2} + \frac{kg}{w} \frac{dy_p}{dt} = -g .$$

Thus,

$$0 + \frac{kg}{w} (C_5) = -g ,$$

and

$$C_5 = -\frac{w}{k} ;$$

so

$$y_p = -\frac{w}{k} t .$$

The subscripts on y refer to the complementary solution (which comes from

the homogeneous equation) and a particular solution.   The complete solution
for y is $y = y_a + y_p$.   Hence,

$$y = C_3 + C_4 e^{-(kg/w)t} - \frac{w}{k} t$$

and

$$\frac{dy}{dt} = -\frac{kg}{w} C_4 e^{-(kg/w)t} - \frac{w}{k} .$$

Now using (b) and (d), namely, when $t = 0$, $y = 0$, and $dy/dt = v_0 \sin \theta$,
we get

$$0 = C_3 + C_4 ,$$
$$v_0 \sin \theta = -\frac{kg}{w} C_4 - \frac{w}{k} ;$$
$$C_3 = -C_4 = \frac{w}{kg} \left(v_0 \sin \theta + \frac{w}{k} \right)$$

and

$$y = \frac{w}{kg} \left(v_0 \sin \theta + \frac{w}{k} \right) \left(1 - e^{-(kg/w)t} \right) - \frac{w}{k} t .$$

The parametric form of the solution to our problem is

$$x = \frac{w}{kg} v_0 (\cos \theta) (1 - e^{-(kg/w)t})$$

$$y = \frac{w}{kg} \left(v_0 \sin \theta + \frac{w}{k} \right) \left(1 - e^{-(kg/w)t} \right) - \frac{w}{k} t .$$ \hspace{1cm} (4)

Obtaining a rectangular form by eliminating the parameter t would not serve
any useful purpose.

    To find the range we need first to find that value of t (say, t = T)
which makes $y = 0$, and then substitute that value in the equation for x.

    From the y equation of Eqs. (4) with $y = 0$, we get

$$T = \frac{1}{g} \left(v_0 \sin \theta + \frac{w}{k} \right) \left(1 - e^{-(kg/w)T} \right) .$$ \hspace{1cm} (5)

    Expanding Eq. (5) in series form and assuming that k is small enough
for second and higher degree terms in k to be negligible, we get

$$T \approx \frac{2}{g} v_0 \sin \theta \left(1 - \frac{k}{3w} v_0 \sin \theta\right). \tag{6}$$

(See Technical Note D-1 for a development of the approximation.)

The x equation of Eqs. (4), when expanded in a Taylor's series in t, gives

$$x = \frac{w}{kg} (v_0 \cos \theta) \left[1 - \left(1 - \frac{kg}{w} t + \frac{k^2 g^2}{w^2} \frac{t^2}{2} - \cdots\right)\right],$$

and neglecting terms involving k^2, k^3, ..., we have

$$x \approx (v_0 \cos \theta) \left(t - \frac{1}{2} \frac{kg}{w} t^2\right). \tag{7}$$

Substituting the value of $t = T$ from Eq. (6) into Eq. (7) for x, we obtain the range R:

$$R \approx (v_0 \cos \theta) \left[\frac{2}{g} v_0 \sin \theta \left(1 - \frac{k}{3w} v_0 \sin \theta\right)\right.$$
$$\left. - \frac{1}{2} \frac{kg}{w} \left(\frac{2}{g} v_0 \sin \theta\right)^2 \left(1 - \frac{k}{3w} v_0 \sin \theta\right)^2\right]$$
$$\approx \frac{2}{g} v_0^2 (\cos \theta \sin \theta) \left(1 - \frac{4k}{3w} v_0 \sin \theta\right)$$
$$R = R(\theta).$$

To find the value of θ which maximizes $R(\theta)$, call it θ^*, we set $R'(\theta^*) = 0$ and solve for θ^*:

$$R'(\theta) \approx \frac{2v_0^2}{g} \left[\cos \theta \sin \theta \left(-\frac{4k}{3w} v_0 \cos \theta\right)\right.$$
$$\left. + \left(1 - \frac{4k}{3w} v_0 \sin \theta\right)(\cos^2 \theta - \sin^2 \theta)\right]$$
$$= \frac{2v_0^2}{g} \left[\frac{4kv_0}{3w} \sin^3 \theta\right.$$
$$\left. + \left(1 - \frac{8k}{3w} v_0 \sin \theta\right) \cos^2 \theta - \sin^2 \theta\right]$$
$$R'(\theta) \approx \frac{2v_0^2}{g} \left[\frac{4kv_0}{w} \sin^3 \theta - 2\sin^2 \theta - \frac{8kv_0}{3w} \sin \theta + 1\right].$$

Now, replacing θ by $\theta*$, equating $R'(\theta*)$ to zero, and dividing by $2v_0^2/g$, we get

$$\frac{4kv_0}{w} \sin^3 \theta* - 2\sin^2 \theta* - \frac{8kv_0}{3w} \sin \theta* + 1 = 0 . \tag{8}$$

We now need appropriate values for the constants w, k, and v_0. Suppose we decide to consider a shot as our projectile. If "number 7 shot" has 300 pellets per ounce, then $w = (1/300) \times (1/16) = 1/4,800 \approx 0.00021$ lbs. or 2.1×10^{-4} lbs. Let us suppose that $v_0 = 870$ ft/sec and $k = 9 \times 10^{-8}$ lb-sec/ft. For convenience, write $\sin \theta* = z$. Eq. (8) becomes

$$1.5z^3 - 2z^2 - z + 1 = 0 .$$

From the "theory of equations" usually found in a college algebra text, we note that this equation has two positive roots and one negative root. The negative root implies a negative angle for θ and is eliminated. One positive root lies between zero and one, the other between one and two. Since $z = \sin \theta*$, the root between one and two is discarded. Thus, we see that our solution for z is a number between zero and one. Using an iterative method (or simply by trial and error), we find $z \approx 0.60$ and, hence, $\theta* \approx 37°$ is our approximate solution for the angle which maximizes the range under the stated conditions.

[*Acknowledgment:* Indebtedness is expressed to C. Alex McMahan for assistance involving the physics of this problem. While expressing appreciation, he also should be thanked for (anonymously) contributing many photographs for this book.]

For convenience of the reader, the details of obtaining the approximation shown in Eq. (6) are presented in this note.

From Eq. (5),

$$T = \frac{1}{g}\left(v_0 \sin \theta + \frac{w}{k}\right)\left(1 - e^{-(kg/w)T}\right).$$

Now
$$1 - e^{-(kg/w)T} = 1 - \left[1 - \frac{kg}{w}T + \frac{1}{2}\left(\frac{kg}{w}\right)^2 T^2\right.$$
$$\left. - \frac{1}{6}\left(\frac{kg}{w}\right)^3 T^3 + \cdots\right]$$
$$= \frac{kg}{w}T\left[1 - \frac{1}{2}\frac{kg}{w}T + \frac{1}{6}\left(\frac{kg}{w}\right)^2 T^2 - \cdots\right].$$

So
$$T = \frac{kT}{w}\left(v_0 \sin \theta + \frac{w}{k}\right)\left[1 - \frac{1}{2}\frac{kg}{w}T + \frac{1}{6}\left(\frac{kg}{w}\right)^2 T^2 - \cdots\right].$$

Dividing through by T, we get

$$1 = \left(\frac{k}{w}v_0 \sin \theta + 1\right)\left[1 - \frac{1}{2}\frac{kg}{w}T + \frac{1}{6}\left(\frac{kg}{w}\right)^2 T^2 - \cdots\right]$$
$$= \frac{k}{w}v_0 \sin \theta + 1 - \frac{1}{2}\frac{kg}{w}T\left(1 + \frac{k}{w}v_0 \sin \theta\right)$$
$$+ \frac{1}{6}\left(\frac{kg}{w}\right)^2 T^2 \left(1 + \frac{k}{w}v_0 \sin \theta\right) - \cdots.$$

Hence,

$$\frac{1}{2}\frac{kg}{w}T\left(1 + \frac{k}{w}v_0 \sin \theta\right) = \frac{k}{w}v_0 \sin \theta$$
$$+ \frac{1}{6}\left(\frac{kg}{w}\right)^2 T^2\left(1 + \frac{k}{w}v_0 \sin \theta\right) - \cdots$$

and

$$T\left(1 + \frac{k}{w}v_0 \sin \theta\right) = \frac{2}{g}v_0 \sin \theta$$
$$+ \frac{1}{3}\frac{kg}{w}T^2\left(1 + \frac{k}{w}v_0 \sin \theta\right) - \cdots.$$

If we let $k \to 0$, in the limit we get

$$T \ = \ \frac{2v_0}{g} \sin \theta \ .$$

If we consider the case in which k is small, T will approximately equal
$(2v_0/g) \sin \theta$. If we use this approximate value to obtain the second-order
term in T ,   we have

$$T\left(1 + \frac{k}{w} v_0 \sin \theta\right) \ \approx \ \frac{2v_0}{g} \sin \theta$$

$$+ \ \frac{1}{3} \frac{kg}{w} \left(\frac{2v_0}{g} \sin \theta\right)^{2} \left(1 + \frac{k}{w} v_0 \sin \theta\right)$$

or

$$T \ \approx \ \frac{2v_0}{g} \sin \theta \left\lfloor \left(1 + \frac{k}{w} v_0 \sin \theta\right)^{-1} + \frac{2}{3} \frac{k}{w} v_0 \sin \theta \right] \ .$$

Expanding $\left(1 + \frac{k}{w} v_0 \sin \theta\right)^{-1}$,

$$T \ \approx \ \frac{2v_0}{g} \sin \theta \left[1 - \frac{k}{w} v_0 \sin \theta \ + \frac{k^2}{w^2} v_0^2 \sin \theta^2 \ - \ \dots \right.$$

$$\left. + \ \frac{2}{3} \frac{k}{w} v_0 \sin \theta \right] \ .$$

If we disregard terms involving k^2 and higher degree terms in k,   we
obtain Eq. (6):

$$T \ \approx \ \frac{2}{g} v_0 \sin \theta \left(1 \ - \ \frac{k}{3w} v_0 \sin \theta\right) \ .$$

APPENDIX E

TIDBITS FROM
MY BRITISH JOURNAL

The reader who has been with me thus far knows that this book is a curious mixture of tall tales, science, art, philosophy, mathematics, probability, statistics, ... , results of research, and yes, even opinion. Undoubtedly, some readers would be interested in selected experiences of mine which might possibly have influenced those implicit and explicit opinions. Hence, partly for that reason, in this appendix I have attempted to share (with those readers so motivated) a few of my personal experiences with selected British retriever enthusiasts which well could have influenced my thinking on retrievers. [See notes at the end of this appendix on some British publications which also have probably influenced my thinking over the years.]

Some Background on English Retriever-Masters

In 1961, I decided that I could no longer delay taking a first-hand look at retrievers and retriever field trials in Great Britain. To initiate my abridged report, really not even a complete outline, of that venture, I shall "do a little name-dropping." This is dangerous and possibly even unkind because each and every British field-trialer was so very nice to me; nevertheless, I do need selected names to describe my visit. My sincere apologies are extended to those individuals whose names I deliberately deleted from my manuscript. [The order of introduction and references are for convenience only.]

Retriever Championship.--For most of the period under discussion, the International Gundog League (IGL) promoted the Retriever Championship in Great Britain; an American counterpart of the IGL is the National Retriever Club Incorporated.

Judges and prizes.--Both amateur and professional trainers (handlers) undertake judging assignments in British retriever trials. Moreover, there may be cash prizes associated with retriever field trials.

The Chudleys.--"Among shooting and field trial folk, the name Chudley is synonymous with top quality gundog work, ... The history of the Harpersbrook Kennels reads like a success story. Jack set up in business in 1947, thanks to the encouragement of Major Hugh Peacock (of "Greatford" fame), and was shortly joined by Keith .... ."[1]

Jack Chudley has contributed a monthly page on "Gundog Training" to *The Gamekeeper and Countryside* for more than a decade (it seems to me). [*Addendum:* In 1969, he initiated a regular contribution, at monthly intervals, to *The Field.*]

Jack and Keith were two of four judges for the Retriever Championship in 1968.

Major Hugh M. Peacock.--Greatford Teal, owned and handled by Major Peacock, won the Retriever Championship at Sandringham in 1955.

Hon. Lady Joan Hill-Wood and Miss Anne Hill-Wood.--These are the people who stand back of the label "Hiwood." As I recall, Miss Anne Hill-Wood personally accompanied Hiwood Storm (whelped in 1957) to the United States, and I seem to recall that she ran him in trials here in the late 1950's.

Hiwood Dipper, owned and handled by the Hon. Lady Joan Hill-Wood, won the Retriever Championship in 1960. (Miss Anne Hill-Wood's retriever, Hiwood Dacre Frank, won the Retriever Championship in 1964; he was handled to that win by the Hon. Lady Hill-Wood.)

R. S. Wilkins, Esquire.--Mr. Wilkins and the shooting syndicate were hosts for the All Aged Stake of the Essex Field Trial Society that I attended in the fall of 1961.

Mr. R.G. Baldwin.-- Mr. Baldwin is the distinguished trainer and handler for Mr. Wilkins.

LEADING LADY.   The Hon. Lady Joan Hill-Wood in action when her
Labrador, Hiwood Dipper, won the Championship in 1960. Photographed
by John Tarlton; courtesy of John Tarlton. Courtesy also The Field.

*Winner of the Retriever Championship, promoted by the Interna-
tional Gundog League, December 7 and 8, 1965: Mr. R. S. Wilkins's
Labrador dog, Sendhurst Sweep, with R. G. Baldwin, his handler. Photograph by C. M. Cooke and Son; courtesy C. M. Cooke and Son and* The
Field.

Mr. Vincent Routledge.--Hallingbury Blackbird won the Retriever Championship in 1962 ; Mr. Routledge himself handled this retriever. The four judges were the Hon. Lady Hill-Wood, Major Peacock, Mrs. W. A. Fellowes, and Mr. R. G. Baldwin.[2]

Retriever Championship, 1965.--Mr. R. S. Wilkins' Labrador dog, Sendhurst Sweep, with Mr. R. G. Baldwin as handler, won the Retriever Championship (December 7 and 8, 1965) at Grimsthrope, Bourne, in Lincolnshire.[3]

Retriever Championship, 1968.--Again in 1968, Dick Wilkins' Sendhurst Sweep, again under handler Bob Baldwin, won the Retriever Championship.

It is worth noting, Sweep was bred by the late Vincent Routledge; moreover, Sweep was sired by the 1962 winner of the Retriever Championship, Hallingbury Blackbird.

VISIT TO ENGLAND, 1961

For several days, I stopped at the Park Lane Hotel, Piccadilly, London W.1. It was a "short walk" from the Park Lane to the editorial offices of *The Field* at the Harmsworth Press, Ltd., 8 Stratton Street, Piccadilly, W.1. Close by "the home" of *The Field* is the Kennel Club, 1-4 Clarges Street, Piccadilly, London W.1.

During the first week of October (1961), I visited the offices of *The Field*, picked up the current issue, and "visited with" some of the staff. Then I walked over to the Kennel Club. There I collected some of their publications; to list a few: *Kennel Gazette*, Volume LXXXII, No. 977, August, 1961; *Kennel Gazette, Breed Records Supplement*, Volume LXXXII, No. 977, August, 1961; *Kennel Club Field Trial Rules* (24 May 1960); *Field Trial Council Recommendations; Guide to Field Trial Judges*; and others. Personnel at the Kennel Club treated me most cordially.

Friday, October 6.--I visited the Hon. Lady Joan Hill-Wood and her daughter, Miss Anne Hill-Wood, at Dacre Farm. I recall seeing several Hiwood retrievers, in particular, Hiwood Dipper and Hiwood Peggy, the distinguished dam of Galleywood Shot and three other field trial champions. (See excerpts from a letter reproduced on page 841.)

October 7.--Early Saturday morning, I took a train from London to Peterborough. [*Aside:* I thought that travel by train in Britain was great; I found it fast, economical, convenient, and comfortable, although many of my British colleagues (non-retriever enthusiasts) complained about the railroads.] Through previous arrangements with, and the kind assistance of, Major Hugh M. Peacock and his daughter, I was collected at the railroad station and taken to "spend the day" with Jack and Keith Chudley, Harpersbrook Kennels. "We trained" retrievers and spaniels, worked spaniels in the rabbit pen, walked up and shot pheasant, and shot woodpigeon.

Sunday, October 8.--Visited with Mr. Bob Baldwin. Went into the field with him and his retrievers; saw Galleywood Shot (winner of the Retriever Championship, 1957 and 1958) in action. When we returned to Mr. Baldwin's home, I spent several pleasant hours with Mr. and Mrs. Baldwin, Mr. Dick Wilkins, and Mr. Wilkins' brother, Pat. Mr. Dick Wilkins invited me to be his guest at the field trial the next day.

Field Trial.--The "official card," that we in America refer to as "the program," for that trial at Audley End, Saffron Walden, is reproduced on the following four pages. As I recall, there were six Guns, four handlers, each with one retriever, and four judges (and other personnel) in the line; moreover, the judges worked in pairs. [*Aside:* I hope that I won't offend Lady Elizabeth Simpson (wife of Sir Joseph Simpson, Chief Commissioner, Scotland Yard) by recording that I vividly recall that her entry, Number 6, Foxhanger Mascot, "ran in" that day ("broke" to my American colleagues).]

Lunch break.-- Lunch was served in a large farm building. This was not "lunch on the grounds" in the usual American sense; this was *a luncheon*. A bar was set up; tables were set complete with ster-

OFFICIAL CARD 2/6

ESSEX FIELD TRIAL SOCIETY

President :
Col. SIR JOHN RUGGLES BRISE, BART, C.B., O.B.E., T.D., J.P.
(Lord Lieutenant of Essex)

Vice-Presidents :
SIR CHARLES S. ROWLEY, BART   R. S. WILKINS, ESQ.
Committee : Mr W. Lawrence Taylor (Chairman), Mr D. F. Cock (Vice-Chairman), Messrs A. J. Andrew, E. R. Benson, D.S.O., D.F.C., R. G. Baldwin, Capt C. F. Crawshay, T. L. Tetlow, W. Grant Fiske, Dr J. Hurndall Gann, R. J. Harvey, John Kent, Capt G. B. Kent, S. R. H. Little, Mr J. M. Lukies, Capt J. McMullen, Mr F. Mason Prime, Mr C. J. Morehouse, Sir Charles S. Rowley, Bt., and Mr Andrew Wylie.
Hon. Vet. Surgeon : Mr J. A. Fleming, M.Sc., M.R.C.V.S.

PROGRAMME
of

Retriever Trial

Under Kennel Club Field Trial Rules

ALL AGED STAKE

On MONDAY & TUESDAY, 9th & 10th OCTOBER, 1961

at

AUDLEY END, SAFFRON WALDEN

By kind permission of R. S. Wilkins, Esq., and the Shooting Syndicate
Meet 9.30 a.m.   First Day.   The Dutch Barn, Clanver End Road
Meet 9.30 a.m.   Second Day.   The Fighting Cocks
Judges : Messrs R. G. Baldwin, P. Fraser, J. A. Taylor and W. L. Woodward
Headquarters : Rose & Crown Hotel, Saffron Walden
Chief Steward : Mr S. R. H. Little
Luncheons, Licensed Bar and Teas on the ground

Annual Dinner, 9th October, Town Hall, Saffron Walden, 7.15 for 7.45 p.m.
Hon. Secretary and Treasurer :
A. R. Heasman, St Aubyns, Saffron Walden   (Tel. 2064)

SPECTATORS ARE INVITED TO JOIN THE SOCIETY
Subscription : One Guinea   Bona-fide Gamekeepers, 5/-

TRANSHALER by Courtesy of

Telecommunications

ALL AGED STAKE
(Limited to 24 dogs)

First Prize: £30   Second Prize : £20   Third Prize : £10
                        Fourth Prize : £5

1. **F. T. Ch. Nazeing Mick.** Mrs R. Crawshay's Labrador d., born 1/5/56, by Greatford Kip—F. T. Ch. Nazeing Soot.
   Breeder: Owner. Handler : Owner.

2. **Wilby Peter.** Mrs E. R. George's Labrador d., born 17/7/58, by F. T. Ch. Harpersbrook Poacher—Meadowcourt Monica.
   Breeder : Mr R. B. Weston-Webb. Handler : Mr T. Arnold.

3. **F. T. Ch. Hiwood Dipper.** Lady Hill-Wood's Labrador d., born 28/1/56, by F. T. Ch. Greatford Teal—F. T. Ch. Hiwood Gypsey.
   Breeder : Owner. Handler : Owner.

4. **Holway Sally.** Mr M. Atkinson's Golden Retriever b., born 8/6/58, by Dual Ch. David of Westley—Irish F. T. Ch. Holway Legato.
   Breeder : Mr F. Dobson. Handler : Owner.

5. **Merry of Chrishall.** Mr John Kent's Labrador b., born 2/7/58, by F. T. Ch. Brackenbank Merry—Alltmor Meg.
   Breeder : Mr A. P. Dick. Handler : Owner.

6. **Foxhanger Mascot.** Lady Simpson's Labrador d., born 29/5/57, by Copperhill Cheerful—Foxhanger Lass.
   Breeder : Owner. Handler : Owner.

7. **Treunair Texa.** Sir J. Landale Train's Golden Retriever d., born 19/5/59, by Stubblesdown Kite—Gay Sandra.
   Breeder : Mrs Wagstaff. Handler : Mrs E. J. C. Lumsden.

8. **Cornbury Regent.** Mr O. P. Watney's Labrador d., born 11/3/58, by F. T. Ch. Galleywood Shot—Polebrooke Garlennick Smog.
   Breeder Owner. Handler : Mr A. C. White-Robinson.

9. **Grattonfield Belle.** The Lord Rank's Labrador b., born 7/3/58, by Scotney Dusty—Madcap Moya.
   Breeder : Lt.-Col. F. M. Bucher. Handler : Mr W. C. Brunt.

10. **Ch. Claverdon Jorrocks of Lilling.** Dr N. Laughton's Flatcoat d., born 27/5/57, by Pewcroft Page—Ch. Claverdon Powder Box.
    Breeder : Mrs J. Wood. Handler : Owner.

11. **Strattonley Flip.** Mrs D. Purbrick's Labrador b., born 24/2/57, by F. T. Ch. Greatford Teal—Strattonley Reedling.
    Breeder : Owner. Handler : Owner.

12. **Wincote Sam.** Mr A. W. C. Thursby's Labrador d., born 5/11/57, by Hiwood Reeve—East Roy Flight.
    Breeder : Mrs E. P. Wilson. Handler : Owner.

13. **Greatford Park.** Mr F. George's Labrador d., born 13/2/59, by Greatford Glenfare Brent—Greatford Gerda.
    Breeder : Mr U. R. Paravicini. Handler : Mr J. Chudley.

14. **Ballyduff Glenfarg Brambling.** Dr T. S. Acheson's Labrador b., born 6 3 58, by Oxenden Shadow— F. T. Ch. Norham Blackie.
Breeder : Mrs B. Harcourt Wood. Handler : Mr J. Greaves.

15. **Greatford Ednaston Rory.** Major H. Peacock's Labrador d., born 14 2 58, by F. T. Ch. Glenhead Zuider— Burdock's Black Beauty.
Breeder : Major A. J. Crewdson. Handler : Mr K. Chudley.

16. **Holway Lancer.** Mrs J. R. Atkinson's Golden Retriever d., born 21 5 59, by F. T. Ch. Stubblesdown Larry— Holway Melody Maker of Wynford.
Breeder : Mr M. Atkinson. Handler : Owner.

17. **Staindrop Woodstain Tern.** Mrs E. Winter's Labrador b., born 9 3 58, by Hiwood Scoter— Staindrop Nipsy.
Breeder : Mr J. Donaldson. Handler : Mrs J. M. Hayes.

18. **Hallingbury Tern.** Mrs A. N. Gardiner's Labrador d., born 4 3 57, by F. T. Ch. Galleywood Shot— Galleywood Pigeon.
Breeder : Mr W. Lawrence Taylor. Handler : Owner.

19. **Marshlands Sandpiper.** Mr G. G. Lawrence's Golden Retriever d., by Holway Leo— Marshlands Starlight.
Breeder : Mrs D. J. French. Handler : Mr P. F. Dobbs.

20. **Earl Soham Plover.** Major R. S. Schreiber's Labrador b., born 5 3 58, by Pinehawk Ben— Shepreth Pamela.
Breeder : Mrs A. Daniell. Handler : Owner.

21. **Templegrafton Scotney Bobbin.** Capt. T. L. Lonsdale's Labrador d., born 14 5 57, by F. T. Ch. Hanlye Bobby— Scotney Jam.
Breeder : The Lord Rank. Handler : Owner.

22. **Pinehawk Galleywood Jack.** Mr A. Wylie's Labrador d., born 6 4 58, by F. T. Ch. Galleywood Shot— Whittlemoor Lady.
Breeder : Mr A. E. Curtis. Handler : Owner.

23 **Nazeing Peep.** Capt. C. F. Crawshay's Labrador b., born 1 6 57, by Greatford Kip— F. T. Ch. Nazeing Soot.
Breeders : Capt. and Mrs C. F. Crawshay. Handler : Owner.

24. **Holcot Ruff of Birdshill.** Dr W. C. M. Berridge's Labrador b., born 17 4 56, by F. T. Ch. Glenhead Zuider— Greatford Jenny.
Breeder : Major F. Howlett. Handler : Owner.

Reserves

25. Major R. S. Schreiber.   26. Mr A. C. Greenhow.

27. Mrs M. O. Ridding.   28. Capt. C. P. Kirk, etc., etc.

General Regulations

1. All persons attending the Trials must consider themselves absolutely under the orders of the Officials **and must follow and remain close to the spectators red flag.**

2. Spectators and Competitors must make their own arrangements for transport and luncheon.

3. Only Officials, Handlers and Owners of competing dogs actually under Judge's orders and accredited members of the Press will be allowed in the firing line.

4. All dogs suffering from hysteria must be removed immediately from the ground and from the Trials.

5. All dogs off the lead, hunting ground behind the line are liable to disqualification.

6. The system of Judging will be entirely at the discretion of the Judges and in accordance with the Kennel Club Field Trial Rules.

7. The Judges are empowered to turn out of the Stake any dog whose handler does not obey them, or wilfully interferes with another competitor or his dog.

Hatts, Printers, Saffron Walden

MR. JOHN KENT is the doyen of gundog trainers. He trained the first cocker spaniel to win the title of Field Trial Champion in 1906 and the first yellow Labrador to do likewise, in 1926. Only last year he won the Spaniel Test at the Game Fair with his English springer Wad of Chrishall. He is held in immense respect by his rivals, both professional and amateur.

He has farmed on the Hertfordshire/Essex border nearly all his life, though his son has now succeeded him in farming at Chrishall, near Royston. Mr. Kent now lives with his daughter, Mrs. P. de Beer, and continues to train retrievers and spaniels. He is 80.

(Source: The Field, April 7, 1966, p. 601; photograph courtesy of The Field.) [Comment: Mr. Kent attended the trial at Saffron Walden which I attended in 1961; I was indeed fortunate to have a pleasant and informative visit with him.]

YORKSHIRE SHOOT: BETWEEN DRIVES AT MARSTON MANOR, 1965.

From a color transparency by John Tarlton; courtesy John Tarlton and The Field.

ling flatware; and a complete serving staff was on-hand. I was impressed!

Later in October, after I returned home, I wrote four letters which are reproduced here (in part) because they provide additional information.

Flat-Coated Retrievers

I wanted to get a first-hand look at some flatcoats on this trip. After all, the wavy-coated retriever (flatcoat) has been a companion and useful gundog to my family since the last quarter of the nineteenth century--for nearly a hundred years. At the time (1961), I felt that he was not the ideal for winning and placing in American trials as they are currently conducted; in short, he was not the acme of perfection for everyone. Nevertheless, I felt, and still feel, that it is not by chance that a gundog fanatic has the privilege of walking through life with a flatcoat at heel and otherwise. The flatcoat is for the privileged few who have a genuine use for him and who can really appreciate his unique characteristics. But I wanted to *see* for myself.

As it turned out, I saw only one flat-coated retriever this trip (see entry Number 10, Official Card, Essex Field Trial Society, All Aged Stake, October 9 and 10, 1961). Accordingly, I decided then and there to explicitly *plan* to see some flatcoats on my next visit to England ("if and when").

VISIT TO ENGLAND AND SCOTLAND, 1965

The "if" came to be, and the "when" was autumn, 1965. Shortly after arrival in London, I visited the offices of *The Field* where I had an appointment with the editor of *The Field*. The editor is a well-known retriever field trial enthusiast and fancier of flat-coated retrievers. He invited me to have dinner with him at the Kennel Club.

6356 Bellaire Drive
New Orleans 24, Louisiana
October 18, 1961

R. S. Wilkins, Esq.

Dear Mr. Wilkins:

    During the last few days, the thought has crossed my mind many times concerning my good fortune to make your acquaintance on my recent trip to England. It was most generous and hospitable of you to accept me, a total stranger, so completely and for you to go "all out" in orienting me concerning your retrievers (I think you have some wonderful dogs) and your field trials. Thank you for the drinks, for a fine lunch, and especially for taking time out to see that I met so many people, as well as for seeing that I got "into the line." My visits to Bishop's Stortford and Saffron Walden were highlights of my trip; I shall cherish always the memories of the experiences which you provided for me.

    I was impressed with Bob as a trainer and as a person; he was most kind to me and I have written him a note of appreciation. Please give Pat my regards and I hope that I shall have the pleasure of seeing all of you again in the not too distant future. Again, I thank you.

                    Sincerely,

                    /s/

                    C. A. McMahan

CAMcM/lkh

6356 Bellaire Drive
New Orleans 24, Louisiana
October 18, 1961

Mr. R. J. Baldwin

Dear Mr. Baldwin:

This is just a note to let you know how very much I appreciate the courteous and warm treatment you accorded me on my recent visit to England. I sincerely appreciate your taking in a stranger and making him feel welcome to your home, to your kennels, and to your field trial. Thank you for all the transportation which you provided me, for the fine exhibition of your dogs on Sunday morning (I was tremendously impressed with your retrievers--even the spaniel), for the many introductions at the trial, and for so many other courtesies which I shall not attempt to enumerate. Thank you and Mr. Wilkins especially for inviting me into the line at the trial and for permitting me to view the trial "close-up."

Please remember me to Mrs. Baldwin and thank her for inviting me to lunch that Sunday. I regret that I could not accept the invitation. . . . .

Thank you for everything.

Sincerely,

/s/

C. A. McMahan

CAMcM/lkh

6356 Bellaire Drive
New Orleans 24, Louisiana
October 19, 1961

Mr. Jack Chudley
Mr. Keith Chudley
Harpersbrook Kennels

Dear Jack and Keith:

Obviously a letter can't do the job, but this letter is written as a token reminder to you that I sincerely appreciate the efforts which you went to on my behalf when I visited you recently. You were most kind to exhibit your dogs for me, to permit me to accompany you on a "hunt," and to allow me to see your retrievers work under actual field conditions. I admired greatly the conformation of your Labradors as well as their competence in the field.

When I saw you at the trial, it was like renewing a friendship of long standing. I haven't received news concerning the placings that day but I do hope that the judges ruled favorably for you.

Thank you for the use of the rubber trousers and for the ride to the train on Saturday afternoon. Keith, be sure to tell your wife that I surely did enjoy the tea and "cookies."

It was certainly nice to see both of you fellows. Be sure to look me up when you get to the States.

Sincerely,

/s/

C. A. McMahan

CAMcM/lkh

6356 Bellaire Drive
New Orleans 24, Louisiana
October 16, 1961

Lady Joan Hill-Wood
Dacre Farm

Dear Lady Hill-Wood:

I returned to New Orleans on Friday from Paris; consequently, this is the first opportunity which I have had to write to you and to tell you how very much I enjoyed my recent visit to your home. Thank you for picking me up at the station, for showing me your dogs, for giving me a chance to walk through fields and to shoot a shotgun in England, and for inviting me to lunch. Please thank Anne for taking me to see the pups over at Major Wilson's. That was an enjoyable ride and a pleasant experience "talking dogs" with Anne. .... .

Saturday was spent with the Chudleys but I missed seeing Major Peacock. I spent Sunday with Mr. Baldwin and had a chance to visit with Mr. Wilkins. On Monday I went to the trial at Saffron Walden and had a wonderful time; Mr. Wilkins and Mr. Baldwin placed me in the line so I got a close-up view. Mr. Thursby sought me out and spoke to me; he indicated that you had called him the night before and told him to look out for me--thank you.

In summary, I thought England was great.

Sincerely,

/s/

C. A. McMahan

CAMcM/lkh

High on my priority list was to obtain some clothing and equipment suitable for excursions into the field with retrievers. Hence, I made appropriate purchases at Austin Reed of Regent Street; J. C. Cording and Co., Ltd., 19 Piccadilly, London, W. 1.; and Cogswell and Harrison Ltd., 168 Piccadilly, London, W. 1. Next, in order to have it ready when I had to return home, I purchased a Webley and Scott shotgun from John Wilkes Gun and Rifle Makers, 79 Beak Street, Regent Street, London, W. 1.

Sunday, October 10.--In planning my 1965 trip, I had written an inquiry to, and received a reply from, the Hon. Secretary, the Hon. Mrs. D. C. G. Jessel, of the Flatcoated Retriever Society. As a consequence, Mr. D. C. G. Jessel and the Hon. Mrs. Jessel invited me to come to their home, be their guest overnight, and accompany them to the field trial (limited to flat-coated retrievers) on Monday, October 11.

On Sunday afternoon, I went by means of British Railways (say, the 1:27). Mr. Jessel collected me at the station.

That afternoon the Jessels demonstrated their flatcoats to me-- on both land and water. Mr. Jessel let me "handle" and inspect a matched pair of beautiful "best made" shotguns that John Wilkes had manufactured for him and delivered just a few months earlier.

Around dusk, four other guests (with their retrievers) arrived, namely, Brigadier F. W. Clowes and Mrs. Clowes, and Dr. Nancy Laughton, and Miss G. M. Knight.

Monday, October 11.--Early Monday morning, I rode with Mr. Jessel in his car to the trial grounds; early arrival was required on his part because he was not only the field trial secretary but an invited Gun as well (I labelled him "number three Gun").

This was a 12-dog stake. According to my recollection, there were 6 Guns, 3 judges, and 6 handlers with one retriever each (and other personnel) in the line. Two handlers (each with one retriever) seemed to be under the jurisdiction of each judge. In the early part of the trial, it appeared to me that no retriever was allowed

more than two retrieves until he was rotated from the line. I walked
in the line and carried a board which was hoisted high to indicate the
number of the retriever that was currently "down" (working).

During the lunch break selected guests were invited to lunch at
the home of the host; I had a wonderful lunch on the grounds with colleagues who had brought lunch along.

After the luncheon break, the trial was resumed. At the conclusion of the trial, Hartshorn Sorrel was awarded first place, and she
impressed me as being a first-rate retriever. In fact, she had been
"put on ice" after her distinguished morning performance. In the
afternoon, after two retrievers had failed to find a marked fall, she
was called back to the line and put down. She found the bird (a blind)
in short order--an eye-wipe.

I said to myself: "That bitch looks like a real comer. I'd like to
take her home with me. Reckon she can pass on her good qualities to
her offspring?" But "talk" is cheap. What operational evidence do I
have that I thought she was a top retriever? I decided then and there
that I wanted a *bitch* puppy (obviously) out of that bitch and I set the
wheels in motion to obtain one, if and when. I discussed the matter
with Mr. Wilson Stephens; after all, he had bred Hartshorn Sorrel
and Major H. A. Wilson (Nesfield House, ... , Northern Ireland)
was his uncle. Moreover, the owner of Hartshorn Sorrel was Miss
Helen Wilson, Major Wilson's daughter.

After the trial was over, I had the pleasure of riding back (to a
station close to London) with two of the judges, Dr. W. C. M. Berridge
and G. Williams, Esq. During that ride, I learned a considerable
amount about the "thinking of the judges" that day. The card for that
stake is reproduced on the next four pages.

Wednesday, October 13. -- While in Cambridge attending to business,
I spent a pleasant hour at Gallyon and Sons, Ltd. , Gun and Cartridge
Makers, 66 Bridge Street (Cambridge).

Thursday, October 14. -- Because Mr. Stephens, the Jessels, and
others, had recommended Mr. Colin Wells as being an excellent

FLATCOATED RETRIEVER SOCIETY
PRESIDENT: BRIGADIER F. W. CLOWES

THIRTY FOURTH
FIELD TRIAL
MEETING

(Under Kennel Club Field Trial Rules and Regulations and Rules of the Flatcoated Retriever Society)

OPEN STAKE FOR FLATCOATED RETRIEVERS
By kind invitation of The Hon. V. P. H. Wills
ON MONDAY, 11TH OCTOBER 1965.

JUDGES
Dr. W. C. M. Berridge.   Capt. T. L. Lonsdale.
G. Williams, Esq.

HON. FIELD TRIAL SECRETARY
D. C. G. Jessel, Esq.

ONLY OFFICIALS AND HANDLERS UNDER JUDGES' ORDERS
ALLOWED IN THE LINE

PRICE: 2/6d.

COMPETITORS

1. MRS. W. STEPHENS'--HARTSHORN MOONSHINE--bitch. 3.2.
    61. by Ch. Woodlark X Nesfield Stratton. Breeder: Mr. W.
    Stephens. Trainer/Handler: owner.

2. DR. N. LAUGHTON'S--CLAVERDON JORROCKS JUNIOR--dog.
    1.4.62 by Ch. Claverdon Jorrocks of Lilling X Claverdon
    Bronte. Breeder: Mr. D. Henry. Trainer/Handler: owner.

3. MISS H. WILSON'S--HARTSHORN SORREL--bitch. 3.4.62. by
    Teal of Hawk's Nest X Nesfield Stratton. Breeder: Mr. W.
    Stephens. Trainers: H. A. and Helen Wilson. Handler: Major
    H. A. Wilson.

4. MR. WILSON STEPHENS'--HARTSHORN BLUEBELL--bitch.
    8.2.64. by Teal of Hawk's Nest X Hartshorn Moonshine.
    Breeder: Mrs. W. Stephens. Trainer/Handler: owner.

5. MR. BRENDAN ROBINSON'S--CH. CLAVERDON COMET--dog.
    1.3.59. by Bob of Riverglad X Claverdon Turtledove. Breeder:
    Dr. N. Laughton. Trainer/Handler: owner.

6. MR. BRENDAN ROBINSON'S--JET OF ARDILEA--dog. 25.4.
    63. by Ch. Claverdon Comet X Meg of Riverdene. Breeder:
    Mr. Grayson. Trainer/Handler: Mr. P. Parsons.

7. THE HON. MRS. JESSEL'S--CH. COLLYERS BLAKEHOLME
    BREWSTER--dog. 4.12.62. by Blakeholme Jem X Rettendon
    Spoon-Bill. Breeder: Miss C. B. Hall. Trainer/Handler:
    owner.

8. MAJOR H. A. WILSON'S--HARTSHORN MIDNIGHT--bitch. 3.2.
    61. by Ch. Woodlark X Nesfield Stratton. Breeder: Mr. W.
    Stephens. Trainer/Handler: owner.

9. AIR-CDRE. W. H. HUTTON'S--BLACK PRINCE OF YARLAW--
    dog. 16.5.62. by Ch. Woodlark X Ch. Pewcroft Prop of Yar-
    law. Breeder/Trainer/Handler: owner.

10. DR. N. LAUGHTON'S--CLAVERDON CINDY--bitch. 1.3.59 by
    Bob of Riverglade X Claverdon Turtledove. Breeder/Trainer:
    owner. Handler: Miss G. M. Knight.

11. BRIG. F. W. CLOWES'--ALBIFRONS--dog. 19.6.61. by Verney Bruce X Selford Promise. Breeder: Mr. J. P. Williams. Trainer/Handler: owner.

12. MRS. E. M. COX'S--BEECHSHAW RIVERSEDGE JESS--bitch. 25.4.63. by Ch. Claverdon Comet X Meg of Riverdene. Breeder: Mr. Grayson. Trainer/Handler: Mr. J. E. Cox.

. . . .

RESERVES

13. BRIG. F. W. CLOWES'--BLACK JACK OF YARLAW--dog. 16.5.62. by Ch. Woodlark X Ch. Pewcroft Prop of Yarlaw. Breeder: Air-Cdre. Hutton. Trainer/Handler: owner.

14. MR. R. FLOWERS'--FENRIVERS FERN--dog. 4.9.62. by Fenrivers Black Tulip X Fenrivers Evergreen. Breeder/Trainer/Handler: owner.

15. THE HON. MRS. JESSEL'S--COLLYERS PATCH--bitch. 20.8. 61. by Claverdon Skipper X Ch. Asperula. Breeder/Trainer/Handler: owner.

16. MR. W. STEPHENS'--HARTSHORN SOU'WESTER--bitch. 3.4. 62. by Teal of Hawk's Nest X Nesfield Stratton. Breeder/Trainer/Handler: owner.

17.   . . . .

FOR QUALIFYING CERTIFICATES

Mrs. G. Fletcher & Mr. A. Davis'--Sh. Ch. Rungles Wag--dog. 27.9.59. by Waterboy of Pringon X Ch. Happy Wanderer. Breeders: owners. Trainer/Handler: Mr. R. Duckworth.

CHALLENGE CUPS & SPECIAL PRIZES

The Winch Cup for the best Working Retriever.

The Patrick Barrett Memorial Cup given by the late Mr. and Mrs. Birch for the best dog handled by a gamekeeper.

The Oliver Challenge Cup for the best Retriever handled by a lady.

The Birch Challenge Cup for the best Retriever handled by its owner who must be an amateur.

The Birch Puppy Cup for the best Puppy.

A Challenge Cup given by the St. Hubert Club for the best working Retriever which has won at least one Challenge Certificate.

The British Field Sports Society Medal to be awarded to the winner.

£1 offered by Brig. F. W. Clowes for the best dog or bitch on a runner.

£1 offered by Mr. D. C. G. Jessel for the quietest handler.

£1 offered by Dr. N. Laughton for Reserve in the Stake.

The Winner obtains a B qualification and the second a C qualification towards the International Gundog League Retriever Championship.

. . . .

ADDRESSES OF COMPETITORS

[Not reproduced here.]

breeder of flat-coated retrievers, I arranged to spend a day with him. He collected me at the station at Grantham in a Land Rover and drove me to his home. He "drove" me around the estate, showed me his birds, indicated where some of the drives were conducted, showed me his ornamental game, some of his game-rearing techniques, and the like.

He demonstrated his flat-coated retrievers and told me about some of his other activities.

In the afternoon, we went by to see the Hon. Lady Hill-Wood and Miss Anne Hill-Wood; they had relocated near Grantham in the period intervening since my last trip to England.

Monday, October 18. -- I visited John Dickson and Son, 21 Frederick Street, Edinburgh, Scotland.

Nesfield Pontchippi Wynk

To make a long story short, Hartshorn Sorrel (winner of the 1965 trial which I attended) was bred to Mr. Wells' Woodlark in the spring of 1966. Four puppies were whelped, two dogs and two bitches. The bitch puppies were not for sale. Mr. Wells sold me the (dog) stud puppy, and (after many delays due to transcontinental airlines strikes) Wynk finally arrived in New Orleans in October, 1966, a year after my return from England.

Additional Information

Several (excerpts from) letters I wrote after I returned home in 1965 are reproduced on the following pages because they provide some additional insights.

Excerpt

My judgment that Hartshorn Sorrel was a first-rate retriever was confirmed by her continued high-class performance; see the excerpt which follows.

BELVOIR CASTLE
GRANTHAM

AERIAL VIEW OF THE CASTLE

Home of the Duke of Rutland for whom Mr. Colin Wells is Game-keeper. (Note: I was informed that Belvoir is pronounced "beaver.")

The flying belly-buster. *Even after being made to gee and haw for two years, Wynk still shows off when he enters the water.*

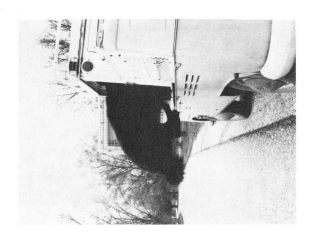

Two attempts to photograph Wynk jumping into his compartment, 1970.

RETRIEVER AND WOODCOCK

*From an old color print in the author's private Pontchippi
Collection. Painting by Sir Edwin Landseer (1802-1873); engraved by
Thomas Landseer.*

6356 Bellaire Drive
New Orleans, Louisiana 70124
November 17, 1965

[Editor]
The Field
8 Stratton Street
London, W. 1., England

Dear   :

Thank you for your time, your courteous and warm treatment, and the sound and straightforward guidance which you gave me when I visited England and Scotland recently. You certainly sent me to see "just the right people" .... I do appreciate your helpful advice.

. . .

After delays occasioned by fog and mechanical trouble, we arrived in New Orleans a day and a half after scheduled time of departure. In view of the fatal crash at London Airport that Tuesday night, I am glad that Pan American decided not to fly. In fact, after checking in at the London Airport on Tuesday, October 26, we were transferred to Gatwick, later transported by bus to Brighton where we spent the night, and finally took off from Gatwick on Wednesday. ....

Again, thank you for making my visit to England a great experience.

Sincerely,

/s/

C. A. McMahan

CAMcM/lkh

6356 Bellaire Drive
New Orleans, Louisiana 70124
October 30, 1965

Mr. D. C. G. Jessel
and the Hon. Mrs. Jessel

Dear Mr. and Mrs. Jessel:

. . .

Thank you for the courteous and warm treatment which you accorded me on my recent visit. Explicitly, thank you for honoring me by inviting me into your home, for showing me your dogs and guns, for securing the crowns for me, for transporting me to the field trial and for allowing me to walk in the line, for the delicious lunch on the grounds, and for all of the other nice things which you did for me.

On Thursday after the trial, I spent a very pleasant day with Mr. Colin Wells.

If your rules permit, I would appreciate becoming a member of the Flatcoated Retriever Society. If this is not permissible, I would like to receive the materials which you mail out. Enclosed is a draft to cover membership and/or mailing expenses.

Sincerely,

/s/

C. A. McMahan

CAMcM/lkh

Enclosure

6356 Bellaire Drive
New Orleans, Louisiana 70124
November 17, 1965

Mr. Colin Wells
Headkeeper to the Duke of Rutland

Dear Mr. Wells:

Thank you for a great day in England. I surely enjoyed the visit with you. Please thank Mrs. Wells for coffee and lunch; it was great to be invited into your home. Also, please thank Mr. B., ... , for the tour of the castle.

When you get that good male with the "not too heavy a coat" for me, if you can bring yourself to it, I would appreciate your registering it as follows:

PONTCHIPPI WYNK

and I shall call him "Wink." This will give my prefix and your W.

Mr. Stephens was real kind when he sent me to see you; that was a stroke of genuine luck for me.

Enclosed are some materials from two field trials.

Sincerely,

/s/

C. A. McMahan

CAMcM/lkh

Enclosures

AT LAST, A FLATCOAT FIELD TRIAL CHAMPION

By winning the Ulster two-day open stake for all varieties of retriever, Miss Helen Wilson's bitch, Hartshorn Sorrel, achieved the title of Field Trial Champion, and is said to be the first flatcoat to do so since before the First World War. Her success marks a new stage in the long-delayed return of this once pre-eminent variety of retriever to all-breed competition.

Four years old, Hartshorn Sorrel was bred by Mr. W. Stephens and is by Teal of Hawk's Nest (owned by Mr. Brian Farr, the bloodstock breeder of Worksop Manor, Nottingham) out of Nesfield Stratton. This breeding preserves a notable line of flatcoat working blood. Its exploitation has proved something of a family affair.

Teal of Hawk's Nest is the last surviving son of Gaff of Riverside, himself one of the last litter bred in Shropshire by the late Mr. H. Reginald Cooke, whose kennel polarised flatcoat breeding for half a century. His influence was such that for many years flatcoats of quality were concentrated in the hands of a small circle of owners. Nesfield Stratton, dam of the new Field Trial Champion, was bred by Major H. A. Wilson, of Lambeg, Co. Antrim, who has handled Hartshorn Sorrel in all her trials for his daughter, to whom she belongs.

Nesfield Stratton's record as a brood bitch is to have produced, in two litters, the winners of 25 Field Trial awards (Hartshorn Sorrel 9, Hartshorn Moonshine 8, Hartshorn Midnight 4 and Hartshorn Sou'wester 4) and two Show Champions (Hartshorn Mudlark and Stolford Hartshorn Memory). The latter are exhibited respectively by Mr. Keith Hart and Mrs. P. J. Robertson, the Hartshorn-owned dogs being seldom entered at shows.

F. Warner Hill

Source: *The Field*, Vol. 228, No. 5945, December 22, 1966, p. 1302.

A pittance of practice may be worth a tome of theory.

Hartshorn Sorrel, a four-year-old flatcoat, retrieves in the International Gundog League Championship Stake at Cromlix, Perthshire, 1966, in which she won a Diploma of Merit. Photo by C. M. Cooke and Son; courtesy C. M. Cooke and Son and The Field.

Dropping to shot

— Vernon Stokes

DROPPING TO SHOT

An old signed print by G. Vernon Stokes in the author's private Pontchippi Collection.

REFERENCES

1. Moxon, P. R. A. "Professional Handling at its Best," *Shooting Times and Country Magazine* (October 6, 1966), pp. 1300-1301.

2. Parsons, Fred. "The Retriever Championship," *The Field* (December 20, 1962), p. 1262.

3. Hill, F. Warner. "A Great Retriever Championship," *The Field* (December 16, 1965), pp. 1294-1295.

[*Note:* Appreciation is expressed to GEC Jr. for photographic assistance in the final process of assembling the book.]

NOTES TO APPENDIX E

Some Background

As stated elsewhere, I have been interested in gundogs as long as I can remember. In 1931, as a 17-year-old youngster on my first trip to Washington, D. C., I chanced across some British publications, to include *The Field*, in the Library of Congress. [*Aside:* The first issue of *The Field* appeared January 1, 1853. Each 1,000 issues spans about 20 years. The six-thousandth issue appeared January 11, 1968, up to which time there had been 10 editors.]

Shortly afterwards, I was introduced to what is called (as of this writing, 1968) *Shooting Times and Country Magazine* (established 1882). The *Shooting Times* (for short) is the official organ of the Wildfowlers Association of Great Britain and Ireland (WAGBI--analogous to "Ducks Unlimited") and the Clay Pigeon Shooting Association. About that same time someone introduced me to what is today called *The Gamekeeper and Countryside* (which stated "Seventy Second Year" in 1968). In short, since 1931 or thereabouts, I have been a regular reader of these three particular British publications (as well as others on occasion).

From this body of British writings (in combination with American publications), it is clear to me now how, in the 1930's, my interests broadened from hounds, pointing breeds, and retrievers, to spaniels. In fact, we bred our first cocker bitch in the fall of 1937.

After World War II, when it became practical for me to again take special interest in retrievers, I systematically went through every issue of *The Field* (one issue each week over nearly a century) in the Library of Congress. I essentially repeated this very same exercise (and broadened the coverage to other publications) in the 1950's. One could assert that I spent many "pleasant hours" in the dust and grime of the "basement" (of the Library of Congress) where these volumes are housed--and apparently seldom used. [Moreover, periodically during recent years, a colleague and I spent many hours in the "rare book" room of the Library of Congress enduring all the red-tape and inconvenience associated with it. All of this to gain further insight into both the American and British retriever, the retriever field trial

game, and the judging process.   *Aside:* The New York City Library turned
out to be an excellent source of useful materials, with much less red-tape.]

Now I am confused!
My first impression of
Retriever Theory *was that it*
is much easier to actually
judge than to write a
model of (and understand)
the judging process.
I'm not so sure any more!

INDEX OF TERMS

Remark: Many terms used in this book appear again and again on multiple pages. A term may be mentioned both as a topic of study and as an element in examining other concepts. For convenience, the number of references to a particular term has been limited; at most there are six.

THE DEMOGRAPHER: BEFORE RETRIEVER THEORY, *1952*

THE DEMOGRAPHER: AFTER RETRIEVER THEORY, 1970

"All broken down by age, ... , and retrievers."

NOTES ABOUT THE AUTHOR

Professor C. A. McMahan, a dedicated and active "gundog man" all his life, has also accumulated a long list of accomplishments outside the realm of breeder-owner-trainer-handler-judge of gundogs and gundog activities.

Born Chalmers Alexander McMahan to Archibald Alexander and Jessie (Chalmers) McMahan on July Fourth, 1914, near Seneca, South Carolina, he manifested a major interest in high school and college athletics as well as in "hunting." Professor McMahan disavows having been outstanding as an athlete, but college annuals indicate he lettered in major sports all three varsity years; set a new school record in the high jump; ... ; won the gold medal at the (old) Southern Conference Championship; and the list goes on. He maintained his interest in sports with a successful high school coaching career in Georgia concurrently with his pursuit of graduate study at Duke University and the University of Georgia after graduation from Clemson (B.S., 1935).

Called to active duty shortly before World War II, Professor McMahan served as Lieutenant, Captain, and Major in the U. S. Army, 1941-1946, and as a statistical control officer, AFWESPAC HQS, Manila, P. I.

Upon his return to civilian life, he completed work for and received his M.A. degree from the University of Georgia (1946), then obtained his Ph.D. (following a General Education Board fellowship, 1947-48) from Vanderbilt University, 1949. Professor McMahan served on the staff and faculty of the University of Georgia from 1946 to 1953. He was the recipient of the M. G. Michael Award in 1951. From 1953 to 1957, Professor McMahan was chief, manpower division, Air University; then joined the faculty of Louisiana State University Medical Center, New Orleans, in 1957, where he is professor and head of the Department of Biometry (established 1962), director of the Biometry Computing Center (established 1961), director of the Clinical Trials Research Center, LSU (established 1964), ...

To list Professor McMahan's professional publications is a mountainous, albeit surmountable, task; to mention only one scientific paper, as early as 1957 (before the days of "Sputnik"), he presented a paper entitled "Astronautical Manpower in the United States" at the Scientific Manpower Conference held during the meeting of the American Association for the Advancement of Science, Washington. To itemize his contributions to the professional community is an impossible task. Suffice it to say that Professor McMahan is a highly esteemed demographer and applied statistician, an internationally recognized authority on measurement and error (especially in the study of atherosclerosis and cancer), and an incurable student of judging.

Date Due